CONCORDIA UNIVERSITY
3 4211 00130 1541
W9-DEE-190
WITHDRAWN

ESSENTIAL BUSINESS MATHEMATICS

ESSENTIAL BUSINESS MATHEMATICS

THIRD EDITION

Llewellyn R. Snyder
CITY COLLEGE OF SAN FRANCISCO

1958

McGraw-Hill Book Company, Inc., New York, Toronto, London

ESSENTIAL BUSINESS MATHEMATICS

Library of Congress Catalog Card Number: 57-10920

THE MAPLE PRESS COMPANY, YORK, PA.

PREFACE

The essential purpose of this textbook is to provide knowledge and skill in the computation of practical financial problems of a business, civic, and personal nature. As in the first two editions, no attempt has been made to provide an all-inclusive study of the various topics presented. The material has been so prepared that it should form a sound basis for either subsequent or concurrent courses in accounting, investments, business finance, money and banking, insurance, real estate, statistics, retailing, and related business subjects.

Students who have completed this text enter courses in accountancy and other specialized business training with a background of general knowledge that enables them to understand more readily and progress more rapidly, and instructors in such courses need not relinquish a portion of their classroom time to the teaching of arithmetical computation but may devote their entire efforts to the teaching of their subjects proper.

It is the experience of the author that many students lack satisfactory accuracy, speed, and knowledge in basic arithmetic. Therefore, Part I of "Essential Business Mathematics" contains review material for students who are deficient in the fundamental processes, fractions, decimals, percentage, and problem solving.

Part I should be omitted for students who have a satisfactory background in arithmetic. Such students should begin their studies immediately with Part II, which contains the essential material of this text—the application of arithmetic to typical business problems and procedures.

Appendix I contains illustrative examples and optional exercises in most of the better known multiplication short cuts, and short methods of adding two fractions and subtracting fractions that have proved to be of interest to many students.

Appendix II contains an explanation and optional exercise in powers and roots; also tables, formulas, and optional exercises in measurements.

The presentation throughout is almost entirely arithmetical in nature. The author has designed both explanation and exercises so that a prior knowledge of algebra is not required of the students.

Within each general topic, the text, examples, and problems have been closely correlated. Thus, explanation immediately precedes each student assignment. Each unit represents one full assignment except where units are divided into parts each of which represents a full assignment: The exercises contain a large number of practical business problems generally arranged from simplest to most difficult. When the instructor finds it desirable or necessary to condense the time allowed for the course, it is suggested that the selection of alternating problems will provide a satisfactory variety of work for the students. It should be noted that answers to the odd-numbered problems are provided in the back of the text.

The use of the "Workbook for Essential Business Mathematics" is optional with the instructor. Assignments in the workbook are similar to the exercises in each chapter in the text.

In preparing this third edition of "Essential Business Mathematics," the author is indebted to the many teachers and businessmen who so kindly took the time and effort to make constructive criticisms and suggestions for improvement of the second edition. Specifically, the author wishes to thank his friend and colleague, Edward W. Larson, for technical advice and help in the preparation of Chapter XI, Transactions in Corporate Securities. Insofar as practicable within the confines of space limitation, the author has adopted such recommendations in this third edition.

Llewellyn R. Snyder

CONTENTS

PART I

ESSENTIALS OF BUSINESS ARITHMETIC

CHAPTER I

MECHANICS OF COMPUTATION

UNIT 1. Using Numbers in Business—Addition and Subtraction

GENERAL DEFINITIONS

A *unit* is one, a single thing, a single quantity. In 7 gallons, the unit is 1 gallon. In $5, the unit is $1.

A *number* is a unit or a group of the same kind of units.

An *abstract number* is one not applied to any thing or object, as 5, 12, 3, etc.

A *concrete number* is one applied to some thing or object, as 15 oranges, 8 chairs, 4 gallons, etc.

In adding or subtracting, care must be taken to use only like numbers. Thus 6 may be added to or subtracted from 12, or 3 apples may be added to or subtracted from 9 apples. But the abstract number 3 cannot be added to or subtracted from 5 gallons, nor can 6 quarts be added to or subtracted from 8 dozen.

In multiplication or division, concrete numbers may be multiplied or divided by abstract numbers. Thus 9 apples may be multiplied or divided by 3, or 10 oranges may be multiplied or divided by 5. Note, however, that concrete numbers cannot be multiplied or divided by concrete numbers. Thus 9 apples cannot be multiplied or divided by 3 apples, nor can 10 oranges be multiplied or divided by 5 oranges.

Notation is the method of writing numbers by means of symbols other than words.

Numeration is the method of reading or naming numbers.

Numbers may be expressed in three ways:

In *words*, as five, thirty-one, three-eighths, etc.
In *figures* (arabic), as 1, 9, 47, 802, etc.
In *letters* (roman), as L, V, X, M, C, etc.

DECIMAL SYSTEM OF NOTATION

The decimal system of notation, probably originating in India, was transmitted to Europe by the Arabs. The digits 1, 2, 3, 4, 5, 6, 7, 8, 9, and 0 are called Arabic or Hindu-Arabic numerals.

The starting point is the decimal indicated by a dot (.). The integral numbers 0 to 9 are written in the first place to the left. Tens, hundreds, thousands, tens of thousands, hundreds of thousands, etc., are written to the immediate left in the second, third, fourth, fifth, sixth, etc., places. Their quantities in tens, hundreds, thousands, etc., are indicated by the digits 0 to 9.

The decimal point is used to separate whole numbers and decimal fractions. Thus the digits to the right of the decimal point in the first, second, third, fourth, etc., places indicate the numbers of ten*ths*, hundred*ths*, thousand*ths*, ten-thousand*ths*, etc.

The following table shows the names and values of some of the places in the decimal system. You will note that the value of each place (both whole numbers and decimal fractions) is ten (10) times that of the next place to the right and one-tenth times that of the next place to the left.

Billions	Hundred millions	Ten millions	Millions	Hundred thousands	Ten thousands	Thousands	Hundreds	Tens	Units	Decimal Point	Tenths	Hundredths	Thousandths	Ten-thousandths	Hundred-thousandths
2	5	6	3	8	9	4	7	1	6	.	4	7	1	8	5

In order to distinguish more easily between the various quantities, a name is given to each group of three digits, and they are usually separated by the use of commas into groups of three to the left of the decimal point.

The word "and" in numeration of the decimal system should be used to indicate the separating point between the whole number and the decimal (or fractional ending). Thus in the preceding illustration the number 2,563,894,716.47185 would be read, "two billion, five hundred sixty-three million, eight hundred ninety-four thousand, seven hundred sixteen, *and* forty-seven thousand, one hundred eighty-five hundred-thousandths." Note that a hyphen (-) is used in writing compound numbers less than 100. Thus 34 is thirty-four, 78 is seventy-eight, .0062 is sixty-two ten-thousandths, etc.

In complex decimals (numbers such as .35$\frac{5}{6}$, 52.87$\frac{1}{3}$, and .0056$\frac{4}{7}$), the word "and" is also used to indicate the separation between the decimals and the fractional endings.

Examples: Give the correct numeration of (*a*) .25$\frac{2}{7}$ and (*b*) 25.00$\frac{2}{7}$.
(*a*) Twenty-five hundred*ths* and two-sevenths of one hundred*th*

Or: Twenty-five and two-sevenths hundred*ths*
(*b*) Twenty-five and two-sevenths of one hundred*th*
Or: Twenty-five and two-sevenths hundred*th*

In (*a*) and (*b*) you will notice that the second forms of numeration given are much alike, the only difference being the ending *ths* or *th.* Because they are so similar, the hearer is likely to misunderstand. Since the first forms of numeration as given in (*a*) and (*b*) are clearer to most people, it is recommended that you use them when giving oral numeration of complex decimals.

NOTE: From the examples, it should be apparent that $.00\frac{1}{2}$ is one-half of one hundredth, *not* one-half of one thousandth; and $.0\frac{2}{3}$ is two-thirds of one tenth, *not* two-thirds of one hundredth; etc.

ARITHMETIC APPROXIMATION

The functions of arithmetic in business do not end with exact solution of a specific problem, for the average businessman is often called upon to think in terms of comparative costs, general market trends, relative values, approximate weights or distances, etc. The development of "figure sense," the ability to recognize significant figures, is of great importance in arriving at decisions and in carrying on intelligent business conversation.

Visualization of the relationships existing between quantities and qualities is a major part of everyone's daily life. Such a concept is dependent upon the ability to make rough estimates. It is therefore desirable that you develop skill in approximation, so that this proficiency may be carried over from your study of arithmetic and utilized in solving the problems that will confront you in the future.

Essential to approximation is the ability to recognize significant figures in a given number. Thus if the number of shares sold on the stock market during a given day is 596,376, the significant figures sufficiently accurate for general information are 600,000. If an automobile is priced at $1,018.95, the significant figures are $1,000; if a sweater is priced $4.75, the significant figure is $5; if the length of a fence is 469.364 ft., the significant figures for most purposes will be 475 ft., or, even less accurately, 450 or 500 ft.

ROUNDING OFF NUMBERS

The rounding off of a given number is simply the determination of its significant figures, as illustrated in the preceding paragraph. Whether a given quantity or value should be rounded off to thousands, to hundreds, to units, to tenths, to hundredths, etc., depends upon the purpose that the numerical value serves.

To round off numbers:

1. Drop all figures beyond the desired unit of accuracy if they are to the right of the decimal point; change them to zeros if they are to the left of the decimal point.

2. If the portion to be dropped off begins with the digit 5 or more, add 1 to the last figure retained.

3. If the portion to be dropped off begins with a digit less than 5, discard it and retain the last figure as is.

Examples:

Rounded off to thousands			*Rounded off to tenths*		
565,743	to	566,000	.356	to	.4
27,499	to	27,000	27.04	to	27.0
5,500	to	6,000	3.051	to	3.1
1,695.62	to	2,000	.049	to	.0

Rounded off to tens			*Rounded off to hundredths*		
27.25	to	30	.4739	to	.47
434.95	to	430	5.626	to	5.63
8.47	to	10	854.3	to	854.30
2056.75	to	2060	9.994	to	9.99

ADDITION

Addition is the process of combining two or more numbers and expressing the result as a single quantity.

Addends are the numbers to be added.

The *sum* or *amount* or *total* is the result of the process of adding.

The sign in addition is "+." In reading, this sign is usually called "plus" or "and." Thus 8 + 5 is 8 plus 5, or 8 and 5.

Examples:

276	Addend	4,638 lb.
+482	Addend	+ 563 lb.
758	Sum or amount or total	5,201 lb.

Adding Decimals. The addition of decimals requires that the following rule be observed: *Place decimals of the same power in the same vertical column.* Thus, in the addends and in the sum, the decimal points must be placed directly above or below one another.

It is apparent that tenths are added to tenths, hundredths to hundredths, thousandths to thousandths, etc.

Example 1: Find the sum of 2.35 and 354.4.

```
  2.35
354.4
------
356.75
```

Example 2: Find the amount of 8,567.0138 and 28.97631.

```
8,567.0138
   28.97631
-----------
8,595.99011
```

Example 3: Find the sum of .067, 1.11, 54, .5678, and 324.6.

```
   .067
  1.11
 54.
   .5678
324.6
--------
380.3448
```

Proving Addition. Two methods of proving addition are in common use: (1) reverse-order check and (2) casting-out-nines check.

The *reverse-order* check is accomplished by adding again in the reverse direction. Thus if a column of figures has been added from bottom to top, reverse the operation and add from top to bottom. If the sums agree, it may be assumed that the answer is correct.

The *casting-out-nines* check is accomplished by eliminating nines or multiples of nine from the addends and the sum. The total of the remainders of the addends when nines have also been eliminated will be equal to the remainder in the sum.

Casting out nines may be done by division by 9, by horizontal addition, or by cancellation combined with addition. As an illustration, consider the numbers 30, 43, 72, 546, 712, 2,516, and 46,622.

Division by 9

Numbers	*Remainders*
30	3
43	7
72	0
546	6
712	1
2,516	5
46,622	2

Horizontal addition

Numbers		*Remainders*
30	3 + 0 =	3
43	4 + 3 =	7
72	7 + 2 = 9 and 9 ÷ 9 :	0[1]
546	5 + 4 + 6 = 15 and 1 + 5 =	6
712	7 + 1 + 2 = 10 and 1 + 0 =	1
2,156	2 + 5 + 1 + 6 = 14 and 1 + 4 =	5
46,622	4 + 6 + 6 + 2 + 2 = 20 and 2 + 0 =	2

Canceling and adding

Numbers	*Remainders*
3 0	3 + 0 = 3
4 3	4 + 3 = 7
~~7~~ ~~2~~	= 0
~~5~~ ~~4~~ 6	= 6
~~7~~ 1 ~~2~~	= 1
~~2~~ 5 ~~1~~ ~~6~~	= 5
~~4~~ ~~6~~ ~~6~~ ~~2~~ 2	= 2

As you will observe, the remainders are the same, regardless of the method used. The "canceling-plus-adding" method is preferred by most people. Note that cancellation may be employed regardless of the number of digits combined to total 9, 18, 27, or any other multiple of 9, the remaining digits not canceled being added to determine the remainder. Thus in the number 2,877,556 the digits 2 + 7 = 9 might be canceled, 7 + 5 + 6 = 18 might be canceled, leaving the digits 8 + 5 = 13, and 1 + 3 may be added (or divided) to give the remainder 4.

The following example will illustrate the use of the casting-out-nines check (*a*) by division, (*b*) by addition, and (*c*) by cancellation plus addition.

Example: Add 376, 842, 936, and 742, proving by the casting-out-nines check.

(*a*) By division:

		Remainders
	376 ÷ 9	7
	842 ÷ 9	5
	936 ÷ 9	0
	742 ÷ 9	4
Sum =	2,896	16 = total of remainders in addends

Total of remainders in addends 16 ÷ 9, remainder of 7

Sum of 2,896 ÷ 9, remainder of 7

The checking number is 7.

[1] In adding, when the sum is 9, 18, 27, or any multiple of 9, the remainder is 0.

(*b*) By addition:

		Remainders
376	$3 + 7 + 6 = 16$, and $1 + 6 =$	7
842	$8 + 4 + 2 = 14$, and $1 + 4 =$	5
936	$9 + 3 + 6 = 18$, and $1 + 8 = 9$ or	0
742	$7 + 4 + 2 = 13$, and $1 + 3 =$	4
Sum = 2,896		16 = total of remainders in addends

Total of remainders in addends = 16, and $1 + 6 = 7$
Sum = 2,896, and $2 + 8 + 9 + 6 = 25$, and $2 + 5 = 7$
The checking number is 7.

(*c*) By cancellation plus addition:

	Cancel and add:		*Remainders*
376	~~3~~ 7 ~~6~~		= 7
842	8 4 2	$8 + 4 + 2 = 14$, and $1 + 4 =$	~~5~~
936	~~9~~ ~~3~~ ~~6~~		= 0
742	~~7~~ 4 ~~2~~		= ~~4~~
Sum = 2,896			7

Total of remainders in addends (cancel $5 + 4$) = 7
Sum = 2,896, cancel 28~~9~~6, and $2 + 8 + 6 = 16$, and $1 + 6 = 7$
The checking number is 7.

The checking number obtained for both the sum and the total of remainders in the addends must be the same. If they are different, the work is incorrect, there being an error in the sum, in the check, or in both.

All methods of proving addition give only reasonable assurance of accuracy. Identical or coinciding mistakes will invalidate the reverse-order check. Shifting of decimals, reversing of numbers such as 74 for 47 (difference of 27 or three 9's), or any error totaling 9's in the sum will result in an error that will not be indicated when the casting-out-nines check is used.

For most problems in addition, the reverse-order check is the more satisfactory. However, when long columns of addends that are quite large must be totaled, the casting-out-nines check may be preferable.

Two Methods of Adding Long Columns:

In adding long columns it is sometimes helpful to divide the columns into two or more parts, obtaining a subtotal for each part and then adding these subtotals to obtain the sum total. (See following page.)

Another method of increasing accuracy is to total each digit column separately and then to obtain the sum total. This is helpful in doing a reverse-order check as it records subtotals by columns. (See following page.)

Example:

4,276	
3,849	
7,827	
4,834	
4,229	25,015 (subtotal)
2,275	
4,832	
7,439	
1,001	
8,157	23,704 (subtotal)
	48,719 Sum total

Example:

4,276	
3,849	
7,827	
4,834	
4,229	
2,275	
4,832	
7,439	
1,001	
8,157	
59	Subtotals of each column
36	
43	
44	
48,719	Sum total

SUBTRACTION

Subtraction is the process of finding the difference between numbers.

The sign used in subtraction is "−." In reading, this sign is usually called "less," or "minus." Thus 7 − 3 is 7 less 3, or 7 minus 3.

The *minuend* is the number from which the subtraction is made.

The *subtrahend* is the number subtracted.

The *remainder* is the difference between the minuend and subtrahend.

The minuend is equal to the sum of the subtrahend and the remainder. The subtrahend is equal to the difference between the minuend and the remainder.

Proving Subtraction. In proving subtraction, the most desirable method is to add the remainder to the subtrahend. The result should equal the minuend.

Example:

Minuend	458,914	
Subtrahend	− 290,478	
Remainder	168,436	
	+ 290,478	Add subtrahend to remainder
	458,914	Sum equals minuend (check)

Since proving in subtraction is so easily accomplished, it is advisable to use this check frequently. The avoidance of errors will more than compensate for the time taken in checking.

Decimals in Subtraction. When there are decimals in subtraction, the rule that must be observed is the same rule used for the addition of decimals: *Place decimals of the same power in the same vertical column.* Thus in minuend, subtrahend, and remainder, decimal points must be placed directly above or below one another.

Since only like numbers may be subtracted, tenths are subtracted from tenths, hundredths from hundredths, thousandths from thousandths, etc.

Example 1: Subtract 47,062 from 1,549.23.

```
            1549.230 (annex 0)
            −47.062
Remainder   1502.168
```

Example 2: Subtract 356.1 from 4,823.15.

```
            4823.15
            −356.1
Remainder   4467.05
```

Example 3: From 129.67 take 73.6438.

```
            129.6700 (annex 00)
            −73.6438
Remainder    56.0262
```

Example 4: From 78,97825 subtract 9.387.

```
            78.97825
            −9.387
Remainder   69.59125
```

Note that the annexation of zeros to digits to the right of the decimal point as in Examples 1 and 3 does not change the value of the decimal.

EXERCISE 1

A. Write the correct verbal form of the following:

1. 374 **2.** 2605.71 **3.** $.547\frac{4}{9}$ $48.03\frac{2}{7}$

B. Write the following as arabic numbers:

1. Two hundred twenty-three ten-thousandths
2. Four hundred twenty-one and nine thousandths
3. Eight thousand five hundred seven and six and one-third hundredths
4. Three million and two tenths

C. Round off the following numbers as indicated:

To hundredths	*To thousands*	*To tens*
1. 8.6053 =	**1.** 4,338,296 =	**1.** 467.83 =
2. .22495 =	**2.** 01,597.6 =	**2.** 306,755 =
3. 73.207 =	**3.** 500.109 =	**3.** 4.5968 =
4. 1.0049 =	**4.** 8,940,521 =	**4.** 529,505 =

To tenths	*To hundreds*	*To units*
1. .30357 =	1. 49.8406 =	1. 703.64 =
2. 33.467 =	2. 8,678,149 =	2. 3.1987 =
3. 921.14 =	3. 24,657.6 =	3. 01.509 =
4. 073.55 =	4. 450.001 =	4. 5,593.6 =

D. Add and prove each problem by the reverse-order check:

1.	2.	3.	4.
763.54	673.33	717.051	557.342
954.28	494.38	114.95	65.729
714.55	363.76	5,432.57	987.0
897.65	400.43	0.0083	5.95
765.89	893.49	92.83	87.005
782.71	144.99	183.92	1,056.925
172.78	617.93	4,298.763	9.0871
778.21	936.71	627.367	1,498,9204
421.87	737.36	29.76	377.695

E. Add and prove each problem by the casting-out-nines check:

1.	2.	3.	4.
68.07	1.021	63.540	353.7000
5.9782	1.0063	9,284.25	216.039
105.6321	5.0408	6.003	62.938
72.6976	7.0321	728.995	176.83
81.7749	14.9825	39.875	78.37
47.32	4.93	1,489.92	99.43
.0041	187.54	429.875	871.69
63.496	3.976	938.625	.3134
5.201	0.842	1,487.333	15.9721

F. Subtract and prove each problem by adding remainder to subtrahend:

1. 86,325.18 18,493.77	2. 53,975.76 1,494.89	3. 496,584.90 9,795.92	4. 2,980.357 97.568
5. 738,445.73 556.80	6. 28,400. 19,598.95	7. 5,630.975 576.899	8. 5,398.656 9.767
9. 2,005. 1,996.055	10. 4,936.285 957.	11. 839.2691 643.29	12. 895.9275 .0089
13. 973.68776 4.798	14. 387.853 298.80077	15. 9,362.448 63.369	16. 78.4 59.50476

UNIT 2. Multiplication and Division

MULTIPLICATION

Multiplication is the process of taking one number as many times as there are units in another number.

It is a form of abbreviated addition. Thus, 5 × 3 means 3 added five times, or 5 added three times. 5 + 5 + 5 = 15, or 5 multiplied by 3 = 15. Also 3 + 3 + 3 + 3 + 3 = 15, or 3 multiplied by 5 = 15.

A sign used in multiplication is "×." In reading, this sign is usually called "times." Thus 4 × 6 is 4 times 6, or 6 times 4.

The *multiplicand* is the number multiplied.

The *multiplier* is the number multiplied by (the number of times the multiplicand "is taken").

The *product* is the result of multiplication.

The *factors* in multiplication are the multiplicand and the multiplier. They are the numbers which when multiplied together result in the product.

Example: Multiply 24 by 6, or 6 times 24, or 24 × 6.

Factor	24	Multiplicand
Factor	6	Multiplier
	144	Product

Partial products are the result of multiplication of the multiplicand by the single digits composing the multiplier.

Example: Multiply 24 by 56.

24	
56	
144	Partial product
120	Partial product
1344	

When Multiplicand or Multiplier Ends in Zeros. Multiplication may be simplified when either or both factors end in zeros. In such instances it is desirable to omit the ending zeros from the process of multiplication, the required product then being determined by annexing the number of zeros omitted.

Example 1: Multiply 7,200 by 23 (one factor ending in zeros).

7200	Factor	23
23	Factor	7200
216		46
144		161
165600	Product	165600 (00 annexed)

Multiplication Table

	Products you must know								Products you should know							Products worth your effort to know								
	2	3	4	5	6	7	8	9	10	11	12	13	14	15	16	17	18	19	20	21	22	23	24	**25**
2	**4**	6	8	10	12	14	16	18	20	22	24	26	28	30	32	34	36	38	40	42	44	46	48	50
3	6	**9**	12	15	18	21	24	27	30	33	36	39	42	45	48	51	54	57	60	63	66	69	72	75
4	8	12	**16**	20	24	28	32	36	40	44	48	52	56	60	64	68	72	76	80	84	88	92	96	100
5	10	15	20	**25**	30	35	40	45	50	55	60	65	70	75	80	85	90	95	100	105	110	115	120	125
6	12	18	24	30	**36**	42	48	54	60	66	72	78	84	90	96	102	108	114	120	126	132	138	144	150
7	14	21	28	35	42	**49**	56	63	70	77	84	91	98	105	112	119	126	133	140	147	154	161	168	175
8	16	24	32	40	48	56	**64**	72	80	88	96	104	112	120	128	136	144	152	160	168	176	184	192	200
9	18	27	36	45	54	63	72	**81**	90	99	108	117	126	135	144	153	162	171	180	189	198	207	216	225
10	20	30	40	50	60	70	80	90	**100**	110	120	130	140	150	160	170	180	190	200	210	220	230	240	250
11	22	33	44	55	66	77	88	99	110	**121**	132	143	154	165	176	187	198	209	220	231	242	253	264	275
12	24	36	48	60	72	84	96	108	120	132	**144**	156	168	180	192	204	216	228	240	252	264	276	288	300
13	26	39	52	65	78	91	104	117	130	143	156	**169**	182	195	208	221	234	247	260	273	286	299	312	325
14	28	42	56	70	84	98	112	126	140	154	168	182	**196**	210	224	238	252	266	280	294	308	322	336	350
15	30	45	60	75	90	105	120	135	150	165	180	195	210	**225**	240	255	270	285	300	315	330	345	360	375
16	32	48	64	80	96	112	128	144	160	176	192	208	224	240	**256**	272	288	304	320	336	352	368	384	400
17	34	51	68	85	102	119	136	153	170	187	204	221	238	255	272	**289**	306	323	340	357	374	391	408	425
18	36	54	72	90	108	126	144	162	180	198	216	234	252	270	288	306	**324**	342	360	378	396	414	432	450
19	38	57	76	95	114	133	152	171	190	209	228	247	266	285	304	323	342	**361**	380	399	418	437	456	475
20	40	60	80	100	120	140	160	180	200	220	240	260	280	300	320	340	360	380	**400**	420	440	460	480	500
21	42	63	84	105	126	147	168	189	210	231	252	273	294	315	336	357	378	399	420	**441**	462	483	504	525
22	44	66	88	110	132	154	176	198	220	242	264	286	308	330	352	374	396	418	440	462	**484**	506	528	550
23	46	69	92	115	138	161	184	207	230	253	276	299	322	345	368	391	414	437	460	483	506	**529**	552	575
24	48	72	96	120	144	168	192	216	240	264	288	312	336	360	384	408	432	456	480	504	528	552	**576**	600
25	50	75	100	125	150	175	200	225	250	275	300	325	350	375	400	425	450	475	500	525	550	575	600	**625**

Example 2: Multiply 6,400 by 850 (both factors ending in zeros).

6400	Factor	850
850	Factor	6400
320		340
512		510
5440000	Product	5440000 (000 annexed)

Decimals in Multiplication. Because one of the factors in multiplication must always be an abstract number, only after the digits comprising the product have been determined is it necessary to locate the position of the decimal point. Therefore it is immaterial whether the decimal points in the multiplicand and multiplier are in any particular position with respect to one another.

Thus the rule to observe when there are decimals in multiplication is, *A product will have as many decimal places as there are decimal places in the two factors together.*

If there are not so many decimals in the product as in both the multiplier and multiplicand together, then prefix as many zeros to the product as are necessary.

Example 1: Find the product of 12.0765 and 2.31.

```
 12.0765
    2.31
 -------
  120765
 362295
241530
--------
27896715
```

Since there are six decimal places in the two factors, there should be six decimal places in the product. The correct answer would be

Product = 27.896715

Example 2: Multiply 92.007 by .000032.

```
  92.007
 .000032
 -------
  184014
 276021
 -------
 2944224
```

Since the sum of the number of decimal places in the multiplicand and multiplier is nine, there should be nine decimal places in the product. As there are only seven digits in the product, two zeros are prefixed:

Product = .002944224

Proving the Product of Multiplication. There are a number of commonly accepted ways of proving the result of multiplication. Among the most frequently used checks are the following:

Transposing the Factors and Again Multiplying. If the products are the same, it may be assumed that the multiplication is correct.

Example:

```
  285            Check:    36
 ×36                     ×285
 1710                     180
 855                     288
10260                    72
                        10260
```

Division of the Product by Either of the Factors (preferably by the multiplier). The quotient thus obtained should equal the remaining factor.

Example:

```
  95        Check:     95       Or check:     42
  42               42)3990             95)3990
 190                  378                 380
380                    210                 190
3990                   210                 190
```

Casting Out Nines. This check is recommended only when the multiplier and multiplicand are large figures. If both factors exceed three digits, this check is sometimes the most desirable means of proving. The casting-out-nines check may be accomplished as follows:

1. Use either the dividing, adding, or canceling-plus-adding method to cast out nines from the multiplicand and the multiplier.
2. Multiply one remainder by the other and again cast out nines.
3. Cast out nines from the product.

The final remainder found in (2) should equal the remainder in the product (3).

Example:

```
   7819  Remainder =  7
  ×281   Remainder = ×2
   7819              16  Remainder = 5
  62552
 15638
2197139  Remainder in the product = 5
```

NOTE: A zero remainder in either factor would immediately indicate that the remainder in the product must also be zero.

Useful Short Methods of Multiplying. There are many short cuts in multiplication, but unless one is constantly working with figures, they are not easily recalled. For the average individual, it is quicker and more accurate to use the longer, more familiar methods. However, there are a few practical short cuts that everyone should know and use. A number of other short cuts in multiplication are illustrated in Appendix I.

Shorts Cuts Based on 10 *and Powers of* 10.

1. *To multiply by* 10, 100, 1,000, *etc.* To multiply by 10 or powers of 10, move the decimal point in the multiplicand to the *right* as many places as there are zeros in the multiplier.

Examples:

$$42 \times 100 = 4{,}200; \qquad 27.6543 \times 1{,}000 = 27{,}654.3$$

This rule is reversed for division by 10 or powers of 10, the decimal point in the dividend being moved to the *left* as many places as there are zeros in the divisor.

2. *To multiply by aliquot parts of* 100 (or 10 or any power of 10):

a. To multiply by 50: multiply by 100 and divide by 2.
b. To multiply by 25: multiply by 100 and divide by 4.

Example a:

$742 \times 50 = (742 \times 100) \div 2 =$
$74{,}200 \div 2 = 37{,}100$

Example b:

$624 \times 25 = (624 \times 100) \div 4 =$
$62{,}400 \div 4 = 15{,}600$

Note: This procedure may be used whenever the multiplier is an aliquot part of 10, 100, 1,000, etc. See section on Aliquot Parts, pages 71–76, for an explanation of aliquot parts, their multiples, and their use in multiplication and division.

3. *To multiply by a number slightly more or less than* 10, 100, 1,000, *etc.*:

a. To multiply by 11: multiply by 10 and add multiplicand.
b. To multiply by 101: multiply by 100 and add multiplicand.
c. To multiply by 99: multiply by 100 and subtract multiplicand.
d. To multiply by 98: multiply by 100 and subtract 2 times the multiplicand.

Example a:

$437 \times 11 = (437 \times 10) + 437 =$
$4{,}370 + 437 = 4{,}807$

Example b:

$38 \times 101 = (38 \times 100) + 38 =$
$3{,}800 + 38 = 3{,}838$

Example c:

$52 \times 99 = (52 \times 100) - 52 =$
$5{,}200 - 52 = 5{,}148$

Example d:

$27 \times 98 = (27 \times 100) - (2 \times 27) =$
$2{,}700 - 54 = 2{,}646$

Note: Variations in this procedure may be used for numbers such as 102, 110, 89, 1,011, 199, etc.

DIVISION

Division is the process of finding how many times one number is contained within another number.

It is a short method of subtraction. Thus, 9 may be subtracted 3 times from 27, or 27 may be divided 3 times by 9.

A sign used in division is "÷," and in reading, this is usually called "*divided by*." Thus 9 ÷ 3 is read "9 divided by 3."

The *dividend* is the number divided.

The *divisor* is the number divided by.

The *quotient* is the result of division.

The *remainder* is the amount by which the dividend exceeds the product of the divisor and the quotient.

Division may also be thought of as the process of finding the unknown factor in a multiplication in which one of the factors and the product are known. For example, in dividing 324 by 6, the divisor 6 is the known factor; the dividend 324 is the known product; and the quotient, which is 54, is the unknown factor. Thus the *divisor* is a given factor; the *dividend* is the given product; and the *quotient* is therefore the required factor.

Short Division. If the divisor is a single digit, do the operation mentally.

Example: Divide 1,981 by 7.

```
Divisor  7)1981  Dividend
            283  Quotient
```

Think as follows: "7 into 19 is 2, and 5 over. Carry 5 to 8, making 58. 7 into 58 is 8, and 2 over. Carry 2 to 1, making 21. 7 into 21 is 3. The quotient is 283."

Long Division. If 748 is multiplied by 362, the product will be 270,776. Therefore if 270,776 is divided by 362, the quotient will be 748. In solving long-division problems, adept estimation is helpful. The following examples illustrate incorrect and correct estimating:

Example 1 (incorrect):

```
            6
362)270776
     2172
      535
```

The number 6 is not large enough since the remainder of 535 is greater than the divisor.

Example 2 (incorrect):

```
            8
362)270776
     2896
```

The number 8 is too large since the product of $8 \times 362 = 2{,}896$ and is larger than the dividend 2,707.

Example 3 (correct):

```
                 748  Quotient
Divisor  362)270776  Dividend
             2534
              1737
              1448
               2896
               2896
```

The procedure in solving Example 3 is as follows:

363 goes into 2,707 seven times. Place 7 above the ending digit of 2,707. Multiply 362 by 7 and place the product 2,534 with its right digit below the right digit of 2,707. Subtract and obtain 173. Annex 7 from the dividend, to obtain the number 1,737. Continue this process to obtain the final answer or quotient of 748.

When the Divisor Ends in Zeros. If the divisor ends in zeros, cancellation may be employed to simplify the process of division. Consider the following:

$600 \div 200 = 3$	$1{,}440 \div 500 = 2.88$	$3{,}280 \div 1{,}600 = 2.05$
$60 \div 20 = 3$	$144 \div 50 = 2.88$	$328 \div 160 = 2.05$
$6 \div 2 = 3$	$14.4 \div 5 = 2.88$	$32.8 \div 16 = 2.05$

It is evident that cancellation (rejection) of 10, 100, 1,000, etc., from both dividend and divisor does not affect the quotient. Moving the decimal point in both divisor and dividend to the left one, two or three places, etc., is equivalent to dividing by 10, 100, 1,000, etc.

The following rule may be applied to all problems in division: *The quotient will remain the same if both dividend and divisor are divided by the same number.*

Examples:

Without canceling:

```
5472000 ÷ 300
        18240
  300)5472000
      300
      2472
      2400
       720
       600
       1200
       1200
```

With canceling:

```
5472ØØØ ÷ 3ØØ
     18240
 3ØØ)5472ØØØ
     3
     24
     24
      7
      6
      12
      12
```

Remainder. If the divisor is not contained an integral (whole) number of times in the dividend, there will be a remainder.

This remainder may be expressed in two ways: (1) as a common fraction with a numerator that is the remainder and a denominator that is the divisor; or (2) as a decimal fraction remainder that is stated in tenths, hundredths, thousandths, etc.

The decimal remainder, or decimal fraction, is determined by placing a decimal point after the units digit (last whole digit) of the dividend and the quotient. Then annex zeros to the dividend and continue dividing until the number of decimal places in the quotient is sufficiently accurate.

Example 1 (common-fraction remainder): Divide 136 by 25.

```
      5
25)136
    125
     11   Remainder
```

$$\text{Complete quotient} = 5\frac{11}{25}$$

The complete expression of this quotient would include the remainder. That is, 25 goes into 136 five times and eleven over. This is more simply stated as five and eleven twenty-fifths.

Example 2 (decimal-fraction remainder): Divide 136 by 25.

```
       5.44
25)136.00
    125
     110
     100
      100
      100
```

Complete quotient = 5.44

This decimal remainder could be expressed to nearest tenths as 5.4 or five and four-tenths; in hundredths (as above) as 5.44, or five and forty-four hundredths; in thousandths as 5.440, or five and four hundred forty thousandths, etc.

Decimals in the Divisor. When decimals occur in the divisor, they may be eliminated by increasing both dividend and divisor proportionately. Consider the following:

$$12 \div 6 = 2 \qquad 25 \div 5 = 5$$
$$120 \div 60 = 2 \qquad 250 \div 50 = 5$$
$$1{,}200 \div 600 = 2 \qquad 2{,}500 \div 500 = 5$$

It is evident that multiplication of both dividend and divisor by the same number does not affect the quotient.

The following rule is applicable not only to division problems that contain decimals in dividend or divisor, or both, but to all problems in division: *The quotient will remain the same if both dividend and divisor are multiplied by the same number.*

If the divisor contains decimals, it is recommended that they be eliminated by (1) moving the decimal point to the right to make it a whole number, (2) moving the decimal point in the dividend the same number of places to the right, annexing as many zeros as may be necessary, and (3) placing the decimal point of the quotient directly above the decimal point in this new dividend.

Note that each digit in the quotient must be placed directly over the right-hand digit of its product.

Example 1: Divide 259.2386 by .542, giving the answer to tenths.

Change the divisor to whole numbers and move the decimal point in the dividend an equal number (3) of places to the right.

```
          478.3
    542)259238.6
        2168
         4243
         3794
          4498
          4336
           1626
           1626
```

This quotient is in tenths. If the answer is desired in hundredths, another zero is annexed to the dividend (259238.60). The quotient is then expressed in hundredths (478.30).

Example 2: Divide 29.10489 by 3.81, giving answer to nearest thousandths.

Change the divisor to whole numbers and move the decimal point in the dividend an equal number (2) to places to the right.

```
          7.639
    381)2910.489
        2667
         2434
         2286
          1488
          1143
           3459
           3429
             30  Remainder
```

The quotient is to the nearest thousandths, for the remainder is less than half of 381; the correct answer is therefore 7.639. If the remainder were greater than one-half of 381, it would be proper to add one-thousandth to the quotient, giving an answer of 7.640.

If the answer is desired to the nearest hundredths, the remainder would be 345.9, more than half of 381, and the final digit or hundredth would be correctly increased from 3 to 4 so that the quotient would be 7.64.

Proving Division by Multiplying Factors. Since the dividend equals the product of the divisor (given factor) and the quotient (required factor), proof of accuracy in division may be determined by multiplying one factor by the other (preferably using the divisor as the multiplier) and then adding the remainder, if any. This number should equal the dividend.

Proof of Example 1 (page 21):

```
  478.3     Factor
   .542     Factor
  -----
   9566
  19132
 23915
--------
259.2386    Product = dividend
```

Proof of Example 2 (page 21):

```
   7.639   Factor
    3.81   Factor
   -----
    7639
   61112
 22917
--------
29.10459   Product
      30   Remainder
--------
29.10489   Product + remainder = dividend
```

If the product plus the remainder fails to equal the dividend, the division or the check, or both, are incorrect.

Proving Division by Casting Out Nines. The casting-out-nines check is recommended only when the divisor and the quotient are large figures. If both exceed three figures, this check is sometimes desirable. The casting-out-nines check may be accomplished as follows:

1. Use either the dividing, adding, or canceling-plus-adding method to cast out nines from the quotient and the divisor.
2. Multiply one remainder by the other and again cast out nines.
3. Cast out nines from the remainder (of the division problem) and add this remainder to the product of (2).

4. Cast out nines from the sum totaled in (3).
5. Cast out nines in the dividend.

The final remainder in (4) should equal the remainder in the dividend (5).

Example:

2353	*Check*
3287)7734912	
6574	Quotient = 4
11609	
9861	Divisor = ×2
17481	8
16435	
10462	Remainder = +7
9861	15 = 6
601	Dividend = 6

EXERCISE 2

A. Multiply and then check by transposing the factors and multiplying:

1. 567,009 × 25.08
2. 3,245.45 × 79.32

B. Multiply and then check by dividing the product by the multiplier:

1. 428,756 × 37.08
2. 7.96573 × .7904

C. Multiply and then check by casting out nines:

1. 768.765 × 7.06
2. 456.7285 × .0037
3. 847.25 × 347.6
4. .62807 × 20.178
5. 6,439.82 × 6,003
6. 2.36507 × 9,805

D. Divide, finding quotient to decimal point only, and then check by multiplication of quotient by divisor:

1. 96,564 ÷ 96
2. 4,355.4 ÷ 8.2
3. .707)86.354
4. 85.9)9,390.7

E. Divide, finding quotient to decimal point only, and then check by casting out nines:

1. 61,021 ÷ 58
2. 5,698.2 ÷ .74
3. .819)82.983
4. .0834)67.495

UNIT 3. Common Factors and Divisibility of Numbers

One of the most serious of the arithmetical deficiencies of many students is lack of knowledge and understanding of factors and multiples. Skill in recognizing factors common to both numerator and denominator is very helpful in solving problems in which cancellation may be employed and also in reducing fractions to lower terms. The solution of certain problems in proportion and, more important, of many problems in adding or subtracting and even in multiplying or dividing fractions may depend largely upon the selection of a common denominator, the finding of which often requires a knowledge of factors.

A *factor* of a number is an exact divisor of that number. Numbers multiplied together that produce a certain number are *factors* of that number.

A *prime number* is a number that has no factors other than itself and 1. Thus 1, 2, 3, 5, 7, 11, 13, 17, 19, 23, etc., are prime numbers. Each is divisible without remainder only by 1 and itself.

A *composite number* is a number that may be formed as the product of two or more factors other than 1 and itself. Thus 4, 6, 8, 9, 10, 12, 14, 15, 16, 18, etc., are composite numbers, since $2 \times 2 = 4$, $3 \times 2 = 6$, $2 \times 2 \times 2 = 8$, $3 \times 3 = 9$, $2 \times 5 = 10$, $2 \times 2 \times 3 = 12$, etc.

RULES OF DIVISIBILITY

Divisibility by Prime Numbers. To find the factors of a number, there are several rules of divisibility that will enable you to determine readily whether a number is divisible without remainder by the smaller prime number 2, 3, 5, or 11.

A number is divisible without remainder by 2 if the ending digit is divisible by 2 without remainder. Thus, 386 is divisible by 2 without remainder, but 385 and 387 are not divisible by 2 into quotients expressed in whole numbers without remainder, since neither 5 nor 7 is divisible by 2 without remainder.

A number is divisible without remainder by 3 if the sum of its digits is divisible by 3 without remainder. Thus, 387 is divisible by 3 without remainder, since the sum of its digits $(3 + 8 + 7)$ totals 18, a number divisible by 3 without remainder. Since the digits in 385 total 16 and in 386 total 17, and since neither 16 nor 17 is divisible by 3 without remainder, the numbers 385 and 386 cannot be divided by 3 into quotients expressed in whole numbers without remainder.

A number is divisible without remainder by 5 if the ending digit is 5 or 0. Thus 745 and 1,180 are each divisible by 5 without remainder. But 746 or 1,179 cannot be divided by 5 into quotients expressed in whole numbers without remainder, since their ending digits are neither 5 nor 0.

A number is divisible without remainder by 11 if the difference between the sums of the digits of odd and even order is divisible by 11 without remainder. Thus, 22 is divisible by 11 without remainder, since the difference between 2 and 2 is 0, and $0 \div 11 = 0$. And 32,758 is divisible by 11 without remainder, since $8 + 7 + 3 = 18$, $5 + 2 = 7$, and the difference between 18 and 7 is 11, a number divisible by 11 without remainder.

Other prime numbers such as 7, 13, 17, 19, etc., which may also be factors of any given number, may best be determined by trial and error. Thus 91 is divisible by 7 and 13 but not by 17 or 19 into quotients expressed in whole numbers without remainder.

Table of Prime Numbers from 1 to 1,000

1	59	139	233	337	439	557	653	769	883
2	61	149	239	347	443	563	659	773	887
3	67	151	241	349	449	569	661	787	907
5	71	157	251	353	457	571	673	797	911
7	73	163	257	359	461	577	677	809	919
11	79	167	263	367	463	587	683	811	929
13	83	173	269	373	467	593	691	821	937
17	89	179	271	379	479	599	701	823	941
19	97	181	277	383	487	601	709	827	947
23	101	191	281	389	491	607	719	829	953
29	103	193	283	397	499	613	727	839	967
31	107	197	293	401	503	617	733	853	971
37	109	199	307	409	509	619	739	857	977
41	113	211	311	419	521	631	743	859	983
43	127	223	313	421	523	641	751	863	991
47	131	227	317	431	541	643	757	877	997
53	137	229	331	433	547	647	761	881	

Divisibility by Composite Numbers. In addition to the preceding rules of divisibility by prime numbers, there are also several helpful rules to aid in determining divisibility without remainder by the composite numbers 4, 8, 6, 9, and 10.

A number is divisible without remainder by 4 if the last two digits are divisible by 4 without remainder. Thus 132, 9,720, 8,516, and 992 are all divisible by 4 without remainder.

A number is divisible without remainder by 8 if the last three digits are divisible by 8 without remainder. Thus 7,104, 52,480, 1,328, and 69,064 are all divisible by 8 without remainder.

A number is divisible without remainder by 6 if it is an even number and if the sum of the digits is divisible by 3 without remainder. Thus 5,718, 3,414, 8,190, and 7,416 are all divisible by 6 without remainder.

A number is divisible without remainder by 9 if the sum of the digits is divisible by 9 without remainder. Thus 7,110, 522, 9,153, and 62,874 are all divisible by 9 without remainder.

A number is divisible without remainder by 10 if the ending digit is 0. Thus 40, 110, 550, and 3,170 are all divisible by 10 without remainder. (If the ending digits are 00, as in 500, 1,200, and 17,900, the number is also divisible by 100; if the ending digits are 000, as in 6,000, 27,000, and 14,000, the number is divisible by 1,000 as well as by 10 and 100, etc.)

Note that there are no exceptions to the preceding rules. Commit these rules of divisibility to memory. Their usefulness will become very apparent to you in the work that follows.

COMMON FACTORS OR COMMON DIVISORS

The terms "common factor" and "common divisor" mean much the same thing and are often used synonymously. If two or more numbers are divisible by the same number (have the same number as a factor), this number is a common divisor (common factor).

Examples:

5 is a common divisor of 5, 25, and 40
7 is a common factor of 14, 21, and 49
9 is a common divisor of 18, 63, and 90
3, 6, and 9 are common factors of 18, 36, 54, 72, and 144
2, 6, and 15 are common divisors of 30, 60, 150, and 240
4, 8, and 3 are common factors of 24, 48, 144, and 168

The Greatest Common Divisor. The term "greatest common divisor" (g.c.d.) is synonymous in general use with the term "highest common factor" (h.c.f.).

The *greatest common divisor* is the largest number that can be divided into each of two or more numbers. The g.c.d. of two or more numbers is the product of all the prime factors common to all the numbers.

Examples:

2 is the greatest common divisor of 4, 8, and 10
6 is the highest common factor of 12, 18, and 30
10 is the greatest common divisor of 10, 30, and 70

One of the most important uses of the g.c.d. is to reduce a fraction to its lowest terms in a single operation. If the g.c.d. is not known, it is possible to reduce a fraction to its lowest terms by dividing both numerator and denominator by their common factors. These common factors may not be apparent readily, and the reduction will then be accomplished only after considerable effort by the trial-and-error method.

Finding the G.C.D. The following is recommended as the most desirable method to use in reducing fractions to lowest terms if the common divisors of the numerator and denominator are not apparent, since it definitely determines the largest possible number that may be divided into the two terms of the fraction. If this method is used, you can be certain that you have found the g.c.d. and that the quotients of the numerator and denominator of the fraction after being divided by the g.c.d. will be the fraction reduced to the lowest possible terms.

The procedure is as follows:

1. Divide the larger number by the smaller.
2. Divide the divisor (the smaller number) by the remainder and continue this operation until there is no remainder (a 0 remainder).

The last divisor will be the g.c.d. (or h.c.f.).

Example 1: Find the g.c.d. of 108 and 744.

```
        6
  108)744
      648   1
       96)108
           96  8
           12)96
              96
               0
```

G.c.d. is 12.

$\frac{108}{744}$ could be reduced to its lowest terms by dividing its numerator and denominator by 12 = $\frac{9}{62}$.

Example 2: Find the h.c.f. of 9,230 and 639.

```
        14
  639)9230
      639
      2840
      2556   2
       284)639
           568   4
            71)284
               284
                 0
```

H.c.f. is 71.

$\frac{9230}{639}$ could be reduced to its lowest terms by dividing its numerator and denominator by 71 $= \frac{130}{9} = 14\frac{4}{9}$.

Example 3: Find the g.c.d. of 313 and 701.

```
        2
   313)701
       626    4
        75)313
           300   5
            13)75
               65   1
               10)13
                  10   3
                   3)10
                      9   3
                      1) 3
                         3
                         0
```

G.c.d. is 1.

$\frac{313}{701}$ is already reduced to its lowest terms, since the numerator and denominator divided by 1 $= \frac{313}{701}$.

EXERCISE 3

A. Find which of the prime numbers 2, 3, 5, 7, and 11 are factors in each of the following:

1. 42,386	**2.** 1,760	**3.** 1,257,120	**4.** 9,084,702	**5.** 2,801,470
6. 87,687	**7.** 2,354	**8.** 297	**9.** 75,852	**10.** 9,548,769

B. Find which of the composite numbers 4, 6, 8, 9, and 10 are factors in each of the following:

1. 679,128	**2.** 2,174,316	**3.** 942	**4.** 940,016	**5.** 1,862,172
6. 724,920	**7.** 5,466,180	**8.** 8,536,518	**9.** 64,387	**10.** 9,082,530

C. Find which of the numbers 2, 3, 4, 5, 6, 7, 8, 9, 10, and 11 are factors in each of the following:

1. 753,445	**2.** 337,428	**3.** 154,504	**4.** 453,120	**5.** 728,640
6. 647,568	**7.** 740,160	**8.** 100,344	**9.** 807,680	**10.** 121,030

D. Find the g.c.d. and then reduce each of the following fractions to lowest terms:

1. $\frac{39}{143}$	**2.** $\frac{1,118}{1,290}$	**3.** $\frac{142}{355}$	**4.** $\frac{604}{1,089}$	**5.** $\frac{413}{649}$
6. $\frac{6,270}{3,990}$	**7.** $\frac{187}{2,890}$	**8.** $\frac{1,441}{3,013}$	**9.** $\frac{265}{1,113}$	**10.** $\frac{279}{465}$

UNIT 4. Multiples and Cancellation

MULTIPLES AND COMMON MULTIPLES

A *multiple* of a number is the product of that number and any multiplier. That is, the number multiplied any number of times will give a product which is a multiple of that number. Thus:

Multiples of 4 are 4, 8, 12, 16, 20, etc.
Multiples of 6 are 6, 12, 18, 24, 30, etc.
Multiples of 10 are 10, 20, 30, 40, 50, etc.

A *common multiple* of two or more numbers is a number which is a multiple of each of the numbers. It is a number into which each of the numbers will divide without a remainder. Thus:

Common multiples of 4 and 6 are 12, 24, 36, 48, etc.
Common multiples of 5 and 7 are 35, 70, 105, 140, etc.
Common multiples of 3, 4, and 5 are 60, 120, 180, 240, etc.
Common multiples of 2, 4, and 9 are 36, 72, 108, 144, etc.

A common multiple is used frequently in the addition or subtraction of fractions. The common denominator used to reduce two or more fractions to like terms is a common multiple of the denominators of the fractions.

The *least common multiple* (l.c.m.) of two or more numbers is the smallest number into which each number can be divided without remainder.

Adding or subtracting fractions is greatly simplified if a "lowest common denominator" can be determined. A *lowest common denominator* (l.c.d.) is the least common multiple of the denominators of two or more fractions. Thus:

4 is the least common multiple of 2 and 4
12 is the least common multiple of 2, 3, 4, 6, and 12
35 is the least common multiple of 5, 7, and 35

Method of Finding the L.C.M. or L.C.D. When two or more numbers are relatively prime to one another (have no common factor other than 1), their product is the l.c.m. (or l.c.d.). Thus:

6 is the least common multiple of 2 and 3
35 is the least common multiple of 5 and 7
36 is the least common multiple of 4 and 9

But 24 is not the least common multiple of 4 and 6, because 2 is a common factor of 4 and 6, and therefore 4 and 6 are not prime to one another.

When three or more numbers are each prime to the other numbers, their product is the l.c.m. Thus 84 is the l.c.m. of 3, 4, and 7; 360 is the l.c.m. of 8, 9, and 5.

When the l.c.m. is not apparent by inspection, it may be found by determining the product of the prime factors of the numbers, each taken as many times as it occurs most frequently in any of the numbers.

A recommended method of finding the l.c.m. (or a lowest common denominator) is as follows:

1. Write the numbers in a horizontal row and then divide by a prime factor common to any two or more of the numbers.

2. Continue this process of division until there are no two quotients divisible by any prime number (other than 1).

The product of the prime factors and the final quotients will equal the l.c.m.

Example 1: Find the l.c.m. of 36, 12, 32, and 48.

2)	36	12	32	48
2)	18	6	16	24
2)	9	3	8	12
2)	9	3	4	6
3)	9	3	2	3
	3	1	2	1

$$\text{L.c.m.} = 2 \times 2 \times 2 \times 2 \times 3 \times 3 \times 2 = 288$$

Example 2: Find the l.c.d. of $\frac{1}{7}$, $\frac{5}{12}$, $\frac{3}{8}$, $\frac{1}{9}$, $\frac{5}{6}$, and $\frac{3}{14}$.

2)	7	12	8	9	6	14
2)	7	6	4	9	3	7
3)	7	3	2	9	3	7
7)	7	1	2	3	1	7
	1	1	2	3	1	1

$$\text{L.c.d.} = 2 \times 2 \times 3 \times 7 \times 2 \times 3 = 504$$

Shortening the Process of Finding the L.C.M. The process of solving for the l.c.m. may be shortened in two ways:

1. *Cancellation:*

a. Rejecting those given numbers which are factors of other numbers under consideration.

b. Rejecting obtained quotients which are factors of other obtained quotients.

2. *Dividing by composite numbers:*

a. Dividing by a composite number *if* it is divisible into all of the retained given numbers or obtained quotients.

b. Dividing by a composite number *if* the numbers not so divided are prime to the composite number.

Example 3: Same problem as Example 1.

4)36	~~12~~	32	48
3) 9		8	12
3		8	~~4~~

L.c.m. = 4 × 3 × 3 × 8 = 288

Example 4: Same problem as Example 2.

2)7	12	8	9	~~6~~	14
2)	6	4	9		7
	~~3~~	2	9		7

L.c.d. = 2 × 2 × 2 × 9 × 7 = 504

Example 5: Find the l.c.m. of 48, 20, 32, 30, 15, and 40.

2)48	~~20~~	32	30	~~15~~	40
4)24		16	15		20
2) 6		4	15		~~5~~
~~3~~		2	15		

L.c.m. = 2 × 4 × 2 × 2 × 15 = 480

Example 6: Find the l.c.d. of fractions which have denominators of 14, 64, 56, 16, 42, and 80.

2)~~14~~	64	56	~~16~~	42	80
4)	32	28		21	40
2)	8	7		21	10
	4			21	5

L.c.d. = 2 × 4 × 2 × 4 × 21 × 5 = 6,720

CANCELLATION

Cancellation is the rejection of equal factors in both dividend and divisor before division takes place.

The result of cancellation is to simplify materially the computations necessary in division, for it reduces the size of the calculations, often eliminating entirely some of the given factors from the process of division.

Either prime or composite numbers may be the rejected factors. The procedure is to place the factors of the dividend above a horizontal line and the factors of the divisor below; equal factors are then eliminated from both dividend and divisor.

As is illustrated in the following examples, cancellation does not affect the quotient.

Example 1: Divide $12 \times 6 \times 2$ by $6 \times 2 \times 4$.

$$144 \div 48 = 3$$

$$\text{(Canceling)} \frac{\overset{3}{\cancel{12}} \times \cancel{6} \times \cancel{2}}{\cancel{6} \times \cancel{2} \times \cancel{4}} = \frac{3}{1} = 3$$

Example 2: Divide $8 \times 6 \times 5 \times 4$ by $4 \times 10 \times 6 \times 2$.

$$960 \div 480 = 2$$

$$\text{(Canceling)} \frac{\overset{2}{\cancel{8}} \times \cancel{6} \times \cancel{5} \times \overset{2}{\cancel{4}}}{\cancel{4} \times \underset{2}{\cancel{10}} \times \cancel{6} \times \cancel{2}} = \frac{2}{1} = 2$$

Cancellation may also be profitably employed in the multiplication and division of fractions. Undoubtedly you will recall that a fraction is merely another form by which division may be indicated and that the bar or line between the upper portion (numerator) and the lower portion (denominator) of a fraction has the same significance as the usual division sign. Thus the following have the same meaning:

$$\frac{4}{5} \text{ and } 4 \div 5; \quad \frac{3}{7} \text{ and } 3 \div 7; \quad \frac{11}{8} \text{ and } 11 \div 8$$

When multiplying by one or a series of fractions, it is desirable to employ cancellation whenever possible. Suppose it is required that 360 be multiplied by $\frac{3}{4}$, that their product be multiplied by $\frac{5}{6}$, and that this second product be multiplied by $\frac{2}{5}$. Each multiplication (and cancellation) could be performed separately as follows:

$$\overset{90}{\cancel{360}} \times \frac{3}{\cancel{4}} = 270$$

$$\overset{45}{\cancel{270}} \times \frac{5}{\cancel{6}} = 225$$

$$\overset{45}{\cancel{225}} \times \frac{2}{\cancel{5}} = 90$$

Preferably, more factors could be rejected through cancellation if all the multiplications are performed jointly as follows:

$$\overset{90}{\cancel{360}} \times \frac{\cancel{3}}{\cancel{4}} \times \frac{\cancel{5}}{\underset{2}{\cancel{6}}} \times \frac{2}{\cancel{5}} = 90$$

Even more desirable as a form for cancellation would be to place all the numerators above and all the denominators below a single horizontal bar or line.

$$\frac{\overset{90}{\cancel{360}} \times \cancel{3} \times \cancel{5} \times \cancel{2}}{\cancel{4} \times \cancel{6} \times \cancel{5} \atop 2} = 90$$

It will be apparent to you that the immediately preceding illustration (originally a problem in multiplication by fractions) is solved in exactly the same manner as might be used for the problem of dividing 360 × 3 × 5 × 2 by 4 × 6 × 5. Note also that the sequence in which the factors are multiplied or rejected may be changed without affecting the result. Thus:

$$\frac{5 \times 3 \times \overset{\overset{\overset{3}{\cancel{15}}}{\cancel{90}}}{\cancel{360}} \times 2}{\cancel{5} \times \cancel{6} \times \cancel{4}} = 90$$

Before factors are rejected through cancellation, the given quantities (or values) in both dividend and divisor must be expressed in like terms. Thus if the given quantities are in both dollars and cents, express all such terms in either dollars or cents; if the given quantities are in both inches and feet, express all such terms in either inches or feet.

Take special note that cancellation cannot be performed when any one of the numbers in the numerator or denominator is separated by division (÷), addition (+), or subtraction (−) signs. Thus cancellation cannot be performed in the following until the operations indicated in the numerators and denominators have been completed:

Examples:

(*a*) $\dfrac{24}{17 - (2 \times 4)}$ (*b*) $\dfrac{32 - (8 \div 4)}{6}$ (*c*) $\dfrac{[(5 \times 6) - 9] \times [(90 \div 5) \div 3]}{(4 \times 12) - [48 \div (4 \times 2)]}$

When the numerator or denominator or both contain signs other than multiplication (×), complete the operations indicated in the numerator and denominator in the following order:

1. Clear quantities within signs of aggregation such as parentheses ( ), brackets [ ], and braces { }—that is, perform the operations indicated.
2. Do all the multiplication (in any order desired).
3. Do all division in the order in which it occurs.

4. Do all addition and subtraction (in any order desired). Thus in solving the preceding examples:

$$(a)\quad \frac{24}{17-(2\times 4)} = \frac{24}{17-8} = \frac{\overset{8}{\cancel{24}}}{\underset{3}{\cancel{9}}} = \frac{8}{3} = 2\frac{2}{3}$$

$$(b)\quad \frac{32-(8\div 4)}{6} = \frac{32-2}{6} = \frac{\overset{5}{\cancel{30}}}{\cancel{6}} = \frac{5}{1} = 5$$

$$(c)\quad \frac{[(5\times 6)-9]\times[(90\div 5)\div 3]}{(4\times 12)-[48\div(4\times 2)]} = \frac{(30-9)\times(18\div 3)}{48-(48\div 8)}$$

$$= \frac{21\times 6}{48-6} = \frac{\overset{3}{\cancel{21}}\times\cancel{6}}{\underset{2}{\cancel{42}}} = \frac{3}{1} = 3$$

EXERCISE 4

A. Find the l.c.m. of the following groups of numbers:

1. 12 16 30 **2.** 42 78 66

3. 8 18 6 4 9 **4.** 48 80 72 96

5. 216 360 504 648 **6.** 3 5 18 10 7

B. Find the l.c.d. of the following fractions:

1. $\frac{11}{18}\quad\frac{7}{27}\quad\frac{13}{63}$ **2.** $\frac{1}{2}\quad\frac{5}{6}\quad\frac{5}{3}\quad\frac{7}{9}\quad\frac{17}{12}$ **3.** $\frac{4}{7}\quad\frac{5}{24}\quad\frac{7}{6}\quad\frac{9}{8}\quad\frac{1}{9}$

4. $\frac{23}{38}\quad\frac{11}{46}\quad\frac{65}{54}\quad\frac{13}{18}$ **5.** $\frac{43}{315}\quad\frac{171}{180}\quad\frac{883}{630}\quad\frac{29}{270}$ **6.** $\frac{15}{16}\quad\frac{9}{7}\quad\frac{29}{14}\quad\frac{3}{8}\quad\frac{41}{32}$

C. Solve the following by cancellation:

1. $\frac{4\times 6\times 12\times 18}{6\times 3\times 8\times 2\times 4}$ **2.** $(9\times 8\times 7\times 15)\div(12\times 14\times 3\times 4)$

3. $\frac{375\times 50\times 80\times 120\times 66}{125\times 50\times 22\times 3\times 10\times 5}$ **4.** $\frac{1{,}250\times 144\times 375\times 39\times 102}{250\times 34\times 13\times 36\times 75}$

5. If a cord of wood requires a space equivalent to 8 by 4 by 4 ft., how many cords are contained in a stack of wood 64 ft. long, 30 ft. wide, and 27 ft. high?

6. A warehouse is 120 ft. long, 42 ft. wide, and 18 ft. 9 in. high. How many boxes 15 by 24 by 45 in. will it contain? (12 in. = 1 ft.)

7. A farmer sold 175 bu. of wheat at $2.50 per bushel, taking his pay in flour at 12.5 cents per pound. How many 100-lb. sacks of flour did he receive? NOTE: Express the price factors in the same kind of terms, *e.g.*, in dollars or in cents.

8. A store manager exchanged 225 yards of silk purchased at $1.80 per yard for percale at 37.5 cents per yard. How many yards of percale did he receive?
9. Find the cost of 150 pieces of lumber that are 2 in. thick, 6 in. wide, and 16 ft. long, if the price is $80 for 1,000 board feet. NOTE: A board foot is 1 in. by 1 ft. by 1 ft. By definition, it is an exception to the rule requiring the use of like terms for operations in weights and measures. Therefore in this problem use

$$\frac{\text{Thickness in inches} \times \text{width in inches} \times \text{length in feet}}{12}$$

10. A solid-brick wall is 36 ft. long, 8 ft. high, and 16 in. wide. If each brick requires 2 by 4 by 8 in. of space, find the number of bricks in the wall.

UNIT 5. Fractions: Fundamental Principles, Reduction, Addition

To begin your study of fractions, read the following definitions carefully. Be sure that you understand the relationship expressed by the two terms of a fraction.

A *fraction* is an indicated division. It is one or more fractional units. It is a part or portion of the whole of anything.

The *terms* of a fraction are the numerator and denominator.

The *numerator* shows the number of fractional units taken. Think of the numerator as representing the number of equal parts or equal portions that have been taken of the whole.

The *denominator* shows the number of fractional units into which the whole is divided. Think of the denominator as representing the number of equal parts or equal portions into which the whole has been divided.

The *fractional unit* has 1 for the numerator and any number for the denominator. Its denominator indicates the exact number of times that the fractional unit is contained in the whole (1 unit).

Example 1: A pie is divided into 5 equal portions. If one portion is eaten, the remainder may be expressed as a fractional part of the pie:

$$\text{Remainder} = \frac{4}{5}$$

4 is the numerator, or number of equal portions remaining of the whole.

5 is the denominator, or number of equal portions into which the pie was divided.

$$\text{Fractional unit} = \frac{1}{5}$$

Example 2: As is indicated by Example 1, a fraction or indicated division is usually written by placing a line between the numerator and the denominator. Thus:

$$\frac{7}{10} \text{ is the same as } 7 \div 10$$

7 is the numerator and is equivalent to a dividend.
10 is the denominator and is equivalent to a divisor.

$$\text{Fractional unit} = \frac{1}{10}$$

Example 3: If the operations indicated by the line or bar (—) in Examples 1 and 2 are completed, the fractions would then be expressed as *decimal fractions.* Thus:

$$\frac{4}{5} = 4 \div 5 = .8 \text{ or } .80 \text{ or } .800, \text{ etc.}$$

$$\frac{7}{10} = 7 \div 10 = .7 \text{ or } .70 \text{ or } .700, \text{ etc.}$$

In a decimal fraction, the denominator is 10 or some power of 10 (100, 1,000, 10,000, etc.), but it is omitted and its value is indicated by means of the decimal point (see page 62).

KINDS OF FRACTIONS

Fractions other than decimal fractions are known as *common* fractions. There are several types of common fractions, each distinguished by its own name.

A *proper fraction* is one in which the numerator is less than the denominator. Thus:

$$\frac{2}{3}, \frac{6}{7}, \frac{21}{22}, \frac{1}{9}, \frac{7}{12} \text{ are proper fractions}$$

An *improper fraction* is one in which the numerator is equal to or more than the denominator. Thus:

$$\frac{5}{3}, \frac{8}{7}, \frac{21}{8}, \frac{6}{6}, \frac{11}{9} \text{ are improper fractions}$$

A *complex fraction* is a fraction in which the numerator or denominator, or both, are fractional. Thus:

$$\frac{\frac{3}{4}}{10}, \frac{7}{\frac{2}{3}}, \frac{\frac{4}{5}}{\frac{8}{9}}, \frac{\frac{1}{2} \times \frac{2}{7}}{\frac{2}{3} - \frac{1}{4}} \text{ are complex fractions}$$

A *mixed number* is the sum of an integer (whole number) and a fraction. Thus:

$$7\frac{1}{4} \text{ is a mixed number equivalent to } 7 + \frac{1}{4}$$

$$23\frac{2}{3} \text{ is a mixed number equivalent to } 23 + \frac{2}{3}$$

A mixed number may also be expressed as (reduced to) an improper fraction; *e.g.*, $2\frac{1}{4}$, equivalent to $2 + \frac{1}{4}$, may be reduced to $\frac{9}{4}$. The mixed number $1\frac{2}{3} = \frac{5}{3}$; the mixed number $3\frac{3}{5} = \frac{18}{5}$, etc.

FUNDAMENTAL PRINCIPLES OF FRACTIONS

In working with fractions, it is necessary to know and understand certain general principles that may be applied to all fractions. These principles are

1. The value of the fraction is not changed by multiplying both numerator and denominator by the same number. Thus:

$$\frac{1}{2} = \frac{2}{4} \text{ or } \frac{3}{6} \text{ or } \frac{4}{8} \text{ (multipliers are 2, 3, and 4, respectively)}$$

$$\frac{2}{3} = \frac{4}{6} \text{ or } \frac{10}{15} \text{ or } \frac{14}{21} \text{ (multipliers are 2, 5, and 7, respectively)}$$

2. The value of the fraction is not changed by dividing both numerator and denominator by the same number. Thus:

$$\frac{32}{40} = \frac{16}{20} \text{ or } \frac{8}{10} \text{ or } \frac{4}{5} \text{ (divisors are 2, 4, and 8, respectively)}$$

$$\frac{75}{150} = \frac{25}{50} \text{ or } \frac{5}{10} \text{ or } \frac{1}{2} \text{ (divisors are 3, 15, and 75, respectively)}$$

3. An improper fraction may be expressed either as an integer (whole number) or as a mixed number, if the numerator is divided by the denominator. Thus:

$$\frac{24}{6} = 24 \div 6 = 4 \qquad \frac{23}{6} = 23 \div 6 = 3\frac{5}{6}$$

$$\frac{35}{7} = 35 \div 7 = 5 \qquad \frac{36}{7} = 36 \div 7 = 5\frac{1}{7}$$

4. An integer (whole number) may be stated as a fraction. Thus:

$$1 = \frac{1}{1} \text{ or } \frac{2}{2} \text{ or } \frac{3}{3}, \text{ etc.}$$

$$3 = \frac{3}{1} \text{ or } \frac{6}{2} \text{ or } \frac{9}{3}, \text{ etc.}$$

$$7 = \frac{7}{1} \text{ or } \frac{14}{2} \text{ or } \frac{21}{3}, \text{ etc.}$$

In performing this operation (called reducing a whole number, or integer, to a fraction), the numerator is determined by the product of the integer and the given denominator. Thus,

$$\text{Reduce 8 to sevenths: } 8 = \frac{8 \times 7}{7} = \frac{56}{7}$$

$$\text{Reduce 5 to ninths: } 5 = \frac{5 \times 9}{9} = \frac{45}{9}$$

GENERAL RULE FOR OPERATION IN FRACTIONS

Solution of many problems in fractions is dependent on a knowledge of the following general rule (which may be developed from the fundamental principles): *Fractions having a common denominator are in the same ratio to each other as are their numerators.* Thus:

$$\frac{3}{6} \text{ is to } \frac{4}{6} \text{ as 3 is to 4;} \qquad \frac{6}{2} \text{ is to } \frac{1}{2} \text{ as 6 is to 1}$$

From this general rule, the following two very important applications may be made.

1. To apportion numbers, money, objects, or things in fractional ratios, reduce the fractions to fractions having a common denominator and use the numerators as integers in determining the proper apportionment.

Thus, if a sum of money is divided so that John has $\frac{1}{4}$, Mary $\frac{1}{3}$, and James the remainder, the problem of determining what fractional part of the whole sum belongs to James may be solved as follows:

A common denominator of 3 and 4 is 12. Therefore John has $\frac{1}{4}$, or $\frac{3}{12}$; and Mary has $\frac{1}{3}$, or $\frac{4}{12}$. Both John and Mary together have $\frac{7}{12}$ of the whole. Since 1, or the whole sum of money, is equivalent to $\frac{12}{12}$, then the remainder is $\frac{12}{12}$ less $\frac{7}{12}$, or $\frac{5}{12}$. James's share is the remainder, or $\frac{5}{12}$.

Restated, it may be said that if the money is divided into 12 equal portions, then John has 3 portions, Mary has 4 portions, and James has the remainder of 5 portions, since

$$12 - (3 + 4) = 5$$

2. To add, subtract, divide, or multiply two or more fractions, reduce them to fractions having common denominators and then add, subtract,

divide, or multiply by the numerators. However, the reduction of fractions to fractions expressed in common denominators is not necessary before dividing or multiplying by fractions, and is not frequently a desirable method to use in multiplication.

NOTE: In multiplying, the denominator is squared, cubed, etc., if a common denominator is found. Example: $\frac{4}{12} \times \frac{3}{12} \times \frac{1}{12} = \frac{12}{1728} = \frac{1}{144}$. Thus:

$$\text{To add: } \frac{1}{3} + \frac{1}{4} = \frac{4}{12} + \frac{3}{12} = \frac{7}{12}$$

$$\text{To subtract: } \frac{1}{3} - \frac{1}{4} = \frac{4}{12} - \frac{3}{12} = \frac{1}{12}$$

$$\text{To divide: } \frac{1}{3} \div \frac{1}{4} = \frac{4}{12} \div \frac{3}{12} = \frac{4}{3} = 1\frac{1}{3}$$

$$\text{To multiply: } \frac{1}{3} \times \frac{1}{4} = \frac{4}{12} \times \frac{3}{12} = \frac{12}{144} = \frac{1}{12}$$

REDUCTION OF FRACTIONS

An often misunderstood mathematical term, very frequently used in connection with operations in fractions, is the word "reduce." In mathematics, "reduce" means to change the denominations of a quantity or the form of an expression without changing the value.

Thus, by definition, the term "reduce" when used in arithmetic does not necessarily mean "to make smaller or lower." Fractions or any numbers may be reduced to higher or to lower terms.

Reducing to higher terms (reduction ascending):

$$\frac{1}{2} \text{ may be reduced to } \frac{2}{4}, \frac{3}{6}, \frac{4}{8}, \frac{5}{10}, \text{ etc.}$$

$$\frac{2}{3} \text{ may be reduced to } \frac{4}{6}, \frac{6}{9}, \frac{8}{12}, \frac{10}{15}, \text{ etc.}$$

$$4 \text{ may be reduced to } \frac{8}{2}, \frac{12}{3}, \frac{16}{4}, \frac{20}{5}, \text{ etc.}$$

Reduced to lower terms (reduction descending):

$$\frac{9}{18} \text{ may be reduced to } \frac{8}{16}, \frac{7}{14}, \frac{6}{12}, \frac{5}{10}, \text{ etc.}$$

$$\frac{18}{27} \text{ may be reduced to } \frac{16}{24}, \frac{14}{21}, \frac{12}{18}, \frac{10}{15}, \text{ etc.}$$

$$\frac{36}{9} \text{ may be reduced to } \frac{32}{8}, \frac{28}{7}, \frac{24}{6}, \frac{20}{5}, \text{ etc.}$$

To reduce an improper fraction to a whole or mixed number, divide the numerator by the denominator. Thus:

$$\frac{18}{6} = 18 \div 6 = 3$$

$$\frac{22}{5} = 22 \div 5 = 4\frac{2}{5}$$

To reduce a mixed number to an improper fraction, multiply the whole number by the denominator of the fraction, add the numerator of the fraction of this product, and then place this sum over the given denominator of the fraction. Thus:

$$5\frac{1}{4} = \frac{(5 \times 4) + 1}{4} = \frac{20 + 1}{4} = \frac{21}{4}$$

$$17\frac{2}{3} = \frac{(17 \times 3) + 2}{3} = \frac{51 + 2}{3} = \frac{53}{3}$$

To reduce a fraction to a fraction in which the denominator is a multiple, multiply the given numerator by the quotient of the required denominator divided by the given denominator and then place this product (required numerator) over the required denominator. Thus:

$$\frac{4}{7} \text{ expressed in 21sts: } \frac{(21 \div 7) \times 4}{21} = \frac{3 \times 4}{21} = \frac{12}{21}$$

$$\frac{7}{8} \text{ expressed as 40ths: } \frac{(40 \div 8) \times 7}{40} = \frac{5 \times 7}{40} = \frac{35}{40}$$

To reduce a fraction to lower terms, divide both terms by a common factor. Note that both numerator and denominator must be divisible by the number used as a factor. Thus:

$$\frac{12}{30} \text{ can be reduced by dividing both terms by } 2 = \frac{6}{15}$$

$$\frac{12}{30} \text{ can be reduced by dividing both terms by } 3 = \frac{4}{10}$$

$$\frac{12}{30} \text{ can be reduced by dividing both terms by } 6 = \frac{2}{5}$$

To reduce a fraction to its lowest terms, divide both terms by a common factor; then divide the result by a common factor and continue this process until the terms are prime to each other. Thus:

$$\frac{20}{40}, \text{ both terms divided by } 2 = \frac{10}{20}$$

$$\frac{10}{20}, \text{ both terms divided by } 2 = \frac{5}{10}$$

$$\frac{5}{10}, \text{ both terms divided by } 5 = \frac{1}{2}$$

To reduce a fraction to its lowest terms by use of only one divisor, divide both terms by their greatest common divisor (highest common factor). Thus:

$$\frac{12}{30}, \text{ both terms divided by } 6 = \frac{2}{5}$$

$$\frac{20}{40}, \text{ both terms divided by } 20 = \frac{1}{2}$$

From the immediately preceding examples, it is obvious that the use of the greatest common divisor saves time and effort in reducing a fraction to its lowest terms.

If you do not have a thorough knowledge of the rules of divisibility for both prime and composite numbers (pages 24–26), review them now, for their use will be of greatest assistance in completing the exercises that follow.

If it is required to reduce fractions to their lowest terms and you are not sure that both factors are prime to each other (that the fraction cannot be expressed in lower terms), find the greatest common divisor by the division method (pages 27–28). Use of this method will determine definitely the lowest terms to which any fraction can be reduced.

ADDITION OF FRACTIONS[1]

Proper fractions, improper fractions, and mixed numbers after reduction to improper fractions may be added by using the following order of procedure:

1. Reduce all addends to fractions with a common denominator (unless they are already so reduced).
2. Add the numerators of the addends to determine the numerator of the required sum.

The denominator of the required sum will be the common denominator of the addends.

The obtained sum will be a proper or improper fraction which should be reduced to lowest terms if it is not already shown thus.

Example 1: Add $\frac{2}{5}$, $\frac{4}{5}$, and $\frac{1}{5}$.

$$\begin{array}{l} \frac{2}{5} \\ \frac{4}{5} \\ \frac{1}{5} \\ \hline \frac{7}{5} = 1\frac{2}{5} \end{array}$$

Example 2: Add $\frac{2}{3}$, $\frac{1}{2}$, and $\frac{5}{6}$.

$$\begin{array}{l} \frac{2}{3} = \frac{4}{6} \\ \frac{1}{2} = \frac{3}{6} \\ \frac{5}{6} = \frac{5}{6} \\ \hline \quad \frac{12}{6} = 2 \end{array}$$

[1] See Appendix I for a short method of adding two fractions.

Example 3: Add $4\frac{1}{4}$, $\frac{13}{6}$, $3\frac{1}{3}$, and $\frac{9}{2}$.

$$4\frac{1}{4} = \frac{17}{4} = \frac{51}{12}$$
$$\frac{13}{6} = \frac{26}{12}$$
$$3\frac{1}{3} = \frac{10}{3} = \frac{40}{12}$$
$$\frac{9}{2} = \frac{54}{12}$$
$$\frac{171}{12} = 14\frac{3}{12} = 14\frac{1}{4}$$

Addition of Mixed Numbers. Mixed numbers need not be reduced to improper fractions before they are added, for the addition of mixed numbers may be accomplished in two steps.

1. Find the sum of the fractional parts of the addends.
2. Add this sum to the whole digits of the addends.

If the sum of the fractional parts is an improper fraction, it may be reduced to a mixed number before it is added to the whole numbers of the addends (see Example 2, below). In any event, the sum should be reduced to lowest terms if it is not already shown thus.

Example 1: Add $1\frac{1}{3}$, $5\frac{1}{8}$, $3\frac{2}{5}$, and $9\frac{1}{10}$.

$$1\frac{1}{3} = 1\frac{40}{120}$$
$$5\frac{1}{8} = 5\frac{15}{120}$$
$$3\frac{2}{5} = 3\frac{48}{120}$$
$$9\frac{1}{10} = 9\frac{12}{120}$$
$$18\frac{115}{120} = 18\frac{23}{24}$$

Example 2: Add $\frac{3}{2}$, $\frac{6}{5}$, $\frac{9}{4}$, and $\frac{17}{10}$.

$$\frac{3}{2} = 1\frac{1}{2} = 1\frac{10}{20}$$
$$\frac{6}{5} = 1\frac{1}{5} = 1\frac{4}{20}$$
$$\frac{9}{4} = 2\frac{1}{4} = 2\frac{5}{20}$$
$$\frac{17}{10} = 1\frac{7}{10} = 1\frac{14}{20}$$
$$5\frac{33}{20} = 6\frac{13}{20}$$

(NOTE: $\frac{33}{20} = 1\frac{13}{20}$ which added to whole digit total of 5 = $6\frac{13}{20}$)

When the given addends are mixed numbers or improper fractions that are the equivalent of large whole or mixed numbers, addition as mixed numbers rather than as improper fractions is recommended except when the given improper fractions have the same denominator.

EXERCISE 5

A. Reduce to common denominators in adding each of the following, and then express each obtained sum in lowest terms as a proper fraction or mixed number.

1. $\frac{1}{7} + \frac{1}{11}$	**2.** $\frac{1}{9} + \frac{1}{12}$	**3.** $\frac{9}{11} + \frac{4}{7}$	**4.** $\frac{8}{9} + \frac{11}{12}$
5. $8\frac{2}{5} + \frac{1}{9}$	**6.** $\frac{3}{11} + 5\frac{1}{6}$	**7.** $3\frac{1}{2} + 6\frac{3}{4}$	**8.** $7\frac{2}{5} + 9\frac{1}{3}$
9. $1/15 + 1/3$	**10.** $1/17 + 1/16$	**11.** $2/3 + 7/13$	**12.** $5/16 + 9/17$
13. $4\ 2/3 + 5/8$	**14.** $4/9 + 2\ 1/4$	**15.** $5\ 1/5 + 6\ 2/3$	**16.** $4\ 3/4 + 2\ 5/6$
17. $\frac{1}{8} =$	**18.** $\frac{1}{5} =$	**19.** $\frac{8}{9} =$	**20.** $\frac{11}{12} =$
$\frac{1}{4} =$	$\frac{1}{7} =$	$\frac{5}{24} =$	$\frac{2}{7} =$
21. $4\frac{3}{22} =$	**22.** $\frac{5}{8} =$	**23.** $7\frac{8}{9} =$	**24.** $6\frac{13}{18} =$
$\frac{9}{11} =$	$9\frac{1}{2} =$	$5\frac{4}{15} =$	$8\frac{9}{10} =$

B. Add and express sums as mixed numbers reduced to lowest terms:

1.	**2.**	**3.**	**4.**
$\frac{1}{5}$	$\frac{2}{7}$	$\frac{5}{12}$	$\frac{1}{3}$
$\frac{2}{3}$	$\frac{1}{4}$	$\frac{2}{7}$	$\frac{5}{6}$
$\frac{1}{4}$	$\frac{5}{8}$	$\frac{1}{16}$	$\frac{1}{4}$
$\frac{5}{6}$	$\frac{1}{9}$	$\frac{3}{4}$	$\frac{1}{13}$

5.	**6.**	**7.**	**8.**
$\frac{1}{4}$	$\frac{1}{14}$	$\frac{11}{15}$	$\frac{15}{16}$
$\frac{3}{5}$	$\frac{3}{13}$	$\frac{1}{8}$	$\frac{1}{4}$
$\frac{5}{8}$	$\frac{1}{17}$	$\frac{2}{9}$	$\frac{3}{8}$
$\frac{3}{7}$	$\frac{3}{26}$	$\frac{1}{12}$	$\frac{5}{12}$
$\frac{1}{6}$	$\frac{5}{7}$	$\frac{5}{24}$	$\frac{7}{8}$

C. Add and express sums as mixed numbers reduced to lowest terms:

1.	2.	3.
$\frac{1}{4}$	$5\frac{1}{4}$	$81\frac{1}{5}$
$2\frac{1}{3}$	$3\frac{1}{8}$	$16\frac{2}{3}$
$\frac{1}{5}$	$7\frac{1}{12}$	$3\frac{1}{3}$
$3\frac{1}{7}$	$14\frac{1}{24}$	$83\frac{1}{3}$
$8\frac{3}{5}$	$3\frac{4}{9}$	$19\frac{8}{15}$

4.	5.	6.
$\frac{67}{6}$	$11\frac{1}{9}$	$3\frac{7}{8}$
$\frac{88}{9}$	$\frac{73}{4}$	$4\frac{5}{6}$
$\frac{45}{4}$	$10\frac{2}{3}$	$2\frac{7}{12}$
$\frac{38}{3}$	$127\frac{1}{8}$	$5\frac{3}{16}$
$\frac{11}{2}$	$45\frac{11}{12}$	$\frac{295}{12}$

UNIT 6. Subtraction of Fractions and Rounding Off Fractions

SUBTRACTION OF FRACTIONS[1]

Proper fractions, improper fractions, and mixed numbers after reduction to improper fractions may be subtracted by using the following order of procedure:

1. Reduce minuend and subtrahend to fractions with a common denominator (unless they are already so reduced).
2. Find the difference between the numerators of the minuend and subtrahend to determine the numerator of the required remainder.

[1] See Appendix I for a short method of subtracting fractions.

The denominator of the required remainder will be the common denominator of the minuend and subtrahend.

The obtained remainder will be a proper or improper fraction which should be reduced to lowest terms if it is not already shown thus.

Example 1: Subtract $\frac{1}{4}$ from $\frac{3}{4}$.

$$\begin{array}{r} \frac{3}{4} \\ -\frac{1}{4} \\ \hline \frac{2}{4} = \frac{1}{2} \end{array}$$

Example 2: From $\frac{7}{8}$ subtract $\frac{2}{3}$.

$$\begin{array}{r} \frac{7}{8} = \frac{21}{24} \\ -\frac{2}{3} = \frac{16}{24} \\ \hline \frac{5}{24} \end{array}$$

Example 3: Subtract $\frac{4}{5}$ from 8.

$$\begin{array}{r} 8 = \frac{40}{5} \\ -\frac{4}{5} \\ \hline \frac{36}{5} = 7\frac{1}{5} \end{array}$$

Example 4: Subtract $\frac{3}{4}$ from $\frac{14}{5}$.

$$\begin{array}{r} \frac{14}{5} = \frac{56}{20} \\ -\frac{3}{4} = \frac{15}{20} \\ \hline \frac{41}{20} = 2\frac{1}{20} \end{array}$$

Example 5: From $\frac{37}{5}$ subtract $2\frac{1}{6}$.

$$\begin{array}{r} \frac{37}{5} = \frac{222}{30} \\ -2\frac{1}{6} = \frac{13}{6} = \frac{65}{30} \\ \hline \frac{157}{30} = 5\frac{7}{30} \end{array}$$

Example 6: Subtract $1\frac{3}{4}$ from $5\frac{1}{3}$.

$$\begin{array}{r} 5\frac{1}{3} = \frac{16}{3} = \frac{64}{12} \\ -1\frac{3}{4} = \frac{7}{4} = \frac{21}{12} \\ \hline \frac{43}{12} = 3\frac{7}{12} \end{array}$$

ROUNDING OFF FRACTIONS

In computing, a portion beyond the desired unit of accuracy will frequently be expressed as a fraction. Thus, it may be necessary to round off such numbers as $7\frac{2}{3}$ ft., $19\frac{7}{16}$ lb., $43.06\frac{5}{11}$ per cent, \$2.37$\frac{1}{2}$. The rules to be followed in most types of business transactions (expressed as the fractional equivalents of the rules for rounding off decimals, page 6) are as follows:

1. If the portion to be dropped off is the fractional equivalent of $\frac{1}{2}$, or more, add 1 to the preceding digit.

2. If the portion to be dropped off is less than the fractional equivalent of $\frac{1}{2}$, discard it, leaving the preceding digit as is.

Examples of Fractions Rounded Off:

Given	*Round off to*	*Given*	*Round off to*
$62\frac{1}{2}$	63	\$ $3.06\frac{1}{3}$	\$ 3.06
$25\frac{7}{16}$	25	\$$57.83\frac{5}{9}$	\$57.84
$452\frac{7}{13}$	453	$15\frac{3}{8}$%	15%
$\frac{9}{20}$	0	$46.12\frac{5}{8}$%	46.13%

In business the most common exceptions to the rules for rounding off fractions or decimal equivalents occur in transactions involving weights and measures or between consumer and retailer. In such cases, the general practice is to raise by 1 unit any digit followed by a fraction, no matter how small that fraction may be. Thus, the purchaser of terra-cotta pipe priced in yard lengths will be required to purchase 14 yards of pipe even though only 13 yards and a very small fraction over is desired; and a purchaser of $2{,}415\frac{1}{4}$ board feet of lumber will be charged for 2,416 board feet; the retail purchaser of canned milk will usually pay 9 cents per can if the price is 3 cans for 25 cents (an average of $8\frac{1}{3}$ cents per can).

SUBTRACTION OF MIXED NUMBERS

Mixed numbers need not be reduced to improper fractions before subtracting. The subtraction of mixed numbers may be accomplished in two steps, provided that the fractional part of the minuend is greater than the fractional part of the subtrahend. If the fractional part of the minuend is not the greater (or if there is no fractional part in the minuend), it may be made greater by reducing the given minuend to its equivalent expressed as 1 *integer less* but with a fractional ending as an improper fraction with a value of 1 *integer* more. This may be accomplished as follows:

If the fractional part of the minuend is smaller than the fractional part of the subtrahend:

1. Subtract 1 integer from the whole integers of the minuend.
2. To the numerator of the fractional part in the minuend, add the denominator (equivalent to 1 integer).

Examples:

Given minuend	*Equivalent minuend*
$7\frac{1}{3}$	$6\frac{4}{3}$
$18\frac{3}{4}$	$17\frac{7}{4}$
$42\frac{4}{5}$	$41\frac{9}{5}$

If there is no fractional part in the minuend:

1. Subtract 1 integer from the whole integers of the minuend.
2. Write a fractional part with *both* numerator and denominator in the same numerical value (equivalent to 1 integer) as the denominator of the fractional part of the subtrahend.

Examples:

Given subtrahend	*Given minuend*	*Equivalent minuend*
$6\frac{3}{7}$	10	$9\frac{7}{7}$
$21\frac{5}{8}$	22	$21\frac{8}{8}$
$57\frac{1}{12}$	85	$84\frac{12}{12}$

When the minuend has been reduced to an equivalent minuend with a greater fractional part or when the *given* minuend already has a greater fractional part than the fractional part of the subtrahend, the procedure in subtracting mixed numbers is as follows:

1. Find the difference between the fractional parts of the minuend and the subtrahend.
2. Add this difference to the difference between the whole integers of the minuend and the subtrahend.

In the following three examples, each given minuend has a fractional part greater than the fractional part (if any) in each subtrahend.

Example 1: Subtract 6 from $15\frac{3}{4}$.

$$\begin{array}{r} 15\frac{3}{4} \\ -\ 6 \\ \hline 9\frac{3}{4} \end{array}$$

Example 2: From $7\frac{2}{5}$ subtract $2\frac{1}{6}$.

$$\begin{array}{rcr} 7\frac{2}{5} & = & 7\frac{12}{30} \\ -2\frac{1}{6} & = & 2\frac{5}{30} \\ \hline & & 5\frac{7}{30} \end{array}$$

Example 3: Subtract $\frac{319}{3}$ from $208\frac{3}{5}$.

$$\begin{array}{rcrcr} & & 208\frac{3}{5} & = & 208\frac{9}{15} \\ -\frac{319}{3} & = & 106\frac{1}{3} & = & 106\frac{5}{15} \\ \hline & & & & 102\frac{4}{15} \end{array}$$

In the following three examples, the fractional part of each subtrahend is greater than the fractional part (if any) in each given minuend. These given minuends must first be reduced to equivalent minuends in which the fractional parts are greater than the fractional parts in the respective subtrahends.

Example 1: Subtract $3\frac{1}{7}$ from 18.

$$\begin{array}{rcr} 18 & = & 17\frac{7}{7} \\ & - & 3\frac{1}{7} \\ \hline & & 14\frac{6}{7} \end{array}$$

Example 2: From $5\frac{1}{3}$ subtract $1\frac{3}{4}$.

$$\begin{array}{rcrcr} 5\frac{1}{3} & = & 5\frac{4}{12} & = & 4\frac{16}{12} \\ -1\frac{3}{4} & = & 1\frac{9}{12} & = & 1\frac{9}{12} \\ \hline & & & & 3\frac{7}{12} \end{array}$$

Example 3: Subtract $3\frac{5}{6}$ from $\frac{125}{2}$.

$$\begin{array}{rcrcrcr} \frac{125}{2} & = & 62\frac{1}{2} & = & 62\frac{3}{6} & = & 61\frac{9}{6} \\ - & & 3\frac{5}{6} & = & 3\frac{5}{6} & = & 3\frac{5}{6} \\ \hline & & & & & & 58\frac{4}{6} = 58\frac{2}{3} \end{array}$$

From the preceding explanation and examples, subtraction of mixed numbers may appear to be more cumbersome and less desirable than reduction of mixed numbers to improper fractions before subtraction. In actual practice, however, when the minuend or the subtrahend is the equivalent of large mixed numbers, it is undoubtedly preferable to perform the required subtraction with minuend and subtrahend in the form of mixed numbers, even though given improper fractions may have to be reduced to whole or mixed numbers. The exception would be when the improper fractions are already expressed in the same denominator.

EXERCISE 6

A. Reduce to common denominators in subtracting each of the following, and then express each obtained remainder in lowest terms:

1. $\frac{7}{8} - \frac{2}{3}$ 2. $\frac{7}{16} - \frac{5}{12}$ 3. $\frac{13}{8} - \frac{5}{14}$ 4. $\frac{7}{3} - \frac{17}{21}$

5. 63/500 − 1/8 6. 1/7 − 3/28 7. 33/100 − 97/300 8. 29/24 − 13/12

9. $\frac{18}{19} =$ 10. $\frac{5}{7} =$ 11. $\frac{25}{13} =$ 12. $\frac{23}{15} =$

$\frac{3}{4} =$ $\frac{5}{8} =$ $\frac{17}{12} =$ $\frac{11}{8} =$

B. Round off the fractions or common fractional endings of the following (see pages 45–46 of text):

1. $\frac{3}{4}$ 2. $\frac{3}{8}$ 3. $3\frac{5}{9}$ 4. $5\frac{8}{17}$

5. $4\frac{173}{345}$ 6. $57.24\frac{3}{5}$ 7. $\$1.99\frac{8}{15}$ 8. $\$0.76\frac{235}{476}$

C. Perform the indicated subtraction *first* and then round off the remainder to nearest whole units:

1. $38 - 16\frac{2}{5}$ 2. $55\frac{4}{11} - 18$ 3. $25\frac{4}{7} - 19\frac{9}{11}$ 4. $\$32\frac{2}{3} - \$18\frac{5}{7}$

D. Subtract the following. (Reduce answers to lowest terms expressing any improper fractions as mixed numbers.)

1. $42\frac{3}{7}$ − 9 2. $38\frac{41}{43}$ − 24 3. $65\frac{17}{26}$ − 13 4. $93\frac{15}{19}$ − 51

5. 46 − $\frac{10}{11}$ 6. 375 − $\frac{11}{15}$ 7. 94 − $\frac{5}{13}$ 8. 254 − $\frac{5}{9}$

9. $14\frac{3}{7}$ − $11\frac{4}{15}$ 10. $95\frac{5}{7}$ − $84\frac{3}{19}$ 11. $15\frac{2}{3}$ − $8\frac{8}{9}$ 12. $197\frac{11}{13}$ − $105\frac{7}{11}$

13. $19\frac{3}{5}$ − $12\frac{4}{5}$ 14. $22\frac{1}{3}$ − $5\frac{1}{2}$ 15. $89\frac{9}{22}$ − $74\frac{41}{44}$ 16. $999\frac{8}{9}$ − $111\frac{10}{11}$

17. $\frac{185}{5}$	**18.** $\frac{69}{11}$	**19.** $\frac{59}{3}$	**20.** $\frac{575}{20}$
$\frac{165}{15}$	$\frac{85}{25}$	$\frac{187}{25}$	$\frac{135}{15}$
21. $325\frac{3}{4}$	**22.** $215\frac{1}{4}$	**23.** $28\frac{5}{9}$	**24.** $36\frac{2}{21}$
$\frac{155}{101}$	$\frac{465}{12}$	$\frac{525}{25}$	$12\frac{1}{3}$

UNIT 7. Multiplication of Fractions

In multiplying fractions there is no need for the denominators to be common, as in adding or subtracting fractions.

To multiply one fraction by another, find the product of the numerators to determine the new numerator and then find the product of the denominators to determine the new denominator.

In order to simplify the operation of multiplication, cancellation should be employed whenever practicable.

Example 1: Proper or improper fractions. Multiply $\frac{4}{5}$ by $\frac{7}{3}$; $\frac{4}{7}$ by $\frac{8}{9}$.

$$\frac{4}{5} \times \frac{7}{3} = \frac{4 \times 7}{5 \times 3} = \frac{28}{15} = 1\frac{13}{15}$$

$$\frac{4}{7} \times \frac{8}{9} = \frac{4 \times 8}{7 \times 9} = \frac{32}{63}$$

Mixed numbers may be multiplied in either of two ways: (1) by making each mixed number an improper fraction and then proceeding as above, *or* (2) by multiplying by the fractions, then by the whole numbers, and finally adding the partial products.

Example 2: Reducing mixed numbers to improper fractions. Multiply $3\frac{1}{2}$ by $4\frac{1}{3}$.

$$3\frac{1}{2} \times 4\frac{1}{3} = \frac{7}{2} \times \frac{13}{3} = \frac{7 \times 13}{2 \times 3} = \frac{91}{6} = 15\frac{1}{6}$$

Example 3: Using mixed numbers (the partial-product method). Multiply $21\frac{1}{5}$ by $17\frac{2}{3}$.

$$
\begin{array}{rll}
 & 21\frac{1}{5} & \\
 & 17\frac{2}{3} & \\
\hline
\text{Partial products} \left\{ \begin{array}{l} \\ \\ \\ \\ \\ \end{array} \right. & \frac{2}{15} & \left(\frac{1}{5} \times \frac{2}{3}\right) \\
 & 14 & \left(21 \times \frac{2}{3}\right) \\
 & 3\frac{6}{15} & \left(\frac{1}{5} \times 17 = 3\frac{2}{5} = 3\frac{6}{15}\right) \\
 & 147 & (21 \times 7) \\
 & 21 & (21 \times 1) \\
\hline
\text{Product} = & 374\frac{8}{15} &
\end{array}
$$

The methods illustrated by Examples 2 and 3 are optional. Notice that in Example 3 the ending digits in the partial products of the fractional endings of both multiplicand and multiplier are placed directly over the ending digit of the partial product derived from the ending whole digit in the multiplier. Thus, to avoid errors, place fractional endings in the partial products directly below the fractional ending in the multiplier and place the digits representing units, tens, hundreds, etc., directly below the corresponding units, tens, hundreds, etc., in the multiplier.

Note that the fractional endings in the partial products should be reduced to fractions with common denominators before the partial products are added to obtain the final product. The lowest common denominator of the fractional endings in the several partial products may be determined as soon as the first partial product (of the fractional endings in the multiplicand and multiplier) has been obtained. The l.c.d. will be the least common multiple of the fractional endings in the given multiplicand and multiplier *or* the denominator of the fractional ending in the first partial product when it has been reduced to lowest terms, *whichever is larger*.

Example 4: Using cancellation.

Multiply $\frac{3}{7}$ by $\frac{14}{27}$

$$\frac{\cancel{3}}{7} \times \frac{\overset{2}{\cancel{14}}}{\underset{9}{\cancel{27}}} = \frac{2}{9}$$

Multiply $7\frac{1}{2}$ by $1\frac{3}{5}$

$$7\frac{1}{2} \times 1\frac{3}{5} = \frac{\overset{3}{\cancel{15}}}{\cancel{2}} \times \frac{\overset{4}{\cancel{8}}}{\cancel{5}} = 3 \times 4 = 12$$

When more than two fractions are to be multiplied together, the following is the usually preferred form because cancellation may be more easily accomplished:

Multiply $3\frac{1}{4}$ by $2\frac{1}{3}$ by $\frac{9}{26}$ by 5.

$$\frac{\cancel{13} \times 7 \times \overset{3}{\cancel{9}} \times 5}{4 \times \cancel{3} \times \underset{2}{\cancel{26}}} = \frac{105}{8} = 13\frac{1}{8}$$

Common fractions may often be conveniently reduced to decimal fractions and then multiplied.

EXERCISE 7

A. Multiply, reducing answers to lowest terms:

1. $\frac{1}{7} \times \frac{1}{6}$
2. $\frac{1}{8} \times \frac{1}{9}$
3. $\frac{1}{5} \times \frac{1}{2}$
4. $\frac{1}{3} \times \frac{1}{4}$
5. $\frac{2}{3} \times \frac{3}{4}$
6. $\frac{2}{3} \times \frac{3}{5}$
7. $\frac{4}{5} \times \frac{5}{9}$
8. $\frac{6}{7} \times \frac{7}{8}$
9. $\frac{8}{9} \times \frac{11}{12}$
10. $\frac{5}{11} \times \frac{8}{17}$
11. $\frac{21}{25} \times \frac{3}{4}$
12. $\frac{5}{6} \times \frac{2}{13}$
13. $\frac{1}{3} \times \frac{1}{5}$
14. $\frac{8}{9} \times \frac{5}{6}$
15. $\frac{11}{17} \times \frac{5}{9}$

B. Multiply, reducing answers to lowest terms as proper fractions or whole or mixed numbers:

1. $\frac{11}{13} \times \frac{3}{2}$
2. $\frac{5}{12} \times \frac{8}{3}$
3. $\frac{2}{5} \times \frac{7}{4}$
4. $\frac{8}{5} \times \frac{5}{9}$
5. $\frac{9}{8} \times \frac{6}{5}$
6. $\frac{17}{11} \times \frac{9}{4}$
7. $\frac{25}{21} \times \frac{17}{6}$
8. $\frac{9}{8} \times \frac{12}{11}$
9. $\frac{125}{21} \times \frac{2}{3}$
10. $\frac{145}{35} \times \frac{5}{9}$
11. $\frac{3}{4} \times \frac{39}{11}$
12. $\frac{9}{10} \times \frac{14}{3}$
13. $\frac{14}{13} \times \frac{7}{8}$
14. $\frac{9}{2} \times \frac{13}{10}$
15. $\frac{7}{3} \times \frac{15}{8}$
16. $\frac{129}{38} \times \frac{455}{25}$

C. Multiply, without changing factors to improper fractions (see Example 3, pages 50–51). Reduce answers to lowest terms as whole or mixed numbers.

1. $52\frac{1}{2} \times 16$
2. $37\frac{1}{3} \times 39$
3. $24 \times 16\frac{2}{3}$
4. $84 \times 12\frac{1}{14}$
5. $24\frac{1}{3} \times 15\frac{1}{4}$
6. $45\frac{4}{9} \times 36\frac{4}{15}$
7. $37\frac{1}{3} \times 98\frac{2}{9}$
8. $28\frac{2}{7} \times 14$
9. $44\frac{5}{9} \times 27$
10. $95 \times 47\frac{1}{5}$
11. $78 \times 11\frac{5}{13}$
12. $36\frac{1}{5} \times 25\frac{3}{4}$
13. $90\frac{1}{7} \times 14\frac{7}{10}$
14. $12\frac{1}{11} \times 43\frac{1}{2}$
15. $84\frac{2}{7} \times 28\frac{9}{14}$
16. $425\frac{1}{3} \times 21\frac{3}{17}$

UNIT 8. Division of Fractions

Division by (or of) fractions may be accomplished in several ways, the generally used methods of solution being

1. Multiplication of the dividend by the reciprocal of the divisor.
2. Reduction of both dividend and divisor to a common denominator before division.
3. Reduction of both dividend and divisor to integers before division.

No one means is preferable in all instances, and therefore you should be familiar with all three methods and develop facility in their use.

Use of Reciprocal in Division. The method commonly used to accomplish division by fractions is based upon a principle that may be explained as follows:

A *reciprocal* is the quotient of one unit divided by any quantity.

When the product of two numbers is 1, the numbers are said to be *reciprocals* of each other. Thus:

$$\frac{1}{4} \times 4 = 1; \quad \frac{2}{3} \times \frac{3}{2} = 1; \quad \frac{8}{3} \times \frac{3}{8} = 1$$

Therefore $1 \div \frac{1}{4} = 4;\quad 1 \div \frac{2}{3} = \frac{3}{2};\quad 1 \div \frac{8}{3} = \frac{3}{8}$

and $1 \div 4 = \frac{1}{4};\quad 1 \div \frac{3}{2} = \frac{2}{3};\quad 1 \div \frac{3}{8} = \frac{8}{3}$

a. It is obvious that the unit 1 will be contained as many times in a given dividend as there are units in the dividend. Thus:

1 is contained 9 times in 9; 1 is contained 25 times in 25

1 is contained $\frac{3}{4}$ times in $\frac{3}{4}$; 1 is contained $\frac{7}{2}$ times in $\frac{7}{2}$

b. From the examples preceding (*a*), it is apparent that the reciprocal of the number used as a divisor indicates the number of times that the divisor is contained in the unit 1. Thus:

$\frac{1}{3}$ is contained 3 times in 1; $\frac{2}{5}$ is contained $\frac{5}{2}$ times in 1

9 is contained $\frac{1}{9}$ times in 1; $\frac{7}{6}$ is contained $\frac{6}{7}$ times in 1

The problem of dividing a dividend of 8 by a divisor of $\frac{2}{3}$ might be reasoned as follows:

a. The unit 1 is contained 8 times in 8 (or the dividend 8 contains 8 units).

b. In each unit 1, $\frac{2}{3}$ is contained $\frac{3}{2}$ times.

Therefore $\frac{2}{3}$ will be contained in 8 units, 8 times as often as it will be contained in 1 unit. Since $\frac{2}{3}$ is contained $\frac{3}{2}$ times in 1 unit and there are 8 units in 8,

$$8 \div \frac{2}{3} =$$

$$8 \times \frac{3}{2} = \frac{24}{2} = 12$$

From the preceding, it may be seen that division, either by a whole number or by a fraction, may be accomplished by multiplying the dividend by the reciprocal of the divisor. Note that the reciprocal of a fraction (or whole number) may be formed by transposing the terms. When the terms of a fraction have been so interchanged, the fraction is said to have been *inverted.*

Hence the following rule (with which you are probably familiar): *To divide by a fraction, invert the terms of the fraction and proceed as in the multiplication of fractions.*

This rule may be applied to any operation in division. Thus, if there is a whole or mixed number in either dividend or divisor, reduce it (or both) to an improper fraction, invert the terms of the divisor, and multiply.

The same operations are required if the rule for division is stated as follows: *To divide by a fraction, multiply by its reciprocal.*

Example 1: Proper or improper fractions. Divide $\frac{5}{7}$ by 2; 5 by $\frac{3}{4}$, $\frac{3}{4}$ by $\frac{2}{3}$; $\frac{5}{2}$ by $\frac{9}{7}$.

$$\frac{5}{7} \div 2 = \frac{5}{7} \div \frac{2}{1} = \frac{5}{7} \times \frac{1}{2} = \frac{5}{14}$$

$$5 \div \frac{3}{4} = \frac{5}{1} \div \frac{3}{4} = \frac{5}{1} \times \frac{4}{3} = \frac{20}{3} = 6\frac{2}{3}$$

$$\frac{3}{4} \div \frac{2}{3} = \frac{3}{4} \times \frac{3}{2} = \frac{9}{8} = 1\frac{1}{8}$$

$$\frac{5}{2} \div \frac{9}{7} = \frac{5}{2} \times \frac{7}{9} = \frac{35}{18} = 1\frac{17}{18}$$

Example 2: Reducing mixed numbers to improper fractions before division. Divide $6\frac{1}{4}$ by $3\frac{2}{7}$.

$$6\frac{1}{4} \div 3\frac{2}{7} = \frac{25}{4} \div \frac{23}{7} = \frac{25}{4} \times \frac{7}{23} = \frac{175}{92} = 1\frac{83}{92}$$

Reduction to a Common Denominator before Division. The general rule, *Fractions having a common denominator are to each other as are their numerators,* may be applied to division as well as to other operations in fractions. Thus fractions may be divided by reducing them to fractions which have a common denominator, discarding the common denominators, and then dividing by the numerators. Preferably, the common denominator used will be the lowest common denominator.

Example 1: Divide 23 by $\frac{2}{3}$ (*a*) by multiplying by the reciprocal of the divisor and (*b*) by reducing both dividend and divisor to fractions with a common denominator, discarding the common denominators and then dividing by the numerators.

$$(a)\ 23 \div \frac{2}{3} = 23 \times \frac{3}{2} = \frac{69}{2} = 34\frac{1}{2}$$

$$(b)\ 23 \div \frac{2}{3} = \frac{69}{\not{3}} \div \frac{2}{\not{3}} = 34\frac{1}{2}$$

Example 2: Divide $32\frac{1}{2}$ by $5\frac{2}{3}$ (*a*) by multiplying by the reciprocal of the divisor and (*b*) by reducing both dividend and divisor to fractions with a common denominator, discarding the common denominators and then dividing by the numerators.

$$(a)\ 32\frac{1}{2} \div 5\frac{2}{3} = \frac{65}{2} \div \frac{17}{3} = \frac{65}{2} \times \frac{3}{17} = \frac{195}{34} = 5\frac{25}{34}$$

$$(b)\ 32\frac{1}{2} \div 5\frac{2}{3} = \frac{65}{2} \div \frac{17}{3} = \frac{195}{\not 6} \div \frac{34}{\not 6} = 5\frac{25}{34}$$

Reduction to Integers before Division. It is a fact that the product of a fraction and any multiple of that fraction's denominator will be an integer (whole number). As examples:

$$\frac{3}{4} \times 4 = 3; \quad \frac{3}{4} \times 8 = 6; \quad \frac{3}{4} \times 12 = 9; \quad \frac{3}{4} \times 16 = 12; \text{ etc.}$$

$$\frac{7}{5} \times 5 = 7; \quad \frac{7}{5} \times 10 = 14; \quad \frac{7}{5} \times 15 = 21; \quad \frac{7}{5} \times 20 = 28; \text{ etc.}$$

A rule of division (see page 21) applying to fractions as well as to whole numbers is, *The quotient will remain the same if both dividend and divisor are multiplied by the same number.*

Thus both dividend and divisor will always be reduced to integers when they are multiplied by a common multiple of their denominators, and the quotient of the dividend and divisor will remain the same. Preferably, the common multiple used will be the least common multiple.

Example 1: Divide 12 by $\frac{4}{5}$ (*a*) by multiplying by the reciprocal of the divisor and (*b*) by multiplying both dividend and divisor by a common multiple of their denominators, and then performing the indicated division.

$$(a)\ 12 \div \frac{4}{5} = \overset{3}{\cancel{12}} \times \frac{5}{\cancel{4}} = 15$$

$$(b)\ 12 \div \frac{4}{5} = (12 \times 5) \div \left(\frac{4}{\cancel{5}} \times \cancel{5}\right) = 60 \div 4 = 15$$

Example 2: Divide $16\frac{3}{5}$ by $7\frac{1}{3}$ (*a*) by reducing both dividend and divisor to fractions with a common denominator, discarding the common denominators and then dividing by the numerators and (*b*) by multiplying both dividend and divisor by a common multiple of their denominators and then performing the indicated division.

$$(a)\ 16\frac{3}{5} \div 7\frac{1}{3} = \frac{83}{5} \div \frac{22}{3} = \frac{249}{\cancel{15}} \div \frac{110}{\cancel{15}} = 2\frac{29}{110}$$

$$(b)\ 16\frac{3}{5} \div 7\frac{1}{3} = \left(16\frac{3}{5} \times 15\right) \div \left(7\frac{1}{3} \times 15\right) = 249 \div 110 = 2\frac{29}{110}$$

$$\text{or } (b)\ 16\frac{3}{5} \div 7\frac{1}{3} = \frac{83}{5} \div \frac{22}{3} = \left(\frac{83}{\cancel{5}} \times \overset{3}{\cancel{15}}\right) \div \left(\frac{22}{\cancel{3}} \times \overset{5}{\cancel{15}}\right) = 249 \div 110 = 2\frac{29}{110}$$

From Example 2, it will be apparent that the methods of dividing fractions by first reducing them to fractions with a common denominator or by first reducing them to whole numbers are much the same and require almost identical computations.

No single method of performing division in fractions will always be most desirable. It is recommended that you become thoroughly familiar with the use of the reciprocal (inverted divisor), of the common denominator, and of the common multiple in the division of fractions. Sometimes one method will be distinctly preferable, and only experience will enable you to select the best solution.

Common fractions may also be divided after they have been reduced to decimal fractions.

EXERCISE 8

A. Divide by the use of the reciprocal. (Express quotients in lowest terms as proper fractions or whole or mixed numbers.)

1. $\frac{1}{7} \div \frac{1}{6}$ **2.** $\frac{1}{3} \div \frac{1}{5}$ **3.** $\frac{2}{3} \div \frac{3}{4}$ **4.** $\frac{5}{8} \div \frac{7}{9}$

5. $\frac{21}{23} \div \frac{3}{4}$ **6.** $\frac{6}{7} \div \frac{11}{17}$ **7.** $\frac{75}{81} \div \frac{5}{9}$ **8.** $\frac{250}{255} \div \frac{50}{765}$

9. $\frac{5}{8} \div 60$ **10.** $\frac{7}{12} \div 42$ **11.** $\frac{8}{15} \div 72$ **12.** $\frac{5}{14} \div 15$

13. $95 \div \frac{19}{25}$ **14.** $18 \div \frac{9}{11}$ **15.** $39 \div \frac{13}{17}$ **16.** $24 \div \frac{6}{7}$

17. $\frac{19}{6} \div 2\frac{1}{4}$ **18.** $\frac{21}{5} \div 8\frac{1}{3}$ **19.** $2\frac{4}{5} \div \frac{14}{3}$ **20.** $12\frac{3}{4} \div \frac{7}{2}$

21. $5\frac{2}{3} \div 4\frac{1}{5}$ **22.** $6\frac{3}{4} \div 2\frac{1}{4}$ **23.** $8\frac{2}{7} \div 5\frac{1}{4}$ **24.** $9\frac{3}{4} \div 4\frac{2}{9}$

B. Divide after reduction to a common denominator. (Express quotients in lowest terms as proper fractions or whole or mixed numbers.)

1. $\frac{1}{4} \div \frac{1}{3}$ **2.** $\frac{3}{5} \div \frac{2}{3}$ **3.** $\frac{14}{25} \div \frac{8}{9}$ **4.** $\frac{45}{14} \div \frac{90}{420}$

5. $\frac{1}{4} \div 8$ **6.** $\frac{2}{3} \div 16$ **7.** $84 \div \frac{21}{25}$ **8.** $35 \div \frac{5}{7}$

9. $\dfrac{\frac{29}{7}}{5\frac{1}{8}}$ **10.** $\dfrac{8\frac{1}{7}}{\frac{18}{5}}$ **11.** $\dfrac{2\frac{1}{3}}{3\frac{1}{4}}$ **12.** $\dfrac{7\frac{4}{5}}{18\frac{2}{3}}$

C. **Divide** after reduction to integers. (Express quotients in lowest terms as proper fractions or whole or mixed numbers.)

1. $\frac{1}{2} \div \frac{1}{5}$
2. $\frac{8}{9} \div \frac{1}{3}$
3. $\frac{2}{3} \div \frac{3}{5}$
4. $\frac{25}{31} \div \frac{50}{62}$
5. $\frac{3}{5} \div 9$
6. $\frac{2}{7} \div 20$
7. $6 \div \frac{1}{2}$
8. $12 \div \frac{3}{5}$
9. $\dfrac{\frac{11}{5}}{3\frac{1}{4}}$
10. $\dfrac{5\frac{1}{6}}{\frac{17}{6}}$
11. $\dfrac{3\frac{1}{4}}{2\frac{1}{7}}$
12. $\dfrac{8\frac{5}{9}}{15\frac{1}{4}}$

UNIT 9. Simplifying Complex Fractions

A *complex fraction* is a fraction which has a fraction or mixed number as numerator or denominator, or both. Thus the following are complex fractions:

$$\dfrac{7}{\frac{5}{6}}; \quad \dfrac{\frac{2}{3}}{4}; \quad \dfrac{\frac{3}{5}}{\frac{7}{4}}; \quad \dfrac{\frac{8}{3}}{2\frac{1}{2}}$$

As you know, the bar or line between the numerator and denominator of a fraction is merely another means of indicating division. Thus the preceding "complex" fractions are really no more complex than equivalent problems in the division of fractions.

$$\dfrac{7}{\frac{5}{6}} = 7 \div \frac{5}{6}; \quad \dfrac{\frac{2}{3}}{4} = \frac{2}{3} \div 4; \quad \dfrac{\frac{3}{5}}{\frac{7}{4}} = \frac{3}{5} \div \frac{7}{4}; \quad \dfrac{\frac{8}{3}}{2\frac{1}{2}} = \frac{8}{3} \div 2\frac{1}{2}$$

The fractions in the numerator or denominator of a complex fraction may be reduced to integers and the complex fraction thus simplified into its equivalent in the form of a proper or improper fraction. This simplification is accomplished by performing the division operation indicated, namely, dividing the numerator by the denominator.

As with any division involving fractions, there is a choice of methods, based upon the use of a reciprocal of the denominator (divisor), a common denominator of the numerator (dividend) and denominator, or a common multiple of the numerator and denominator.

Example 1: Simplifying by the use of the reciprocal.

$$(a)\ \frac{7}{\frac{5}{6}} = 7 \div \frac{5}{6} = 7 \times \frac{6}{5} = \frac{42}{5}$$

$$(b)\ \frac{\frac{2}{3}}{4} = \frac{2}{3} \div 4 = \frac{2}{3} \times \frac{1}{4} = \frac{2}{12} = \frac{1}{6}$$

$$(c)\ \frac{\frac{3}{5}}{\frac{7}{4}} = \frac{3}{5} \div \frac{7}{4} = \frac{3}{5} \times \frac{4}{7} = \frac{12}{35}$$

$$(d)\ \frac{\frac{8}{3}}{2\frac{1}{2}} = \frac{8}{3} \div 2\frac{1}{2} = \frac{8}{3} \div \frac{5}{2} = \frac{8}{3} \times \frac{2}{5} = \frac{16}{15}$$

Example 2: Simplifying by the use of a common denominator.

$$(a)\ \frac{7}{\frac{5}{6}} = \frac{\frac{42}{\cancel{6}}}{\frac{5}{\cancel{6}}} = \frac{42}{5} \qquad (b)\ \frac{\frac{2}{3}}{4} = \frac{\frac{2}{\cancel{3}}}{\frac{12}{\cancel{3}}} = \frac{1}{6}$$

$$(c)\ \frac{\frac{3}{5}}{\frac{7}{4}} = \frac{\frac{12}{\cancel{20}}}{\frac{35}{\cancel{20}}} = \frac{12}{35} \qquad (d)\ \frac{\frac{8}{3}}{2\frac{1}{2}} = \frac{\frac{8}{3}}{\frac{5}{2}} = \frac{\frac{16}{\cancel{6}}}{\frac{15}{\cancel{6}}} = \frac{16}{15}$$

Example 3: Simplifying by the use of a common multiple.

$$(a)\ \frac{7}{\frac{5}{6}} = \frac{7 \times 6}{\frac{5}{\cancel{6}} \times \cancel{6}} = \frac{42}{5} \qquad (b)\ \frac{\frac{2}{3}}{4} = \frac{\frac{2}{\cancel{3}} \times \cancel{3}}{4 \times 3} = \frac{2}{12} = \frac{1}{6}$$

$$(c)\ \frac{\frac{3}{5}}{\frac{7}{4}} = \frac{\frac{3}{\cancel{5}} \times \overset{4}{\cancel{20}}}{\frac{7}{\cancel{4}} \times \underset{5}{\cancel{20}}} = \frac{12}{35} \qquad (d)\ \frac{\frac{8}{3}}{2\frac{1}{2}} = \frac{\frac{8}{3}}{\frac{5}{2}} = \frac{\frac{8}{\cancel{3}} \times \overset{2}{\cancel{6}}}{\frac{5}{\cancel{2}} \times \underset{3}{\cancel{6}}} = \frac{16}{15}$$

Complex fractions are sometimes expressed as follows:

$$\frac{\frac{1}{2} - \frac{1}{3}}{\frac{2}{5} \div \frac{1}{2}}; \qquad \frac{\frac{2}{3} + \frac{3}{4}}{\frac{1}{6} \times 1\frac{2}{3}}$$

This type of complex fraction is also known as a "compound" or "compound-complex" fraction. When expressed in this manner, the procedure in simplifying is to clear (perform the operations indicated) the numerator and denominator, and then solve by any of the methods used to divide fractions.

Examples:

$$\frac{\frac{1}{2} - \frac{1}{3}}{\frac{2}{5} \div \frac{1}{2}} = \frac{\frac{1}{6}}{\frac{4}{5}}$$, and then proceed as in Example 1, 2, or 3

$$\frac{\frac{2}{3} + \frac{3}{4}}{\frac{1}{6} \times 1\frac{2}{3}} = \frac{\frac{17}{12}}{\frac{5}{18}}$$, and then proceed as in Example 1, 2, or 3

EXERCISE 9

A. Simplify the following complex fractions by the use of the reciprocals. With a compound-complex fraction, clear the numerator and denominator before simplification by any method desired. Reduce answers to lowest terms as proper fractions or mixed numbers.

1. $\dfrac{3\frac{3}{4}}{100}$
2. $\dfrac{5\frac{1}{6}}{7\frac{3}{8}}$
3. $\dfrac{15\frac{1}{4} \times 3\frac{1}{6}}{8\frac{1}{3} \div 2\frac{1}{7}}$
4. $\dfrac{6\frac{3}{100}}{\frac{67}{360} \times \frac{9}{200}}$

B. Simplify the following complex fractions by reduction to a common denominator. With a compound-complex fraction, clear the numerator and denominator before simplification by any method desired. Reduce answers to lowest terms as proper fractions or mixed numbers.

1. $\dfrac{5\frac{1}{2}}{100}$
2. $\dfrac{1\frac{5}{7}}{15\frac{1}{14}}$
3. $\dfrac{\frac{5}{8} \times \frac{3}{4}}{2\frac{1}{3} - 1\frac{1}{4}}$
4. $\dfrac{2\frac{1}{20}}{\frac{41}{360} \times \frac{3}{40}}$

C. **Simplify** the following complex fractions by reduction to integers. With a compound-complex fraction, clear the numerator and denominator before simplification by any method desired. Reduce answers to lowest terms as proper fractions or mixed numbers.

1. $\dfrac{3\frac{1}{3}}{100}$ 2. $\dfrac{12\frac{1}{5}}{2\frac{1}{15}}$ 3. $\dfrac{\frac{7}{8} \times \frac{6}{7}}{3\frac{1}{4} \div 2\frac{1}{5}}$ 4. $\dfrac{8\frac{27}{50}}{\frac{61}{360} \times \frac{3}{25}}$

D. **Solve** the following:

1. A farmer sold $\frac{5}{8}$ of his 280-ton crop of hay. If he sold 45 tons at \$18$\frac{3}{5}$ per ton, 60 tons at \$17$\frac{3}{4}$ per ton, $\frac{4}{7}$ of the remainder at \$16$\frac{1}{2}$ per ton, and the balance at \$16$\frac{2}{3}$ per ton, how much did he receive?
2. Mr. Brown, owning $\frac{3}{7}$ of a store, sold $\frac{2}{5}$ of his share to Mr. Jones for \$648. Find the total value of the store.
3. A partnership realized a profit of \$9,240. If each partner's share in the profits was the fraction proportionate with his original investment to the total investment made by all the partners, what was each partner's profit in dollars if A invested $\frac{1}{3}$, B invested $\frac{5}{11}$, and C the remainder?
4. A man paid \$11,900 for a house and lot. If the house was valued at 2$\frac{1}{2}$ times as much as the lot, find (*a*) the value of the lot and (*b*) the value of the house.
5. A speculator in the stock market lost $\frac{7}{9}$ of his investment. He recovered \$4,400 of his loss, and then had $\frac{3}{8}$ of his original investment. How much was his original investment?
6. Mr. Smith left a will providing his widow with $\frac{3}{7}$ of his estate, his son $\frac{4}{7}$ of the remainder, and his daughter the balance of the estate. If the daughter received \$2,156 less than the son, what was the value of the estate?

UNIT 10. Decimal Fractions and Repetends

Reading and writing of decimals have already been discussed (see pages 4 and 5). Placement of the decimal point in addition, subtraction, multiplication, and division was treated in connection with the fundamental processes. Restated briefly:

In adding decimals place the decimal points in the addends and sum in the same vertical column.

In subtracting decimals place the decimal points in minuend, subtrahend, and remainder in the same vertical column.

In multiplying decimals place the decimal point in the product (after multiplication) so that the product will contain the same number of decimal places as the factors combined.

In dividing decimals clear the divisor of decimals (by multiplying divisor and dividend by 10, 100, 1,000, or some other power of 10), thus placing the decimal point in the quotient directly above the relocated decimal point in the dividend *before* beginning the process of division.

A *decimal fraction* is a fraction with a denominator of 10 or some power of 10 which is not expressed by numbers but is shown by the placing of a decimal point.

The digits to the right of the decimal point are really fractions with a numerator of the number indicated by those digits, and a denominator of 1 with as many zeros annexed as there are decimal places in the given decimal. Thus:

$$12.4 = 12\frac{4}{10}; \qquad 6.25 = 6\frac{25}{100}; \qquad .007 = \frac{7}{1000}$$

Kinds of Decimals (Decimal Fractions). Just as fractions are classified as proper fractions, improper fractions or mixed numbers, and complex fractions, so may decimal fractions be classified as pure decimals, mixed decimals, and complex decimals.

Pure decimals	*Mixed decimals*	*Complex decimals*
.5	3.1	$.0\frac{2}{3}$
.12	25.07	$.675\frac{1}{7}$
.375	1.402	$4.3\frac{1}{6}$
.06	860.3125	$18.91\frac{5}{9}$

Note that there is no classification of decimals similar to improper fractions. The decimal equivalent of an improper fraction will be a mixed decimal or complex decimal.

Reduction of Decimals to Common Fractions. Since a decimal is a fraction with a denominator of 10 or some power of 10, to reduce from a decimal-fraction form to a common-fraction form, proceed as follows:

1. Write the figures in the given decimal as a numerator.
2. Write 1 in the denominator and annex as many zeros as there are decimal places in the given decimal (decimal fraction).

The obtained fraction will then be expressed in tenths, hundredths, thousandths, etc. If it is complex, simplify it (see pages 58–60). If it can be reduced to lower terms, reduce it.

Decimals

(a) $.4 = \frac{4}{10} = \frac{2}{5}$

(b) $.056 = \frac{56}{1000} = \frac{7}{125}$

Mixed decimals

(a) $9.25 = 9\frac{25}{100} = 9\frac{1}{4}$

or $9.25 = \frac{925}{100} = 9\frac{1}{4}$

(b) $14.625 = 14 + \frac{625}{1000} = 14\frac{5}{8}$

or $14.625 = \frac{14625}{1000} = 14\frac{5}{8}$

Complex decimals[1]

(a) $.3\frac{1}{3} = \frac{3\frac{1}{3}}{10} = \frac{10}{30} = \frac{1}{3}$

(b) $8.28\frac{4}{7} = 8 + \frac{28\frac{4}{7}}{100} = 8\frac{200}{700} = 8\frac{2}{7}$

or $8.28\frac{4}{7} = \frac{828\frac{4}{7}}{100} = \frac{5{,}800}{700} = 8\frac{2}{7}$

Note that a mixed decimal or complex decimal containing a whole integer may be reduced to a mixed number in two ways:

1. By directly reducing only the decimal fraction ending of the mixed decimal (or complex decimal) to its common-fraction equivalent and then adding this equivalent to the whole integers.

2. By first reducing the entire mixed decimal (or complex decimal) to an improper fraction and then reducing.

It is obvious that the first method is the more desirable.

Reduction of Common Fractions to Decimals. To reduce from a common-fraction form to a decimal-fraction form, proceed as follows:

1. Write the numerator of the common fraction as a dividend, annexing as many zeros as decimal places are desired in the decimal fraction.

2. Divide this obtained dividend by the denominator of the common fraction.

If it is desired to express the decimal fractions in tenths, annex one zero to the dividend; to express in hundredths, annex two zeros; to express in thousandths, annex three zeros; etc.

[1] After a complex decimal is reduced to a fraction, it will be first in a complex fraction form. This complex fraction may be simplified by any of the methods illustrated on pp. 58–60, but the reduction of both numerator and denominator to whole integers by multiplying by a common multiple is probably the easiest and most desirable method.

Tenths

(a) $\frac{2}{5} = 5\overline{)2.0}$ = .4

(b) $\frac{8}{3} = 3\overline{)8.0}$ = $2.6\frac{2}{3}$

(c) $5\frac{3}{7} = 5 + 7\overline{)3.0}$ (= $.4\frac{2}{7}$) $= 5.4\frac{2}{7}$

or $5\frac{3}{7} = \frac{38}{7} = 7\overline{)38.0}$ = $5.4\frac{2}{7}$

Hundredths

(a) $\frac{3}{4} = 4\overline{)3.00}$ = .75

(b) $\frac{11}{6} = 6\overline{)11.00}$ = $1.83\frac{1}{3}$

(c) $3\frac{5}{8} = 3 + 8\overline{)5.00}$ (= $.62\frac{1}{2}$) $= 3.62\frac{1}{2}$

or $3\frac{5}{8} = \frac{29}{8} = 8\overline{)29.00}$ = $3.62\frac{1}{2}$

Thousandths

(a) $\frac{7}{20} = 20\overline{)7.000}$ = .350

(b) $\frac{32}{9} = 9\overline{)32.000}$ = $3.555\frac{5}{9}$

(c) $12\frac{5}{6} = 12 + 6\overline{)5.000}$ (= $.833\frac{1}{3}$) $= 12.833\frac{1}{3}$

or $12\frac{5}{6} = \frac{77}{6} = 6\overline{)77.000}$ = $12.833\frac{1}{3}$

Note that mixed numbers may be reduced to decimals in two ways:

1. By reducing only the fractional ending of the mixed number to its decimal equivalent and then adding this equivalent to the whole integers in the mixed number.

2. By first expressing the mixed number as an improper fraction and then reducing this improper fraction to its decimal equivalent.

The first method is preferable.

Repetends or Circulating Decimals. As you know, some common fractions when reduced to decimals do not terminate but continue repeating. Decimals that will not terminate are "repetends." They are also commonly known as "circulating decimals," sometimes as "periodic decimals."

The fraction $\frac{1}{3}$ expressed decimally is .333, etc. And $\frac{1}{6}$ is expressed decimally as .1666, etc. Such fractions will not reduce to exact or "finite decimals." Some fractions may be reduced to finite decimals. Thus, $\frac{1}{2}$ is exactly .5; $\frac{3}{8}$ is exactly .375; and $\frac{3}{40}$ is exactly .075. Such fractions do terminate when expressed as decimals.

Any common fraction, expressed in lowest terms, will not reduce to a finite decimal if its denominator has in it any other prime factors than 2 or 5. Thus the fractions $\frac{1}{7}$, $\frac{5}{12}$, $\frac{2}{3}$, $\frac{11}{15}$, etc., will not terminate if reduced to decimals. But any common fraction, expressed in lowest terms, will reduce to a finite decimal if its denominator has in it only the prime factors 2 or 5, or 2 and 5. Thus, the fractions $\frac{1}{8}$, $\frac{9}{10}$, $\frac{4}{25}$, $\frac{3}{4}$, etc., will terminate if carried sufficient places when reduced to decimals.

If the denominator of a fraction contains neither a 2 nor a 5 as a factor, it will be a *pure* circulate. For example, $\frac{5}{9}$ is expressed decimally as .555, etc.; and $\frac{1}{7}$ as .142857 142857 142857, etc.

If the denominator contains only 2's and/or 5's as factors, there will be as many places in the decimal as there are 2's *or* 5's in the denominator. Thus, $\frac{1}{10}$, containing a 2 and a 5 (2 × 5), is expressed decimally as .1; $\frac{3}{8}$, containing three 2's (2 × 2 × 2), is expressed decimally as .375; and $\frac{1}{20}$, containing two 2's and a 5 (2 × 2 × 5), is expressed decimally as .05.

If the denominator contains 2's or 5's and some other factor or factors, the decimal will be a *mixed circulate;* that is, it will be part finite and part circulating. Thus, $\frac{1}{6}$ containing one 2 (2 × 3) may be expressed as $.1\frac{2}{3}$; $\frac{1}{15}$, containing one 5 (5 × 3) may be expressed as $.0\frac{2}{3}$; and $\frac{1}{36}$, containing two 2's (2 × 2 × 3 × 3), may be expressed as $.02\frac{7}{9}$.

Indicating a Repetend. To indicate a repetend, place a dot (.) above the figure or figures that constitute the circulating portion of the decimal.

Examples:

$$\frac{1}{9} = .\dot{1}; \qquad \frac{2}{7} = .\dot{2}8571\dot{4}; \qquad \frac{11}{6} = 1.8\dot{3}$$

$$\frac{7}{30} = .2\dot{3}; \qquad \frac{5}{24} = .208\dot{3}; \qquad \frac{17}{110} = .1\dot{5}\dot{4}$$

Reducing a Repetend. Circulating decimals may be reduced to fractions as follows:

1. Use the repetend as the numerator.
2. For the denominator, write as many 9's as there are places in the repetend.

Examples:

$$.\dot{3} = \frac{3}{9} = \frac{1}{3}; \qquad 1.\dot{2}\dot{5} = 1\frac{25}{99}; \qquad .2\dot{6} = .2\frac{6}{9} = .2\frac{2}{3}$$

$$7.6\dot{1}2\dot{3} = 7.6\frac{123}{999} = 7.6\frac{41}{333}$$

It will be observed that, in so reducing, a pure circulate will be expressed as a proper fraction or mixed number, and a mixed circulate will be expressed as a complex decimal fraction. A mixed circulate, when reduced to an equivalent complex decimal fraction, may then be reduced to a proper fraction or mixed number.

However, a mixed circulate may be directly reduced to a proper fraction or mixed number by the following procedure:

1. From the decimals (including repetend), subtract the finite decimals and use this remainder as a numerator.

2. For the denominator, write as many 9's as there are places in the repetend and *annex* as many zeros (0) as there are finite decimal places.

Examples:

$$.1\dot{6} = \frac{(16 - 1)}{90} = \frac{15}{90} = \frac{1}{6}; \qquad .43\dot{5}1\dot{8} = \frac{(43{,}518 - 43)}{99{,}900} = \frac{43{,}475}{99{,}900} = \frac{47}{108}$$

$$4.8\dot{3} = 4 + \frac{(83 - 8)}{90} = 4\frac{75}{90} = 4\frac{5}{6}; \qquad 5.\dot{1}5\dot{4} = 5 + \frac{(154 - 1)}{990} = 5\frac{153}{990} = 5\frac{17}{110}$$

EXERCISE 10

A. Reduce to common-fraction equivalents expressed in lowest terms. If equivalents are improper fractions, express as mixed numbers.

1. .71	2. .44	3. .35	4. .075
5. 5.52	6. 7.25	7. $.00\frac{2}{3}$	8. $.19\frac{3}{7}$
9. $.85\frac{5}{9}$	10. $1.08\frac{1}{3}$	11. $2.87\frac{1}{2}$	12. $7.95\frac{3}{4}$

B. Reduce to decimal-fraction equivalents (work to nearest ten-thousandths):

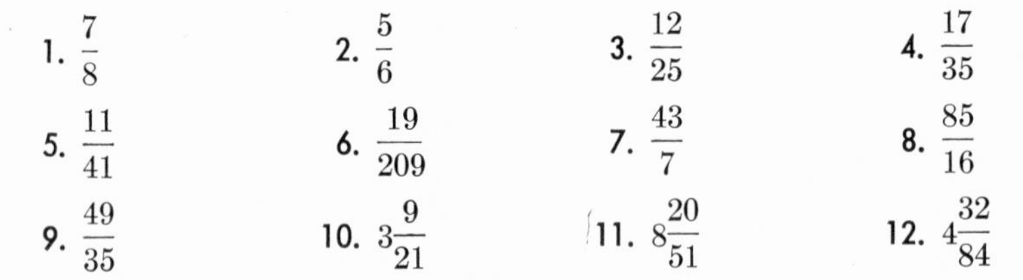

1. $\frac{7}{8}$	2. $\frac{5}{6}$	3. $\frac{12}{25}$	4. $\frac{17}{35}$
5. $\frac{11}{41}$	6. $\frac{19}{209}$	7. $\frac{43}{7}$	8. $\frac{85}{16}$
9. $\frac{49}{35}$	10. $3\frac{9}{21}$	11. $8\frac{20}{51}$	12. $4\frac{32}{84}$

C. Reduce the following fractions to circulating decimals. Indicate repetends by placement of dot or dots.

1. $\frac{5}{6}$	2. $\frac{2}{9}$	3. $\frac{4}{7}$	4. $\frac{2}{15}$
5. $\frac{11}{75}$	6. $\frac{7}{27}$	7. $\frac{43}{12}$	8. $\frac{263}{150}$

D. Reduce only the repetends in the following to common fractions or fractional endings expressed in lowest terms:

1. $.\dot{5}$	**2.** $.\dot{2}5\dot{0}$	**3.** $.1\dot{6}$	**4.** $.4\dot{1}2\dot{3}$
5. $.35\dot{5}\dot{4}$	**6.** $.03\dot{8}\dot{1}$	**7.** $4.8\dot{7}$	**8.** $2.0\dot{3}1\dot{2}$

E. Reduce the following mixed circulates to common fractions or mixed numbers expressed in lowest terms:

1. $.4\dot{7}$	**2.** $.25\dot{3}$	**3.** $.01\dot{3}$	**4.** $.6\dot{8}\dot{1}$
5. $.08\dot{5}\dot{4}$	**6.** $.1\dot{0}3\dot{7}$	**7.** $4.0\dot{2}\dot{7}$	**8.** $7.4\dot{0}\dot{9}$

CHAPTER II

FUNDAMENTALS OF PROBLEM SOLVING

UNIT 1. Finding a Required Quantity When the Quantity of a Fractional Equivalent Is Known

If the quantity (or value) of a fractional equivalent is known, the *whole* quantity may be found by either the fractional-unit method or by the "reciprocal method." Each solution requires exactly the same computations, but each follows a somewhat different mental approach or line of reasoning.

Fractional-unit Method:

1. Divide the known quantity by the numerator of the fractional equivalent to find the quantity contained in a fractional unit.
2. Multiply this obtained quantity by the denominator of the fractional unit to find the *whole* quantity.

Reciprocal Method:

1. Find the reciprocal of the fractional equivalent.
2. Multiply the known quantity by this reciprocal to find the *whole* quantity.

Example 1: If $\frac{2}{5}$ of a cake costs 30 cents, find the cost of the whole cake.

Fractional-unit method:

$$\text{(1) Cost of } \frac{1}{5} \text{ of cake} = 30¢ \div 2 = 15¢$$

$$\text{(2) Cost of } \frac{5}{5} \text{ or whole cake} = 15¢ \times 5 = 75¢$$

Reciprocal method:

$$\text{(1) The reciprocal of } \frac{2}{5} \text{ is } \frac{5}{2}$$

$$\text{(2) Cost of whole cake} = \overset{15}{\cancel{30}}¢ \times \frac{5}{\cancel{2}} = 75¢$$

Example 2: The value of $\frac{7}{16}$ ownership of a store is \$12,600. Find the value of the whole store.

Fractional-unit method:

$$(1)\ \text{Value of } \frac{1}{16} \text{ ownership} = \$12{,}600 \div 7 = \$1{,}800$$

$$(2)\ \text{Value of } \frac{16}{16} \text{ or whole store} = \$1{,}800 \times 16 = \$28{,}800$$

Reciprocal method:

$$(1)\ \text{The reciprocal of } \frac{7}{16} \text{ is } \frac{16}{7}$$

$$(2)\ \text{Value of whole store} = \overset{1{,}800}{\cancel{\$12{,}600}} \times \frac{16}{\cancel{7}} = \$28{,}800$$

When it is desired to find *more* or *less* than a whole quantity, the fractional-unit method is perhaps the more desirable if the fractional equivalent of the required quantity has the same denominator as the given fractional equivalent. If the denominator of the required fractional equivalent is not the same, the reciprocal method may offer greater opportunity for cancellation and thus be preferable.

Example 1: Finding fractional quantity. If $\frac{5}{12}$ yard of silk costs \$.80, find the cost of $\frac{7}{12}$ yard.

Fractional-unit method:

$$(1)\ \text{Cost of } \frac{1}{12} \text{ yard} = \$.80 \div 5 = \$.16$$

$$(2)\ \text{Cost of } \frac{7}{12} \text{ yard} = \$.16 \times 7 = \$1.12$$

Reciprocal method:

$$(1)\ \text{The reciprocal of } \frac{5}{12} \text{ is } \frac{12}{5}$$

$$(2)\ \text{Cost of } \frac{12}{12} \text{ or whole yard} = \overset{.16}{\cancel{\$.80}} \times \frac{12}{\cancel{5}} = \$1.92$$

$$(3)\ \text{Cost of } \frac{7}{12} \text{ yard} = \overset{.16}{\cancel{\$1.92}} \times \frac{7}{\cancel{12}} = \$1.12$$

$$\text{or combining (2) and (3): } \overset{.16}{\cancel{\$.80}} \times \frac{\cancel{12}}{\cancel{5}} \times \frac{7}{\cancel{12}} = \$1.12$$

Example 2: Finding fractional quantity. John earned \$14.40, or $\frac{3}{5}$ as much as Mary. Henry earned $\frac{11}{8}$ times as much as Mary. Find the earnings of Mary and of Henry.

Fractional-unit method:

$$(1)\ \frac{1}{5} \text{ of Mary's earnings} = \$14.40 \div 3 = \$4.80$$

$$(2)\ \frac{5}{5} \text{ or Mary's whole earnings} = \$4.80 \times 5 = \$24.00$$

$$(3)\ \frac{11}{8} \text{ Mary's earnings or Henry's earnings} = \overset{3.00}{\cancel{\$24.00}} \times \frac{11}{\cancel{8}} = \$33.00$$

Reciprocal method:

$$(1)\ \text{The reciprocal of } \frac{3}{5} \text{ is } \frac{5}{3}$$

$$(2)\ \text{Mary's earnings} = \overset{4.80}{\cancel{\$14.40}} \times \frac{5}{\cancel{3}} = \$24.00$$

$$(3)\ \text{Henry's earnings} = \overset{3.00}{\cancel{\$24.00}} \times \frac{11}{\cancel{8}} = \$33.00$$

EXERCISE 1

A. Find the whole quantity of each of the following by the fractional-unit method:

1. $\frac{1}{7}$ of a quantity $= 21$

2. $\frac{4}{5}$ of a quantity $= 360$

3. $\frac{5}{9}$ of a quantity $= 15\frac{1}{2}$

4. $\frac{7}{13}$ of a quantity $= \$60.34$

5. $\frac{9}{4}$ of a quantity $= 18\frac{1}{3}$

6. $1\frac{2}{3}$ times a quantity $= 240$

B. Find the whole quantity of each of the following by the reciprocal method:

1. $\frac{1}{3}$ of a quantity $= 15$

2. $\frac{4}{7}$ of a quantity $= 252$

3. $\frac{8}{11}$ of a quantity $= 16\frac{1}{2}$

4. $\frac{5}{16}$ of a quantity $= \$49.60$

5. $\frac{6}{5}$ of a quantity $= 30\frac{1}{3}$

6. $1\frac{3}{4}$ times a quantity $= 420$

C. Solve the following by any method.

If:	*Find the quantity of the following whole quantities or fractional parts of the whole quantities:* (*a*)	(*b*)	(*c*)
1. $\frac{2}{3}$ of a quantity = 21	1	$\frac{5}{3}$	$\frac{6}{7}$
2. $\frac{5}{2}$ of a quantity = 36	$\frac{5}{12}$	$2\frac{1}{4}$	$\frac{3}{8}$
3. $\frac{9}{40}$ of a quantity = 801	$\frac{3}{20}$	1	$6\frac{1}{4}$
4. $\frac{1}{6}$ of a quantity = \$72	$\frac{1}{2}$	$4\frac{1}{3}$	$\frac{4}{5}$
5. $\frac{10}{3}$ of a quantity = \$$45\frac{1}{2}$	$\frac{5}{6}$	$\frac{4}{9}$	$1\frac{1}{10}$
6. $2\frac{1}{5}$ times a quantity = \$66	$3\frac{1}{4}$	$\frac{5}{12}$	$\frac{14}{3}$

UNIT 2. Aliquot Parts

An *aliquot part* is a number contained in another number without remainder.

Thus $3\frac{1}{3}$ is an aliquot part of 10, $12\frac{1}{2}$ is an aliquot part of 100, and $166\frac{2}{3}$ is an aliquot part of 1,000; for $3\frac{1}{3}$ is contained exactly 3 times in 10, $12\frac{1}{2}$ is contained exactly 8 times in 100, and $166\frac{2}{3}$ is contained exactly 6 times in 1,000. Also, $3\frac{1}{3}$ is equivalent to $\frac{1}{3}$ of 10, $12\frac{1}{2}$ is equivalent to $\frac{1}{8}$ of 100, and $166\frac{2}{3}$ is equivalent to $\frac{1}{6}$ of 1,000.

It is the aliquot parts of 1, 10 and the powers of 10 (10, 100, 1,000, 10,000) which frequently occur in business computations which are of particular interest, for the necessary operations in multiplication and division by such fractional parts may be accomplished by a short cut known as the "aliquot-parts method."

However, if this short cut is to be of any practical value, it is necessary that the more often occurring aliquot parts be committed to memory. In the table on page 72 it is suggested that you memorize first the aliquot parts and their fractional equivalents of the basic number 100. As you will observe, a knowledge of these aliquot parts of 100 may be extended readily to the adjoining columns which list the aliquot parts of the basic numbers 1, 10, 1,000, and 10,000.

Table of Certain Aliquot Parts

Aliquot fractions	The basic numbers				
	1	10	100	1,000	10,000
$\frac{1}{2}$	.50	5	50	500	5,000
$\frac{1}{3}$	$.33\frac{1}{3}$	$3\frac{1}{3}$	$33\frac{1}{3}$	$333\frac{1}{3}$	$3,333\frac{1}{3}$
$\frac{1}{4}$	.25	$2\frac{1}{2}$	25	250	2,500
$\frac{1}{5}$	.20	2	20	200	2,000
$\frac{1}{6}$	$.16\frac{2}{3}$	$1\frac{2}{3}$	$16\frac{2}{3}$	$166\frac{2}{3}$	$1,666\frac{2}{3}$
$\frac{1}{7}$	$.14\frac{2}{7}$	$1\frac{3}{7}$	$14\frac{2}{7}$	$142\frac{6}{7}$	$1,428\frac{4}{7}$
$\frac{1}{8}$	$.12\frac{1}{2}$	$1\frac{1}{4}$	$12\frac{1}{2}$	125	1,250
$\frac{1}{9}$	$.11\frac{1}{9}$	$1\frac{1}{9}$	$11\frac{1}{9}$	$111\frac{1}{9}$	$1,111\frac{1}{9}$
$\frac{1}{10}$	.10	1	10	100	1,000
$\frac{1}{12}$	$.08\frac{1}{3}$	$\frac{5}{6}$	$8\frac{1}{3}$	$83\frac{1}{3}$	$833\frac{1}{3}$
$\frac{1}{16}$	$.06\frac{1}{4}$	$\frac{5}{8}$	$6\frac{1}{4}$	$62\frac{1}{2}$	625

Note that the numerator of an aliquot fraction is 1, and the basic numbers in the preceding table are 1, 10, 100, 1,000, and 10,000.

Multiples of Aliquot Parts. It is often possible to recognize that a number is a multiple of an aliquot part. When such a number is a factor in multiplication or a divisor in division, it may be advantageous to multiply or divide by the aliquot-parts method.

Those multiples of aliquot parts which are most useful are the multiples of the aliquot parts of 1 and of 100. The following table includes some of the multiples which occur most frequently and with which you should be familiar. Note that the fractional equivalent of a multiple of an aliquot fraction always has a numerator other than 1.

To Multiply by an Aliquot Part or Its Multiple:

1. Find the product of the multiplicand and the basic number.
2. Multiply this product by the fractional equivalent (the aliquot fraction or its multiple).

If the basic number is 1, 10, 100, 1,000, or 10,000, finding the product of the multiplicand and the basic number may be accomplished by

Table of Multiples of Certain Aliquot Parts

Multiples of aliquot fractions	The basic numbers				
	1	10	100	1,000	10,000
$\frac{2}{3}$	$.66\frac{2}{3}$	$6\frac{2}{3}$	$66\frac{2}{3}$	$666\frac{2}{3}$	$6,666\frac{2}{3}$
$\frac{3}{4}$	.75	$7\frac{1}{2}$	75	750	7,500
$\frac{2}{5}$	.40	4	40	400	4,000
$\frac{3}{5}$	.60	6	60	600	6,000
$\frac{4}{5}$	.80	8	80	800	8,000
$\frac{5}{6}$	$.83\frac{1}{3}$	$8\frac{1}{3}$	$83\frac{1}{3}$	$833\frac{1}{3}$	$8,333\frac{1}{3}$
$\frac{3}{8}$	$.37\frac{1}{2}$	$3\frac{3}{4}$	$37\frac{1}{2}$	375	3,750
$\frac{5}{8}$	$.62\frac{1}{2}$	$6\frac{1}{4}$	$62\frac{1}{2}$	625	6,250
$\frac{7}{8}$	$.87\frac{1}{2}$	$8\frac{3}{4}$	$87\frac{1}{2}$	875	8,750
$\frac{2}{9}$	$.22\frac{2}{9}$	$2\frac{2}{9}$	$22\frac{2}{9}$	$222\frac{2}{9}$	$2,222\frac{2}{9}$
$\frac{4}{9}$	$.44\frac{4}{9}$	$4\frac{4}{9}$	$44\frac{4}{9}$	$444\frac{4}{9}$	$4,444\frac{4}{9}$
$\frac{5}{9}$	$.55\frac{5}{9}$	$5\frac{5}{9}$	$55\frac{5}{9}$	$555\frac{5}{9}$	$5,555\frac{5}{9}$
$\frac{7}{9}$	$.77\frac{7}{9}$	$7\frac{7}{9}$	$77\frac{7}{9}$	$777\frac{7}{9}$	$7,777\frac{7}{9}$
$\frac{8}{9}$	$.88\frac{8}{9}$	$8\frac{8}{9}$	$88\frac{8}{9}$	$888\frac{8}{9}$	$8,888\frac{8}{9}$
$\frac{5}{12}$	$.41\frac{2}{3}$	$4\frac{1}{6}$	$41\frac{2}{3}$	$416\frac{2}{3}$	$4,166\frac{2}{3}$
$\frac{7}{12}$	$.58\frac{1}{3}$	$5\frac{5}{6}$	$58\frac{1}{3}$	$583\frac{1}{3}$	$5,833\frac{1}{3}$
$\frac{11}{12}$	$.91\frac{2}{3}$	$9\frac{1}{6}$	$91\frac{2}{3}$	$916\frac{2}{3}$	$9,166\frac{2}{3}$
$\frac{3}{16}$	$.18\frac{3}{4}$	$1\frac{7}{8}$	$18\frac{3}{4}$	$187\frac{1}{2}$	1,875
$\frac{5}{16}$	$.31\frac{1}{4}$	$3\frac{1}{8}$	$31\frac{1}{4}$	$312\frac{1}{2}$	3,125
$\frac{7}{16}$	$.43\frac{3}{4}$	$4\frac{3}{8}$	$43\frac{3}{4}$	$437\frac{1}{2}$	4,375
$\frac{9}{16}$	$.56\frac{1}{4}$	$5\frac{5}{8}$	$56\frac{1}{4}$	$562\frac{1}{2}$	5,625
$\frac{11}{16}$	$.68\frac{3}{4}$	$6\frac{7}{8}$	$68\frac{3}{4}$	$687\frac{1}{2}$	6,875
$\frac{13}{16}$	$.81\frac{1}{4}$	$8\frac{1}{8}$	$81\frac{1}{4}$	$812\frac{1}{2}$	8,125
$\frac{15}{16}$	$.93\frac{3}{4}$	$9\frac{3}{8}$	$93\frac{3}{4}$	$937\frac{1}{2}$	9,375

moving the decimal point in the multiplicand as many places to the *right* as there are zeros in the basic number.

As an *aliquot* fraction always has 1 for a numerator, multiplying by an aliquot fraction is equivalent to dividing by the denominator of the aliquot fraction. Hence the second step, if applied only to aliquot parts, could be stated, *Divide this product by the denominator of the aliquot fraction.*

With practice, you will find that much or all of the necessary computation may be made mentally or with a minimum of pencil work.

Example 1: Aliquot part. Multiply 497.62 by $14\frac{2}{7}$.

$$14\frac{2}{7} \text{ is } \frac{1}{7} \text{ of the basic number } 100$$

$$(1)\ 497.62 \times 100 = 49{,}762$$

$$(2)\ 49{,}762 \times \frac{1}{7} = 7{,}108\frac{6}{7}$$

$$\text{or } \frac{497.62 \times 100}{7} = \frac{49{,}762}{7} = 7{,}108\frac{6}{7}$$

Example 2: Aliquot part. Multiply $166\frac{2}{3}$ by .075678.

$$166\frac{2}{3} \text{ is } \frac{1}{6} \text{ of the basic number } 1{,}000$$

$$(1)\ .075678 \times 1{,}000 = 75.678$$

$$(2)\ 75.678 \times \frac{1}{6} = 12.613$$

$$\text{or } \frac{.075678 \times 1{,}000}{6} = \frac{75.678}{6} = 12.613$$

As is illustrated by Example 2, the factors may be transposed, with the multiplicand considered as the multiplier.

Multiplication by a *multiple* of an aliquot part does not lend itself quite so readily to mental computation as does multiplication by an aliquot part, for the multiple always has a numerator of more than 1. Nevertheless, in many instances the aliquot-parts method will save considerable time and effort.

Example 3: Multiple of an aliquot part. Multiply 76.3 by $37\frac{1}{2}$.

$$37\frac{1}{2} \text{ is } \frac{3}{8} \text{ of the basic number } 100$$

$$(1)\ 76.3 \times 100 = 7{,}630$$

$$(2)\ \overset{3{,}815}{\cancel{7{,}630}} \times \frac{3}{\underset{4}{\cancel{8}}} = \frac{11{,}445}{4} = 2{,}861\frac{1}{4}$$

Example 4: Multiple of an aliquot part. Multiply $83\frac{1}{3}$ by 390.

$$83\frac{1}{3} \text{ is } \frac{5}{6} \text{ of the basic number 100}$$

$$(1)\ 390 \times 100 = 39{,}000$$

$$(2)\ \overset{6{,}500}{\cancel{39{,}000}} = \frac{5}{\cancel{6}} = 32{,}500$$

Note that in Example 4, $83\frac{1}{3}$ is also an aliquot part, namely, $\frac{1}{12}$ of 1,000. If 1,000 is considered the basic number, the computations would be $390 \times 1{,}000 \times \frac{1}{12} = 32{,}500$. Many aliquot parts and their multiples may be expressed as an aliquot part of some other power of 10. Thus, $3\frac{1}{3}$ (or $\frac{1}{3}$ of 10) is also $\frac{1}{30}$ of 100; $66\frac{2}{3}$ (or $\frac{2}{3}$ of 100) is also $\frac{1}{15}$ of 1,000.

To Divide by an Aliquot Part or Its Multiple:

1. Find the quotient of the dividend divided by the basic number.
2. Divide this quotient by the fractional equivalent (the aliquot fraction or its multiple).

Division of the dividend by the basic number may be accomplished by moving the decimal point in the dividend as many places to the *left* as there are zeros in the basic number.

Dividing by an *aliquot* fraction is equivalent to multiplying by its denominator. Thus, the second step, if applied only to aliquot parts, could be stated, *Multiply this quotient by the denominator of the aliquot fraction.*

Example 1: Aliquot part. Divide 432.24 by $3\frac{1}{3}$.

$$3\frac{1}{3} \text{ is } \frac{1}{3} \text{ of the basic number 10}$$

$$(1)\ 432.24 \div 10 = 43.224$$

$$(2)\ 43.224 \div \frac{1}{3} = 43.224 \times \frac{3}{1} = 129.672$$

$$\text{or } \frac{432.24}{10} \times 3 = 43.224 \times 3 = 129.672$$

Example 2: Aliquot part. Divide 97,645 by $8\frac{1}{3}$.

$$8\frac{1}{3} \text{ is } \frac{1}{12} \text{ of the basic number 100}$$

$$(1)\ 97{,}654 \div 100 = 976.54$$

$$(2)\ 976.54 \div \frac{1}{12} = 976.54 \times \frac{12}{1} = 11{,}718.48$$

$$\text{or } \frac{97{,}654}{100} \times 12 = 976.54 \times 12 = 11{,}718.48$$

Division by a *multiple* of an aliquot part is somewhat more difficult to compute mentally than is division by an aliquot part. However, in division as with multiplication by a multiple of an aliquot part, the aliquot-parts method will often save both time and effort.

Example 3: Multiple of an aliquot part. Divide 4,800 by $87\frac{1}{2}$.

$$87\frac{1}{2} \text{ is } \frac{7}{8} \text{ of the basic number } 100$$

$$(1)\ 4{,}800 \div 100 = 48$$

$$(2)\ 48 \div \frac{7}{8} = 48 \times \frac{8}{7} = \frac{384}{7} = 54\frac{6}{7}$$

Example 4: Multiple of an aliquot part. Divide 278 by $666\frac{2}{3}$.

$$666\frac{2}{3} \text{ is } \frac{2}{3} \text{ of the basic number } 1{,}000$$

$$(1)\ 278 \div 1{,}000 = .278$$

$$(2)\ .278 \div \frac{2}{3} = \overset{.139}{\cancel{.278}} \times \frac{3}{\cancel{2}} = .417$$

It must be emphasized that the aliquot-parts method of multiplying and dividing is of little value unless the user has thoroughly memorized the tables of the more frequently occurring aliquot parts (of 1, 10, and the powers of 10) and their multiples.

Finally, summarizing the steps in solution:

To multiply (the multiplicand):

1. Multiply by basic number.
2. Multiply by fractional equivalent.

To divide (the dividend):

1. Divide by basic number.
2. Divide by fractional equivalent.

EXERCISE 2

A. Multiply by the aliquot-parts method. Use only *aliquot* parts.

1. $24 \times 3\frac{1}{3}$ **2.** $72 \times 166\frac{2}{3}$

3. $2\frac{1}{2} \times 76$

4. $.12\frac{1}{2} \times 5.60$

5. $26.1 \times 333\frac{1}{3}$

6. $54 \times 1{,}111\frac{1}{9}$

7. $66 \times .16\frac{2}{3}$

8. $6\frac{1}{4} \times 65.6$

9. $833\frac{1}{3} \times 53.1$

10. $.976 \times 625$

B. **Divide** by the aliquot-parts method. Use only *aliquot* parts.

1. $75 \div 1\frac{2}{3}$

2. $36 \div 83\frac{1}{3}$

3. $488 \div .16\frac{2}{3}$

4. $336 \div 62\frac{1}{2}$

5. $96 \div 8\frac{1}{3}$

6. $738 \div 166\frac{2}{3}$

7. $54.4 \div .12\frac{1}{2}$

8. $99 \div 3{,}333\frac{1}{3}$

9. $27 \div 111\frac{1}{9}$

10. $46.4 \div 1{,}250$

C. **Multiply** by the aliquot-parts method. Use only *multiples* of aliquot parts.

1. $66 \times 66\frac{2}{3}$

2. $41\frac{2}{3} \times 3.72$

3. $72 \times .31\frac{1}{4}$

4. $18\frac{3}{4} \times 17.6$

D. **Divide** by the aliquot parts method. Use only *multiples* of aliquot parts.

1. $56 \div 37\frac{1}{2}$

2. $24 \div .83\frac{1}{3}$

3. $72 \div 58\frac{1}{3}$

4. $4.64 \div 62\frac{1}{2}$

E. **Solve** the following by the aliquot-parts method.

1. A salesman received a commission of $\frac{1}{20}$ of his sales. If he sold 576 articles at $16\frac{2}{3}$ cents each, find (*a*) his total sales and (*b*) his total commission.
2. A manufacturer agreed to take back 1,218 items and credit a merchant with the retail sales price of $33\frac{1}{3}$ cents less a discount of $\frac{2}{7}$. Find (*a*) the total retail selling price of the items, (*b*) the total discount, and (*c*) the total credit.
3. A piece of property costing \$17,500 was valued (assessed) for tax purposes at

$\frac{11}{25}$ of its cost. If the tax was $83\frac{1}{3}$ cents on each \$100 of assessed value, find (*a*) the assessed value and (*b*) the total tax on the property.

4. A workman was paid at the rate of $66\frac{2}{3}$ cents per hour with a bonus of one-fourth for every hour of work in excess of 40 hours per week. During one week he worked $47\frac{1}{2}$ hours. Find (*a*) his pay for 40 hours, (*b*) his overtime pay, and (*c*) his total pay for the week.
5. A produce house paid a farmer $\$.41\frac{2}{3}$ each for 2,496 crates of lettuce and $\$1.58\frac{1}{3}$ each for 768 lug boxes of tomatoes. The lettuce cost the farmer $\$.29\frac{1}{6}$ per crate and the tomatoes cost him $\$1.39\frac{7}{12}$ per lug box. Find (*a*) the total amount he received from the produce house and (*b*) his total profit. (NOTE: When cents expressed as \$0.00 are an aliquot part of \$1.00, then \$1 or 1 is the basic number.)
6. A home costing \$25,600 is given an assessed value of $.18\frac{3}{4}$ of its cost. If the county tax rate is \$3.75 for each \$100 of assessed value, and the city tax rate is $\$3.12\frac{1}{2}$ for each \$100 of assessed value, find (*a*) the county tax and (*b*) the city tax.

UNIT 3. Simple Equations and Use of Formulas

The solution to any given problem is often found through the determination of the quantity or value of an unknown part of an equation.

An *equation* expresses the equality of two quantities or values. Thus the following are equations:

$$8 = 6 + 2; \qquad 12 = 4 \times 3$$
$$6 = 8 - 2; \qquad 4 = 12 \div 3$$

The two parts (left and right of the = sign) are known as the *sides* or *members* of the equation.

In arithmetical computations, usually the problem (and the equation) is satisfied if the value of some one unknown is found. This unknown may be named, as "retail," "cost," "area," "length," etc., or it may be indicated by a symbol or abbreviation such as R, C, A, l, etc. This symbol may or may not be mnemonic (when letter or letters indicate the meaning of the unknown, as R, C, A, or l), and frequently such letters as X, y, A, b, C, d, etc., are used to symbolize the unknown quantity or value without in themselves implying what the unknown represents. The symbols x, y, or z are commonly used to represent such an unknown.

Formulas. Many operations and definitions in mathematics lend themselves to expression in equation form. When rules or methods of solution are so indicated, they are known as "*formulas*." Frequently, formulas will contain signs of aggregation, such as parentheses ( ), brackets [ ], and braces { }, which are used to simplify and make plain the order of operations to be performed. When a formula contains such a sign of aggregation, all quantities within the sign are to be treated as a single quantity and the operations indicated should be performed first.

After substituting known quantities in a formula, solve by applying the following order of procedure:

1. Clear quantities within signs of aggregation (perform the operations indicated).
2. Raise to powers indicated. (See Appendix II for explanation of powers.)
3. Do all multiplication (in any order desired).
4. Do all division in the order in which it occurs.
5. Do all addition and subtraction (in any order desired).

Note that multiplication should be performed before division. Thus $24 \div 3 \times 2 = 24 \div 6 = 4$ (not $8 \times 2 = 16$).

And division should be performed in the order in which it occurs. Thus $48 \div 4 \div 2 = 12 \div 2 = 6$ (not $48 \div 2 = 24$).

However, factors may be rejected (canceled) from dividend and divisor before the indicated operations are performed:

$$\overset{\overset{4}{\cancel{8}}}{\cancel{24}} \div \cancel{3} \times \cancel{2} = 4 \qquad \text{or} \qquad \overset{\overset{4}{\cancel{12}}}{\cancel{24}} \div \cancel{3} \times \cancel{2} = 4$$

The dividend is 24
The divisor is 3×2

$$\overset{\overset{6}{\cancel{12}}}{\cancel{48}} \div \cancel{4} \div \cancel{2} = 6 \qquad \text{or} \qquad \overset{\overset{6}{\cancel{24}}}{\cancel{48}} \div \cancel{4} \div \cancel{2} = 6$$

The dividend is 48
The divisors are 4 and 2

Ordinarily, problems are so stated that there will be no uncertainty as to their meanings. Thus the preceding might have been written:

$$24 \div (3 \times 2), \text{ or } \frac{24}{3 \times 2}; \qquad (48 \div 4) \div 2, \text{ or } \frac{48 \div 4}{2}, \text{ or } \frac{\frac{48}{4}}{2}$$

Observe that the following formulas are expressed in two forms, each form having the same meaning:

$$V = \frac{1}{3} \times b \times h \quad \text{or} \quad V = \frac{1}{3} bh \text{ or } \frac{bh}{3}$$

$$S = B \times (1 + r) \quad \text{or} \quad S = B(1 + r)$$

$$2s = 2 \times (1 + i)^n \quad \text{or} \quad 2s = 2(1 + i)^n$$

$$B = P \div r \quad \text{or} \quad B = \frac{P}{r}$$

$$P = I \div n \times i \quad \text{or} \quad P = \frac{I}{ni}$$

Generally, formulas are written as in the right-hand grouping. As you will observe, the multiplication sign × need not be used between an abstract number and symbol, between symbols, or between a symbol or abstract number and a sign of aggregation. Also, as is indicated, the division process is ordinarily shown in the fractional form rather than by the division sign ÷.

Since both parts of an equation are equalities, the unknown may be placed in either side of the equation, but it is customary to place the unknown in the left side and then substitute all known quantities before proceeding with the solution.

Solving Simple Equations. The following axioms (established truths) are used in solving simple equations:

1. The same number may be added to both members of an equation without destroying the equality. Thus:

If $8 = 6 + 2$ then $8 + 4 = 6 + 2 + 4$ If $A = 9 - 2$ then $A + 3 = 9 - 2 + 3$

2. The same number may be subtracted from both members of an equation without destroying the equality. Thus:

If $6 = 8 - 2$ then $6 - 3 = 8 - 2 - 3$ If $B = 12 \times 5$ then $B - 7 = 12 \times 5 - 7$

3. Both members of an equation may be multiplied by the same number without destroying the equality. Thus:

If $12 = 4 \times 3$ then $2 \times 12 = 2(4 \times 3)$ If $C = 6 + 4$ then $5C = 5(6 + 4)$

4. Both members of an equation may be divided by the same number without destroying the equality. Thus:

If $4 = 12 \div 3$ then $4 \div 2 = (12 \div 3) \div 2$ If $D = 15 \times 5$ then $\frac{D}{3} = \frac{15 \times 5}{3}$

There are several mechanical methods that may be used to solve simple equations. Two of these are

1. *Transposition.* A term may be transposed from one member of an equation to another if the sign is changed to its opposite (from $+$ to $-$; from $-$ to $+$; from $\times$ to $\div$; from $\div$ to $\times$). Thus:

$$\begin{array}{rl} \text{If} & 8 = 6 + 2 \\ \text{then} & 8 - 2 = 6 \\ \text{and} & 8 - 6 = 2 \end{array} \qquad \begin{array}{rl} \text{If} & c = a + b \\ \text{then} & c - b = a \\ \text{and} & c - a = b \end{array}$$

$$\begin{array}{rl} \text{If} & 12 = 4 \times 3 \\ \text{then} & 12 \div 3 = 4 \\ \text{and} & 12 \div 4 = 3 \end{array} \qquad \begin{array}{rl} \text{If} & x = yz \\ \text{then} & x \div z = y \\ \text{and} & x \div y = z \end{array}$$

2. *Cancellation.* A term (with the same sign of operation) appearing in both members of an equation may be canceled. Thus:

$$\begin{array}{rl} \text{If} & 8 + \cancel{4} = 6 + 2 + \cancel{4} \\ \text{then} & 8 = 6 + 2 \end{array} \qquad \begin{array}{rl} \text{If} & X + \cancel{3} = 7 + \cancel{3} \\ \text{then} & X = 7 \end{array}$$

$$\begin{array}{rl} \text{If} & 6 - \cancel{3} = 8 - 2 - \cancel{3} \\ \text{then} & 6 = 8 - 2 \end{array} \qquad \begin{array}{rl} \text{If} & Y - \cancel{6} = 9 - \cancel{6} \\ \text{then} & Y = 9 \end{array}$$

$$\begin{array}{rl} \text{If} & \cancel{2} \times 12 = \cancel{2}(4 \times 3) \\ \text{then} & 12 = 4 \times 3 \end{array} \qquad \begin{array}{rl} \text{If} & \cancel{7}A = \cancel{7} \times 5 \\ \text{then} & A = 5 \end{array}$$

$$\begin{array}{rl} \text{If} & 4 \div \cancel{2} = (12 \div 3) \div \cancel{2} \\ \text{then} & 4 = 12 \div 3 \end{array} \qquad \begin{array}{rl} \text{If} & B \div \cancel{9} = 2 \div \cancel{9} \\ \text{then} & B = 2 \end{array}$$

Finding One Unit (Whole or 100 Per Cent) of the Unknown. If in solving, the unknown is expressed as a multiple (or fractional part), the quantity of value of *one unit* (a whole unit) of the unknown may be found by applying Axiom 3 (multiplying by the reciprocal), Axiom 4 (dividing by the multiple or fractional part), or by transposition. As you know, $4A$ means 4 times A, $6Y$ means 6 times Y, $\frac{2}{3}B$ means $\frac{2}{3}$ times B, etc.

Examples: Find the quantities of C in the following equations by applying Axiom 3, Axiom 4, and transposition: (*a*) $4C = 35$; (*b*) $\frac{3}{4}C = 26$.

By Axiom 3 (multiplying by reciprocal):

(*a*)
$$4C = 35$$
$$\frac{1}{\cancel{4}} \times \cancel{4}C = \frac{1}{4} \times 35$$
$$C = 8\frac{3}{4}$$

(*b*)
$$\frac{3}{4}C = 26$$
$$\frac{\cancel{3}}{\cancel{4}}C \times \frac{\cancel{4}}{\cancel{3}} = 26 \times \frac{4}{3}$$
$$C = \frac{104}{3} = 34\frac{2}{3}$$

By Axiom 4 (dividing by multiple or fractional part):

(a)
$$4C = 35$$
$$\frac{4C}{4} = \frac{35}{4}$$
$$C = 8\frac{3}{4}$$

(b)
$$\frac{3}{4}C = 26$$
$$\frac{3}{4}C \div \frac{3}{4} = 26 \div \frac{3}{4}$$
$$\frac{3}{4}C \times \frac{4}{3} = 26 \times \frac{4}{3}$$
$$C = \frac{104}{3} = 34\frac{2}{3}$$

By transposition (changing signs):

(a)
$$4C = 35$$
$$C = \frac{35}{4}$$
$$C = 8\frac{3}{4}$$

(b)
$$\frac{3}{4}C = 26$$
$$C = 26 \div \frac{3}{4}$$
$$C = 26 \times \frac{4}{3}$$
$$C = \frac{104}{3} = 34\frac{2}{3}$$

As is illustrated by these examples, the method of solution is optional. You may prefer to solve by the mechanical rule for transposition.

EXERCISE 3

A. Find the value of a in each of the following equations:

1. $5a = 15 \times 6$

2. $3a - 2 = 10$

3. $7 + 9a + 3 = 56 - 4 + 3$

4. $30a - 10 = 14 - 18a$

5. $20(a + 5) = 5(2a + 80)$

6. $\frac{8a}{2} = \frac{4(a + 2)}{2}$

7. $\frac{6(a + 7)}{3} = 3 \times 9 + 1$

8. $\frac{15a \div 3}{5} = \frac{24 \times 3}{2}$

B. Find the numerical value of each of the following if $a = 5$, $b = 3$, $c = 4$, $x = 10$, and $y = 2$:

1. $a + b$

2. $2a + 3y$

3. $x - 4y$

4. $ab + c - x$

5. $abc - xy$

6. $\frac{4a}{c} + \frac{x}{y}$

7. $\frac{y}{x} + \frac{c}{a}$

8. $\frac{2\left(\frac{cx}{y} - a + bc\right)}{cy + x}$

C. Select the appropriate formula from the following listing and then solve for the required quantities or values:

$P = S - D$	Proceeds of bank discount = maturity value − bank discount
$A = lw$	Area of a rectangle = length × width
$d = rt$	Distance = rate × time
$I = Pni$	Interest in dollars = principal × time in years × rate of interest
$l = \frac{A}{w}$	Length of a rectangle = area ÷ width
$V = \frac{1}{3}Bh$	Volume of a regular pyramid = one-third area of base × height
$P = a + b + c$	Perimeter of a triangle = sum of lengths of three sides (a, b, c, respectively)
$w = \frac{A}{l}$	Width of a rectangle = area ÷ length
$A = \frac{1}{2}bh$	Area of a triangle = half base × height
$M = R - C$	Markup in dollars = retail price − cost

1. A rectangular garden plot is 40 ft. long and 30 ft. wide. Find the area in square feet.
2. A concrete monument is shaped in the form of a regular pyramid. If the base has an area of 64 sq. ft. and the height is 12 ft., find the number of cubic feet of concrete that compose the monument.
3. A boat has a triangular sail with a base of 5 yards and a height of $7\frac{1}{2}$ yards. Find the area of the sail in square yards.
4. Find the width of a desk top in inches if the surface area of the desk top is 1,260 sq. in. and its length is 42 in.
5. What will be the simple interest charge for the use of $2,400 for 3 years if the rate of interest is 6 per cent (equivalent to .06 or $\frac{6}{100}$)?
6. A train averaged $43\frac{1}{2}$ miles per hour for $2\frac{3}{4}$ hours. How many miles did the train travel?
7. A bank discounted a note with a maturity value of $1,246.75 and charged a discount of $73.42. What were the proceeds?
8. A radio with a retail price of $178.50 cost $122.75. Find the markup in dollars.

UNIT 4. Ratio and Proportion

A convenient way of comparing the size or magnitude of like quantities (or values) is to state the ratio of one to the other.

The *ratio* of one number to another is the quotient of the first number divided by the second number.

By definition, it is apparent that a ratio may be considered as a fraction, and hence problems that involve ratios may be solved by application of the same principles that are used for fractions (see pages 37–38). Thus the ratio of 2 to 6 is $\frac{1}{3}$, and may be stated as 2:6 or $\frac{2}{6}$. In either case it may be read, "the ratio of 2 to 6."

When the ratio of two numbers is given and an unknown term (quantity or value) has the same ratio to some known term, the unknown may be found by the use of proportion.

Proportion is an equality of ratios (or fractions).

From the definitions of ratio and proportion, it is evident that the reduction of a fraction to its equivalent may be considered as a problem in proportion. You will recall that to reduce a fraction to a fraction in which the denominator is a multiple, the rule is, *Multiply the given numerator by the quotient of the required denominator divided by the given denominator and then place this product (required numerator) over the required denominator* (see page 40). Thus in reducing $\frac{4}{8}$ to sixteenths:

(*a*)
$$\frac{4}{8} = \frac{x}{16}$$
$$x = 4(16 \div 8) = 4 \times 2 = 8$$
and therefore
$$\frac{4}{8} = \frac{8}{16}$$

If it were required to reduce $\frac{4}{8}$ to twelfths (which are not a multiple of eighths) the same rule might be used.

(*b*)
$$\frac{4}{8} = \frac{x}{12}$$
$$x = 4(12 \div 8) = 4 \times 1\frac{1}{2} = 6$$
and therefore
$$\frac{4}{8} = \frac{6}{12}$$

As you will observe from this reduction of $\frac{4}{8}$ to its equivalent $\frac{6}{12}$, the preceding rule for the reduction of a fraction is not limited to fractions in which the denominator is a multiple of the fraction to be reduced. Thus this rule may be applied to the finding of any required equivalent, regardless of that equivalent's denominator.

Further, had the numerators in the required equivalents been known and the denominators unknown, the denominators could have been found by a quite similar procedure.

(c) $\frac{4}{8} = \frac{8}{x}$

$x = 8(8 \div 4) = 8 \times 2 = 16$

and $\frac{4}{8} = \frac{8}{16}$

(d) $\frac{4}{8} = \frac{6}{x}$

$x = 8(6 \div 4) = 8 \times 1\frac{1}{2} = 12$

and $\frac{4}{8} = \frac{6}{12}$

However, it may be readily perceived that when the required denominator is not a multiple of the given denominator (and likewise when the required numerator is not a multiple of the given numerator), this method may not be satisfactory.

Consider another method by which the unknown numerators in the preceding illustrations might have been found.

(a) $\frac{4}{8} = \frac{x}{16}$

$8x = 4 \times 16$

$x = \frac{4 \times \cancel{16}^{2}}{\cancel{8}} = 8$

and $\frac{4}{8} = \frac{8}{16}$

(b) $\frac{4}{8} = \frac{x}{12}$

$8x = 4 \times 12$

$x = \frac{\cancel{4} \times \cancel{12}^{6}}{\cancel{8}_{\cancel{2}}} = 6$

and $\frac{4}{8} = \frac{6}{12}$

The unknown denominators may also have been found by this method.

(c) $\frac{4}{8} = \frac{8}{x}$

$4x = 8 \times 8$

$x = \frac{8 \times \cancel{8}^{2}}{\cancel{4}} = 16$

and $\frac{4}{8} = \frac{8}{16}$

(d) $\frac{4}{8} = \frac{6}{x}$

$4x = 8 \times 6$

$x = \frac{\cancel{8}^{2} \times 6}{\cancel{4}} = 12$

and $\frac{4}{8} = \frac{6}{12}$

This latter method of finding the unknown quantity (or value) is nothing more nor less than the way by which problems in proportion may be solved.

Proportion is commonly expressed in a form other than fractionally.

$$5:15::12:36 \qquad \text{or} \qquad 5:15 = 12:36$$

It is read, "5 is to 15 as 12 is to 36." It means that 5 has the same ratio to 15 as 12 has to 36. It also means that the ratio of 5 to 15 equals the ratio of 12 to 36.

Stated fractionally, it would be

$$\frac{5}{15} = \frac{12}{36}$$

Just as each term in a fraction is given a name (numerator or denominator), so are the terms in a proportion named.

The *extremes* are the first and fourth terms. In the preceding, 5 and 36 are the extremes.

The *means* are the second and third terms. In the preceding, 15 and 12 are the means.

The first term (5) is sometimes called the *first cause;* the second term (15) the *first effect;* the third term (12) the *second cause;* and the fourth term (36) the *second effect.* When each term is so thought of, it is referred to as the "cause-and-effect" method of solving by proportion.

The basic rule used to solve problems in proportion is: *The product of the means equals the product of the extremes.*

Thus in the proportion 5:15::12:36,

$$5 \times 36 = 15 \times 12$$
$$180 = 180$$

When two quantities are related to each other and the first becomes greater when the second also becomes greater (or smaller when the first becomes smaller), it is known as a *direct proportion.*

Example 1: Direct proportion. A well produces 4,800 gal. of water in 120 min. How long will it take to produce 5,700 gal. of water?

$$\frac{120}{x} = \frac{4{,}800}{5{,}700}$$
$$4{,}800x = 120 \times 5{,}700$$
$$x = \frac{120 \times 5{,}700}{4{,}800} = 142.5 \text{ (min.)}$$

Example 2: Direct proportion. An investment of \$3,000 yields a return of \$240. At the same rate of return what will be the yield of an investment of \$2,100?

$$\frac{3{,}000}{2{,}100} = \frac{240}{x}$$
$$3{,}000x = 240 \times 2{,}100$$
$$x = \frac{240 \times 2{,}100}{3{,}000} = 168 \text{ (dollars)}$$

When two quantities are related to each other and the first becomes greater *but* the second becomes smaller (or greater when the first becomes smaller), it is known as an *inverse proportion.*

Example 3: Inverse proportion. If 60 men can do a job in 8 days, how many men will be required to do the job in 5 days?

$$\frac{x}{60} = \frac{8}{5}$$

$$5x = 60 \times 8$$

$$x = \frac{60 \times 8}{5} = 96 \text{ (men)}$$

Example 4: Inverse proportion. An airplane travels from one city to another in 160 min. at the rate of 270 miles per hour. How long will it take to make the return trip if its speed is decreased to 240 miles per hour?

$$\frac{160}{x} = \frac{240}{270}$$

$$240x = 160 \times 270$$

$$x = \frac{160 \times 270}{240} = 180 \text{ (min.)}$$

From the preceding examples, it is apparent that in solving a problem by proportion it must first be determined whether it is a direct or an inverse proportion. You may prefer to handle such problems in their entirety as problems in fractions. If so, it is necessary only to *determine whether the answer should be greater or smaller.* As problems in fractions the preceding examples would appear:

Example 1:

$$\frac{5{,}700}{4{,}800} \times 120 = 142.5 \text{ min.}$$

Example 2:

$$\frac{2{,}100}{3{,}000} \times 240 = 168 \text{ dollars}$$

Example 3:

$$\frac{8}{5} \times 60 = 96 \text{ men}$$

Example 4:

$$\frac{270}{240} \times 160 = 180 \text{ min.}$$

When Proportional Parts Are Expressed as Fractions Totaling More or Less than a Whole Unit (1). The following type of problem is confusing to many: "$460 is divided among A, B, and C in the ratios of $\frac{2}{3}$, $\frac{3}{4}$, and $\frac{1}{2}$, respectively. How much does each receive?" This is a logical problem and may be solved readily by the use of proportion.

If the problem were worded "$460 is divided among A, B, and C in the ratios of 8, 9, and 6, respectively. How much does each receive?" the solution might be as follows:

$$8 + 9 + 6 = 23 \text{ shares} = \$460$$

$$\frac{8}{23} = \frac{\text{A's share}}{\$460}$$

$$23 \text{ A's share} = 460 \times 8$$

$$\text{A's share} = \frac{\overset{20}{\cancel{460}} \times 8}{\cancel{23}} = \$160$$

$$\frac{9}{23} = \frac{\text{B's share}}{\$460}$$

$$23 \text{ B's share} = 460 \times 9$$

$$\text{B's share} = \frac{\overset{20}{\cancel{460}} \times 9}{\cancel{23}} = \$180$$

$$\frac{6}{23} = \frac{\text{C's share}}{\$460}$$

$$23 \text{ C's share} = 460 \times 6$$

$$\text{C's share} = \frac{\overset{20}{\cancel{460}} \times 6}{\cancel{23}} = \$120$$

Check:

A's share	$160
B's share	180
C's share	120
Total	$460

The general rule for operations in fractions (page 38) is: *Fractions having a common denominator are in the same ratio to each other as are their numerators.* From this rule the following application is made: *To apportion numbers, money, objects, or things in fractional ratio, reduce the fractions to fractions having a common denominator and use the numerators as integers in determining the proper apportionment.*

$$\text{Thus } \frac{2}{3}:\frac{3}{4}:\frac{1}{2} \text{ as } \frac{8}{12}:\frac{9}{12}:\frac{6}{12}$$

Applying the preceding rule for operations in fractions, the shares of A, B, and C, given as $\frac{2}{3}$, $\frac{3}{4}$, and $\frac{1}{2}$, respectively, are in the ratios of 8, 9, and 6, respectively. The procedure of solving by proportion may then be as illustrated, A receiving $160, B receiving $180, and C receiving $120.

EXERCISE 4

A. Express the ratios of the following in fractional form reduced to lowest terms:

1. 210 to 30 =

2. 15 to 75 =

3. 36 to 99 =

4. $8\frac{3}{4}$ to $3\frac{1}{2}$ =

5. $6\frac{8}{9}$ to $48\frac{2}{9}$ =

6. $\frac{3}{8}$ to $\frac{5}{12}$ =

7. $\frac{8}{3}$ to $\frac{11}{8}$ =

8. 1.34 to 2.01 =

9. $5.0\frac{2}{3}$ to 8.8 =

10. $\frac{3}{16}$ to 18.75 =

B. Find the missing quantities in each of the following:

1. $\frac{1{,}800}{400} = \frac{1{,}350}{x}$

2. $\frac{540}{108} = \frac{x}{30}$

3. $\frac{51.3}{x} = \frac{142.2}{47.4}$

4. $\frac{x}{3\frac{3}{4}} = \frac{10}{15}$

5. $\frac{\frac{4}{3}}{\frac{16}{9}} = \frac{84}{x}$

6. $\frac{.38}{x} = \frac{7.6}{2.2}$

7. $\frac{\frac{9}{8}}{\frac{3}{4}} = \frac{x}{\frac{17}{2}}$

8. $\frac{x}{1.66\frac{2}{3}} = \frac{166.6\frac{2}{3}}{8.3\frac{1}{3}}$

C. Solve the following problems in ratio and proportion:

1. If $1,500 is received as the profit on an investment of $5,000, what return might be expected on an investment of $3,850?
2. Jones invests $3,000 and Smith $3,900 in a partnership. If profits are to be shared in the ratio that each partner's investment bears to the total investment, what return should Smith receive if Jones's share of the profits is $350?
3. Mr. Brown invested $37,500 in an apartment house earning a profit of $3,200 yearly. He invests $24,500 in another apartment house, expecting to earn a profit one-fifth larger in ratio to the amount invested. How much yearly profit does Mr. Brown expect on the second apartment house?
4. In a partnership, A invested $4,000; B invested $3,000; and C invested $2,500. If their profits totaled $12,000, how much did each receive if the profits were divided in the ratio that each partner's investment bore to the total investment?
5. The framework of a building will require the labor of 28 men for 18 days. If it is desired to complete the job in 4 days less time, how many men will be needed?
6. Two flywheels are joined by a belt. The circumference of the larger is 186 in., and it makes 54 revolutions per minute. Find how many revolutions per minute the smaller flywheel makes if its circumference is 81 in.
7. A gain of $15,400 is to be divided among A, B, and C, in the ratios of $\frac{2}{3}$, $\frac{3}{4}$, and $\frac{4}{5}$, respectively. How much should each receive?

8. An estate of $85,000 is left to five heirs, A, B, C, D, and E. It is to be divided in the ratios of $\frac{1}{3}$, $\frac{1}{2}$, $\frac{2}{3}$, $\frac{3}{4}$, and $\frac{4}{5}$, respectively. What inheritance should each heir receive?

UNIT 5. Percentage: General Rules; Aliquot Parts of 1.00 and 100 Per Cent

In business, it is essential to use a common means of expressing the relationships among different departments and within different departments.

Costs, expenses, profits, sales, etc., are often stated in *per cents* allowing a ready means of comparison. Similarly, per cents are used to indicate differences or likenesses in fiscal periods, among industries, and for other purposes in which comparison, proportion, or ratio is of use.

Interest rates are spoken of as 6 per cent, 8 per cent, etc., not as 6 hundredths, 8 hundredths, etc. Discounts are likewise stated as 25 per cent, 15 per cent, etc., not as 25 hundredths, 15 hundredths, etc.

Per cent is symbolized by the use of the sign or character "%."

A unit or whole is conceived as containing 100 equal parts, each part being one hundredth or 1 per cent of the whole. Therefore 1 per cent = $\frac{1}{100}$ or .01 parts of the whole. Thus:

$$1\% = .01 = \frac{1}{100}$$

$$5\% = .05 = \frac{5}{100}$$

$$12\% = .12 = \frac{12}{100}$$

$$75\% = .75 = \frac{75}{100}$$

$$125\% = 1.25 = \frac{125}{100}, \text{ etc.}$$

The *base* is the quantity regarded as a unit or as a whole. It is always 100 per cent of itself. It may be either an abstract or a concrete number.

Other like quantities are compared with the base, and their relationship as a fractional part, as equal to or as in excess to the base, is expressed by means of per cents. Thus, if the dollar cost of transportation, rent, publicity, administration, etc., is compared with the dollar sales, then the amount of sales in dollars is the base and is expressed by the whole unit 1 or 100 per cent. If the comparison were with the dollar cost, then the amount of the cost in dollars would be the base and would be expressed by the whole unit 1 or 100 per cent.

The *rate* is the number of hundredths of the base used. It is an abstract number expressed as per cent and is the per cent equivalent of the percentage.

$$\frac{1}{100} = .01 \text{ or } 1\%$$
$$\frac{17}{100} = .17 \text{ or } 17\%$$
$$\frac{125}{100} = 1.25 \text{ or } 125\%, \text{ etc.}$$

Percentage is the product of the base and the rate. It is the result of taking so many hundredths (rate) of a given number (base). It is the quantity (or value) equivalent of the rate. By formula,

$$P = Br$$

Thus if the base is $240 and the rate 5 per cent, the percentage is $12.

Think of percentage as the product in a multiplication in which the multiplier is hundredths. It is a product that will be expressed in the same kind of terms as the base, and like the base it may be expressed either as a concrete or as an abstract number.

Per cent, however, is an abstract number and refers merely to the number of hundredths (number of equal portions of a hundred) applied as a factor (the other factor being the base) in determining the percentage.

Amount is the sum of the base and the percentage. By formula,

$$A = B + P$$

Thus if the base is $240 and the percentage is $12, the amount is $252.

Difference is the base less the percentage. By formula,

$$D = B - P$$

Thus if the base is $240 and the percentage is $12, the difference is $228.

Expressed in per cents, the base is always 100 per cent of itself and the rate is the per cent equivalent of the percentage. Note that there is no name such as "rate" to indicate the per cent equivalents of the amount or difference, and thus such per cent equivalents are stated in terms as "the per cent equivalent of the amount," "the per cent equivalent of the difference," etc.

GENERAL RULES FOR THE CONVERSION OF PER CENTS TO OR FROM FRACTIONS AND DECIMALS

To reduce a proper or improper fraction to a decimal fraction, divide the numerator by the denominator.

Example 1: Express $\frac{1}{2}$ as a decimal fraction.

$$2\overline{)1.0} = .5$$

Example 2: Express $\frac{3}{8}$ as a decimal fraction.

$$8\overline{)3.000} = .375$$

Example 3: Express $\frac{15}{4}$ as a decimal fraction.

$$4\overline{)15.00} = 3.75$$

To reduce a mixed number to a decimal fraction, (*a*) reduce the mixed number to an improper fraction and then divide the numerator by the denominator, or (*b*) divide the numerator of the fractional ending by its denominator and *annex* this quotient to the whole integer of the mixed number.

Example 1: Express $8\frac{2}{5}$ as a decimal fraction.

Method (*a*)

$$8\frac{2}{5} = \frac{42}{5}$$

$$5\overline{)42.0} = 8.4$$

Method (*b*)

$$5\overline{)2.0} = .4$$

.4 annexed to 8 = 8.4

Example 2: Express $19\frac{3}{16}$ as a decimal fraction.

Method (*a*)

$$19\frac{3}{16} = \frac{307}{16}$$

$$16\overline{)307.0000} = 19.1875$$

Method (*b*)

$$16\overline{)3.0000} = .1875$$

.1875 annexed to 19 = 19.1875

To reduce a decimal fraction to a per cent, move the decimal point two places to the right and annex the per cent sign (%).

Example 1: Express .5 as a per cent.

$$.5 = 50\%$$

Example 2: Express $1.25\frac{1}{3}$ as a per cent.

$$1.25\frac{1}{3} = 125\frac{1}{3}\ \%$$

If the decimal fraction is a mixed or complex decimal expressed only to tenths, it must be extended to hundredths before this rule may be applied.

Example: Express $3.2\frac{2}{3}$ as a per cent.

$$3.2\frac{2}{3} = 3.26\frac{2}{3}$$

$$3.26\frac{2}{3} = 326\frac{2}{3}\ \%$$

To reduce a per cent to a decimal fraction, move the decimal point two places to the left and omit the per cent sign (%).

Example 1: Express 62.5% as a decimal fraction.

$$62.5\% = .625$$

Example 2: Express 837.625% as a decimal fraction.

$$837.625\% = 8.37625$$

Example 3: Express $.07\frac{1}{3}$ % as a decimal fraction.

$$.07\frac{1}{3}\ \% = .0007\frac{1}{3}$$

To reduce a decimal fraction to a common fraction or mixed number, omit the decimal point and write the decimal fraction as a numerator with a denominator of 1, annexing as many zeros as there are decimal places in the decimal fraction. Finally, reduce the obtained proper, improper, or complex fraction to its lowest terms.

Example 1: Express .85 as a proper fraction reduced to lowest terms.

$$.85 = \frac{85}{100} = \frac{17}{20}$$

Example 2: Express 3.625 as a mixed number reduced to lowest terms.

$$3.625 = \frac{3625}{1000} = \frac{29}{8} = 3\frac{5}{8}$$

$$\text{or } 3.625 = 3 + \frac{625}{1000} = 3\frac{5}{8}$$

Example 3: Express $4.26\frac{2}{3}$ as a mixed number reduced to lowest terms.

$$4.26\frac{2}{3} = \frac{426\frac{2}{3}}{100} = \frac{1,280}{300} = \frac{64}{15} = 4\frac{4}{15}$$

$$\text{or } 4.26\frac{2}{3} = 4 + \frac{26\frac{2}{3}}{100} = 4 + \frac{80}{300} = 4\frac{4}{15}$$

To reduce a fractional per cent to a common fraction, drop the per cent sign (%) and annex two zeros to the denominator. Reduce this obtained proper fraction to its lowest terms.

Example 1: Express $\frac{2}{7}$ per cent as a proper fraction reduced to lowest terms.

$$\frac{2}{7}\% = \frac{2}{700} = \frac{1}{350}$$

Example 2: Express $\frac{50}{81}$ per cent as a proper fraction reduced to lowest terms.

$$\frac{50}{81}\% = \frac{50}{8100} = \frac{1}{162}$$

ALIQUOT PARTS OF 1.00 OR 100% AND THEIR MULTIPLES

In many computations involving per cents, the use of aliquot parts or their multiples will greatly shorten the time required for solution. Since per cent is equivalent to hundredths, it is the aliquot parts of 1.00 and their multiples that will be of particular value.[1]

The basic number of the table on page 95 is 1.00 (or 100 per cent); that is, each fraction represents that fractional part of 1.00 (and 100 per cent). Included are the aliquot parts of 1.00 (and 100%) and their multiples that are most likely to prove useful.

In the table, the *first vertical column* (at the left) indicates the denominators of the fractional equivalents of 1.00 and 100 per cent; the *first horizontal column* (at the top) indicates the numerators of the fractional equivalents of 1.00 and 100 per cent. The aliquot parts and multiples of aliquot parts are shown in the squares at which the two columns meet.

Thus .50 is $\frac{1}{2}$ of 1.00, or 50 per cent is $\frac{1}{2}$ of 100 per cent; $.33\frac{1}{3}$ is $\frac{1}{3}$ of 1.00, or $33\frac{1}{3}$ per cent is $\frac{1}{3}$ of 100 per cent; .25 is $\frac{1}{4}$ of 1.00, or 25 per cent is $\frac{1}{4}$ of 100 per cent; .50 and .75 are multiples of .25; 50 per cent and 75 per cent are multiples of 25 per cent; etc. Notice that the fractional equivalents are not necessarily reduced to lowest terms, $\frac{2}{4}$, $\frac{3}{6}$, $\frac{4}{8}$, etc., being equivalent to $\frac{1}{2}$; $\frac{2}{6}$, $\frac{3}{9}$, $\frac{4}{12}$, etc., being equivalent to $\frac{1}{3}$; etc.

[1] See pp. 71–76 for a complete explanation of the use of aliquot parts and their multiples in both multiplication and division.

Table of Certain Aliquot Parts of 1.00 or 100% and Their Multiples

(The basic number is 1.00 or 100%)

1.00 or 100%	1	2	3	4	5	6	7	8	9	10	11	12	13	14	15
2	.50 50%														
3	.33 1/3 33 1/3%	.66 2/3 66 2/3%													
4	.25 25%	.50 50%	.75 75%												
5	.20 20%	.40 40%	.60 60%	.80 80%											
6	.16 2/3 16 2/3%	.33 1/3 33 1/3%	.50 50%	.66 2/3 66 2/3%	.83 1/3 83 1/3%										
7	.14 2/7 14 2/7%	.28 4/7 28 4/7%	.42 6/7 42 6/7%	.57 1/7 57 1/7%	.71 3/7 71 3/7%	.85 5/7 85 5/7%									
8	.12 1/2 12 1/2%	.25 25%	.37 1/2 37 1/2%	.50 50%	.62 1/2 62 1/2%	.75 75%	.87 1/2 87 1/2%								
9	.11 1/9 11 1/9%	.22 2/9 22 2/9%	.33 1/3 33 1/3%	.44 4/9 44 4/9%	.55 5/9 55 5/9%	.66 2/3 66 2/3%	.77 7/9 77 7/9%	.88 8/9 88 8/9%							
10	.10 10%	.20 20%	.30 30%	.40 40%	.50 50%	.60 60%	.70 70%	.80 80%	.90 90%						
11	.09 1/11 9 1/11%	.18 2/11 18 2/11%	.27 3/11 27 3/11%	.36 4/11 36 4/11%	.45 5/11 45 5/11%	.54 6/11 54 6/11%	.63 7/11 63 7/11%	.72 8/11 72 8/11%	.81 9/11 81 9/11%	.90 10/11 90 10/11%					
12	.08 1/3 8 1/3%	.16 2/3 16 2/3%	.25 25%	.33 1/3 33 1/3%	.41 2/3 41 2/3%	.50 50%	.58 1/3 58 1/3%	.66 2/3 66 2/3%	.75 75%	.83 1/3 83 1/3%	.91 2/3 91 2/3%				
13	.07 9/13 7 9/13%	.15 5/13 15 5/13%	.23 1/13 23 1/13%	.30 10/13 30 10/13%	.38 6/13 38 6/13%	.46 2/13 46 2/13%	.53 11/13 53 11/13%	.61 7/13 61 7/13%	.69 3/13 69 3/13%	.76 12/13 76 12/13%	.84 8/13 84 8/13%	.92 4/13 92 4/13%			
14	.07 1/7 7 1/7%	.14 2/7 14 2/7%	.21 3/7 21 3/7%	.28 4/7 28 4/7%	.35 5/7 35 5/7%	.42 6/7 42 6/7%	.50 50%	.57 1/7 57 1/7%	.64 2/7 64 2/7%	.71 3/7 71 3/7%	.78 4/7 78 4/7%	.85 5/7 85 5/7%	.92 6/7 92 6/7%		
15	.06 2/3 6 2/3%	.13 1/3 13 1/3%	.20 20%	.26 2/3 26 2/3%	.33 1/3 33 1/3%	.40 40%	.46 2/3 46 2/3%	.53 1/3 53 1/3%	.60 60%	.66 2/3 66 2/3%	.73 1/3 73 1/3%	.80 80%	.86 2/3 86 2/3%	.93 1/3 93 1/3%	
16	.06 1/4 6 1/4%	.12 1/2 12 1/2%	.18 3/4 18 3/4%	.25 25%	.31 1/4 31 1/4%	.37 1/2 37 1/2%	.43 3/4 43 3/4%	.50 50%	.56 1/4 56 1/4%	.62 1/2 62 1/2%	.68 3/4 68 3/4%	.75 75%	.81 1/4 81 1/4%	.87 1/2 87 1/2%	.93 3/4 93 3/4%

EXERCISE 5

A. Find the missing terms in the following equivalents: F, common fractions (or mixed numbers); D, decimal fractions (or mixed decimals); and P, per cents. Reduce decimals to hundredths showing all fractional remainders in lowest terms.

F =	D =	P	D =	P =	F	P =	F =	D
1. $\frac{1}{2}$	—	—%	2. .2	—%	—	3. 25%	—	—
4. $\frac{9}{8}$	—	—%	5. .625	—%	—	6. $83\frac{1}{3}$ %	—	—
7. $\frac{3}{40}$	—	—%	8. 1.75	—%	—	9. 137.5%	—	—
10. $\frac{1}{100}$	—	—%	11. .008	—%	—	12. .015%	—	—

B. Solve the following:

1. Is $\frac{2}{15}$ greater or less than 12 per cent, and by how much, expressed as a common fraction?
2. Is $\frac{1}{80}$ greater or less than $.011\frac{1}{9}$ per cent, and by how much, expressed as a decimal fraction?
3. Is 62.5 per cent greater or less than $\frac{5}{7}$, and by how much, expressed in per cent?
4. From the sum of 52.25 per cent, $.71\frac{1}{3}$, and $\frac{5}{12}$ subtract the sum of 20.75 per cent, $.31\frac{1}{5}$, and $\frac{7}{16}$. Express the difference in per cent.

C. Find the following percentages (express decimally):

1. 40% of 160
2. 25% of 120
3. $3\frac{1}{3}$ % of 270
4. 12.5% of 480
5. $116\frac{2}{3}$ % of 36
6. $\frac{1}{8}$ % of 4.4
7. $\frac{5}{12}$ % of 108
8. .625% of 18
9. 87.5% of .08
10. 250% of .35
11. 1,500% of $15
12. 375% of $424
13. $11\frac{1}{9}$ % of $135
14. .125% of $328
15. $\frac{1}{3}$ % of $411

D. Find 100 per cent (or base) to nearest hundredths by dividing the given percentage by the given per cent expressed decimally:

1. 6% = 84
2. 13% = 78
3. 73% = 219
4. 48% = 5.64
5. 21.2% = 120.6
6. 114% = $39\frac{1}{4}$

E. Find 100 per cent (or base) to nearest hundredths by (*a*) finding the equivalent of 1 per cent to nearest ten-thousandth by dividing the given percentage by the given number of per cent; and (*b*) then multiplying the obtained equivalent of 1 per cent by 100:

1. 7% = 91	2. 15% = 87.5	3. 57% = 162
4. 84% = 9.32	5. 32.3% = 140.4	6. 212% = $45\frac{1}{8}$

F. For the following per cents *a*, *b*, and *c*, **find** the quantity or value equivalents to the nearest dollars and cents *by any method desired:*

	If	*Find* *a*	*b*	*c*
1.	8% = $ 68.00	1%	35%	124%
2.	22% = $ 77.00	23%	100%	225%
3.	130% = $ 25.00	100%	19.4%	$56\frac{1}{4}$ %
4.	$16\frac{2}{3}$ % = $ 45.00	1%	$83\frac{1}{3}$ %	100%
5.	$111\frac{1}{9}$ % = $801.72	283%	1%	2.25%
6.	.3% = $ 6.38	1%	314%	$81\frac{1}{7}$ %

UNIT 6. Formulas in Percentage

The following formulas include all that are most frequently used in solving problems in percentage and should be studied carefully so that you may have a better comprehension of percentage. However, if you understand the various elements comprising problems in percentage, it is not necessary that these formulas be committed to memory.

To know how to apply these formulas is essential, but more important is to train yourself so that you will be able to comprehend a problem, determine a satisfactory method of solution, and perform the necessary operations in arriving at a successful conclusion.

In the following equations, the symbols used are

P = percentage $\quad A$ = amount
r = rate $\quad D$ = difference
B = base $\quad 1$ = 100% of the base expressed decimally

Derivation of Formulas Used in Percentage. By definition (see page 91), you know that

$$P = Br; \qquad A = B + P; \qquad D = B - P$$

From the preceding, the following may be derived:

$$B = \frac{P}{r}; \qquad B = A - P; \qquad B = D + P$$

$$r = \frac{P}{B}; \qquad P = A - B; \qquad P = B - D$$

By substitution of Br for P, the following may be derived:

$$\text{If } A = B + P \quad \text{then } A = B + Br = B(1 + r) \quad \text{and } B = \frac{A}{1 + r}$$

$$\text{If } D = B - P \quad \text{then } D = B - Br = B(1 - r) \quad \text{and } B = \frac{D}{1 - r}$$

Summarizing of Formulas and Examples. The preceding formulas for percentage may be recapitulated as follows:

To find percentage:

	Given	*Solution*
1. $P = Br$	$B = 300;\ r = 6\%$	$P = 300 \times .06 = 18$
2. $P = A - B$	$A = 420;\ B = 390$	$P = 420 - 390 = 30$
3. $P = B - D$	$B = 320;\ D = 280$	$P = 320 - 280 = 40$

To find rate (the per cent equivalent of the percentage):

	Given	*Solution*
1. $r = \frac{P}{B}$	$P = 7.50;\ B = 150$	$r = \frac{7.50}{150} = .05 = 5\%$
2. $r = A\% - 100\%$	$A\% = 115\%$	$r = 115\% - 100\% = 15\%$
3. $r = 100\% - D\%$	$D\% = 76\%$	$r = 100\% - 76\% = 24\%$

To find base (always 100 per cent):

	Given	*Solution*
1. $B = A - P$	$A = 235;\ P = 25$	$B = 235 - 25 = 210$
2. $B = D + P$	$D = 385;\ P = 45$	$B = 385 + 45 = 430$
3. $B = \frac{P}{r}$	$P = 4.80;\ r = 4\%$	$B = \frac{4.80}{.04} = 120$
4. $B = \frac{A}{100\% + r}$	$A = 459;\ r = 2\%$	$B = \frac{459}{1 + .02} = \frac{459}{1.02} = 450$
5. $B = \frac{D}{100\% - r}$	$D = 342;\ r = 5\%$	$B = \frac{342}{1 - .05} = \frac{342}{.95} = 360$

To find amount (the per cent equivalent of the base of 100 per cent plus the rate in per cent):

	Given	Solution
1. $A = B + P$	$B = 325; P = 30$	$A = 325 + 30 = 355$
2. $A\% = 100\% + r$	$r = 20\%$	$A\% = 100\% + 20\% = 120\%$

To find difference (the per cent equivalent of the base of 100 per cent less the rate in per cent):

	Given	Solution
1. $D = B - P$	$B = 45; P = 5$	$D = 45 - 5 = 40$
2. $D\% = 100\% - r$	$r = 8\%$	$D\% = 100\% - 8\% = 92\%$

Although the preceding formulas are not all of those which may be derived, those given, if properly combined, may be used in solving any problem in simple percentage. Take careful note that the rate is the per cent equivalent of the percentage but that there are no special names to indicate the per cent equivalents of the amount or of the difference.

TYPICAL EXAMPLES OF WORD PROBLEMS IN PERCENTAGE

In actual practice, the base, the percentage, the amount, or the difference is not stipulated by name as in the preceding examples and it is necessary in solving problems in percentage to determine the number or quantity to which the per cent or percentage has reference. The following 15 examples of word problems are in the same number sequence as the preceding examples and are typical of the various kinds of problems in percentage.

To Find Percentage

Example 1: If a manufacturer sells his goods at 15 per cent more than they cost him to produce, by how much will his selling price be increased over cost on an article that costs him $25 to produce?

$25 × .15 = $3.75 Increase in selling price over cost

Example 2: If cost + gross profit = selling price, find the gross profit on an item that cost $37.50 and is sold at $55.

$55 − $37.50 = $17.50 Gross profit

Example 3: If Mr. Louis Batmale purchases 20 shares of American Telephone and Telegraph Company common stock at a cost of $182.50 per share and at a later date sells the shares at $168.75 per share, find his loss.

$182.50 × 20 =	$3,650	Cost
168.75 × 20 =	− 3,375	Selling price
	$ 275	Loss

To Find Rate

Example 1: If 264 crates of fruit are spoiled on a truck containing a total of 2,200 crates of fruit, find the per cent of loss due to spoilage.

$$\frac{264}{2{,}200} = .12 = 12\% \quad \text{Spoilage}$$

Example 2: An investor in real estate sold a business lot at 135 per cent of its cost. Find his per cent of gain.

In this problem, cost represents 100 per cent. Therefore:

$$135\% - 100\% = 35\% \quad \text{Gain}$$

Example 3: If after paying his expenses, a salesman had a net income of 62.5 per cent of his commissions, find the per cent that his expenses are of his commissions.

In this problem, commissions represent 100 per cent. Therefore:

$$100\% - 62.5\% = 37.5\% \quad \text{Expenses}$$

To Find Base

Example 1: If principal + interest = maturity value, find the principal of a note on which the interest is $17.25 and the maturity value is $342.65.

$$\$342.65 - \$17.25 = \$325.40 \quad \text{Principal}$$

Example 2: If $416.50 is payment in full of an invoice from which a cash discount of $8.50 has been taken (subtracted), find the amount of the invoice.

$$\$416.50 + \$8.50 = \$425 \quad \text{Amount of the invoice}$$

Example 3: The dividend return per annum on an investment in a preferred stock was $900. If this was an annual return of 6 per cent on the investment, how much did the stock cost?

$$\frac{\$900}{.06} = \$15{,}000 \quad \text{Cost of the stock}$$

Example 4: The gross sales of a store were $72,800 and returns and allowances were 12 per cent of the net sales. If net sales + returns and allowances = gross sales, find the net sales in dollars.

In this problem, net sales represent 100 per cent. Therefore:

$$\frac{\$72{,}800}{1.00 + .12} = \frac{\$72{,}800}{1.12} = \$65{,}000 \quad \text{Net sales}$$

Example 5: A wholesaler sold an odd lot of merchandise for $1,288, a loss of 8 per cent on his original cost. Find the original cost of the merchandise to the wholesaler.

In this problem, the original cost represents 100 per cent. Therefore:

$$\frac{\$1{,}288}{1.00 - .08} = \frac{\$1{,}288}{.92} = \$1{,}400 \quad \text{Original cost}$$

To Find Amount

Example 1: The Warner Company's cost of goods sold was $125,000 and its gross profit was $35,000. If cost + gross profit = sales, find the sales of the Warner Company.

$125,000 + $35,000 = $160,000 Sales

Example 2: If a stock is sold at a gain of 13.5 per cent on its original cost, what per cent was the selling price of the original cost?

In this problem, the original cost represents 100 per cent. Therefore:

100% + 13.5% = 113.5% Selling price per cent of original cost

To Find Difference

Example 1: Mr. John Booher sold his home that cost him $19,750 at a loss of $1,325. For how much did he sell his home?

$19,750 − $1,325 = $18,425 Selling price

Example 2: If an employee who claims no tax exemptions has 18 per cent of his gross earnings withheld by his employer in payment of his Federal income tax, what per cent are his net earnings of his gross earnings?

In this problem, the gross earnings represent 100 per cent. Therefore:

100% − 18% = 82% Per cent net earnings are of gross earnings

EXERCISE 6A

A. Find the percentage to nearest hundredths in each of the following:

1. Base 32, rate 6%
2. Base $6.40, rate 7.5%
3. Rate 175%, base 64
4. Rate 4%, base $140.60
5. What is 9% of 341?
6. 50% of $21 is what?
7. Find 16.2% of 63.9
8. $2\frac{1}{2}$ % of $320 is what percentage?
9. What percentage of 124 is $37\frac{1}{2}$ %?
10. $\frac{5}{6}$ % of $5,400 is what percentage?
11. What is $6\frac{4}{7}$ % of 642.6?
12. Determine $\frac{4}{11}$ % of $1,100
13. Base 360, amount 400
14. Amount $43.20, base $31.80
15. Base 166, difference 140
16. Difference $38.73, base $42.16

B. Find the rate in per cent in each of the following:

1. Percentage 15, base 150
2. Percentage $12, base $160
3. Base 720, percentage 46.8
4. Base $540, percentage $32.40
5. 18 is what per cent of 36?
6. What per cent of $80 is $6?
7. How many per cent of 90 is 4.5?
8. Determine what per cent .23 is of 92
9. What per cent of $480 is $300?
10. $94.08 is what per cent of $784?
11. Find what per cent 18.75 is of 375
12. What per cent is $3.08 of $88?

13. Amount as per cent is 118%
14. Per cent equivalent of amount is 326%
15. Difference as per cent is 88%
16. Per cent equivalent of difference is 59%

C. **Find** the base in each of the following:

1. Amount 430, percentage 30
2. Percentage \$12.60, amount \$94.60
3. Difference 48, percentage 6
4. Percentage \$15, difference \$285
5. Percentage 24, rate 6%
6. Rate $4\frac{1}{2}$ %, percentage \$12.42
7. 72 is 9% of what number?
8. \$7.65 is 9% of how many dollars?
9. \$13 is 1% of what number?
10. 40% of how many dollars is \$14.40?
11. \$.42 is $\frac{2}{7}$ % of how many dollars?
12. $2.93\frac{1}{3}$ is $3\frac{1}{3}$ % of what number?
13. Amount \$416, rate 4%
14. A number increased by 2.5% of itself is 77.9
15. \$778.80 is 18% more than how many dollars?
16. How many dollars plus 8% is \$90.72?
17. Difference 152, rate 5%
18. A number decreased by $7\frac{1}{2}$ % of itself is 416.25
19. \$581.25 is 7% less than how many dollars?
20. How many dollars less 9% is \$101.92?

D. **Find** (*a*) the amount to nearest hundredths and (*b*) the per cent equivalent of the amount in each of the following:

1. Base \$420, percentage \$25.20
2. Increase \$42.50 by \$3.40
3. Base \$180, rate 4%
4. Increase \$75.60 by 5%
5. Percentage \$3.25, rate 5%
6. Increase is \$54.60 and rate is 6.5%

E. **Find** (*a*) the difference to nearest hundredths and (*b*) the per cent equivalent of the difference in each of the following:

1. Base \$180, percentage \$5.85
2. Decrease \$48.25 by \$1.93
3. Base \$620, rate 12%
4. Decrease \$87.50 by 8%
5. Percentage \$32.55, rate 7%
6. Decrease is \$42.75 and rate is 4.5%

EXERCISE 6B

Solve the following:

1. The gross weight of an article is 20 per cent more than the net weight of 860 lb. What is the gross weight in pounds?

2. A finance company lent \$6,000, \$5,000, and \$1,500, charging the borrower $11\frac{1}{2}$ per cent. How much did the finance company charge for the use of its money?
3. The gross profit on some merchandise is 25 per cent of the selling price. If the cost is \$273, what is the gross profit in dollars? (NOTE: Cost + gross profit = selling price.)
4. In a carload of fruit, 15 per cent spoiled, leaving a remainder of 2,040 crates of fruit that were sold at \$7 per crate. What was the loss in dollars and cents due to spoilage?
5. Mr. Smith had \$8,640 in the bank on July 1. On July 5 he withdrew 20 per cent, and on July 18 he withdrew 9 per cent of the remainder. On July 31 he deposited 110 per cent of what he had withdrawn. What was his bank balance?
6. If Mr. Jones had \$24,816 at the end of the year after losing 6 per cent of his original capital, what was the amount of loss in dollars?
7. A wholesaler paid \$3,600 for some merchandise. He sold 25 per cent at a 2 per cent gain on cost, $33\frac{1}{3}$ per cent at a $4\frac{1}{2}$ per cent loss on cost, 15 per cent at a gain of $16\frac{2}{3}$ per cent on cost, and the remainder at a loss of $12\frac{1}{2}$ per cent on cost. Did he gain or lose? Give your answer in dollars.
8. Gross sales of a store were \$132,000. Returns and allowances were 10 per cent of the net sales. (NOTE: gross sales − returns and allowances = net sales.) How much were the returns and allowances in dollars?
9. A merchant forced into insolvency by his creditors had liabilities of \$54,720 and assets of \$45,417.60. What per cent of his debts could he pay?
10. A merchant paid \$15.50 for some goods, which he sold for \$23.25. Find his per cent of gross profit (*a*) on cost and (*b*) on selling price. (NOTE: Cost + gross profit = selling price.)
11. Mr. Smith sold some used furniture for \$225, a loss of \$25 on the original purchase price. What was his per cent of loss?
12. A man's salary is \$225 per month. He spends $16\frac{2}{3}$ per cent for fuel, $25\frac{1}{3}$ per cent for food, 22 per cent for lodging, $15\frac{2}{3}$ per cent for clothing, and 14 per cent for miscellaneous expenses, saving the remainder. What are his savings per year?

EXERCISE 6C

Solve the following:

1. A has \$720, B has \$1,620. A has what per cent of B's money? B has what per cent of A's money?
2. If Mr. Jones spends 35 per cent of his money and then \$1,287 of the remainder and finds that he has \$858 left, what per cent of the original sum of money does he still have?
3. During a journey of 1,500 miles, Mr. Gill traveled 705 miles by train and the remainder by bus. What per cent of the journey was taken by bus?
4. In a school there are 2,640 students, an increase of 240 students over last year. What was the per cent of increase in enrollment?

5. Mr. Smith was given a raise of $960, or 25 per cent increase in salary. What was his former salary?
6. A wholesaler priced his sugar at $7.26 per sack, which was 10 per cent more than it cost. What was the cost per sack?
7. The distance between two points on a railroad is 172.5 miles, or 2.3 per cent of the entire trackage of the railroad. How many miles is the entire length of trackage of the railroad?
8. If this year's sales of $665 are a loss of 5 per cent on last year's sales volume, find last year's sales.
9. A jobber sold some goods for $28.16, a loss of 12 per cent on the original price. What was the original price?
10. A student had $40.80 left after spending 22 per cent of his monthly allowance. How much was his monthly allowance?
11. A manufacturer's sales were $20,460. What was his cost of manufacture if his gross profit was 24 per cent of the cost? (NOTE: Cost + gross profit = selling price.)
12. John had $2.45, which was $16\frac{2}{3}$ per cent more than $\frac{1}{2}$ of what Mary had. How much money had Mary?

EXERCISE 6D

A. **Find** the missing terms in the following:

	Amount	*Base* (*a*)	*Rate, %* (*b*)	*Percentage* (*c*)	*Difference* (*d*)
1	$375.00	$300.00			
2	351.25		40.5		
3	630.00			$30.00	
4	14.42	14.00			
5	237.60		8		
6	221.27			18.27	

B. **Solve** the following:

1. The combined tax rate in a city and county is $2.84 per $100 of assessed value. What will be Mr. Smith's annual tax on a home with an assessed value of $4,750?
2. Last year, overhead expenses in the ABC Company were 32 per cent of the sales. This year, sales were $12,450 and overhead expenses $3,610.50. (*a*) Find this year's per cent rate of overhead. (*b*) If last year's per cent rate of overhead were applied to this year's sales, what would be the loss or gain in dollars?
3. Mr. Brown, a salesman working on commission, receives 8 per cent on sales up to and including $30,000, 10 per cent on the next $10,000, and 15 per cent on all sales above $40,000. His sales this year were $43,490, and he has withdrawn $150 per month in anticipation of his commission. What is the amount due Mr. Brown?

C. Find the missing terms in the following:

	Difference	Base (a)	Rate, % (b)	Percentage (c)	Amount (d)
1	$403.20	$420.00			
2	323.75		$7\frac{1}{2}$		
3	180.50			$ 9.50	
4	23.85	26.50			
5	81.27		3.25		
6	589.68			138.32	

D. Solve the following:

1. John received $120 salary. After paying his board and room, he had $78 left. What per cent of his balance was his board and room?
2. A merchant lost 12 per cent of the cost price on some goods that he sold for $281.60. What did the merchandise cost?
3. The Brown Company purchased some merchandise for $480, which they marked up 25 per cent of the selling price. One-half was sold at this original price, the balance being reduced and sold at 80 per cent of its original price. Was there a gain or a loss, and what per cent was it of the actual selling price?

PART II

ESSENTIALS OF BUSINESS MATHEMATICS

CHAPTER III

SIMPLE INTEREST

UNIT 1. Computing Time; Ordinary and Accurate Interest; Cancellation Method of Computing Interest

If you rent a house, you pay money for the use of the house for fixed periods of time, usually per month. This charge is known as *rent*. If you borrow money, you also pay rent for its use, in the form of a fractional part of the money borrowed. This rental charge for borrowed money is known as *interest*. Thus,

Interest is money (or premium) paid for the use of money.

Banks and other lending agencies are in the business of renting money. Their profits are derived largely from the rent, or interest, that they charge for the use of their own or their depositors' money.

The *principal* is the money borrowed (or obligation incurred).

The *rate of interest* is the per cent per annum of the principal that is charged as rent for its use.

Thus 6 per cent interest means 6 cents rental charge for the use of each $1 of principal borrowed for 1 year's time, and 4 per cent interest means 4 cents rental charge for the use of each $1 of principal borrowed for 1 year's time.

Time is the number of years, months, and/or days for which a principal is borrowed and for which interest may be charged.

Maturity value is the sum (or amount) of the principal plus any interest accumulated at the time at which the obligation is due and payable.

The Gregorian Calendar. Inasmuch as the majority of loans are for periods of not exactly 1 or more years but for a few months or days, it is necessary to know how to compute interest for months or days as well as per year.

Since time is an element in every interest calculation and since time in the modern business world is determined by the Gregorian calendar, the following information is pertinent.

The time required for the earth to make a complete revolution around the sun determines the length of the year. Thus a year is exactly 365 days, 5 hours, 48 minutes, and 46 seconds, almost $365\frac{1}{4}$ days. Because of this fractional part of a day, an extra day is added every 4 years to the years divisible by four, giving the month of February 29 days in leap years instead of the usual 28. An extra day added every 4 years gives a small fraction too much time, amounting to 3 days in 400 years. This is corrected by declaring only century years which are divisible by 400 to be leap years. Thus 1600 was a leap year and 1700, 1800, and 1900 were not leap years. A slight error remaining causes a variation between our calendar years and the position of earth and sun of 1 day in approximately 20,000 years. For practical purposes, the Gregorian calendar is sufficiently accurate.

Table of Time Measurement

60 seconds (sec.)	= 1 minute	(min.)
60 minutes	= 1 hour	(hr.)
24 hours	= 1 day	(da.)
7 days	= 1 week	(wk.)
30 days	= 1 month	(mo.)
52 weeks	= 1 year	(yr.)
12 months	= 1 year	
365 days	= 1 calendar year	
366 days	= 1 leap year	
360 days	= 1 business year	
100 years	= 1 century	

Unless the following information is already known, it should be committed to memory so that it may be recalled instantly:

Calendar quarters	Month number	Month name	Abbreviation	No. of days
First	1	January	Jan.	31
	2	February	Feb.	28 (or 29 in leap years)
	3	March	Mar.	31
Second	4	April	Apr.	30
	5	May	May	31
	6	June	June	30
Third	7	July	July	31
	8	August	Aug.	31
	9	September	Sept.	30
Fourth	10	October	Oct.	31
	11	November	Nov.	30
	12	December	Dec.	31

If the time in dated years is stated, it must be determined whether any are leap years. Unless otherwise stated, February is to be considered as having 28 days. The old rhyme

Thirty days hath September,
April, June, and November;

All the rest have thirty-one,
Excepting February alone,
Which hath but twenty-eight, in fine,
Till leap year gives it twenty-nine

was intended to facilitate the remembering of the number of days in each month.

METHODS OF COMPUTING TIME

Since several methods are used to calculate time, it is necessary that you understand the different ways by which time is determined in actual business practice. Two measurements of time in common use are (1) 30-day-month time and (2) exact time.

Thirty-day-month Time. The year is considered as 360 days, divided into 12 months of 30 days each. Each month, quarter, half-year, or year is considered as having the same number of days as a corresponding period, thus simplifying the comparison of one period with another.

Thirty-day-month time is used most frequently for long-term loans in which periodic payments are made on both principal and interest. Typical examples of periodic payment plans include certain forms of personal borrowing, real-estate loans, and obligations arising out of the purchase of such items as home furnishings, clothing, jewelry, or automobiles. In such instances, interest charges for each month are computed upon the assumption that each month contains 30 days and is $\frac{1}{12}$ year (regardless of whether the month actually is 28, 29, 30, or 31 days). Thirty-day-month time is sometimes called "bond time" because it is always used in computing interest accruing to the seller of commercial bonds.

Usual Method of Computing 30-day-month Time. In calculating short periods of time, particularly those of less than one year, the usual method of computation is recommended.

1. *When the stipulated date of the earlier month* (date of orgin) *is less than the stipulated date of the later month* (due date): determine the time in whole months (each considered as 30 days) from the date of the earlier month *to the same date* in the later month. To this number *add* the difference between the stipulated dates of the earlier month and the later month.

Example 1: Find the time from May 17 to Aug. 26.

$$
\begin{aligned}
&5/17 \text{ to } 8/17 = 3 \text{ months} = 90 \text{ days}\\
&\text{Plus } 26 - 17 \qquad\qquad\quad = \underline{\ \ 9 \text{ days}}\\
&\qquad\qquad\qquad\qquad \text{Time} = 99 \text{ days}
\end{aligned}
$$

2. *When the stipulated date of the earlier month* (date of origin) *is greater than the stipulated date of the later month* (due date): determine the time in whole months (each considered as 30 days) from the date of the earlier month *to the same date* in the later month. From this number *subtract* the difference between the stipulated dates of the earlier month and the later month.

Example 2: Find the time from May 17 to Aug. 6.

5/17 to 8/17 = 3 months	=	90 days
Less 17 − 6 =	=	11 days
Time	=	79 days

In counting, notice that the first day is not counted, but that the last day is included in the total. Also notice that in the preceding examples both May and July, although actually having 31 days, are considered as 30-day months. This is also true of the other 31-day months; and February, whether it has 28 or 29 days, is also considered as a 30-day month *if* 30-day-month time is used.

Compound-time Method of Computing 30-day-month Time. In calculating long periods of time, particularly those in excess of one year, the compound-time method of computation is recommended.

In computing the elapsed time period at 30-day-month time by the compound-time method, change the date of origin if 31 (days) to 30 unless both date of origin and maturity date are 31 (see Example 2 following).

Example 1: Find the number of days at 30-day-month time from Nov. 16, 1957, to May 9, 1962.

Year	*Month*	*Day*
196~~2~~ 1	~~5~~ ~~4~~ 16	~~9~~ 39
1957	11	16
4 yr.	5 mo.	23 da.
(1,440 da.) +	(150 da.) +	(23 da.) = 1,613 days

Since 16 days cannot be subtracted from 9 days, 1 month or 30 days is borrowed from the month column, making 4 the number of months and 39 the number of days. Since 11 months cannot be subtracted from 4 months, 1 year or 12 months is borrowed from the year column, making 1941 the number of years and 16 the number of months.

At this point, the problem is merely that of subtraction and conversion of the remainders in years, months, and days to their equivalent total of days.

Example 2: Find the number of days at 30-day-month time from Oct. 31, 1895, to June 8, 1899.

Year	*Month*	*Day*	
189~~9~~ 8	~~6~~ ~~5~~ 17	~~8~~ 38	
1895	10	~~31~~ 30	(Note: 31 is changed to 30)
3 yr.	7 mo.	8 da.	

(1,080 da.) + (210 da.) + (8 da.) = 1,298 days

Exact Time. Exact time is the actual number of days and is the time basis used for most interest calculations, and in general may be said to be used for most loans except real-estate loans and installment loans.

Since loans, other than security loans, government obligations, real-estate loans, and installment loans rarely extend over time periods in excess of a few months, it is usually not necessary to calculate exact time (with the exception of security loans and government obligations) for periods in excess of 120 to 180 days.

When exact time is used, as with 30-day-month time, the first day is not counted, but the last day is included in the total. The following examples will make it obvious to you why it is necessary that you know the number of days in each month (and whether February falls in a leap year).

Example 1: Find the exact time from June 4 to Sept. 2.

Solution (*a*)		
	June 4 to June 30	= 26 days
	July	= 31 days
	August	= 31 days
	To Sept. 2	= 2 days
	Exact time total	= 90 days

Solution (*b*)			
	June 4 to Sept. 4 is 3 months or approximately		90 days
	But Sept. 2 is due date and 4 − 2	=	− 2 days
	At 30-da.-mo. time, number of days would be		88 days
	For July 31 and Aug. 31, add		+ 2 days
	Exact time total	=	90 days

Example 2: Find the exact time from Jan. 15, 1960 to Mar. 15, 1960.

Solution (*a*)		
	Jan. 15 to Jan. 31	= 16 days
	February	= 29 days (leap year)
	To Mar. 15	= 15 days
	Exact time total	= 60 days

Solution (*b*)			
	Jan. 15 to Mar. 15 is 2 months or approximately		60 days
	For Jan. 31, add 1 day		+ 1 day
	Since Feb. is 29 days subtract only 1 day		− 1 day
	Exact time total	=	60 days

The Date of Origin and the Due Date of a Loan. The *date* (or date of origin) of a loan is the date on which the loan is incurred.

The *due date* (or maturity date) of a loan is the date on which the loan is due and payable.

The time of a loan is frequently expressed in either of two ways: (1) a specified number of days, (2) a specified number of months or years.

When Time of a Note Is Expressed in Days. The time period of most loans is expressed as a stipulated number of days from the date of the loan. Thus the due date of a 30-day loan is *exactly* 30 days after date; the due date of a 72-day loan is exactly 72 days after date; etc.

Example 1: Find the due date of a 45-day loan dated June 25.

June 25 to June 30 = 5 days
July = 31 days
Subtotal = 36 days
45 − 36 = 9 days
To Aug. 9 = 9 days
Total = 45 days
Therefore the due date of the loan is Aug. 9

Example 2: Find the date of origin of a 60-day loan due to Sept. 12.

In September = 12 days
August = 31 days
Subtotal = 43 days
60 − 43 = 17 days
And July 31 − 17 = July 14
July 14 to July 31 = 17 days
Total = 60 days
Therefore the date of origin of the loan is July 14

When Time of a Note Is Expressed in Months (or Years). If the time period of a loan is expressed as a specified number of months (or years), the due date of the loan is found by 30-day-month time. Thus the due date of a 1-month loan dated Jan. 25 would be Feb. 25; the due date of a 3-month loan dated June 7 would be Sept. 7; etc.

If there is not the required number of days in the maturity month, the maturity date is the *last day* of the maturity month. Thus a 1-month loan dated Jan. 31 is due on Feb. 28 (or Feb. 29 in a leap year). And a 4-month loan dated May 31 would fall due on Sept. 30.

Likewise, a 1-year loan falls due on the same date of the following year; a 2-year loan falls due on the same day of the second year following; etc.

Take special note that, *even though the maturity date is established by 30-day-month time, the number of days at interest may be computed by either 30-day-month time or exact time,* the latter being the more frequently used for short-term business and commercial bank transactions.

When the Due Date Is a Nonbusiness Day. If the due date of a loan falls on a nonbusiness day, such as a Sunday or legal holiday, the due date is considered to be the first business day following, and the additional day or days are added to the period for which interest is charged. Thus if a 90-day loan falls due on Dec. 25, the note is considered as due Dec. 26 (if a business day) and interest is charged for 91 days. Similarly, if the due date falls on a Sunday, interest is considered as due the first business day following, and the additional day or days are added to the interest period. In many states, Saturdays as well as Sundays are nonbusiness days.

Example 1: Find the due date on a 2-month loan dated Nov. 1.

2 months after Nov. 1 is Jan. 1.

But Jan. 1 is a legal holiday.

Therefore the due date is considered as Jan. 2 (if a business day), and interest is charged for 61 days if 30-day-month time is used or for 62 days if exact time is used.

Example 2: Find the due date on a 90-day loan dated Apr. 5.

Solution (*a*)		
	Apr. 5 to Apr. 30	= 25 days
	May	= 31 days
	June	= 30 days
	Subtotal	= 86 days
	90 − 86 = 4 days	
	To July 4	= 4 days
	Total	= 90 days

But July 4 is a legal holiday. Therefore the due date would be considered as July 5 (if a business day), and interest would be charged for 91 days.

Solution (*b*) 90 days or approximately 3 months after Apr. 5 is July 5.

But May 31 would add 1 day to 90 days and July 5 would be 91 days after Apr. 5. Therefore the due date would be July 4, except that July 4 is a legal holiday; so July 5 (if a business day) would be the due date, and interest would be charged for 91 days.

CANCELLATION METHOD OF COMPUTING ORDINARY SIMPLE INTEREST AND ACCURATE INTEREST

Simple-interest charges on an identical principal at an identical rate of interest sometimes differ because of the various methods that may be used to determine the time element in the basic interest formula: *Interest equals the product of the principal, time, and rate.* This formula is commonly expressed by means of the following symbols:

I = interest, in dollars
P = principal, in dollars at interest
n = time, in years
i = rate of interest, per annum

And the formula expressed in symbols is

$$I = Pni$$

Since the time element in the equation may be assigned four different values in the equation, there are four possible answers to a given interest problem. These variations are due to the different number of days which may be computed by 30-day-month time and by exact time, and also to the two different bases that may be used in the computation, namely, the business year of 360 days and the calendar year of 365 days (366 in a leap year).

Thus, in a period of time from Apr. 30 to June 30, the time element in the interest formula may be expressed by any of the following combinations:

(a) *Ordinary simple interest at 30-day-month time:*

60	= 30-day-month time from Apr. 30 to June 30 is	60 days
360	= The base or business year is expressed as	360 days

(b) *Ordinary simple interest at exact time:*

61	= The exact time from Apr. 30 to June 30 is	61 days
360	= The base or business year is expressed as	360 days

(c) *Theoretically possible but never used hybrid:*

60	= 30-day-month time from Apr. 30 to June 30 is	60 days
365	= The base or calendar year is expressed as	365 days

(d) *Accurate interest or exact interest* (note similarity in name but difference from interest at exact time):

61	= The exact time from Apr. 30 to June 30 is	61 days
365	= The base or calendar year is expressed as	365 days

It is evident that the interest on \$1,000 at 6 per cent from Apr. 30 to June 30 could be computed as follows:

(a) With 30-day-month time and a 360-day year,

$$I = \$1{,}000 \times \frac{60}{360} \times \frac{6}{100} = \$10$$

(b) With exact time and a 360-day year,

$$I = \$1{,}000 \times \frac{61}{360} \times \frac{6}{100} = \$10.17$$

(*c*) With 30-day-month time and a 365-day year,

$$I = \$1{,}000 \times \frac{60}{365} \times \frac{6}{100} = \$\ 9.86$$

(*d*) With exact time and a 365-day year,

$$I = \$1{,}000 \times \frac{61}{365} \times \frac{6}{100} = \$10.03$$

In computing interest, 30-day-month time is never combined with the calendar year of 365 as the base, and thus solution *c* is a theoretical, not a practical answer.

Ordinary Interest. In business practice, as has already been noted, 360 days is most frequently used as the base of the time element in interest calculations, the numerator being computed either by 30-day-month time or by exact time.

Whether 30-day-month or exact time is used depends primarily upon custom, although in general, *ordinary interest at 30-day-month time* is used only for periodic repayment plans such as monthly payments on real-estate mortgages, installment purchases, and certain types of personal borrowing and in computing accrued interest on commercial bonds. *Ordinary interest at exact time* is commonly used for most commercial, industrial, and personal notes.

As is readily apparent, the lender gains 5 days additional interest yearly by the use of ordinary interest at exact time (365 days for the numerator and 360 days for the denominator).

Accurate Interest or Exact Interest. Although not customary in most business transactions, accurate interest is sometimes used when the borrower is in an advantageous position. Interest payments on government obligations (and also rediscounting of notes for member banks by Federal Reserve banks) are calculated on the basis of the 365-day year. The interest payment is $\frac{5}{365}$ or $\frac{1}{73}$ less than when interest is computed at exact time. Take special note that accurate interest, frequently called *exact interest, is not the same as ordinary interest at exact time.*

Accurate interest is calculated by taking the *exact time* (actual number of days) and using the 365-*day year* as the base.

Cancellation Method of Computing Ordinary Interest. To find the ordinary interest on a given sum at a given rate for a given number of days, use the formula $I = Pni$.

As you will observe in the following Example 1 of ordinary interest at 30-day-month time and Example 2 of ordinary interest at exact time, the denominator is 360 × 100. To simplify the process of cancellation, reject factors of 100 only when it may be reduced to 10 or to 1. Thus do not reject 4 from 100 to obtain 25 unless the 25 may be further reduced to 1;

do not reject 5 from 100 to obtain 20 unless the 20 may be further reduced to 10 or to 1. To increase greatly your speed and accuracy in the use of cancellation in ordinary simple-interest problems, thoroughly memorize all of the factors of 360 that follow, most of which are already known to you:

360	
2	180
3	120
4	90
5	72
6	60
8	45
9	40
10	36
12	30
15	24
18	20

Example 1: Ordinary interest at 30-day-month time. What is the interest, using 30-day-month time, on $720 at 5 per cent from Apr. 25 to June 15?

$$P = \$720$$
$$n = 50 \text{ days (base: 360-day year)}$$
$$i = 5\% = \frac{5}{100}$$
$$I = \overset{2}{\cancel{\$720}} \times \frac{\cancel{50}}{\cancel{360}} \times \frac{5}{\underset{2}{\cancel{100}}} = \$5.00$$

Example 2: Ordinary interest at exact time. What is the interest, using exact time, on $720 at 5 per cent from Apr. 25 to June 15?

$$P = \$720$$
$$n = 51 \text{ days (base: 360-day year)}$$
$$i = 5\% = \frac{5}{100}$$
$$I = \frac{\overset{2}{\cancel{\$720}} \times 51 \times \cancel{5}}{\cancel{360} \times \underset{\underset{10}{\cancel{50}}}{\cancel{100}}} = \frac{51}{10} = \$5.10$$

Cancellation Method of Computing Accurate Interest. Just as in computing ordinary simple interest, to find the accurate (or exact) interest on a given sum at a given rate for a given number days, use the formula $I = Pni$.

When accurate interest is required, it should be noted that the preferred method of computation is cancellation. Since 365 days is used as the base for the time period, the opportunities for cancellation are limited because the factors of 365 are 5×73, both prime numbers. Thus, the numerator of the interest problem must contain 5, 73, 365 or multiples of these numbers if any rejection is to take place. As with problems in ordinary simple interest, reject factors in 100 only when it may be reduced to 10 or to 1.

Example: Accurate interest or exact interest. What is the accurate interest on \$720 at 5 per cent from Apr. 25 to June 15?

$$P = \$720$$
$$n = 51 \text{ days (base: 365-day year)}$$
$$i = 5\% = \frac{5}{100}$$
$$I = \frac{\overset{72}{\cancel{\$720}} \times 51 \times \cancel{5}}{\underset{73}{\cancel{365}} \times \underset{10}{\cancel{100}}} = \frac{3{,}672}{730} = \$5.03$$

Note that in this example, further cancellation could have been employed to reduce $\frac{3{,}672}{730}$ to $\frac{1{,}836}{365}$ but such cancellation would not have simplified the computation.

Relationship of Accurate Interest and Ordinary Interest at Exact Time. If the base for the time calculation is 365 days, the interest charge is $\frac{5}{365}$ or $\frac{1}{73}$ *less* than if 360 days is used as the base for the time calculation. Restated, if the base for the time calculation is 360 days, the interest charge is $\frac{5}{360}$ or $\frac{1}{72}$ *more* than if 365 days is used as the base for the time calculation.

Two rules for conversion would then be

1. To find *accurate interest*, if ordinary interest at exact time is known, deduct $\frac{1}{73}$. Thus, in Example 2 of ordinary interest at exact time, where the interest charge was determined as \$5.10, subtraction of $\frac{1}{73} \times \$5.10$, or \$.07, would give accurate interest of \$5.03.

2. To find ordinary *interest at exact time*, if accurate interest is known, add $\frac{1}{72}$ of the accurate interest to the accurate interest. Thus in Example 3 of accurate interest, where the interest charge was determined as \$5.03, addition of $\frac{1}{73} \times \$5.03$, or \$.07, would give ordinary interest at exact time of \$5.10.

NOTE: These rules for conversion are applicable to ordinary *interest at 30-day-month time* only when the number of days at interest are the same as in accurate interest.

Maturity Value or Amount. By definition, maturity value is the sum (or amount) of the principal plus any interest accumulated at the time at which the obligation is due and payable. If S is used to symbolize maturity value, then

$$S = P + I$$

Since I is usually unknown, most problems in finding maturity value require that the interest be determined and then added to the given principal. Thus:

$$I = Pni$$
$$S = P + I$$

Example 1: Find the maturity value of a note for \$540 at 8 per cent ordinary interest for 135 days.

$$I = \frac{\$540 \times \overset{3}{\cancel{135}} \times \cancel{8}}{\underset{45}{\cancel{360}} \times 100} = \frac{1{,}620}{100} = \$16.20$$

$$S = \$540 + \$16.20 = \$556.20$$

Example 2: Find the amount due at maturity of \$292 at accurate interest for 216 days at 5 per cent.

$$I = \frac{\overset{4}{\cancel{\$292}} \times 216 \times \cancel{5}}{\underset{73}{\cancel{365}} \times 100} = \frac{864}{100} = \$8.64$$

$$S = \$292 + \$8.64 = \$300.64$$

When to Drop Decimals. Although commercial practice varies in computing interest, the preferred and accurate rule to follow is: *Do not drop or raise decimal parts of* 1 *cent until the final result is determined.* With the cent, the smallest coin used in the United States, business practice is as follows: *If the result is a fractional part of* 1 *cent amounting to* \$.005 ($\frac{1}{2}$ *cent) or more, raise the amount* 1 *cent and drop the fraction of a cent; if the result is a fractional part of* 1 *cent amounting to less than* \$.005, *drop the fraction of a cent.* Thus \$10.915 is raised to \$10.92, and \$10.9149 is considered as \$10.91.

Remember, do not drop or raise decimal parts of 1 cent until all computations have been made.

EXERCISE 1A

In computing time in the following exercise, assume Jan. 1, July 4, and Dec. 25 due dates to be the only nonbusiness days.

A. Find 30-day-month time by the compound-time method on the following obligations (*a*) in years, months, and days and (*b*) in total number of days.

Date of origin	*Due date*	*Date of origin*	*Due date*
1. Aug. 5, 1946	Sept. 11, 1959	**2.** Feb. 15, 1949	May 27, 1958
3. Jan. 28, 1944	Feb. 28, 1956	**4.** Jan. 31, 1957	Mar. 17, 1964
5. Nov. 29, 1956	Apr. 15, 1961	**6.** Dec. 14, 1960	Jan. 27, 1961

B. Find the time in total days on the following obligations (*a*) by 30-day-month time and the ordinary method and (*b*) by exact time.

Date of origin	*Due date*	*Date of origin*	*Due date*
1. Dec. 16, 1959	Apr. 28, 1960	**2.** Aug. 31, 1960	Nov. 30, 1960
3. Apr. 22, 1959	July 4, 1959	**4.** Sept. 22, 1959	Mar. 18, 1960
5. July 14, 1956	Feb. 9, 1957	**6.** Sept. 2, 1960	Dec. 25, 1960

C. Find the due dates:

Date of origin	*Time*	*Date of origin*	*Time*
1. 9/9	1 mo.	**2.** 5/22	3 mo.
3. 7/31	2 mo.	**4.** Jan. 4	6 mo.
5. Dec. 13	4 mo.	**6.** Feb. 28	1 mo.

D. Find the dates of origin:

Time	*Due date*	*Time*	*Due date*
1. 4 mo.	5/17	**2.** 2 mo.	11/5
3. 3 mo.	4/30	**4.** 1 mo.	Aug. 21
5. 6 mo.	Jan. 18	**6.** 2 mo.	Oct. 2

E. Find the due dates by *exact time:*

Date of origin	*Time*	*Date of origin*	*Time*
1. 3/12	17 da.	**2.** 10/7	61 da.
3. 4/1	29 da.	**4.** July 6	92 da.
5. Oct. 22	180 da.	**6.** Jan. 2	58 da.

F. Find the dates of origin by *exact time:*

Time	*Due date*	*Time*	*Due date*
1. 127 da.	8/31	**2.** 89 da.	5/4
3. 31 da.	12/19	**4.** 119 da.	May 25
5. 45 da.	Mar. 2	**6.** 63 da.	Dec. 12

G. Find ordinary interest (days in year = 360) on the following using the cancellation method:

1. $6,000 for 144 days at 5%

2. $2,540 for 135 days at 8%

3. $306.75 for 75 days at $4\frac{1}{2}$ %

4. $522.50 for 96 days at 6%

5. $85.35 for 205 days at 4%

6. $213.60 for 252 days at $3\frac{1}{3}$ %

H. Find accurate interest (days in year = 365) on the following using the cancellation method:

1. \$8,000 for 146 days at 5%
2. \$2,190 for 55 days at 7%
3. \$509.25 for 292 days at $3\frac{3}{4}$ %
4. \$105.50 for 8 days at 9%
5. \$92.60 for 219 days at 10%
6. \$454.86 for 195 days at $4\frac{1}{6}$ %

EXERCISE 1B

A. Find ordinary interest at 30-day-month time $\left(\frac{\text{30-da.-mo. time}}{360}\right)$ using the cancellation method

1. \$3,000 at 5%, June 7 to Aug. 7
2. \$596 at $4\frac{1}{2}$ %, Jan. 29 to Mar. 14
3. \$73.50 at 7%, May 4 to Oct. 19

B. Find maturity value at ordinary interest using 30-day-month time $\left(\frac{\text{30-da.-mo. time}}{360}\right)$ and the cancellation method:

1. \$7,200 at 6%, Aug. 20 to Nov. 5
2. \$824 at $7\frac{1}{2}$ %, Feb. 12 to June 18
3. \$80.65 at 4%, Nov. 27 to Mar. 27

C. Find ordinary interest at exact time $\left(\frac{\text{actual number days}}{360}\right)$ using the cancellation method:

1. \$653.20 at 2%, May 5 to Aug. 13
2. \$435.60 at 8%, Sept. 27 to Dec. 11
3. \$6,732.70 at 4%, Feb. 8 to Apr. 9

D. Find maturity value at ordinary interest using exact time $\left(\frac{\text{actual number days}}{360}\right)$ and the cancellation method:

1. \$392.65 at $4\frac{1}{2}$ %, Dec. 3 to Apr. 7
2. \$93.57 at 4%, July 25 to Sept. 2
3. \$8.55 at $7\frac{1}{2}$ %, Jan. 30 to Mar. 14

E. Find accurate interest $\left(\frac{\text{actual number days}}{365}\right)$ using the cancellation method:

1. \$764 at 6%, Dec. 29 to Jan. 4
2. \$987.20 at 5%, Feb. 15 to Mar. 6
3. \$1,876 at $4\frac{1}{2}$ %, June 20 to Sept. 13

F. Find maturity value at accurate interest $\left(\frac{\text{actual number days}}{365}\right)$ using the cancellation method:

1. \$330.50 at $7\frac{1}{2}$ %, Apr. 7 to Nov. 12
2. \$87.56 at 4%, July 13 to Aug. 27
3. \$4,378 at $3\frac{1}{3}$ %, Nov. 23 to Feb. 4

G. Solve the following by the use of cancellation:

1. A \$408.65 note dated June 27 and due Nov. 12 bears ordinary interest at 8 per cent. At 30-day-month time, find (*a*) interest and (*b*) maturity value.
2. Mr. Johnson borrowed \$4,736.85 on July 1 at 7 per cent ordinary interest. He paid his obligation in full on Dec. 6. At exact time, find (*a*) interest and (*b*) maturity value.
3. A taxpayer overpaid his income tax on Apr. 15 by \$673.51. He applied for and received a refund including accurate interest at 6 per cent. If the government computed interest to and including Sept. 8, how much did he receive?

UNIT 2. The 60-day, 6 Per Cent Method of Computing Ordinary Interest[1]

Those people who are required to make many calculations of ordinary interest have developed special methods of finding interest at certain rates, which are often much shorter and easier than the use of the cancellation method. All such short cuts are based on a 360-day year (denominator), but the time at interest (numerator) may be computed by 30-day-month time or by exact time.

[1] Certain other frequently occurring interest rates lend themselves to similar methods. Thus the following could be used, if desired: 90-day, 4 per cent; 80-day, $4\frac{1}{2}$ per cent; 120-day, 3 per cent; 30-day, 12 per cent; etc.

Best known and most widely used short cut, the 60-day, 6 per cent method, finds the ordinary interest on any given sum for the given time at 6 per cent and then converts it to any other per cent that may be required.

Since 6 per cent for 360 days or 12 months would be 1 per cent for 60 days or 2 months, to find the ordinary interest on any sum at 6 per cent, *move* the *decimal point* in the *principal* as follows:

3 places to the left for 6 days $\left(\frac{1}{10}\% \text{ or } .001\right)$
2 places to the left for 60 days (1% or .01)
1 place to the left for 600 days (10% or .1)
Do not move as interest equals principal in 6,000 days (100% or 1.)

The interest for 30 days would be one-half of the interest for 60 days, the interest for 200 days would be one-third of the interest for 600 days, the interest for 12 days would be one-fifth the interest for 60 days or twice the interest for 6 days. Becoming adept in the use of the 60-day, 6 per cent method requires the selection of easy-to-use combinations of factors and multiples of 6, 60, 600, and 6,000 days.

Examples:

10 days $= \frac{1}{6}$ of 60 days

15 days $= \frac{1}{4}$ of 60 days

20 days $= \frac{1}{3}$ of 60 days

45 days $= \frac{1}{4}$ less than 60 days

50 days $= \frac{1}{6}$ less than 60 days

1 day $= \frac{1}{6}$ of 6 days

2 days $= \frac{1}{3}$ of 6 days

3 days $= \frac{1}{2}$ of 6 days

4 days $= \frac{1}{3}$ less than 6 days

5 days $= \frac{1}{6}$ less than 6 days

150 days = 2 × 60 days plus 30 days $\left(\text{or } \frac{1}{4} \text{ of 600 days}\right)$

90 days = 60 days plus 30 days
54 days = 60 days minus 6 days (or 6 days × 9)
183 days = 60 days × 3 plus 3 days
118 days = 60 days × 2 minus 2 days

Example 1: Find the ordinary interest on $800 for 60 days at 6 per cent.

$8.00 = interest for 60 days (point off 2 places)

Example 2: Find the ordinary interest on $560 for 96 days at 6 per cent.

$5.60	=	interest for 60 days (point off 2 places)
2.80	=	interest for 30 days (half of 60 days)
.56	=	interest for 6 days (point off 3 places)
$8.96	=	interest for 96 days

Example 3: Find the ordinary interest on $960 for 673 days at 6 per cent.

$ 96.00	=	interest for 600 days (point off 1 place)
9.60	=	interest for 60 days (point off 2 places)
1.92	=	interest for 12 days (point off 3 places, multiply by 2)
.16	=	interest for 1 day $\left(\frac{1}{6} \text{ of 6 days}\right)$
$107.68	=	interest for 673 days

Dividing the Days. It is possible to select various combinations of days into which the time may be divided. In using the 60-day, 6 per cent method, attempt to select that combination of days which seems easiest to use. Thus if interest at 6 per cent is to be found on $240 for 88 days, the following are among many possible combinations of days that might be used:

a		*b*		*c*	
$2.40 =	60 days	$2.40 =	60 days	$2.40 =	60 days
.80 =	20 days	1.20 =	30 days	.60 =	15 days
.24 =	6 days	3.60 =	90 days	.24 =	6 days
.08 =	2 days	−.08 =	−2 days	.24 =	6 days
$3.52 =	88 days	$3.52 =	88 days	.04 =	1 day
				$3.52 =	88 days

Transposing. Transposition of the principal and the days will often simplify the use of the 60-day, 6 per cent method; *e.g.*, $1 for 360 days will result in the same interest as $360 for 1 day, or $10 for 39 days will result in the same interest as $39 for 10 days, etc.

Example: Find the ordinary interest on $600 for 127 days at 6 per cent.

a

$ 6.00 =	60 days
6.00 =	60 days
.60 =	6 days
.10 =	1 day
$12.70 =	127 days

b

By transposition:

$600 for 127 days = $127 for 600 days

$12.70 = 600 days

Since the principal in many interest problems often lends itself to transposition, always consider whether such a change is advisable before proceeding with the solution.

FINDING ORDINARY INTEREST AT RATES OTHER THAN 6 PER CENT

When the ordinary interest at 6 per cent may be obtained readily because of desirable combinations of days, it is sometimes advantageous to use the 60-day, 6 per cent method and then convert to the desired rate. Thus if the ordinary interest at 6 per cent in the example preceding is \$12.70, the interest at 3 per cent would be one-half as great, or $\$12.70 \div 2 = \$6.35$. A number of interest rates in common use lend themselves to such conversion:

Rate required, %	For the same number of days and the same principal, the interest will be:	Because
1	$\frac{1}{6}$ of the interest at 6%	1 is $\frac{1}{6}$ of 6
$1\frac{1}{2}$	$\frac{1}{4}$ of the interest at 6%	$1\frac{1}{2}$ is $\frac{1}{4}$ of 6
2	$\frac{1}{3}$ of the interest at 6%	2 is $\frac{1}{3}$ of 6
3	$\frac{1}{2}$ of the interest at 6%	3 is $\frac{1}{2}$ of 6
4	6% interest *minus* $\frac{1}{3}$ of interest at 6%	$4 = 6 - \frac{1}{3}$ of 6
$4\frac{1}{2}$	6% interest *minus* $\frac{1}{4}$ of interest at 6%	$4\frac{1}{2} = 6 - \frac{1}{4}$ of 6
5	6% interest *minus* $\frac{1}{6}$ of interest at 6%	$5 = 6 - \frac{1}{6}$ of 6
7	6% interest *plus* $\frac{1}{6}$ of interest at 6%	$7 = 6 + \frac{1}{6}$ of 6
$7\frac{1}{2}$	6% interest *plus* $\frac{1}{4}$ of interest at 6%	$7\frac{1}{2} = 6 + \frac{1}{4}$ of 6
8	6% interest *plus* $\frac{1}{3}$ of interest at 6%	$8 = 6 + \frac{1}{3}$ of 6
9	6% interest *plus* $\frac{1}{2}$ of interest at 6%	$9 = 6 + \frac{1}{2}$ of 6
12	Twice the interest at 6%	$12 = 6 \times 2$

Example 1: Find the ordinary interest on \$240 for 60 days at 7 per cent.

$$\begin{aligned} \$2.40 &= \text{interest for 60 days at } 6\% \\ +\ .40 &= \tfrac{1}{6} \text{ interest at } 6\% = +1\% \\ \hline \$2.80 &= \text{interest for 60 days at } 7\% \end{aligned}$$

Example 2: Find the ordinary interest on \$320 for 93 days at $4\frac{1}{2}$ per cent.

$$
\begin{aligned}
\$3.20 &= \text{interest for 60 days at } 6\% \\
1.60 &= \text{interest for 30 days at } 6\% \left(\frac{1}{2} \text{ of 60 days}\right) \\
.16 &= \text{interest for } \underline{3} \text{ days at } 6\% \left(\frac{1}{10} \text{ of 30 days, or } \frac{1}{2} \text{ of 6 days}\right) \\
\$4.96 &= \text{interest for 93 days at } \quad 6\% \\
-1.24 &= \frac{1}{4} \text{ of interest at } 6\% = \quad -1\frac{1}{2}\% \\
\$3.72 &= \text{interest for 93 days at } \quad 4\frac{1}{2}\%
\end{aligned}
$$

Computing Interest at Rates Not Easily Converted from Interest at 6 Per Cent. A number of interest rates may not be converted readily from 6 per cent, and sometimes the interest at 6 per cent does not lend itself to easy conversion. In any such instances, the interest at the required rate may be found by use of the following formula:

$$\textit{Required interest} = \frac{\textit{interest at } 6\% \times \textit{required rate in number of per cent}}{6}$$

Example 1: Find the ordinary interest on \$920 for 72 days at 3.5 per cent.

$$
\begin{aligned}
\$9.20 &= \text{interest for 60 days at } 6\% \\
1.84 &= \text{interest for } \underline{12} \text{ days at } 6\% \left(\frac{1}{5} \text{ of 60 days, or } 2 \times 6 \text{ days}\right) \\
\$11.04 &= \text{interest for 72 days at } 6\%
\end{aligned}
$$

$$\frac{\overset{1.84}{\cancel{\$11.04}} \times 3.5}{\cancel{6}} = \$6.44$$

Example 2: If the ordinary interest at 6 per cent is exactly \$7.523 find the ordinary interest at 7 per cent.

$$\frac{\$7.523 \times 7}{6} = \frac{52.661}{6} = \$8.78$$

EXERCISE 2A

A. Find the ordinary interest at 6 per cent by the use of the 60-day, 6 per cent method:

1. \$150 for 60 days
2. \$500 for 30 days
3. \$200 for 90 days
4. \$75 for 120 days

5. \$250 for 59 days
6. \$125 for 31 days
7. \$50 for 88 days
8. \$300 for 117 days
9. \$450 for 61 days
10. \$25 for 29 days
11. \$150 for 91 days
12. \$100 for 122 days
13. \$350 for 58 days
14. \$75 for 89 days
15. \$500 for 180 days
16. \$240 for 95 days
17. \$840 for 660 days
18. \$75 for 800 days
19. \$8.95 for 6,000 days
20. \$100.50 for 87 days

B. Find the ordinary interest by the use of the 60-day, 6 per cent method. (Suggestion: When possible, use the table of conversion, page 126.)

1. \$642 for 109 days at 4%
2. \$943 for 87 days at 5%
3. \$637 for 117 days at $4\frac{1}{2}$ %
4. \$439 for 78 days at 3%
5. \$87.56 for 76 days at 2%
6. \$598.50 for 43 days at 3%
7. \$3,700 for 37 days at $7\frac{1}{2}$ %
8. \$6,700 for 96 days at 9%
9. \$954.20 for 101 days at 1%
10. \$6,457.18 for 98 days at 12%

EXERCISE 2B

A. Find the ordinary interest on all the following *at 30-day-month time,* and solve at least half of the problems by the 60-day, 6 per cent method:

1. \$960 at 6%, May 15 to July 14
2. \$86 at $7\frac{1}{2}$ %, Mar. 9 to May 23
3. \$175 at $4\frac{1}{2}$ %, Feb. 14 to Aug. 8
4. \$188 at 3%, Jan. 3 to June 13
5. \$450 at 7%, Aug. 22 to Nov. 15
6. \$145.82 at 5%, Mar. 3 to May 22
7. \$95.85 at 4%, Oct. 13 to Nov. 19
8. \$860.48 at 9%, May 9 to Dec. 24

B. Find the ordinary interest on all the following *at exact time,* and solve at least half of the problems by the 60-day, 6 per cent method:

1. \$406 at $7\frac{1}{2}$ %, June 13 to Aug. 17
2. \$285 at 2%, Feb. 21 to Mar. 20
3. \$345 at 5%, June 27 to Dec. 17
4. \$350 at 7%, Oct. 15 to Nov. 26
5. \$2,500 at $2\frac{1}{2}$ %, May 30 to June 29
6. \$660 at $1\frac{1}{2}$ %, May 7 to June 2
7. \$520 at $4\frac{1}{2}$ %, Jan. 9 to May 6
8. \$800 at $3\frac{1}{2}$ %, June 6 to Aug. 1

C. Solve the following by the use of the 60-day, 6 per cent method:

1. \$8,468.48 is invested at $7\frac{1}{2}$ per cent ordinary interest at 30-day-month time from Oct. 21 to Jan. 18. Find (*a*) interest and (*b*) maturity value.
2. Mr. John Kay borrowed \$34,592.82 at 8 per cent ordinary interest at 30-day-month time from Feb. 13 to Apr. 1. Find (*a*) interest and (*b*) maturity value.
3. Mr. Orrin Shaw obtained a construction loan from his bank at 5 per cent ordinary interest at exact time. If he borrowed \$3,682.71 from Apr. 4 to Aug. 5, how much did he pay (*a*) in interest and (*b*) at maturity?
4. A business firm was able to borrow at $3\frac{1}{3}$ per cent ordinary interest computed at exact time. If \$4,668.19 was borrowed from Oct. 21, 1959, to Mar. 25, 1960, find (*a*) interest and (*b*) the amount due at maturity.

UNIT 3. The Product Method of Computing Ordinary Interest

The product method of computing ordinary interest (also known as the dollar-day method) is preferred by many people to the 60-day, 6 per cent method. As you know, the interest formula is expressed as

$$I = Pni$$

Since n, or time, is expressed as the number of days for which interest is taken, divided by the number of days in the year (360), the formula may be written as follows, letting t represent the number of days:

$$I = Pi\left(\frac{t}{360}\right)$$

And since t is the number of 360ths taken, the equation may also be written

$$I = Pit\left(\frac{1}{360}\right)$$

This is equivalent to

$$I = Pt\left(\frac{1}{360}\,i\right)$$

If the rate of interest (i) is 1 per cent, substituting its equivalent of $\frac{1}{100}$ in the equation gives the following:

$$I = Pt\left(\frac{1}{360} \times \frac{1}{100}\right) = Pt\left(\frac{1}{36{,}000}\right) = \frac{Pt}{36{,}000} = \text{ordinary interest at } 1\%$$

It should be apparent that, if $Pt \div 36{,}000$ is equal to ordinary interest at 1 per cent, then Pt is equal to ordinary interest at 36,000 per cent. And $Pt \div 1{,}000$ will equal ordinary interest at 36 per cent. Thus:

$$\frac{Pt}{1{,}000} = \text{ordinary interest at } 36\%$$

or

$$\frac{\text{Principal} \times \text{days}}{1{,}000} = \text{ordinary interest at } 36\%$$

Once ordinary interest at 36 per cent is known, ordinary interest at many rates in common use may be found quickly by application of the following:

$$\frac{\textit{Ordinary interest at } 36\% \times \textit{required rate in number of per cent}}{36}$$

Examples: Find the ordinary interest on \$720 for 100 days at (a) 6 per cent, (b) 4 per cent, (c) $4\frac{1}{2}$ per cent, and (d) 9 per cent.

Step

(1) Ordinary interest at 36,000% $= \$720 \times 100 = \$72{,}000$

(2) Ordinary interest at 36% $= \frac{\$72{,}000}{1{,}000} = \$72$

(a) $\frac{\$72 \times \not{6}}{\not{36}_{\,6}} = \$12$ (b) $\frac{\$72 \times \not{4}}{\not{36}_{\,9}} = \$8$

(c) $\frac{\$72 \times \not{4\frac{1}{2}}}{\not{36}_{\,8}} = \$9$ (d) $\frac{\$72 \times \not{9}}{\not{36}_{\,4}} = \$18$

Converting from Exactly 36 Per Cent Ordinary Interest to Other Rates. Though the formula preceding the examples may be used in converting from exactly 36 per cent ordinary interest to any required rate of ordinary interest, unless a calculating machine is available it will usually be more desirable to solve interest problems by some other method than the product method if the following table of conversion may not be used.

Rate Required	*To Find Required Interest if Exactly 36% Ordinary Interest is Known*
$\frac{1}{2}\%$	Divide interest at 36% by 72
$\frac{3}{4}\%$	Divide interest at 36% by 48
1%	Divide interest at 36% by 36
$1\frac{1}{2}\%$	Divide interest at 36% by 24
2%	Divide interest at 36% by 18
3%	Divide interest at 36% by 12
4%	Divide interest at 36% by 9
$4\frac{1}{2}\%$	Divide interest at 36% by 8
5%	Divide interest at 36% by 7.2
6%	Divide interest at 36% by 6
$7\frac{1}{2}\%$	Divide interest at 36% by 4.8
8%	Divide interest at 36% by 4.5
9%	Divide interest at 36% by 4
10%	Divide interest at 36% by 3.6
12%	Divide interest at 36% by 3

Example 1: Find the ordinary interest on $985 for 22 days at 6 per cent.

(1) $\$985 \times 22 = \$21{,}670$

(2) $\frac{\$21{,}670}{1{,}000} = \$21.670$

(3) $\frac{\$21.670}{6} = \$3.61$

Example 2: Find the ordinary interest on $455 for 65 days at 4 per cent.

(1) $\$455 \times 65 = \$29{,}575$

(2) $\frac{\$29{,}575}{1{,}000} = \$29.575$ (do not round off)

(3) $\frac{\$29.575}{9} = \$3.29$

Example 3: Find the ordinary interest on $727 for 55 days at 8 per cent.

(1) $\$727 \times 55 = \$39{,}985$

(2) $\frac{\$39{,}985}{1{,}000} = \$39.985$ (do not round off)

(3) $\frac{\$39.985}{4.5} = \$8.89$

As is indicated in these three examples, decimal places in the computations should be retained (not rounded off) until the required interest in dollars and cents has been determined.

Bank clerks and other individuals who find it necessary to make many interest computations often select either the 60-day, 6 per cent method or the product method, employing whichever solution experience and judgment indicate will provide the easier computation. If calculating machines are available, the product method is usually the more desirable.

EXERCISE 3

A. Find the ordinary interest at 6 per cent, using the product method and 30-*day-month time:*

1. $875 from Jan. 11 to May 9
2. $250 from Mar. 1 to Apr. 1
3. $650 from Oct. 12 to Dec. 5
4. $536 from Apr. 27 to July 3
5. $444 from Feb. 23 to Aug. 18
6. $2,700 from June 7 to July 7
7. $96.75 from Sept. 6 to Dec. 16
8. $325.50 from May 11 to Nov. 7
9. $842.23 from Aug. 28 to Sept. 30
10. $698.78 from May 8 to Oct. 26

B. Find the ordinary interest, using the product method and 30-*day-month time:*

1. $253 at 5%, Apr. 27 to July 8
2. $139 at $4\frac{1}{2}$ %, Jan. 3 to Aug. 2
3. $567 at $7\frac{1}{2}$ %, Mar. 19 to May 7
4. $738 at $1\frac{1}{2}$ %, June 3 to July 3
5. $800 at 2%, Oct. 24 to Nov. 27
6. $640 at 7%, Nov. 23 to Dec. 29
7. $300 at 3%, Sept. 18 to Oct. 23
8. $50.95 at 8%, Mar. 6 to July 19
9. $855.75 at 4%, Apr. 9 to May 20
10. $927.93 at 9%, July 5 to Oct. 3

C. Find the ordinary interest, using the product method and *exact time:*

1. $150 at $1\frac{1}{2}$ %, Oct. 8 to Dec. 22
2. $630 at $4\frac{1}{2}$ %, May 27 to Aug. 3
3. $310 at 3%, July 5 to Oct. 16
4. $980 at $7\frac{1}{2}$ %, Apr. 30 to May 5
5. $500 at $7\frac{2}{3}$ %, Feb. 14 to Mar. 6
6. $225 at 6%, Mar. 19 to July 8
7. $460 at 12%, Aug. 12 to Oct. 1
8. $39.25 at 2%, Nov. 19 to Nov. 29
9. $673.85 at 8%, Jan. 9 to May 8
10. $482.67 at 4%, May 7 to June 6

D. Solve the following by the product method:

1. $456.75 is invested at 6 per cent ordinary interest at 30-day-month time from Nov. 16 to June 6. Find (*a*) interest and (*b*) maturity value.

2. Mr. R. E. Maxwell loaned $551.32 at 3 per cent ordinary interest at 30-day-month time from Mar. 25 to July 16. Find (*a*) interest and (*b*) maturity value.

3. Mr. Irwin Johnson made a short-term business loan of $8,254 from his bank. If the bank charged him $4\frac{1}{2}$ per cent ordinary interest computed at exact time and if he borrowed the money on Apr. 17 and paid the loan in full with interest on July 3, how much did he pay (*a*) in interest and (*b*) at maturity?

4. A lending agency charged 8 per cent ordinary interest at exact time. If $5,051.75 was borrowed on Sept. 22 and due on Nov. 27, find (*a*) interest and (*b*) the amount due at maturity.

UNIT 4. Using Tables to Compute Exact Time and Ordinary Interest

Lending agencies and other businesses, having frequent need to figure interest, save time and insure greater accuracy in such calculations by utilizing one or more of the several types of time and interest tables that are available.

To determine the exact number of days between two given dates, the table shown on page 134 is in common use.

To find the exact number of days, use the table as follows:

1. In the left-hand column find the day of the month corresponding to the date of origin.
2. Read horizontally to locate the day of the year underneath the month of origin.
3. In the left-hand column find the day of the month corresponding to the date of maturity.
4. Read horizontally to locate the day of the year underneath the month of maturity.
5. Subtract the figure obtained in step 2 from the figure obtained in step 4.

Example 1: Find the exact time from June 5 to Aug. 27.

(1 and 2) June 5 is 156th day
(3 and 4) Aug. 27 is 239th day
(5) $239 - 156 = 83$ days

Example 2: Find the exact time from Jan. 24, 1956, to Apr. 29, 1956.

(1 and 2) Jan. 24 is 24th day
(3 and 4) Apr. 29 is 119th day, but add 1 day for Feb. 29 is included to make Apr. 29, 1956, the 120th day
(5) $120 - 24 = 96$ days

Table Used to Determine Exact Number of Days

(If a leap year, add 1 day to the terminal date if the time period includes Feb. 29.)

Day of month	J	F	M	A	M	J	J	A	S	O	N	D
1	1	32	60	91	121	152	182	213	244	274	305	335
2	2	33	61	92	122	153	183	214	245	275	306	336
3	3	34	62	93	123	154	184	215	246	276	307	337
4	4	35	63	94	124	155	185	216	247	277	308	338
5	5	36	64	95	125	156	186	217	248	278	309	339
6	6	37	65	96	126	157	187	218	249	279	310	340
7	7	38	66	97	127	158	188	219	250	280	311	341
8	8	39	67	98	128	159	189	220	251	281	312	342
9	9	40	68	99	129	160	190	221	252	282	313	343
10	10	41	69	100	130	161	191	222	253	283	314	344
11	11	42	70	101	131	162	192	223	254	284	315	345
12	12	43	71	102	132	163	193	224	255	285	316	346
13	13	44	72	103	133	164	194	225	256	286	317	347
14	14	45	73	104	134	165	195	226	257	287	318	348
15	15	46	74	105	135	166	196	227	258	288	319	349
16	16	47	75	106	136	167	197	228	259	289	320	350
17	17	48	76	107	137	168	198	229	260	290	321	351
18	18	49	77	108	138	169	199	230	261	291	322	352
19	19	50	78	109	139	170	200	231	262	292	323	353
20	20	51	79	110	140	171	201	232	263	293	324	354
21	21	52	80	111	141	172	202	233	264	294	325	355
22	22	53	81	112	142	173	203	234	265	295	326	356
23	23	54	82	113	143	174	204	235	266	296	327	357
24	24	55	83	114	144	175	205	236	267	297	328	358
25	25	56	84	115	145	176	206	237	268	298	329	359
26	26	57	85	116	146	177	207	238	269	299	330	360
27	27	58	86	117	147	178	208	239	270	300	331	361
28	28	59	87	118	148	179	209	240	271	301	332	362
29	29		88	119	149	180	210	241	272	302	333	363
30	30		89	120	150	181	211	242	273	303	334	364
31	31		90		151		212	243		304		365

If the time period extends from one year into a following year, add 365 (days) to the figure obtained in steps 3 and 4 for each year. As in Example 2, add 1 day for each Feb. 29 that is included in the interest period.

Example 3: Find the exact time from Sept. 21 to May 7 of the following year.

(1 and 2) Sept. 21 is 264th day
(3 and 4) May 7 is 127th day. $127 + 365 = 492$ days
(5) $492 - 264 = 228$ days

When the time in days either by 30-day-month time or exact time is known and it is desired to compute ordinary interest (360-day-year basis), a table similar to the one shown on page 136 taken from a more complete set of tables may be used.

To find ordinary simple interest, use the table as follows:

1. Locate the figures at the intersecting point of the column headed by the given rate of interest and given number of days at interest to be found in the left-hand column headed "Time."
2. Move the decimal point in the obtained figures two places to the left (that is, divide by 100) to find the interest on $1 and then multiply by the given principal.

The obtained product is the required interest.

Thus to find the ordinary interest on $1,000 for 27 days at 5 per cent, locate the figures .3750; move the decimal point two places to the left to obtain .003750; and multiply by $1,000. The product $3.75 is the required interest.

Example 1: Find the ordinary interest on $550.85 for 103 days at $4\frac{1}{2}$ per cent.

3 months or 90 days: 1.1250
13 days: .1625
103 days: 1.2875

Interest on $1 for 103 days at $4\frac{1}{2}\% = \$1.2875 \div 100 = \$.012875$
Interest required $= \$.012875 \times 550.85 = \$7.09$

Example 2: Find the ordinary interest on $706.50 at exact time from July 23 to Oct. 15 at 7 per cent.

From the time table: $288 - 204 = 84$ days
2 months or 60 days: 1.1667
24 days: .4667
84 days: 1.6334

Interest on $1 for 84 days at $7\% = \$1.6334 \div 100 = \$.016334$
Interest required $= \$.016334 \times 706.50 = \$11.54$

Table of Ordinary Simple Interest on $100

(360-day-year basis—for either 30-day-month or exact time)

Time	3%	$3\frac{1}{2}$%	4%	$4\frac{1}{2}$%	5%	$5\frac{1}{2}$%	6%	$6\frac{1}{2}$%	7%
1 da.	.0083	.0097	.0111	.0125	.0139	.0153	.0167	.0181	.0194
2 da.	.0167	.0194	.0222	.0250	.0278	.0306	.0333	.0361	.0389
3 da.	.0250	.0292	.0333	.0375	.0417	.0458	.0500	.0542	.0583
4 da.	.0333	.0389	.0444	.0500	.0556	.0611	.0667	.0722	.0778
5 da.	.0417	.0486	.0556	.0625	.0694	.0764	.0833	.0903	.0972
6 da.	.0500	.0583	.0667	.0750	.0833	.0917	.1000	.1083	.1167
7 da.	.0583	.0681	.0778	.0875	.0972	.1069	.1167	.1264	.1361
8 da.	.0667	.0778	.0889	.1000	.1111	.1222	.1333	.1444	.1556
9 da.	.0750	.0875	.1000	.1125	.1250	.1375	.1500	.1625	.1750
10 da.	.0833	.0972	.1111	.1250	.1389	.1528	.1667	.1806	.1944
11 da.	.0917	.1069	.1222	.1375	.1528	.1681	.1833	.1986	.2139
12 da.	.1000	.1167	.1333	.1500	.1667	.1833	.2000	.2167	.2333
13 da.	.1083	.1264	.1444	.1625	.1806	.1986	.2167	.2347	.2528
14 da.	.1167	.1361	.1556	.1750	.1944	.2139	.2333	.2528	.2722
15 da.	.1250	.1458	.1667	.1875	.2083	.2292	.2500	.2708	.2917
16 da.	.1333	.1556	.1778	.2000	.2222	.2444	.2667	.2889	.3111
17 da.	.1417	.1653	.1889	.2125	.2361	.2597	.2833	.3069	.3306
18 da.	.1500	.1750	.2000	.2250	.2500	.2750	.3000	.3250	.3500
19 da.	.1583	.1847	.2111	.2375	.2639	.2903	.3167	.3431	.3694
20 da.	.1667	.1944	.2222	.2500	.2778	.3056	.3333	.3611	.3889
21 da.	.1750	.2042	.2333	.2625	.2917	.3208	.3500	.3792	.4083
22 da.	.1833	.2139	.2444	.2750	.3056	.3361	.3667	.3972	.4278
23 da.	.1917	.2236	.2556	.2875	.3194	.3514	.3833	.4153	.4472
24 da.	.2000	.2333	.2667	.3000	.3333	.3667	.4000	.4333	.4667
25 da.	.2083	.2431	.2778	.3125	.3472	.3819	.4167	.4514	.4861
26 da.	.2167	.2528	.2889	.3250	.3611	.3972	.4333	.4694	.5056
27 da.	.2250	.2625	.3000	.3375	.3750	.4125	.4500	.4875	.5250
28 da.	.2333	.2722	.3111	.3500	.3889	.4278	.4667	.5056	.5444
29 da.	.2417	.2819	.3222	.3625	.4028	.4431	.4833	.5236	.5639
1 mo.	.2500	.2917	.3333	.3750	.4167	.4583	.5000	.5417	.5833
2 mo.	.5000	.5833	.6667	.7500	.8333	.9167	1.0000	1.0833	1.1667
3 mo.	.7500	.8750	1.0000	1.1250	1.2500	1.3750	1.5000	1.6250	1.7500
4 mo.	1.0000	1.1667	1.3333	1.5000	1.6667	1.8333	2.0000	2.1667	2.3333
5 mo.	1.2500	1.4583	1.6667	1.8750	2.0833	2.2917	2.5000	2.7083	2.9160
6 mo.	1.5000	1.7500	2.0000	2.2500	2.5000	2.7500	3.0000	3.2500	3.5070

EXERCISE 4

Solve the following by the use of the tables on pages 134 and 136.

A. Find the ordinary interest on the following. Use 30-*day-month time* when dates are given.

1. \$800 at 6% for 26 days
2. \$555.25 at 5% for 97 days
3. \$406.60 at $4\frac{1}{2}$ % for 235 days
4. \$56.75 at 3% for 113 days
5. \$2,144 at $6\frac{1}{2}$ %, May 8 to Aug. 2
6. \$2,863.36 at $3\frac{1}{2}$ %, Apr. 7 to Aug. 9
7. \$6,804.32 at $5\frac{1}{2}$ %, July 28 to Sept. 6
8. \$2,746.54 at 7%, Feb. 13 to June 22

B. Find the ordinary interest on the following at *exact time:*

1. \$65 at 6%, May 8 to July 14
2. \$530 at 4%, Nov. 12 to Apr. 7
3. \$80.35 at 7%, Mar. 2 to Aug. 2
4. \$109 at 5%, Dec. 23 to Mar. 8
5. \$214.75 at $5\frac{1}{2}$ %, May 1 to Oct. 3
6. \$220.44 at $4\frac{1}{2}$ %, Sept. 17 to Dec. 2
7. \$728 at 3%, Feb. 10, 1960 to Mar. 29, 1960
8. \$543.63 at $3\frac{1}{2}$ %, Apr. 8, 1964 to Dec. 4, 1964

C. Solve the following:

1. Phelps and Co., manufacturers, charge 5 per cent ordinary interest computed at exact time on overdue bills. Find the sum necessary to pay in full a bill for \$1,875 due on Jan. 18, 1956, but not paid until June 13.
2. A note dated Mar. 21 for \$2,260 is due in 2 months at 4 per cent ordinary interest. Find the maturity value (*a*) at 30-day-month time and (*b*) at exact time.
3. On Sept. 23, a student borrowed \$135 at $4\frac{1}{2}$ per cent ordinary interest in order to pay his tuition. During the Christmas holidays he worked and saved enough to pay in full both debt and interest on Jan. 6. Compute the interest charge (*a*) at 30-day-month time and (*b*) at exact time.
4. The annual tax on a piece of property owned by Mr. McMillan is 7.52 per cent of its assessed value of \$8,350. Taxes are due in two equal payments, the first

on Dec. 5 and the second on Apr. 20. Overdue payments are charged $5\frac{1}{2}$ per cent ordinary interest computed at exact time. If Mr. McMillan makes his first payment on Dec. 31 and his second payment on June 23, find his total payment for the tax year.

5. Mr. Albert Petersen, a masonry contractor, made a short term business loan of $8,460 from his bank. If the bank charged him 4 per cent ordinary interest computed at exact time and he borrowed the money on Jan. 12, 1964, and paid the loan in full with interest on May 18 of the same year, how much did he pay (*a*) in interest and (*b*) at maturity?

UNIT 5. Reverse Operations in Simple Interest

As you know, problems in simple interest are much the same as problems in percentage, with the exception of the added element *time*. The generally accepted symbols used in expressing interest formulas are as follows:

I = interest in dollars
P = principal (or face) in dollars
S = maturity value or amount (principal + interest) in dollars
n = time at interest in years
i = rate of interest per annum (expressed decimally)
1 = 100% of principal expressed decimally

Derivation of Essential Formulas Used in Simple Interest. By definition, the basic formulas for interest and maturity value are as follows:

$$I = Pni \qquad S = P + I$$

From the preceding, the following may be derived:

$$P = \frac{I}{ni} \qquad P = S - I$$

$$n = \frac{I}{Pi} \qquad I = S - P$$

$$i = \frac{I}{Pn}$$

By substitution of Pni for I:

$$\begin{aligned} \text{If } S &= P + I \\ \text{then } S &= P + Pni \\ &= P(1 + ni) \\ \text{and } P &= \frac{S}{1 + ni} \end{aligned}$$

Summarizing of Formulas and Examples. Although a number of other formulas may be derived, the preceding include all those fundamental to the solving of most problems in simple interest. These essential formulas together with examples of their use are recapitulated for your convenience as follows:

To find interest: — *Examples:*

1. $I = Pni$

Let $P = \$600$, time $= 180$ days, $i = 6\%$

$$\text{then } I = \$600 \times \frac{180}{360} \times \frac{6}{100} = \$18$$

2. $I = S - P$

Let $S = \$240$, $P = \$195$

then $I = \$240 - \$195 = \$45$

To find time in years: — *Example:*

$$n = \frac{I}{Pi}$$

Let $I = \$110.25$, $P = \$1{,}500$, $i = 6\%$

$$\text{then } n = \frac{\$110.25}{\$1{,}500 \times \frac{6}{100}} = 1.225 \text{ years}$$

To convert n to days at ordinary interest:

$$\begin{aligned} 1 \text{ year} &= 360 \text{ days} \\ n &= 360 \times 1.225 = 441 \text{ days} \\ \text{or } n &= 360 + (360 \times .225) = 360 + 81 = 441 \text{ days} \end{aligned}$$

To convert n to years, months, and days at ordinary interest at 30-day-month time:

$$\begin{aligned} 1 \text{ year} &= 360 \text{ days} \\ 1 \text{ month} &= 30 \text{ days} \\ n &= 1.225 = 1 \text{ year} + .225 \text{ year} \\ &= 1 \text{ year} + (360 \times .225) = 1 \text{ year} + 81 \text{ days} \\ &= 1 \text{ year} + \frac{81}{30} = 1 \text{ year} + 2 \text{ months} + 21 \text{ days} \end{aligned}$$

Since the time period in ordinary interest problems is likely to be for a fractional part of a year (usually less than 6 months), it is generally desirable to find the time in days directly by modification of the formula to find the time in years. Thus:

$$\text{Time in days} = \frac{I \times 360}{Pi}$$

and the preceding example is solved:

$$\frac{\$110.25 \times 360}{\$1{,}500 \times \frac{6}{100}} = 441 \text{ days}$$

The time in days may then be reduced to years, months, and days at 30-day-month time as follows:

$$\frac{441}{360} = 1 \text{ year } 81 \text{ days}$$

$$\frac{81}{30} = 2 \text{ months } 21 \text{ days}$$

and the answer in years, months, and days: 1 yr. 2 mo. 21 da.

To find rate of interest: (in decimals):

$$i = \frac{I}{Pn}$$

Example:

Let $I = \$3.75$, $P = \$450$, time $= 60$ days

$$\text{then } i = \frac{\$3.75}{\$450 \times \frac{60}{360}} = .05 = 5\%$$

To find principal:

Examples:

1. $P = \dfrac{I}{ni}$

Let $I = \$9$, $n = 4$, $i = 4\frac{1}{2}\%$

$$\text{then } P = \frac{\$9}{4 \times \frac{45}{1000}} = \$50$$

2. $P = S - I$

Let $S = \$156$, $I = \$6$
then $P = \$156 - \$6 = \$150$

3. $P = \dfrac{S}{1 + ni}$

Let $S = \$244.80$, time $= 3$ months, $i = 8\%$

$$\text{then } P = \frac{\$244.80}{1 + \left(\frac{90}{360} \times \frac{8}{100}\right)} = \$240$$

To find maturity value:

Examples:

1. $S = P + I$

Let $P = \$425$, $I = \$36$
then $S = \$425 + \$36 = \$461$

2. $S = P + Pni$

Let $P = \$420$, time $= 135$ days, $i = 8\%$

$$\text{then } S = \$420 + \left(420 \times \frac{135}{360} \times \frac{8}{100}\right) = \$432.60$$

For purposes of consistent illustration in the preceding examples, both time and rate of interest have been expressed as common fractions and the use of the cancellation method is indicated. In many instances decimal fractions, the use of the 60-day, 6 per cent method, the use of the product method, or the use of simple interest tables will provide easier solution.

All of the preceding formulas may be applied to problems in accurate (exact) interest with the symbol n representing the actual number of days (exact time) at interest and a calendar year base of 365 days.

EXERCISE 5A

A. Find the time in days:

	Principal	*Maturity value*	*Ordinary interest*	*Rate, %*
1.	$ 620		$ 6.82	6
2.	810		16.74	4
3.	3,340	$4,275.20		8
4.		85.22	.87	4

B. Solve the following:

1. Mr. Arden paid $203.50 ordinary interest at exact time due on his $7\frac{1}{2}$ per cent note for $5,280. Find the time in days for which interest was paid.
2. A student borrowed $315 at 5 per cent ordinary interest at 30-day-month time in order to pay his tuition charges. At a later date he was unable to make any payment on the principal, but he did pay $34.65, the interest due at that time. How many years, months, and days had elapsed before he made the interest payment?
3. A borrower of $1,725 at 3 per cent ordinary interest cleared his debt and interest due with a payment of $1,796.01. At 30-day-month time, for how many years, months, and days did he have the use of the lender's money?

C. Find the per cent rate of ordinary interest charged on the following notes:

	Principal	*Maturity value*	*Ordinary interest*	*Time in days*
1.	$2,200		$ 39.60	108
2.	2,120		188.44	400
3.	320	$331.08		277
4.		571.36	6.36	135

D. Solve the following:

1. A borrower of $600 made an interest payment of $16.65 due at the end of 222 days. Find the per cent rate of ordinary interest at exact time paid by the borrower.
2. Three months and 27 days after Mr. Kilmer borrowed $427.60, he paid his note in full and ordinary interest at 30-day-month time due in an amount totaling $432.46. Find the per cent rate of interest that was charged Mr. Kilmer.
3. Mr. Saylor paid $48.06 ordinary interest at exact time due for the use of $856.50 for 202 days. What per cent rate of interest did he pay?

EXERCISE 5B

A. Find (*a*) the principal and then (*b*) the maturity value in the following:

	Ordinary interest	*Time in days*	*Rate, %*
1.	$ 20.29	333	4
2.	162.53	788	$4\frac{1}{2}$
3.	6.78	93	$7\frac{1}{2}$
4.	6.99	68	5

B. Solve the following:

1. After 264 days, Mr. Joyce made an ordinary interest payment of $16.81 due on his 3 per cent note. How much was the principal?
2. On the due date, the ordinary interest at 30-day-month time owed after 1 year, 5 months, and 11 days on a 6 per cent note was $322.99. Find the maturity value.
3. Mr. Warren received $23.98 ordinary interest at exact time due after 285 days on a loan that he had made to a friend. If the interest rate was $3\frac{1}{2}$ per cent, how much did he lend his friend?

C. Find the principal on the following notes at ordinary interest:

	Maturity value	*Time in days*	*Rate, %*
1.	$ 141.97	193	2
2.	621.27	424	$4\frac{1}{2}$
3.	649.71	91	6
4.	8,268.08	249	3

D. Solve the following:

1. A bank made a 74-day loan at $1\frac{1}{2}$ per cent ordinary interest at exact time, receiving at maturity an amount of $9,331.81. How much was the principal?
2. One year, 10 months, and 6 days after Mr. Lippitt borrowed some money at 8 per cent ordinary interest at 30-day-month time, he paid off his note in full, including interest due, with a check for $4,018. How much did he borrow?
3. Mr. O'Shaughnessy borrowed some money at 5 per cent ordinary interest at exact time in order to pay cash for some furniture. He cleared the note in full, including the interest due, 67 days later with a payment of $254.43. How much did he borrow?

CHAPTER IV

BANK DISCOUNT, PRESENT VALUE, PARTIAL PAYMENTS, AND PERIODIC PAYMENT PLANS

UNIT 1. Bank Discount: Finding Discount and Proceeds of Non-interest-bearing Notes

Bank discount is the interest on the amount due at maturity for the exact number of days following the discount date to and including the maturity date.

The difference between bank discount and interest is due to the fact that in bank discount the interest charge is based on an amount (principal + interest, if any) and is collected in advance (in cash or as part of a negotiable discounted note), whereas in interest (true discount) the interest charge is based on a principal and is not collected in advance.

If a businessman needs cash to meet current obligations, he may borrow the money from his bank, giving the bank his personal note. Consider the following examples of *notes payable* (Figs. 1 and 2) by a private party to a bank. (From the point of view of the bank, these are notes receivable.)

Example 1: Note payable at interest (Fig. 1).

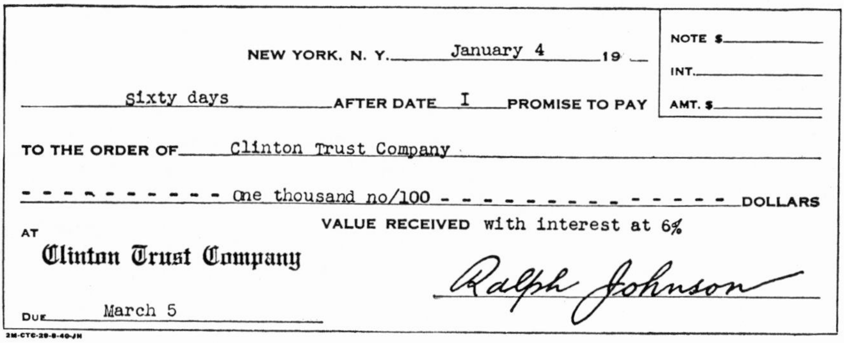

NEW YORK, N. Y. January 4 19__

Sixty days AFTER DATE I PROMISE TO PAY

TO THE ORDER OF Clinton Trust Company

One thousand no/100 DOLLARS

VALUE RECEIVED with interest at 6%

AT Clinton Trust Company

Ralph Johnson

DUE March 5

NOTE $

INT.

AMT. $

2M-CTC-28-8-40-JH

FIG. 1.

Example 2: Discounted note payable (Fig. 2).

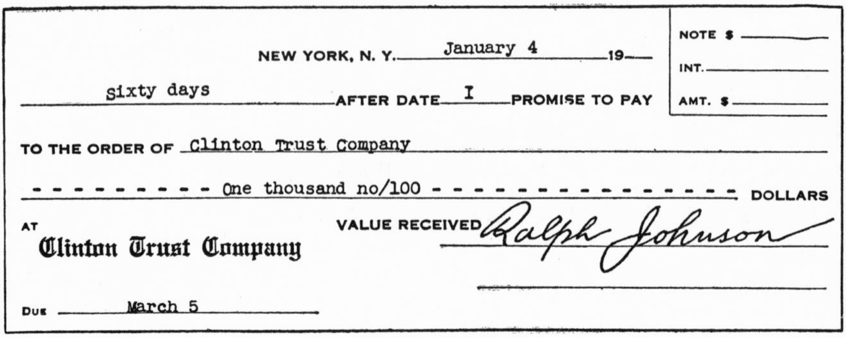

NEW YORK, N. Y. January 4 19__	NOTE $
Sixty days AFTER DATE I PROMISE TO PAY	INT.
	AMT. $

TO THE ORDER OF Clinton Trust Company

- - - - - - - - - - One thousand no/100 - - - - - - - - - - - - - - - - DOLLARS

AT Clinton Trust Company VALUE RECEIVED Ralph Johnson

DUE March 5

FIG. 2.

In Example 1, Ralph Johnson has given a promissory note for \$1,000 with interest at 6 per cent, due in 60 days. Thus *on Mar.* 5, the amount due is

$$\$1,000 + \$10 = \$1,010$$

And Johnson *pays* \$10 interest *after using* \$1,000 for 60 days.

In Example 2, Ralph Johnson has given a promissory note for \$1,000. If it is discounted at 6 per cent, he receives *on Jan.* 4:

$$\$1,000 - \$10 = \$990$$

And Johnson *borrows* \$10 *in advance* to pay for the use of \$990 for 60 days. (Of course, if he preferred, he could pay the \$10 discount in cash out of his own pocket instead of deducting it from the face of the note. He would then receive \$1,000.)

At one time, it was general bank practice to discount almost all personal promissory notes. Today, many banks make it a practice to charge interest rather than discount on loans of this type.

A businessman will frequently accept a note from a customer in payment of merchandise or in settlement of an account. In such a case, the businessman has two options: (1) He may hold the note until maturity (date when due) and then collect it directly from the maker or deposit it with his bank for collection; (2) he may take the note immediately, or at any time prior to maturity, to his bank for discounting. This latter practice, known as the discounting of commercial paper, is the most frequent use of bank discount.

Consider the following examples of *notes receivable* (Figs. 3 and 4):

Example 1: Non-interest-bearing note receivable (Fig. 3).

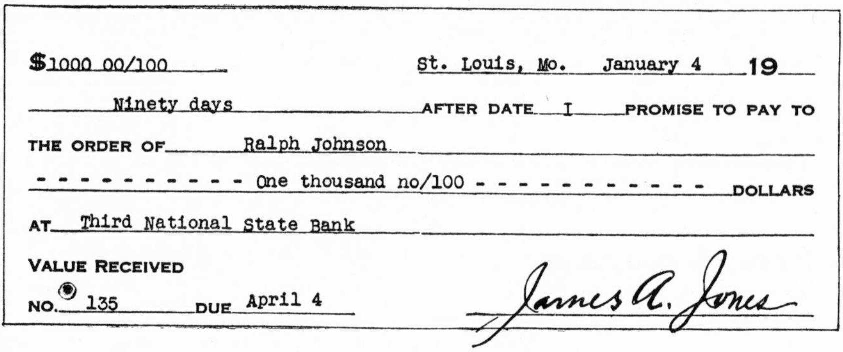

$1000 00/100 St. Louis, Mo. January 4 19

Ninety days AFTER DATE I PROMISE TO PAY TO

THE ORDER OF Ralph Johnson

- - - - - - - - - - - One thousand no/100 - - - - - - - - - - - DOLLARS

AT Third National State Bank

VALUE RECEIVED

NO. 135 DUE April 4 James A. Jones

FIG. 3.

Example 2: Interest-bearing note receivable (Fig. 4).

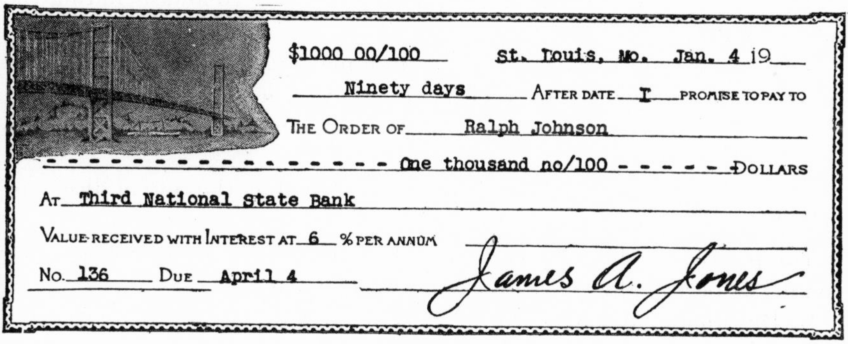

$1000 00/100 St. Louis, Mo. Jan. 4 19

Ninety days AFTER DATE I PROMISE TO PAY TO

THE ORDER OF Ralph Johnson

- - - - - - - - - - - - - - - - - One thousand no/100 - - - - - DOLLARS

AT Third National State Bank

VALUE RECEIVED WITH INTEREST AT 6 % PER ANNUM

No. 136 DUE April 4 James A. Jones

FIG. 4.

The preceding are examples of *notes receivable* to the *payee*, Ralph Johnson, because they are made in his favor and he is to receive payment. The *maker* is James A. Jones. To him, these are *notes payable.*

Example 1 (Fig. 3) is a non-interest-bearing note, and the maturity value on Apr. 4 is $1,000, the same as the face.

Example 2 (Fig. 4) is an interest-bearing note, and the maturity value (or new face) on Apr. 4 is $1,000 plus interest at 6 per cent for 90 days:

$$\$1,000 + \$15 = \$1,015$$

And Jones is obligated to pay to the holder of the note on Apr. 4 the sum of $1,015.

If such a note is endorsed by the payee and accepted by (sold to) his bank for collection or discount, he will be held liable by the bank in the event that the maker fails to meet the obligation when it is due. In such an instance, the bank which has accepted the endorsement will charge back the maturity value of the note to the account of the individual for whom the note was discounted.

Terminology of Bank Discount. The *date* of a note is the date on which it is written (also known as the date of origin).

The *maturity date* (or due date) is the date on which the note is due and payable.

The *discount date* is the date on which the note is discounted (sold).

The *discount term* is the exact number of days, following the date of discount to and including the maturity date, for which bank discount (equivalent to interest on the maturity value) is charged.

The *face* of the note is the number of dollars and cents for which the note is written.

The *maturity value* of a non-interest-bearing note is the same as the face.

The *maturity value* of an interest-bearing note is the sum of the face plus interest based on the face, the time, and the rate of interest.

The *time* of a note is the time following the date to and including the maturity date.

The *discount rate* is the per cent per annum charge for discounting, computed on the maturity value and the discount term (the year expressed as a fraction with the exact number of days for a numerator and 360 days for a denominator).

The *discount* is the product of the maturity value, the rate of discount, and the term of discount.

The *proceeds* is the sum realized by the seller of the note after the discount has been deducted from the maturity value.

To Determine Maturity Date. Any note that falls due on a Sunday (or a Saturday in many states) or on a legal holiday matures on the next business day with interest charged for the additional time. Thus a 60-day note that matures on a Saturday, July 4 (a legal holiday), would be considered as maturing on Monday, July 6. The maker of the note may avoid this situation, if he so desires, by making the note either a 62-day note or a 59-day note that would mature Friday, July 3.

If the time of the note is stipulated as a number of days, *e.g.*, 30 days, 60 days, 90 days, 120 days, etc., the maturity date is that exact number of days after the date of the note (with the exceptions indicated in the previous paragraph).

If the time of the note is stipulated in months, *e.g.*, 1 month, 2 months, 3 months, etc., the maturity date is that number of months to the same date of the maturity month as the date of the month in which the note was written. If there be not the required number of days in the maturity month, the maturity date is the *last day* of the maturity month.

Thus a 30-day note dated Jan. 31 would mature Mar. 2. But a 1-month note dated Jan. 31 (or Jan. 28, 29, 30) would mature Feb. 28. (During a leap year, of course, a 30-day note dated Jan. 31 would mature Mar. 1, and a 1-month note dated Jan. 29, 30, or 31 would mature on Feb. 29.)

To Determine the Term of Discount. The term of discount is found by counting the *exact* number of days following the date the note is presented for discount to and including the maturity date. The actual number of days is always counted *regardless* of whether the maturity date of the note has been determined by exact time (when the time is stipulated in days) or by 30-day-month time (when the time is stipulated in months).

Thus a note discounted on May 30 that matures on June 30 has a term of discount of 31 days; a note discounted on Aug. 15 maturing on Sept. 25 has a term of discount of 41 days; and a note discounted on Sept. 20 maturing on Oct. 15 has a term of discount of 25 days.

To Find Discount and Proceeds of a Non-interest-bearing Note. The proceeds of a non-interest-bearing note is equal to the maturity value (face) less the discount computed on the maturity value at the discount rate for the exact number of days following the discount date to and including the maturity date.

The methods used to find discount or proceeds on either non-interest-bearing or interest-bearing notes may be expressed by the same formulas:

Let D = bank discount in dollars
P = proceeds in dollars[1]
n = term of discount (time in years)
d = rate of discount per annum

S = maturity value in dollars $\begin{cases} \text{face on a non-interest-bearing note} \\ \text{face + interest on an interest-bearing note} \end{cases}$

$$\text{Then } D = Snd$$
$$P = S - D$$

Example 1: A non-interest-bearing note. A \$2,400, 92-day non-interest-bearing note dated May 15 is discounted on June 16 at 5 per cent. Find (*a*) the due date, (*b*) the maturity value, (*c*) the term of the discount, (*d*) the bank discount, and (*e*) the proceeds.

(*a*) 92 days following May 15 is Aug. 15.

(*b*) Since maturity value equals face, it is \$2,400.

(*c*) The exact time (actual number of days) following June 16 to and including Aug. 15 = 60 days.

[1] Note that in this text P is used to symbolize both principal at interest and proceeds at bank discount. This should not be confusing in formulas because *principal* at interest is determined by the presence of I or i in the formulas, while *proceeds* at bank discount is determined by the presence of D or d in the formulas.

(*d*) $$D = \$2{,}400 \times \frac{60}{360} \times \frac{5}{100} = \$20$$

(*e*) $$P = \$2{,}400 - \$20 = \$2{,}380$$

Example 2: A non-interest-bearing note. A $1,000, 4-month non-interest-bearing note dated Mar. 25 is discounted on Apr. 26 at 6 per cent. Find (*a*) the maturity date, (*b*) the maturity value, (*c*) the discount term, (*d*) the bank discount, and (*e*) the proceeds.

(*a*) The due date is the same date of the fourth month following Mar. 25: July 25.

(*b*) The maturity value is the same as the face, or $1,000.

(*c*) The term is the exact number of days following Apr. 26 to and including July 25 = 90 days.

(*d*) $$D = \$1{,}000 \times \frac{90}{360} \times \frac{6}{100} = \$15$$

(*e*) $$P = \$1{,}000 - \$15 = \$985$$

EXERCISE 1

A. The following non-interest-bearing notes were discounted by a bank. For each, **find** (*a*) due date, (*b*) maturity value, (*c*) term of discount, (*d*) bank discount, and (*e*) proceeds.

Note no.	Date	Face	Time	Discount rate, %	Discount date
1	1/3	$200	3 mo.	6	2/2
2	2/7	$325	2 mo.	6	3/5
3	6/13	$700	30 da.	4	6/25
4	3/8	$1,250	9 mo.	5	7/14
5	12/23	$575	60 da.	$4\frac{1}{2}$	12/26
6	7/16	$800	90 da.	$7\frac{1}{2}$	7/31

B. Solve the following problems in bank discount:

1. A manufacturer sold on date of origin to his bank, at 4 per cent bank discount, a 90-day non-interest-bearing note for $1,212.12 that he had received from a wholesaler. Find (*a*) bank discount and (*b*) proceeds.
2. On May 12, the bank discounted at 3 per cent a non-interest-bearing note for $930, dated May 7 and payable in 30 days, that Mr. Marsh had received from a customer. Find (*a*) the discount charge made by the bank and (*b*) the proceeds received by Mr. Marsh.
3. Mr. Ziegler took a non-interest-bearing note that he held to a moneylender, who agreed to discount the note at 8 per cent. If the discount date was

Nov. 4 and the note was a 180-day, $10,000 note dated Aug. 20, find (*a*) the bank discount and (*b*) the proceeds received by Mr. Ziegler.

4. On July 18, the bank discounted at 7 per cent a non-interest-bearing note for $100, dated Apr. 19 and payable in 92 days, that Mr. Harper had received from a customer. What proceeds did Mr. Harper receive?
5. Mr. Bean took a non-interest-bearing note that he held to a moneylender, who agreed to discount the note at 9 per cent. If the discount date was May 17 and the note was a 60-day, $150 note dated May 11, how much did Mr. Bean receive from the moneylender?
6. On Oct. 18, to obtain cash so that he might anticipate some bills, Mr. Sargent, a small manufacturer, took to his bank a 2-month, non-interest-bearing note for $1,000, dated Oct. 5, that he had accepted from a customer. If the bank discounted the note at $4\frac{1}{2}$ per cent, how much was credited to Mr. Sargent's checking account?

UNIT 2. Bank Discount: Finding Discount and Proceeds of Interest-bearing Notes

Since the face of an interest-bearing note and its maturity value are not the same, the first step in computing bank discount and/or proceeds is to determine the maturity value.

The *maturity value* of an interest-bearing note is its face plus interest on the face.

The *time* of an interest-bearing note determines *only* the date of maturity. It is the time (number of days or months) following the date of origin to and including the date of maturity. Take special note that even though the time *on an interest-bearing note* may be stated in months, *the actual number of days* following the date of origin to and including the due date *is counted in determining the time at interest* if it is discounted at a bank.

The *interest rate* is the per cent per annum charge based on the face, exact number of days (numerator), and a 360-day year (denominator), which is added to the face in determining the maturity value. It applies only to an interest-bearing note and must be stipulated on the note.

The *interest* is the product of the face, the rate of interest, and the exact time at interest.

Once the interest has been determined, it is added to the face to determine the maturity value. Using the same symbols and formulas as those given for finding interest and maturity value (page 120) and for finding bank discount and proceeds (page 147), to find discount and proceeds of an interest-bearing note, proceed as follows:

1. $I = Pni$
2. $S = P + I$
3. $D = Snd$
4. $P = S - D$

Example 1: An interest-bearing note. A \$1,000, 120-day, 4 per cent interest-bearing note dated Mar. 25 is discounted on Apr. 26 at 5 per cent. Find (*a*) due date, (*b*) time at interest, (*c*) interest, (*d*) maturity value, (*e*) term of the discount, (*f*) bank discount, and (*g*) proceeds.

(*a*) The due date is 120 days following Mar. 25 = July 23.

(*b*) The time at interest is 120 days.

(*c*) $$I = \$1{,}000 \times \frac{120}{360} \times \frac{4}{100} = \$13.33$$

(*d*) $$S = \$1{,}000 + \$13.33 = \$1{,}013.33$$

(*e*) The term of discount is the exact number of days after Apr. 26 to and including July 23 = 88 days.

(*f*) $$D = \$1{,}013.33 \times \frac{88}{360} \times \frac{5}{100} = \$12.39$$

(*g*) $$P = \$1{,}013.33 - \$12.39 = \$1{,}000.94$$

Example 2: An interest-bearing note. A \$720, 2-month, 6 per cent, interest-bearing note dated June 15 is discounted on July 1 at 9 per cent. Find (*a*) maturity date, (*b*) time at interest, (*c*) interest, (*d*) amount due at maturity, (*e*) discount term, (*f*) bank discount, and (*g*) proceeds.

(*a*) The maturity date is 2 months after June 15 = Aug. 15.

(*b*) But the time at interest is exact time = 61 days (*the actual number of days*).

(*c*) $$I = \$720 \times \frac{61}{360} \times \frac{6}{100} = \$7.32$$

(*d*) $$S = \$720 + \$7.32 = \$727.32$$

(*e*) The discount term is the actual number of days after July 1 to and including Aug. 15 = 45 days.

(*f*) $$D = \$727.32 \times \frac{45}{360} \times \frac{9}{100} = \$8.18$$

(*g*) $$P = \$727.32 - \$8.18 = \$719.14$$

EXERCISE 2

A. The following ordinary interest-bearing notes were discounted by a bank. For each, **find** (*a*) due date, (*b*) actual number of days at interest, (*c*) interest, (*d*) maturity value, (*e*) discount term, (*f*) bank discount, (*g*) proceeds.

Note number	Date	Face	Time	Interest rate, %	Discount rate, %	Discount date
1	Dec. 7	$451	180 da.	6	6	Apr. 12
2	May 21	$927	2 mo.	7	4	July 18
3	Jan. 16	$743	120 da.	$7\frac{1}{2}$	5	May 2
4	Feb. 19	$297	6 mo.	6	$4\frac{1}{2}$	Feb. 19
5	Mar. 9	$375	90 da.	4	3	Apr. 24
6	Apr. 12	$840.50	3 mo.	$4\frac{1}{2}$	6	May 14

B. Solve the following problems in bank discount:

1. On Oct. 31, James Robley took a $698, $4\frac{1}{2}$ per cent ordinary interest-bearing, 30-day note dated Oct. 30 to his bank where it was discounted at 5 per cent. Find (*a*) maturity value, (*b*) bank discount, and (*c*) proceeds received by James Robley.
2. On Feb. 11, a customer gave a 6-month, 8 per cent ordinary interest-bearing note with a face of $1,691.50 to Ben Celli. Seven days later, Ben Celli took the note to his bank, where it was discounted by $4\frac{1}{2}$ per cent. Find (*a*) maturity value, (*b*) bank discount, and (*c*) proceeds received by Ben Celli.
3. On Sept. 14, a manufacturer sold to his bank a 120-day, 6 per cent ordinary interest-bearing note with a face of $612 and dated Aug. 5. If the bank charged 5 per cent bank discount, find the proceeds received by the manufacturer.
4. In order that he might obtain some ready cash, Mr. Evans on June 22 took a 6 per cent ordinary interest-bearing note to a loan agency, where it was discounted at 8 per cent. If the face of the note was for $465.35, the time 120 days, and the date of origin May 23, what proceeds did Mr. Evans receive?
5. On Oct. 27, Mr. James took a $349, $7\frac{1}{2}$ per cent ordinary interest-bearing, 2-month note dated Oct. 26 to his bank, where it was discounted at 5 per cent. Find the proceeds received by Mr. James.
6. On June 15, a customer gave a 3-month, $7\frac{1}{2}$ per cent ordinary interest-bearing note with a face of $675.85 to Mr. Werner. Two days later Mr. Werner took the note to his bank, where it was discounted at $5\frac{1}{2}$ per cent. Find the proceeds received by Mr. Werner.

UNIT 3. Present Value at True Discount

True discount is simple interest on the *present value*.[1] It differs from bank discount in that it is equivalent to simple interest paid at maturity

[1] In this text, the words "present worth" and "present value" are used synonymously. Some authorities distinguish them as follows: present worth is equivalent to principal; present value is equivalent to bank proceeds.

on a *principal*, whereas bank discount is equivalent to simple interest paid in advance on an *amount* (principal + interest, if any).

The term "present value" or "present worth" refers to the sum equal to a principal that, if placed at interest today (at present or now), will amount to a required greater sum at a given future time. Thus if $1,000 is required 1 year from now and if money is worth 6 per cent, the present value will be equivalent to the principal ($943.40) which, if placed at 6 per cent interest for one year, will amount to $1,000.

Since bank discount is interest on an amount and true discount is equivalent to interest on a principal, bank discount, if the sum of money obtained be the same, is always more in dollars and cents than true discount, even though the nominal rate of interest or discount may be the same. Stated in another way, if the nominal rate and the dollars-and-cents cost are the same, the proceeds of bank discount will be a lesser sum than the present value at true discount.

The dissimilarity of the cost of bank discount and true discount is equal to the interest on the true discount; that is, the bank discount is greater because interest is charged on the interest. Thus interest plus interest on the interest is equal to bank discount.

The following example will illustrate the two types of discount. It is based on the sum of $1,000 for 1 year at 6 per cent.

$ 1000 Present value +	$ 60 True discount	= $ 1060 Amount
×.06	×.06	×.06
$60.00 True discount +	$3.60 Interest on true discount	= $63.60 Bank discount

Consider the following statements of fact:

1. If bank discount is taken at 6 per cent for 1 year on a maturity value of $1,000, the proceeds would be $1,000 − $60 = $940.

2. If true discount is taken at 6 per cent for 1 year on $1,000, the "proceeds at true discount" would be $1,000 − $56.60 = $943.40.[1]

The sum of $940 is the *proceeds* of a note with maturity value of $1,000, subject to bank discount at 6 per cent for 1 year. Such "proceeds" are equivalent to "discounted present value."

The sum of $943.40 is the *present value* of a note with maturity value of $1,000 subject to true discount (interest) at 6 per cent for 1 year. Such "present value" is equivalent to principal.

[1] The $56.60 is determined by the present value formula, $\frac{S}{1 + ni}$, and

$$\frac{\$1{,}000}{1 + (1 \times .06)} = \frac{\$1{,}000}{1.06} = \$943.40$$

That is, the true discount on $1,000 for 1 year at 6 per cent equals the interest for 1 year at 6 per cent on $943.40.

Proof: $943.40 × 1 × .06 = $56.60, and $943.40 + $56.60 = $1,000

To Find Present Value. The present value of a *non-interest-bearing* (n.i.b.) note is equal to the face (maturity value) of the note divided by $1 plus the interest on $1 at the specified rate of true discount from the date of discount to the maturity date.

The present value of an *interest-bearing* (i.b.) note is equal to the maturity value (face plus interest) of the note divided by $1 plus the interest on $1 at the specified rate of true discount from the date of discount to the maturity date.

Since true discount is equivalent to interest, problems in present value may also be solved in the same manner as any other interest problem. Thus in the formulas for simple interest (page 138) substitute as follows:

True discount	= I, or interest in dollars
Term of true discount	= n, or term (time of discount) in years
Rate of true discount	= i, or rate of interest per annum
Present value	= P, or principal in dollars
Maturity value	= S, or maturity value in dollars
1	= 100% of present value expressed decimally

Then the formula for the present value of either a non-interest-bearing or an interest-bearing note will be

$$P \text{ or present value} = \frac{S}{1 + ni}$$

$$\text{True discount} = S - P$$

Example 1: A non-interest-bearing note. What are the present value and the true discount on Apr. 26 of a $1,000, 4-month non-interest-bearing note dated Mar. 25 at true discount of 6 per cent?

The due date is the same date of the 4th month following the date of origin = July 25. The term of discount is the actual number of days after Apr. 26 to and including July 25 = 90 days.

$$P \text{ or present value} = \frac{\$1{,}000}{1 + \left(\frac{90}{360} \times \frac{6}{100}\right)} = \$985.22$$

$$\text{True discount} = \$1{,}000 - \$985.22 = \$14.78$$

Example 2: An interest-bearing note. Find the present value and true discount on Apr. 26 of a $1,000, 120-day, 4 per cent ordinary interest-bearing note dated Mar. 25 at true discount of 5 per cent.

$$\begin{aligned} S \text{ or maturity value} &= P + Pni \\ &= \$1{,}000 + \left(\$1{,}000 \times \frac{120}{360} \times \frac{4}{100}\right) \\ &= \$1{,}000 + \$13.33 = \$1{,}013.33 \end{aligned}$$

The due date is 120 days after date = July 23. The term of discount is the actual number of days after Apr. 26 to and including July 23 = 88 days.

$$P \text{ or present value} = \frac{\$1{,}013.33}{1 + \left(\frac{88}{360} \times \frac{5}{100}\right)} = \$1{,}001.09$$

$$\text{True discount} = \$1{,}013.33 - \$1{,}001.09 = \$12.24$$

Compare the present value found in the two preceding problems with the proceeds of bank discount in Example 2, page 148, and in Example 1, page 150. As may be seen readily, *proceeds* is determined by charging bank discount, while *present value* is determined by charging simple interest (true discount).

EXERCISE 3

A. **Find** (*a*) the maturity value and as of June 12 (*b*) the proceeds at 6 per cent bank discount and (*c*) the present value at 6 per cent true discount on the following non-interest-bearing notes:

Note no.	*Date*	*Face*	*Time*
1	Apr. 3	\$5,750	3 mo.
2	May 23	830	60 da.

B. **Solve** the following:

1. Find the present value at 6 per cent true discount on June 12 of a 122-day non-interest-bearing note with a face of \$450 and dated Apr. 24.
2. A non-interest-bearing note for 60 days with a face of \$8,000 and dated May 9 is discounted at 5 per cent true discount on May 15. Find (*a*) the present value as of May 15 and (*b*) the true discount.
3. A 5-month, non-interest-bearing note, dated Feb. 14, has a face of \$12,675. Find as of May 12 (*a*) the bank discount at 5 per cent and (*b*) the true discount at 5 per cent.

C. **Find** (*a*) the maturity value and as of July 28 (*b*) the proceeds at 6 per cent bank discount and (*c*) the present value at 6 per cent true discount on the following ordinary interest-bearing notes. NOTE: Compute interest for the exact number of days, even though time at interest is expressed in months.

Note no.	*Date*	*Face*	*Time*	*Interest rate, %*
1	June 28	\$3,500	60 da.	$4\frac{1}{2}$
2	May 13	2,250	4 mo.	$7\frac{1}{2}$

D. Solve the following:

1. Find the present value at 4 per cent true discount on Apr. 17 of a 4 month, 6 per cent ordinary interest-bearing note with a face of $8,900 and dated Mar. 11.
2. At 4 per cent true discount, find as of Aug. 17 (*a*) the present value and (*b*) the true discount on a 90-day, 3 per cent ordinary interest-bearing note with a face of $14,500 and dated Aug. 8.
3. A 72-day, 5 per cent ordinary interest-bearing note, dated July 3, has a face of $1,980. Find as of July 10 (*a*) the bank discount at 6 per cent and (*b*) the true discount at 6 per cent.

UNIT 4. Reverse Operations in Bank Discount

Since bank-discount problems are much the same as simple interest problems (with the exception that bank discount is equivalent to interest paid in advance and based on an amount known as maturity value, whereas interest is paid at maturity and based on a principal), the solution for maturity value, proceeds, discount rate, term of discount, or discount is found in much the same manner as reverse problems in simple interest (see pages 138–140).

The generally accepted symbols used in expressing formulas in bank discount are as follows:[1]

D = bank discount in dollars
P = proceeds (of discounting) in dollars
S = maturity value in dollars $\begin{cases}\text{face on non-interest-bearing note} \\ \text{face + interest on interest-bearing note}\end{cases}$
n = term of discount in years
d = rate of discount per annum expressed decimally
1 = 100% of maturity value expressed decimally

Derivation of Essential Formulas Used in Bank Discount. By definition, the basic formulas for bank discount and proceeds are as follows:

$$D = Snd \qquad P = S - D$$

[1] Take note that in this text P is used to symbolize principal at interest, present value at true discount, and proceeds of bank discount. This should not be confusing in formulas because P at interest (or true discount) is determined by the presence of I or i in the formulas, while P at bank discount is determined by the presence of D or d in the formulas.

From the preceding, the following may be derived:

$$S = \frac{D}{nd} \qquad S = P + D$$

$$n = \frac{D}{Sd} \qquad D = S - P$$

$$d = \frac{D}{Sn}$$

By substitution of Snd for D:

$$\text{If} \quad P = S - D,$$
$$\text{then } P = S - Snd$$
$$= S(1 - nd)$$
$$\text{and } S = \frac{P}{1 - nd}$$

Summarizing of Formulas and Examples. The essential formulas for the solution of problems in bank discount, together with examples of their use, are recapitulated for your convenience as follows:

To find discount: *Examples:*

1. $D = Snd$

Let $S = \$520$, term $= 66$ days, $d = 3\%$

then $D = \$520 \times \frac{66}{360} \times \frac{3}{100} = \$2.86$

2. $D = S - P$

Let $S = \$324$, $P = \$290$

then $D = \$324 - \$290 = \$34$

To find term in years: *Example:*

1. $n = \frac{D}{Sd}$

Let $D = \$3.90$, $S = \$260$, $d = 4\%$

then $d = \dfrac{\$3.90}{\$260 \times \frac{4}{100}} = .375 \text{ year}$

Term in days at exact time $= 360 \times .375 = 135$ days

Since bank discount is rarely for periods of time in excess of a few months, it is generally desirable to find the term in days (always the actual number of days at bank discount) directly by modification of the formula to find the term in years. Thus,

$$\text{Term in days at exact time} = \frac{D \times 360}{Sd}$$

and the preceding example is solved:

$$\frac{\$3.90 \times 360}{\$260 \times \frac{4}{100}} = 135 \text{ days}$$

To find rate of discount (in decimals):

1. $d = \dfrac{D}{Sn}$

Example:

Let $D = \$4.80$, $S = \$640$, term = 54 days

$$\text{then } d = \frac{\$4.80}{\$640 \times \frac{54}{360}} = .05 = 5\%$$

To find proceeds:

1. $P = S - D$

Examples:

Let $S = \$870$, $D = \$120$
Then $P = \$870 - \$120 = \$750$

2. $P = S - Snd$

Let: $S = \$160$, term = 48 days, $d = 6\%$

$$\text{Then } P = \$160 - \left(\$160 \times \frac{48}{360} \times \frac{6}{100}\right) = \$158.72$$

To find maturity value:

1. $S = \dfrac{D}{nd}$

Examples:

Let $D = \$2.50$, term = 30 days, $d = 6\%$

$$\text{then } S = \frac{\$2.50}{\frac{30}{360} \times \frac{6}{100}} = \$500$$

2. $S = P + D$

Let $P = \$560$, $D = \$60$
then $S = \$560 + \$60 = \$620$

3. $S = \dfrac{P}{1 - nd}$

Let $P = \$743.50$, term = 78 days, $d = 4\%$

$$\text{then } S = \frac{\$743.50}{\left(1 - \frac{78}{360} \times \frac{4}{100}\right)} = \$750$$

For the purpose of consistent illustration in the preceding examples, both the term of discount and the rate of discount have been expressed as common fractions, and the use of the cancellation method is indicated. In many instances, the use of decimal fractions or the 60-day, 6 per cent method or the product method will provide easier solution.

EXERCISE 4

Solve the following problems in bank discount:

1. A note with a maturity value of \$7,200 was discounted at 6 per cent. What was the term of discount in days if the discount was \$79.20?
2. If the discount rate was $4\frac{1}{2}$ per cent, for how many days must a non-interest-bearing note for \$1,620 have been discounted if the proceeds were \$1,601.37?
3. A 90-day note for \$2,500, bearing ordinary interest at 4 per cent, was dis-

counted at 6 per cent, the bank discount being \$15.15. What was the term of discount in days?

4. For how many days must a 60-day, \$1,800, 6 per cent ordinary interest-bearing note have been discounted if the discount rate was 4 per cent and the proceeds were \$1,807.90?
5. A note with maturity value of \$2,640 was discounted for 60 days. The discount was \$22. Find the per cent rate of discount.
6. What was the per cent discount rate on a non-interest-bearing note for \$360 if it was discounted for 48 days and yielded proceeds of \$356.40?
7. A discount clerk discounted a 90-day, 4 per cent ordinary interest-bearing note with a face of \$1,080. The term of the discount was 66 days and the discount was \$6. He failed to record the rate of discount. What was the per cent discount rate?
8. A 120-day, 9 per cent ordinary interest-bearing note with a face of \$3,720 was discounted for 84 days and yielded proceeds of \$3,795.84. What was the per cent discount rate?
9. A note, discounted for 69 days at 6 per cent, yielded a discount of \$10.58. What was the maturity value?
10. What was the maturity value of a note, discounted for 45 days at 3 per cent, if the discount was \$3.30?
11. A merchant offers a manufacturer a 72-day, non-interest-bearing note in payment of a debt. What should be the maturity value of the note if the manufacturer is to discount it on date at 5 per cent at his bank and receive proceeds of \$3,608.55?
12. On July 25, a 60-day note, dated July 5, was sold to a bank at $4\frac{1}{2}$ per cent bank discount and yielded proceeds of \$2,417.85. What must have been the maturity value of the note?

UNIT 5. Finding the Face of a Note Yielding a Given Discount or a Given Proceeds

The determination of the face (or principal) of a note that will yield a given bank discount or given proceeds is primarily dependent upon whether the note is (1) non-interest-bearing or (2) interest-bearing.

Non-interest-bearing Note. Since the face and the maturity value (S) of a non-interest-bearing note are the same, the previously derived formulas for finding the maturity value in bank discount problems may be employed:

$$\text{Face} = \frac{D}{nd}$$

$$\text{or Face} = \frac{P}{1 - nd}$$

Example 1: A non-interest-bearing note. Find the face of a non-interest-bearing note if the bank discount is \$1.35, the term of the discount is 30 days, and the rate of discount is $4\frac{1}{2}$ per cent.

$$\text{Face} = \frac{D}{nd}$$

$$= \frac{\$1.35}{\frac{30}{360} \times \frac{45}{1000}} = \$360$$

Example 2: A non-interest-bearing note. Find the face of a non-interest-bearing note if the bank proceeds are \$831.04, the term of the discount is 96 days, and the rate of discount is 4 per cent.

$$\text{Face} = \frac{P}{1 - nd}$$

$$= \frac{\$831.04}{1 - \left(\frac{96}{360} \times \frac{4}{100}\right)} = \$840$$

Interest-bearing Note. Since the maturity value (S) of an interest-bearing note is the sum of the face (or principal) plus interest, the face may be determined by first finding the maturity value and then solving for the face. Essentially such a problem requires a two-step reverse operation in both bank discount and simple interest. Thus:

$$(a)\quad S \text{ or maturity value} = \frac{D}{nd}$$

$$\text{or } S \text{ or maturity value} = \frac{P}{1 - nd}$$

$$(b)\quad \text{Face or principal} = \frac{S}{1 + ni}$$

Example 1: An interest-bearing note. Find the face of a 120-day, 3 per cent interest-bearing note if the bank discount is \$4.04, the term of the discount is 45 days, and the rate of discount is 4 per cent.

$$(a)\quad S = \frac{D}{nd}$$

$$= \frac{\$4.04}{\frac{45}{360} \times \frac{4}{100}} = \$808$$

$$(b)\quad \text{Face} = \frac{S}{1 + ni}$$

$$= \frac{\$808}{1 + \left(\frac{120}{360} \times \frac{3}{100}\right)} = \$800$$

Example 2: An interest-bearing note. Find the face of a 72-day, 5 per cent interest-bearing note if the proceeds of bank discounting are \$597.92, the term of the discount is 60 days, and the rate of discount is 8 per cent.

$$(a) \qquad S = \frac{P}{1 - nd}$$

$$= \frac{\$597.92}{1 - \left(\frac{60}{360} \times \frac{8}{100}\right)} = \$606$$

$$(b) \text{ Face} = \frac{S}{1 + ni}$$

$$= \frac{\$606}{1 + \left(\frac{72}{360} \times \frac{5}{100}\right)} = \$600$$

If the immediately preceding formulas used to find the face of a note that will yield a given proceeds or a given discount seem too complex or too cumbersome, perhaps the following method of procedure will be more desirable for you:

Divide the given discount (or proceeds) by the discount (or proceeds) of a note with a face of \$1 and all the other elements the same as that of the note to yield the given discount (or proceeds).

Thus in solving the immediately preceding problems:

Example 1: A non-interest-bearing note.

\$1.00 Maturity value
.00375 Discount on \$1 for 30 days at $4\frac{1}{2}\%$

$$\text{Face} = \frac{\$1.35}{.00375} = \$360$$

Example 2: A non-interest-bearing note.

\$1.00	Maturity value
$-.010\frac{2}{3}$	Discount on \$1 for 96 days at 4%
\$ $.989\frac{1}{3}$	Proceeds on \$1

$$\text{Face} = \frac{\$831.04}{.989\frac{1}{3}} = \frac{\$2{,}493.12}{2.968} = \$840$$

Example 1: An interest-bearing note.

$1.00	Face
.01	Interest on $1 for 120 days at 3%
$1.01	Maturity value
.00505	Discount on $1.01 for 45 days at 4%

$$\text{Face} = \frac{\$4.04}{.00505} = \$800$$

Example 2: An interest-bearing note.

$1.00	Face
.01	Interest for 72 days on $1 at 5%
$1.01	Maturity value
$-.0134\frac{2}{3}$	Discount on $1.01 for 60 days at 8%
$ $.9965\frac{1}{3}$	Proceeds on $1

$$\text{Face} = \frac{\$597.92}{.9965\frac{1}{3}} = \frac{\$1793.76}{2.9896} = \$600$$

EXERCISE 5

Solve the following problems in bank discount:

1. What must have been the face of a 60-day, non-interest-bearing note, discounted 12 days after date at 6 per cent, if the discount was $7.68?
2. Find the face of a non-interest-bearing 90-day note, dated May 10, if when discounted on May 28 at 8 per cent the discount was $29.60.
3. Find the face of a non-interest-bearing note for 62 days, dated Nov. 8, if when discounted on Nov. 22 at $4\frac{1}{2}$ per cent it yielded proceeds of $313.11.
4. A borrower wished to postpone payment of his $1,200 bill for 60 days. He offered to give his non-interest-bearing note with a face that would yield proceeds of $1,200 if discounted at 5 per cent immediately at the bank. What should have been the face of the note?
5. What was the original face of a 120-day, 6 per cent ordinary interest-bearing note, discounted for 90 days at $4\frac{1}{2}$ per cent, if the bank discount was $73.44?
6. Find the face of a 60-day, 8 per cent ordinary interest-bearing note, dated June 12, if the discount date is July 6, the discount rate is 5 per cent, and the bank discount is $2.28.
7. What was the original face on a 90-day, 5 per cent ordinary interest-bearing note, discounted on date at 4 per cent, if it yielded proceeds of $4,811.40?
8. Find the face of a 50-day, 4 per cent ordinary interest-bearing note, dated Oct. 28 and discounted at 6 per cent on Nov. 2, if the proceeds of bank discount were $718.57.

UNIT 6. Partial Payments

In bankruptcy settlements in long-term loans, and in the purchase of merchandise and other forms of property, it happens frequently that payments on account are made. The question immediately arises as to the amount of interest and principal that is due at any point in the life of a debt or at its maturity.

A *partial payment*, or payment on account, is the payment of any part of a note or similar obligation.

On non-interest-bearing obligations the computation is of course quite simple, for the partial payment need only be deducted from the sum due in order to obtain the remainder due.

On interest-bearing obligations, the two common methods of finding the amount due are by the United States rule or by the merchants' rule.

The United States Rule. The United States rule was first used as a method of settling government obligations. Its legality, established by the United States Supreme Court, has subsequently been affirmed by many of the states. Hence it is called the United States rule.

The following excerpt from a decision by the United States Supreme Court is the basis for solving partial-payment problems on interest-bearing obligations:

> The rule for casting interest when partial payments have been made is to apply the payment, in the first place, to the discharge of the interest then due.
>
> If the payment exceeds the interest, the surplus goes toward discharging the principal, and the subsequent interest is to be computed on the balance of the principal remaining due.
>
> If the payment is less than the interest, the surplus of interest must not be taken to augment the principal, but the interest continues on the former principal until the period when the payments, taken together, exceed the interest due, and then the surplus is applied toward discharging the principal, and the interest is to be computed on the balance as aforesaid.

It is evident that two fundamental principles must be applied in solving partial-payment problems by the United States rule: (1) accrued interest must be paid before the principal can be diminished and (2) interest must never draw interest.

Therefore the procedure to find the amount due *at any given time* is as follows:

1. Compute the interest on the face of the note following the date of the note to and including the date of the first payment.
2. From the first payment deduct the interest.
3. Apply the remainder of the first payment to reduce the face, obtain-

ing a new face; that is, the excess of the payment over the interest due is subtracted from the previous face to obtain a new face as of the date of the payment.

For any subsequent payments continue the above procedure. The amount due at any time is the sum of the last face plus accrued interest from the date of that face.

If any payment does not equal the interest due at the time the payment is made, no change is made in the face, interest continues on the face, and the payment is held until sufficient payments, taken together, exceed the interest due; at which time the excess is applied to determine a new face, as above.

The Merchants' Rule. Under the merchants' rule, the face of the note draws interest following its date to and including the date of settlement, and each payment draws interest following its date to and including the date of settlement. To determine the amount due at the date of settlement, the sum of the amounts (payment + interest) of the payments is deducted from the amount (face + interest) of the note or obligation.

Therefore the procedure to find the amount due at *any given settlement date* is as follows:

1. Find the amount (face + interest) of the note to the date of settlement.
2. Find the amount (face + interest) of each payment from the date of payment to the date of settlement.
3. From the amount of the note subtract the sum of the amounts of the payments. The remainder is the amount due on the settlement date.

To Compute Time on Partial Payments. You will note that in the preceding explanation of the United States rule, the term "at any given time" was used, and that in the explanation of the merchants' rule, the term "at any given settlement date" was used. These terms, rather than "maturity date," were used on the assumption that the payee would accept final payment prior to any fixed date. Of course, if the final date of payment is the maturity date, the amounts due will be determined by the stipulated maturity date rather than "*any* given time" or "*any* given settlement date."

However, since partial payments are commonly applied on obligations that may have no fixed or predetermined date of maturity, such as payments on merchandise, accounts payable, etc., this terminology is desirable.

Because of banking regulations, most banks prefer to make out entirely new notes at the time of each payment. At times, this is impossible because of the unavailability of one or more of the makers or for other reasons, and in such instance banks will ordinarily apply the United States rule.

In obligations arising from merchandise transactions, businessmen sometimes use the merchants' rule.

For both rules, a 360-day business year and either exact time or 30-day-month time may be used. Although both banks and business concerns generally use exact time, on some occasions 30-day-month time is used.

Example of the United States rule, using exact time (Fig. 5). On Apr. 17 Ralph Johnson contracted the following obligation:

$8500 00/100 San Francisco, Calif. *April 17, 1961*

On or before One Year after date *I* promise to pay to

the order of *American National Bank*

Eighty-Five Hundred and no/100 — Dollars

at American National Bank

Value Received — — — — with interest at *6%*

No. *5736* Due *April 17, 1962*

FIG. 5.

The following payments were endorsed on the back of the note:

7/13/61	$1,200.00
9/22/61	$1,500.00
12/26/61	$2,000.00

Find the amount due at *maturity* using the United States rule and exact time:

Face of note, 4/17/61		$8,500.00
First payment, 7/13/61	$1,200.00	
Interest, 4/17 to 7/13 (87 days on $8,500)	−123.25	
Balance applied to face		−1,076.75
Reduced face of note, 7/13/61		$7,423.25
Second payment, 9/22/61	$1,500.00	
Interest, 7/13 to 9/22 (71 days on $7,423.25)	− 87.84	
Balance applied to face		−1,412.16
Reduced face of note, 9/22/61		$6,011.09
Third payment, 12/26/61	$2,000.00	
Interest, 9/22 to 12/26 (95 days on $6,011.09)	− 95.18	
Balance applied to face		−1,904.82
Reduced face of note, 12/26/61		$4,106.27
Interest, 12/26/61 to maturity 4/17/62 (112 days on $4,106.27)		+ 76.65
Amount due at *maturity*		$4,182.92

Example of the merchants' rule, using 30-day-month time. Compute the amount due at *maturity* on the $8,500 note of Ralph Johnson, using the merchants' rule and 30-day-month time.

Face of note, 4/17/61			$8,500.00
Interest 4/17/46 to maturity 4/17/62			+510.00
Maturity value of note			$9,010.00
First payment, 7/13/61	$1,200.00		
Interest, 7/13/61 to 4/17/62 (274 days)	+54.80		
Amount of first payment		$1,254.80	
Second payment, 9/22/61	$1,500.00		
Interest, 9/22/61 to 4/17/62 (205 days)	+51.25		
Amount of second payment		1,551.25	
Third payment, 12/26/61	$2,000.00		
Interest, 12/26/61 to 4/17/62 (111 days)	+37.00		
Amount of third payment		2,037.00	
Sum of amounts of payments			−4,843.05
Amount due at *maturity*			$4,166.95

EXERCISE 6

1. A 1-year note for $4,750, dated Aug. 13, 1962, and bearing ordinary interest at 7 per cent, had the following payments endorsed on its back:

10/17/62	$ 435.00
12/26/62	$ 950.00
3/11/63	$1,750.00

Compute the amount owed at maturity of this note by the United States rule using exact time.

2. Charles Davis was the maker of a note for $7,325, dated July 16, 1958, and bearing ordinary interest at 6 per cent. Payments were endorsed on the back of the note as follows:

8/22/58	$ 925.00
9/17/58	$ 450.00
11/5/58	$1,540.00

Use the United States rule to compute the amount Charles Davis owed on this note as of Mar. 22, 1959 by exact time.

3. The following payments were made on an 18-month, 7 per cent ordinary interest-bearing note for $3,675, dated Feb. 15, 1958:

8/29/58	$ 625.00
10/14/58	$1,525.00
5/7/59	$ 540.00

Compute the amount due at maturity by the merchants' rule using 30-day-month time.

4. A 5 per cent ordinary interest-bearing note for $5,700, dated Mar. 17, 1960, and due on or before 15 months after date, was given in payment of some merchandise. The following partial payments had been made:

6/24/60	$ 950.00
10/19/60	$ 875.00
3/28/61	$2,750.00

Using the merchants' rule, find the amount of final settlement made on Apr. 2, 1961 computed by exact time.

UNIT 7. Installment Buying and Periodic Payments of Personal Borrowings

Goods sold by stores are purchased either by paying cash or through the medium of credit. When purchased for cash, payment is made at the time of sale and the transaction is closed. When credit is extended, the purchaser usually pays nothing at the time of the sale but is expected to make payment in full on or before the 10th of the following month. There is no direct charge for this credit service, although the price is slightly higher than if the store sold for cash only, because of the costs of additional record keeping and of "bad-debt insurance."

An extension of this monthly-charge-account credit system is found in many businesses. Stores frequently offer goods on "budget terms," "no down payment—pay balance in small monthly payments," "easy-to-buy plan," "use while you pay," etc. To the retailer, such selling terms are known as *installment selling;* to the consuming public, such purchase terms are known as *installment buying* or *installment purchases.*

In installment selling, the seller agrees to extend the period of purchase over a period of weeks, months, or years. To the original purchase price are added the cost of investigating the credit standing of the proposed purchaser, the cost of discounting the order with a loan company or bank, the cost of insuring the sale against loss, the bookkeeping expenses, and other items such as interest on deferred payments and collection charges. The additional amount added to the original selling price is known as the "carrying charge."

A down payment of a stipulated sum or a certain per cent of the purchase price is often required at the time of purchase. The carrying charge, plus interest for the entire period based on the balance, is added to the balance. This total is then divided equally over the agreed number of periods and the buyer signs a conditional sales contract in which the seller retains title to the goods until the account is paid in full.

Since the carrying charges in installment buying may be considered an additional interest charge, you should know how to compute the total increased cost and the effective rate of ordinary interest charged on any given installment purchase.

Example 1: An electric refrigerator is advertised at $275 cash, or $25 down and $30 per month for 10 months on an "easy-pay plan." Find (*a*) the installment cost, (*b*) the interest or carrying charge, (*c*) the cash balance required to pay in full (cash price less down payment), and (*d*) the effective rate of ordinary interest to nearest tenth per cent.

(*a*) Down payment $ 25
Monthly payments: $30 × 10 = 300
$325 Installment cost

(*b*) Installment cost $325
Less cash price 275
$ 50 Interest or carrying charge

(*c*) Cash price $275
Less down payment required 25
$250 Cash balance required to pay in full

(*d*) If it is assumed that each periodic payment includes an equal and constant payment of the cash balance required to make payment in full, and also an equal and constant payment of interest or carrying charge, the solution for the effective rate of ordinary interest may be obtained as follows:

$$\frac{\text{Cash balance}}{\text{Number of monthly payments}} \quad \frac{\$250}{10} = \$25 \text{ Payment to principal each month}$$

$$\frac{\text{Interest}}{\text{Number of monthly payments}} \quad \frac{\$50}{10} = \$5 \text{ Payment to interest each month}$$

End of month	Principal borrowed	Payment to principal	Payment of interest
1	$ 250	$ 25	$ 5
2	225	25	5
3	200	25	5
4	175	25	5
5	150	25	5
6	125	25	5
7	100	25	5
8	75	25	5
9	50	25	5
10	25	25	5
Totals.......	$1,375	$250	$50

From the totals in this table, it is apparent that the combined payments are equivalent to an interest charge of \$50 for the use of \$1,375 for 1 month (one period). The effective rate (per annum) of ordinary interest may then be found as follows:

$$i = \frac{I}{Pn}$$

$$= \frac{\$50}{\$1{,}375 \times \frac{1}{12}} = \frac{12 \times \$50}{\$1{,}375} = \frac{\$600}{\$1{,}375} = .436 = 43.6\%$$

As is illustrated in the table preceding, the computations required to find the effective rate of ordinary interest would be a lengthy and burdensome process if the payments were extended over longer periods of time such as 20 months, 36 months, 78 weeks, etc. Fortunately, a formula may be developed that greatly simplifies the computations necessary.

Formula to Find Effective Rate of Ordinary Interest. If the preceding table is observed, it will be noted that the principal borrowed is reduced month after month by the same amount, namely \$25. That is, the principal borrowed is considered as \$250, then \$225, then \$200, etc., on down to the final principal of \$25 and payment in full at the end of the tenth month.

This is a series of numbers with a common difference (\$25) and thus is an arithmetic progression. In any arithmetic progression, the sum may be obtained by the following formula:

$$\text{Sum} = \text{number of terms} \times \frac{\text{1st term} + \text{last term}}{2}$$

$$\text{Thus the sum} = 10 \times \frac{\$250 + \$25}{2} = \$1{,}375$$

Further, in an arithmetic progression finally *ending* in zero (as is true in Example 1 and the final payment of any debt), the sum may be obtained by the following formula:

$$\text{Sum} = \text{largest term in the series} \times \frac{\text{number of terms} + 1}{2}$$

$$\text{Thus the sum} = \$250 \times \frac{10 + 1}{2} = \$1{,}375$$

Since this latter formula does not necessitate our finding the final principal (\$25 in the illustration), it is to our advantage to use it in determining the sum.

In computing the effective rate of ordinary interest in Example 1, observe that $\frac{12 \times \$50}{\$1{,}375} = 43.6$ per cent, the required answer. Both the numerator and denominator of the fraction (letting i symbolize the effective rate of ordinary interest) may be expressed in words as follows:

$$i = \frac{\text{number of payments that would occur in one year} \times \text{interest in dollars}}{\text{cash balance required to pay in full} \times \dfrac{\text{number of payments} + 1}{2}}$$

This formula may be symbolized as follows:

i = effective rate of ordinary interest per annum (expressed decimally)
m = number of payment periods that would occur in one full year. (Thus, for monthly payments, $m = 12$; for weekly payments, $m = 52$; etc.)
I = interest in dollars, or excess of installment price over cash price
B = cash balance required to pay in full (cash price less down payment, if any)
p = number of periodic payments to be made, not including down payment, if any

Using the symbols, the formula preceding becomes:

$$i = \frac{mI}{B \times \dfrac{p+1}{2}}, \text{ or } i = \frac{mI}{B\left(\dfrac{p+1}{2}\right)}$$

Substituting in the formula,

$$i = \frac{12 \times \$50}{\$250\left(\dfrac{10+1}{2}\right)} = \frac{\$600}{\$250\left(\dfrac{11}{2}\right)} = \frac{\$600}{\$1{,}375} = .436 = 43.6\%$$

Though it is apparent that the formula as developed requires considerably less time than the computations necessary if a table such as that illustrated in Example 1 is prepared, the formula is a complex (or compound-complex) fraction and may be further simplified if both denominator and numerator are multiplied by 2. Thus,

$$i = \frac{mI}{B \times \dfrac{p+1}{2}} = \frac{2mI}{B \times \dfrac{p+1}{2} \times 2} = \frac{2mI}{B(p+1)}$$

Example 2: Use the preceding formula in solving part (*d*) of Example 1.

$$i = \frac{2 \times 12 \times \$50}{\$250(10+1)} = \frac{2 \times 12 \times \$50}{\$250 \times 11} = \frac{\$1{,}200}{\$2{,}750} = \frac{\$600}{\$1{,}375} = .436 = 43.6\%$$

Example 3: A pressure pump is priced at \$310 cash or \$40 down and \$4 per week for 75 weeks on the installment plan. If purchased on the installment plan find the effective rate of ordinary interest to nearest tenth per cent charged on the cash balance required to make payment in full at the time of purchase.

$$\$40 + (\$4 \times 75) = \$340 \text{ Installment-plan cost}$$
$$\$340 - \$310 = \$\ 30 \text{ Interest charge for installment purchase}$$
$$\$310 - \$40 = \$270 \text{ Cash balance needed to pay in full}$$
$$i = \frac{2 \times 52 \times \$30}{\$270(75 + 1)} = \frac{2 \times 52 \times \$30}{\$270 \times 76} = .152 = 15.2\%$$

Personal Borrowing. Personal loan repayment plans are of two kinds: (1) ordinary notes (payment in full at the time loan is due) and (2) periodic payments, usually monthly or weekly.

Ordinary notes are loans with interest computed on the original face. Payment of both principal and interest is made at or before maturity, no intervening payments being required. Such loans are usually for short terms such as 30, 60, or 90 days and are available ordinarily only to borrowers with high credit rating or easily liquidated collateral.

Periodic payments are usually computed at a moderate rate but are based on the *original* face of the loan or are computed on a much higher rate based on the *declining* balance. Borrowers who have poor credit standing or who need an exceptionally long time in which to make repayment are likely to be required to use a periodic-payment plan.

Periodic-payment Plans. Originally, only personal-loan companies made this type of loan, and interest charges were invariably high. Today, many banks also make such personal loans at much more reasonable interest charges, and the entrance of banking institutions into the personal-loan field has caused a decided lowering of charges by most personal-loan companies.

Usually, personal-loan companies and banks indicate the cost of such

Schedule of Typical Personal Finance Company, Flat-payment Plan

Amount of loan	Duration of loan and amount of payments to be made each month					
	4 mo.	6 mo.	10 mo.	12 mo.	15 mo.	18 mo.
$ 25	$ 6.65	$ 4.54	$ 2.86	$ 2.44		
50	13.30	9.09	5.72	4.88		
75	19.95	13.63	8.58	7.33	$ 6.07	$ 5.24
100	26.60	18.18	11.45	9.77	8.10	6.99
125	33.22	22.69	14.28	12.19	10.10	8.71
150	39.82	27.19	17.10	14.59	12.08	10.41
200	53.01	36.17	22.72	19.36	16.02	13.79
300	79.32	54.08	33.90	28.87	23.85	20.51
400	105.63	71.96	45.07	38.36	31.66	27.22
500	131.91	89.94	56.23	47.84	39.47	33.91

borrowing with schedules of flat payments. Banks ordinarily limit the length of time in which payment may be made to not much more than 1 year, but personal-loan companies frequently make loans with payment periods extending to 36 months or even longer when it is legal to do so.

At banks, a typical charge for personal loans is \$6 per \$100 per year, equivalent to 6 per cent per year of the original balance. Thus on a \$100 bank loan of this type for one year, payments would be (\$100 + \$6) ÷ 12 = \$8.83 per month for 12 months. The year is considered to be 12 months of 30 days each.

Example: What payments would a bank require on a \$200 personal loan to be repaid in four equal monthly installments, if the bank charge for such loans is \$6 per \$100 per year?

$$\$6 \text{ per } \$100 \text{ per year} = \frac{\$6}{\$100} = .06 = 6\% \text{ on the original balance}$$

$$\text{Interest charge} = \$200 \times \frac{4}{12} \times \frac{6}{100} = \$4$$

$$\text{Total repayment} = \$200 + \$4 = \$204$$

$$\text{Monthly payment} = \frac{\$204}{4} = \$51$$

Banks have a minimum interest charge that varies between banks and between communities. This minimum charge will ordinarily range between \$.50 to \$2.50.

To Find Effective Rate of Ordinary Interest on Balance if Paid on Periodic-payment Plan. Although there are several optional methods of computing the approximate effective rate of ordinary interest to nearest tenth per cent charged for borrowings repaid through periodic-payment plans, the same method used to determine the approximate effective rate of ordinary interest charged on installment purchases is recommended. Thus:

$$i = \frac{2mI}{B(p+1)}$$

where B = original balance (equivalent to principal at interest or proceeds of discount)

Example 1: Ben Shaw borrows \$600. He obligates himself to make weekly payments of \$19.50 for each of 32 weeks. Find the effective rate of ordinary interest to nearest tenth per cent that he pays.

$$\$19.50 \times 32 = \$624 \text{ Amount (principal + interest) to be paid}$$

$$\$624 - \$600 = \$\ 24 \text{ Total interest payment}$$

$$i = \frac{2 \times 52 \times \$24}{\$600(32+1)} = \frac{2 \times 52 \times \$24}{\$600 \times 33} = .126 = 12.6\%$$

Example 2: Roberta Madden signs a note with a finance company for $50 discounted at 6 per cent for 10 months and agrees to pay $5 at the end of each of the next 10 months. Find the effective rate of ordinary interest to nearest tenth per cent that she pays for the loan.

$$\$50 \times \frac{10}{12} \times \frac{6}{100} = \$2.50 \text{ Discount}$$

$$\$5 \times 10 = \$50 \text{ Amount to be paid}$$

$$\$50 - \$2.50 = \$47.50 \text{ Proceeds of discount (or principal borrowed)}$$

$$i = \frac{2 \times 12 \times \$2.50}{\$47.50(10 + 1)} = \frac{2 \times 12 \times \$2.50}{\$47.50 \times 11} = .115 = 11.5\%$$

Effective Interest Rate Compared to Nominal Interest Rate. When the nominal interest rate charged on the *original* balance and the number and length of the equal periodic payments are known, the effective ordinary interest rate may be found by the use of the following formula in which the nominal interest rate is symbolized by j:

$$i = \frac{2pj}{p + 1}$$

Example 1: Find the effective ordinary interest rate to nearest tenth per cent if a loan company charges 12 per cent nominal interest on the original balance and the loan with interest is to be repaid in 26 equal weekly payments.

$$i = \frac{2 \times 26 \times .12}{26 + 1} = \frac{2 \times 26 \times .12}{27} = .231 = 23.1\%$$

When the effective ordinary interest rate and the number and length of the equal periodic payments are known, the nominal interest rate charged on the original balance may be found by application of the following formula:

$$j = \frac{i(p + 1)}{2p}$$

Example 2: Find the nominal rate of interest to nearest tenth per cent charged on the original balance of an installment purchase if the effective ordinary interest rate is 25 per cent and the obligation including interest is to be paid in 8 equal monthly payments.

$$j = \frac{.25(8 + 1)}{2 \times 8} = \frac{.25 \times 9}{16} = .14\frac{1}{16} = 14.1\%$$

EXERCISE 7

Find the effective rate of ordinary interest to nearest tenth per cent on the following installment purchases and personal loans paid with interest in equal periodic payments:

1. A radio advertised at $130 cash, or $30 down and $5 per month for 24 months.
2. A dining-room set advertised at $89.50 cash, or $9.50 down and $9 per month for 10 months.
3. A washing machine priced at $175 cash, or nothing down and $4 per week for 48 weeks.
4. An automobile priced at $495 cash, or one-third down and $10 per week for 40 weeks.
5. A loan of $250 is paid with interest in an amount of $280 in six equal monthly installments.
6. A non-interest-bearing note for $840 is discounted at a bank on date of origin at 5 per cent and payments are made in 12 equal monthly installments.
7. Mr. Rice purchased a new car, borrowing $950 from the bank which charged him $5 per $100 per year on the first $400 borrowed and $4 per $100 per year on the remainder of the sum borrowed. He paid the amount (principal + interest) due in 10 equal monthly payments.
8. Find the effective ordinary interest rates charged by the Typical Personal Finance Company (page 170) on (*a*) a $100 loan paid in 10 months and (*b*) a $300 loan paid in 10 months.
9. A lending institution charges 8 per cent rate of nominal interest on an original balance paid with interest in 9 equal monthly installments. Find the effective rate of ordinary interest.
10. Find the nominal rate of interest to nearest tenth per cent charged on the original balance of a personal loan if the effective ordinary interest rate is 19.5 per cent and the obligation including interest is paid in 39 equal weekly payments.

CHAPTER V

PAYROLLS, WAGES, AND COMMISSION ACCOUNTS

UNIT 1. Net Pay after Deductions; Change Memorandums

After determining gross wages, further computations are usually necessary in determining the net pay due employees. With the exception of certain exempt services, deductions must be made by employers for Federal old-age, disability, and survivors insurance (Federal Insurance Contributions Act), Federal income tax withholding, and in some states, unemployment and/or disability fund taxes. Additionally, payroll deductions may be made for union dues, group life-insurance premiums, savings plans, hospital- and medical-insurance premiums, etc.

Old-age, Disability, and Survivors Insurance Tax. Federal old-age, disability, and survivors insurance (F.I.C.A. tax) is paid for by a tax on the workers' earnings and matching contributions by the employers—and by self-employed persons on the net earnings from their profession, trade, or business. The self-employed pay $1\frac{1}{2}$ times as much as employees (or employers) would pay on the same earnings, but $\frac{1}{4}$ less than the combined payments of employees and employers. The employees' contributions are deducted from their wages each pay day. The employers send the employees' contributions and their own matching contributions to the Director of Internal Revenue not later than the month following the end of each calendar quarter. The self-employed make their contributions yearly when they file their Federal income tax returns.

The table on page 175 shows the F.I.C.A. tax rates that have been in effect since Jan. 1, 1937 and the scheduled increases.[1]

An employee having more than one employer is taxed separately for the income received from each employer and thus may pay a tax in excess of the stipulated percentage. Any excess payment by the employee beyond maximum contributions required may be applied by the employee as a payment on his Federal income tax return, though the employers may not do so in such instances.

[1] Rates and maximums quoted were in effect through 1957 and may (probably will) be changed by future acts of Congress.

Calendar years	Maximum earnings	Employee, %	Employer, %	Self-employed, %
1937–1950	$3,000	1	1	not covered
1951–1953	3,600	$1\frac{1}{2}$	$1\frac{1}{2}$	$2\frac{1}{4}$
1954	3,600	2	2	3
1955–1956	4,200	2	2	3
1957–1959	4,200	$2\frac{1}{4}$	$2\frac{1}{4}$	$3\frac{3}{8}$
1960–1964	4,200	$2\frac{3}{4}$	$2\frac{3}{4}$	$4\frac{1}{8}$
1965–1969	4,200	$3\frac{1}{4}$	$3\frac{1}{4}$	$4\frac{7}{8}$
1970–1974	4,200	$3\frac{3}{4}$	$3\frac{3}{4}$	$5\frac{5}{8}$
1975 and after	4,200	$4\frac{1}{4}$	$4\frac{1}{4}$	$6\frac{3}{8}$

Those who have earnings from both employment and self-employment pay contributions on their wages from employment and on that part of their self-employment earnings that may be necessary to bring the total earnings up to the maximum ($4,200 as scheduled beginning 1955).

Example 1: Mae Goodan, an office worker, was paid $256.75 per month in January of 1958. Find the F.I.C.A. deduction made from her January salary check.

$$\$256.75 \times .0225 = \$5.78$$

Example 2: Beacham Baker earned $15,000 as division manager of an insurance company in 1960. Find the total F.I.C.A. deductions made from his yearly earnings.

The deductions are limited to the first $4,200 of earnings. Therefore,

$$\$4{,}200 \times .0275 = \$115.50$$

Example 3: H. Glenn Mercer, self-employed as a real-estate broker, had a net business income of $980 in 1960 as well as $3,500 in income as a clerk in an insurance office. Find (*a*) his F.I.C.A. tax as a clerk and (*b*) his F.I.C.A. self-employment tax.

(*a*) $\$3{,}500 \times .0275 = \$96.25$

(*b*) $\$4{,}200 - \$3{,}500 = \$700$ subject to self-employment tax

$\$700 \times .04125 = \$28.875 = \$28.88$

State Unemployment Fund Taxes. In addition to Federal old-age and survivors insurance, the Social Security Act of 1935 established unemployment benefit funds to be administered by the various state unemployment commissions. This has resulted in considerable variation among the states as to the eligibility requirements, employee and employer contributions, minimum and maximum benefits, and the period of time for which unemployment benefits are paid.

Benefits approximate $15 to $40 per week with the number of weekly periods during which payments are made usually limited to not more than

26 weeks. Because of the impossibility of giving qualifications, alternatives, and methods of computation in a brief summary form, the law and the State Employment Security Agency in the state in which you reside should be consulted for authoritative information. In some states weekly compensation is provided for disability as well as unemployment.

In only five states does the employee contribute directly to the unemployment (or disability) fund: Alabama, California, Kentucky, and New Jersey requiring employees to contribute 1 per cent of earnings, usually to a limit of $3,000 earnings; and Rhode Island, requiring employees to contribute $1\frac{1}{2}$ per cent of earnings to a limit of $3,000 earnings.

Example: Duncan Malloch, a carpenter in Rhode Island, earned $113.75 per week. Find (*a*) the state unemployment tax deduction from his weekly pay check, and (*b*) the maximum deduction that will be made in any one calendar year.

(*a*) $\$113.75 \times .015 = \$1.70625 = \$1.71$

(*b*) $\$3{,}000 \times .015 = \$45.00$

Employment excluded from the benefits of the Federal old-age and survivors insurance is generally excluded from unemployment compensation. In many states, employees in certain forms of seasonal work have also been excluded or limited by the various state unemployment commissions in participation in unemployment insurance benefits. Self-employed neither contribute to nor may they receive unemployment compensation.

Federal Income Tax Withholding. The Federal income tax laws require that the employer withhold from his employees' pay certain stipulated amounts or per cents of their earnings which must then be deposited by the employer by the 15th day of each of the first two months of each quarter if in excess of $100 (including old-age and survivors insurance taxes) with a Federal Reserve bank or other authorized bank. Withholdings for the third month of the quarter may be so deposited or paid with the quarterly return (due the month following each calendar quarter) to the offices of the Director of Internal Revenue.

On or before each Jan. 31 or at the end of employment, the employer is required to give each employee a withholding statement in duplicate (Form W-2) showing the total wages subject to income tax withholding, the amount of income tax withheld, and the amount of the F.I.C.A. employee taxes withheld (old-age and survivors insurance taxes). Additionally, on or before Jan. 31, the employer must file a reconciliation of quarterly returns (Form W-3) together with the Director of Internal Revenue's copy (Form W-2*a*) of all withholding statements furnished employees for the preceding calendar year.

The employee in filing his Federal individual income tax return claims credit toward payment or overpayment of his income tax by attaching the original Form W-2's provided to him by his employers.

For income tax withholding, employers are required to allow exemptions to each employee on the basis of a withholding exemption certificate signed by the employee. If an employee fails to furnish a certificate, the employer is required to withhold tax as if the employee had claimed no withholding exemptions.

Each exemption claimed by the employee is a $600 offset against his income and reduces his taxable income by that amount. As a taxpayer, the employee may claim an exemption for himself or herself, for wife or husband, and for each of the following who qualify as dependents by meeting *all four* of the following tests:

1. He or she receives over one-half of support from the taxpayer (employee), and
2. Is "closely related," and
3. Does not have $600 or more gross income during the tax year (unless he or she is a child that has not attained age 19, or if a child of 19 or over attends as a full-time student a recognized educational institution for at least 5 months of the year or pursues a full-time course of institutional on-farm training), and
4. If married, her or his exemption is not already claimed as an employee.

Income tax withholding tables have been prepared by the Bureau of Internal Revenue, U.S. Treasury Department, and are available without charge for the following day periods: weekly, 10-day, biweekly, semimonthly, 28-day, monthly, and daily or miscellaneous.

The table that follows was one in use in early 1958. It is subject to revision, and undoubtedly the same rates may not be in effect at any given time in the future. Nevertheless, it should serve as an illustration of how the employer determines the withholding that he is required to make if he chooses to use the wage-bracket table method of income tax withholding.

If the wages exceed the highest wage bracket in the applicable table, in determining the amount to be deducted and withheld, the wages may, at the election of the employer, be rounded to the nearest dollar.

Example of use of wage-bracket table: In the first week of May, 1958, Wilbur Warner earned $158.40 as an office manager. He claimed three exemptions for himself, his wife, and his wife's dependent mother. Find the Federal income tax withholding by the use of the weekly wage-bracket table.

The bracket of at least $150 but less than $160 in the column indicating three withholding exemptions claimed shows the amount of income tax withholding to be $21.00.

If the Payroll Period with Respect to an Employee Is Weekly

And the wages are		And the number of withholding exemptions claimed is										
At least	But less than	0	1	2	3	4	5	6	7	8	9	10 or more
		The amount of income tax to be withheld shall be										
$ 0	$ 13	18% of wages	$ 0	$ 0	$ 0	$ 0	$ 0	$ 0	$ 0	$ 0	$ 0	$ 0
13	14	$ 2.40	.10	0	0	0	0	0	0	0	0	0
14	15	2.60	.30	0	0	0	0	0	0	0	0	0
15	16	2.80	.50	0	0	0	0	0	0	0	0	0
16	17	3.00	.70	0	0	0	0	0	0	0	0	0
17	18	3.20	.80	0	0	0	0	0	0	0	0	0
18	19	3.30	1.00	0	0	0	0	0	0	0	0	0
19	20	3.50	1.20	0	0	0	0	0	0	0	0	0
20	21	3.70	1.40	0	0	0	0	0	0	0	0	0
21	22	3.90	1.60	0	0	0	0	0	0	0	0	0
22	23	4.10	1.70	0	0	0	0	0	0	0	0	0
23	24	4.20	1.90	0	0	0	0	0	0	0	0	0
24	25	4.40	2.10	0	0	0	0	0	0	0	0	0
25	26	4.60	2.30	0	0	0	0	0	0	0	0	0
26	27	4.80	2.50	.20	0	0	0	0	0	0	0	0
27	28	5.00	2.60	.30	0	0	0	0	0	0	0	0
28	29	5.10	2.80	.50	0	0	0	0	0	0	0	0
29	30	5.30	3.00	.70	0	0	0	0	0	0	0	0
30	31	5.50	3.20	.90	0	0	0	0	0	0	0	0
31	32	5.70	3.40	1.10	0	0	0	0	0	0	0	0
32	33	5.90	3.50	1.20	0	0	0	0	0	0	0	0
33	34	6.00	3.70	1.40	0	0	0	0	0	0	0	0
34	35	6.20	3.90	1.60	0	0	0	0	0	0	0	0
35	36	6.40	4.10	1.80	0	0	0	0	0	0	0	0
36	37	6.60	4.30	2.00	0	0	0	0	0	0	0	0
37	38	6.80	4.40	2.10	0	0	0	0	0	0	0	0
38	39	6.90	4.60	2.30	0	0	0	0	0	0	0	0
39	40	7.10	4.80	2.50	.20	0	0	0	0	0	0	0
40	41	7.30	5.00	2.70	.40	0	0	0	0	0	0	0
41	42	7.50	5.20	2.90	.50	0	0	0	0	0	0	0
42	43	7.70	5.30	3.00	.70	0	0	0	0	0	0	0
43	44	7.80	5.50	3.20	.90	0	0	0	0	0	0	0
44	45	8.00	5.70	3.40	1.10	0	0	0	0	0	0	0
45	46	8.20	5.90	3.60	1.30	0	0	0	0	0	0	0
46	47	8.40	6.10	3.80	1.40	0	0	0	0	0	0	0
47	48	8.60	6.20	3.90	1.60	0	0	0	0	0	0	0
48	49	8.70	6.40	4.10	1.80	0	0	0	0	0	0	0
49	50	8.90	6.60	4.30	2.00	0	0	0	0	0	0	0
50	51	9.10	6.80	4.50	2.20	0	0	0	0	0	0	0
51	52	9.30	7.00	4.70	2.30	0	0	0	0	0	0	0
52	53	9.50	7.10	4.80	2.50	.20	0	0	0	0	0	0
53	54	9.60	7.30	5.00	2.70	.40	0	0	0	0	0	0
54	55	9.80	7.50	5.20	2.90	.60	0	0	0	0	0	0
55	56	10.00	7.70	5.40	3.10	.80	0	0	0	0	0	0
56	57	10.20	7.90	5.60	3.20	.90	0	0	0	0	0	0

If the Payroll Period with Respect to an Employee Is Weekly *(Continued)*

And the wages are		And the number of withholding exemptions claimed is										
At least	But less than	0	1	2	3	4	5	6	7	8	9	10 or more
		The amount of income tax to be withheld shall be										
57	58	10.40	8.00	5.70	3.40	1.10	0	0	0	0	0	0
58	59	10.50	8.20	5.90	3.60	1.30	0	0	0	0	0	0
59	60	10.70	8.40	6.10	3.80	1.50	0	0	0	0	0	0
60	62	11.00	8.70	6.40	4.10	1.70	0	0	0	0	0	0
62	64	11.30	9.00	6.70	4.40	2.10	0	0	0	0	0	0
64	66	11.70	9.40	7.10	4.80	2.50	.20	0	0	0	0	0
66	68	12.10	9.80	7.40	5.10	2.80	.50	0	0	0	0	0
68	70	12.40	10.10	7.80	5.50	3.20	.90	0	0	0	0	0
70	72	12.80	10.50	8.20	5.90	3.50	1.20	0	0	0	0	0
72	74	13.10	10.80	8.50	6.20	3.90	1.60	0	0	0	0	0
74	76	13.50	11.20	8.90	6.60	4.30	2.00	0	0	0	0	0
76	78	13.90	11.60	9.20	6.90	4.60	2.30	0	0	0	0	0
78	80	14.20	11.90	9.60	7.30	5.00	2.70	.40	0	0	0	0
80	82	14.60	12.30	10.00	7.70	5.30	3.00	.70	0	0	0	0
82	84	14.90	12.60	10.30	8.00	5.70	3.40	1.10	0	0	0	0
84	86	15.30	13.00	10.70	8.40	6.10	3.80	1.50	0	0	0	0
86	88	15.70	13.40	11.00	8.70	6.40	4.10	1.80	0	0	0	0
88	90	16.00	13.70	11.40	9.10	6.80	4.50	2.20	0	0	0	0
90	92	16.40	14.10	11.80	9.50	7.10	4.80	2.50	.20	0	0	0
92	94	16.70	14.40	12.10	9.80	7.50	5.20	2.90	.60	0	0	0
94	96	17.10	14.80	12.50	10.20	7.90	5.60	3.30	.90	0	0	0
96	98	17.50	15.20	12.80	10.50	8.20	5.90	3.60	1.30	0	0	0
98	100	17.80	15.50	13.20	10.90	8.60	6.30	4.00	1.70	0	0	0
100	105	18.50	16.10	13.80	11.50	9.20	6.90	4.60	2.30	0	0	0
105	110	19.40	17.00	14.70	12.40	10.10	7.80	5.50	3.20	.90	0	0
110	115	20.30	17.90	15.60	13.30	11.00	8.70	6.40	4.10	1.80	0	0
115	120	21.20	18.80	16.50	14.20	11.90	9.60	7.30	5.00	2.70	.40	0
120	125	22.10	19.70	17.40	15.10	12.80	10.50	8.20	5.90	3.60	1.30	0
125	130	23.00	20.60	18.30	16.00	13.70	11.40	9.10	6.80	4.50	2.20	0
130	135	23.90	21.50	19.20	16.90	14.60	12.30	10.00	7.70	5.40	3.10	.80
135	140	24.80	22.40	20.10	17.80	15.50	13.20	10.90	8.60	6.30	4.00	1.70
140	145	25.70	23.30	21.00	18.70	16.40	14.10	11.80	9.50	7.20	4.90	2.60
145	150	26.60	24.20	21.90	19.60	17.30	15.00	12.70	10.40	8.10	5.80	3.50
150	160	27.90	25.60	23.30	21.00	18.70	16.40	14.10	11.70	9.40	7.10	4.80
160	170	29.70	27.40	25.10	22.80	20.50	18.20	15.90	13.50	11.20	8.90	6.60
170	180	31.50	29.20	26.90	24.60	22.30	20.00	17.70	15.30	13.00	10.70	8.40
180	190	33.30	31.00	28.70	26.40	24.10	21.80	19.50	17.10	14.80	12.50	10.20
190	200	35.10	32.80	30.50	28.20	25.90	23.60	21.30	18.90	16.60	14.30	12.00
		18% of the excess over $200 plus										
$200 and over		$36.00	$33.70	$31.40	$29.10	$26.80	$24.50	$22.20	$19.80	$17.50	$15.20	$12.90

In 1958, the employer who did not use the wage-bracket withholding tables was permitted to compute income tax withholding from employees in accordance with the accompanying table.

Percentage Method Income Tax Withholding Table

Payroll period	*Amount of one withholding exemption*
Weekly	$ 13.00
Biweekly	26.00
Semimonthly	28.00
Monthly	56.00
Quarterly	167.00
Semiannual	333.00
Annual	667.00
Daily or miscellaneous (per day of such period)	1.80

The steps in computing the income tax to be withheld are as follows:

1. Multiply the amount of *one* withholding exemption (see table) by the number of exemptions claimed by the employee.
2. Subtract the amount thus determined from the employee's wages.
3. Multiply the difference by 18 per cent.

In determining the amount of income tax to be deducted and withheld, the employer might elect to reduce to zero the last digit (cents) of the wage amount, or he might compute the wage amount to the nearest dollar. Thus, if the weekly wage were $37.46, the employer might eliminate the last digit and determine the income tax on the basis of a wage payment of $37.40, or he might determine the income tax on the basis of a wage payment of $37.

Example of use of percentage method table: An employee in March of 1958 had a weekly payroll period for which he earned $122.69 gross pay. His withholding exemption certificate then in effect claimed four exemptions. Using the percentage method, compute the income tax withheld (*a*) reducing to zero the last digit of the earnings, (*b*) rounding off to the nearest dollar of earnings, and (*c*) using the exact number of dollars-and-cents earned.

		(*a*)	(*b*)	(*c*)
Total earnings for computation		$122.60	$123.00	$122.69
Amount of one weekly exemption	= $13			
Number of exemptions claimed	×4			
Deduct		−52.00	−52.00	−52.00
Amount subject to withholding		= $ 70.60	$ 71.00	$ 70.69
		×.18	×.18	×.18
Income tax withheld		= $ 12.71	$ 12.78	$ 12.72

It should be understood that the income tax withheld is not ordinarily the exact amount due by the taxpayer (employee). The amounts withheld are credited to the taxpayer's account, and in filing his annual income tax return, he may receive a credit and/or refund for any overpayment and in like manner will be liable for any underpayment of his tax due.

Change Memorandums. Because of the preference of employees, many industrial plants and business concerns meet their payroll by means of cash payments rather than by checks. When cash payment of wages is to be made, the paymaster must determine in advance the quantity of notes (currency) and specie (coin) in each denomination that will be needed to make the exact change necessary for each worker's pay envelope.

Ordinarily, each pay envelope will contain the minimum number of notes and specie that will provide payment. Thus an employee earning $30 will be paid with one $20 note and one $10 note; an employee earning $56.63 will be paid with two $20 notes, one $10 note, one $5 note, one $1 note, one half-dollar, one dime, and three cents.

$2 notes and notes in larger denominations than $20 are rarely used in payment of wages.

Example: Complete the change memorandum in the following net payroll after all deductions have been made: Employee A, $22.75; Employee B, $37.13; Employee C, $48.46; and Employee D, $51.84.

Employee	Net wages	Notes				Specie				
		$20	$10	$5	$1	50¢	25¢	10¢	5¢	1¢
A	$22.75	1			2	1	1			
B	37.13	1	1	1	2			1		3
C	48.46	2		1	3		1	2		1
D	51.84	2	1		1	1	1		1	4
Units of each denomination		6	2	2	8	2	3	3	1	8
Dollars of each denomination		$120	$20	$10	$8	$1	$.75	$.30	$.05	$.08
Total net wages $160.18		Total notes $158				Total specie $2.18				

EXERCISE 1

A. Find the F.I.C.A. tax (use schedule, page 175), unemployment tax (use schedule, page 176), and Federal income tax withholding as requested (use tables, pages 178–180) in the following:

1. Find the F.I.C.A. (old-age and survivors insurance tax) deduction from the gross pay of Ted Lapham who earned $476.29 in January, 1959.

2. In 1960, Carol Booher earned $3,975. Find the total F.I.C.A. deduction from her gross pay.
3. In 1960, Adolph Stoll earned $5,680 gross pay as a bookkeeper with the Acme Company and $1,796 gross pay as a paymaster with the Bentley Construction Corporation. Find (*a*) total F.I.C.A. deduction by the Acme Company, (*b*) total F.I.C.A. deduction by the Bentley Construction Corporation, and (*c*) F.I.C.A. overpayment that he could apply as a payment on his Federal income tax return for 1960.
4. In 1959, Joe Carlstrom earned $2,086 as a salesman in a men's furnishing store and $8,925 as a self-employed insurance broker. Find (*a*) his F.I.C.A. tax as a salesman, (*b*) his F.I.C.A. self-employment tax, and (*c*) his total F.I.C.A. tax for the year.
5. Gerald Cresci, an office manager in Alabama, earned $480 per month in 1960. Find the unemployment tax deducted from his paychecks (*a*) in each of the months January through June, 1960, (*b*) in the month of July, 1960, and (*c*) for the entire year 1960.
6. Edward Sandys, an insurance company office manager, received a salary of $180 per week during 1958. He claimed three withholding exemptions. Use the wage-bracket table on pages 178–179 to determine the Federal income tax withholding in 1958 (*a*) from his weekly paycheck, and (*b*) for the calendar year.
7. Louis and Eleanor Fitzsimmon supported one dependent child and Mrs. Fitzsimmon's dependent mother and father. Louis Fitzsimmon, who earned $91.75 per week in 1959, claimed five exemptions; Eleanor Fitzsimmon, who earned $48.25 per week in 1959, claimed no exemptions. Use the wage-bracket table on pages 178–179 to determine the Federal income tax withholding for the entire year 1959 from (*a*) Mr. Fitzsimmon's earnings and (*b*) Mrs. Fitzsimmon's earnings.
8. Louis Batmale earned $126.88 per week in 1959. Find the Federal income tax withholding from his weekly pay if he claimed three exemptions and his employer used the percentage method income tax withholding table for 1959 (see page 180), basing the computation on the *exact* number of dollars and cents earned.
9. Lucille Mason earned $675.46 per month. She claimed two exemptions. Find the Federal income tax withholding by her employer each month if he used the percentage method income tax withholding table for 1960 (see page 180,), basing the computation on the *nearest* number of dollars earned.
10. Harley Jensen, a draftsman residing in California, earned $136 per week. Find the total of each of the following deductions for the year 1960 from his yearly pay: (*a*) F.I.C.A. tax, (*b*) disability (unemployment) insurance, (*c*) Federal income tax withholding based on four exemptions and use of the wage-bracket withholding table for 1960 (see pages 178–179).

B. The Carson Novelty Company pays its employees in cash. **Prepare and complete** a change memorandum for the net wages paid to the following employees of the shipping department:

Employee number	Net wages after deductions	Notes				Specie				
		$20	$10	$5	$1	50¢	25¢	10¢	5¢	1¢
63	$ 97.50									
64	75.53									
65	66.00									
66	57.65									
67	90.85									
68	59.25									
69	150.69									
Units of each denomination...										
Dollars of each denomination..		$	$	$	$	$	$	$	$	$
Total net wages $		Total notes $				Total specie $				

UNIT 2. The Time Basis for Wage Payments

The term *wages*, although technically including all forms of payment for all kinds of services, is generally used in a more restricted sense as applying to the compensation of labor.

Today, as in the past, most workers in this country are compensated for their efforts by means of an hour- or day-rate wage-payment plan. Output or performance is not considered in the wage calculation, although wages are varied in amounts in recognition of the differing degrees of time, effort, or skill required and the value of the services rendered.

Straight Hour (or Day) Rate. The method of payment by hour or day rate may be expressed by the following formula if overtime hours do not receive a higher rate of pay per hour:

$$W = R_h \times H_w$$

Wages equal rate per hour multiplied by hours worked.

Example: George O'Reilly was paid $2.87\frac{1}{2}$ per hour. Find his gross pay for (*a*) a day during which he worked 7 hr., and (*b*) a week during which he worked 42 hr.

(a) $$W = \$2.87\frac{1}{2} \times 7 = \$20.12\frac{1}{2} = \$20.13$$

(b) $$W = \$2.87\frac{1}{2} \times 42 = \$120.75$$

Salaried Earnings. Salaries, a form of time payment for services, are paid usually on the basis of weekly, biweekly, semimonthly, or monthly periods. Expressed as a formula:

$$W = R_p$$

Wages equal a stipulated amount per period.

Example: Leland Eisan received a weekly salary of \$80; Roberta Madden received a biweekly salary of \$150; John Lippitt received a semimonthly salary of \$160; and John O'Shaughnessy received a monthly salary of \$330. For each worker, find earnings (*a*) per year, (*b*) per month, and (*c*) per week.

Leland Eisan:
(*a*) \$80 × 52 = \$4,160 per yr.
(*b*) \$4,160 ÷ 12 = \$346.67 per mo.
(*c*) \$80 per wk.

Roberta Madden:
(*a*) \$150 × 26 = \$3,900 per yr.
(*b*) \$3,900 ÷ 12 = \$325 per mo.
(*c*) \$150 ÷ 2 = \$75 per wk.

John Lippitt:
(*a*) \$160 × 24 = \$3,840 per yr.
(*b*) \$160 × 2 = \$320 per mo.
(*c*) \$3,840 ÷ 52 = \$73.85 per wk.

John O'Shaughnessy:
(*a*) \$330 × 12 = \$3,960 per yr.
(*b*) \$330 per mo.
(*c*) \$3,960 ÷ 52 = \$76.15 per wk.

Salaries *plus* commissions or bonuses (see page 200) are frequently employed as a method of incentive payment for the sale or purchase of goods, increased profits, decreased expenses, and other exceptional services performed. Workers in responsible executive or administrative positions are rewarded in many instances in such manner, the commissions or bonuses for high productivity often being equal to or many times greater than the nominal earnings from the base salaries.

Overtime Pay and Overtime Excess Pay. Frequently it is provided that work after the usual working period is completed is paid at a higher rate than the regular rate. Many and differing arrangements are made, but ordinarily this higher rate is for work in excess of the standard work day (usually 8 hr.) or the standard work week (usually 40 hr.). This higher rate is commonly half again or twice as much as the regular rate. In accordance with the Federal Wage and Hour Law, employees engaged in work or services that enter interstate commerce must be paid a rate not less than 50 per cent greater than the regular hourly rate for all work in excess of 40 hr. during a work week.

Two general methods are used in computing total pay for employees who have worked longer than the stipulated standard time period. The original and still used method is to compute the pay for the regular work period and then add to it the *overtime pay*. A later and increasingly used method is to compute the pay for the total time at the regular rate and then add to it the *overtime excess* (bonus) *pay*.

Overtime Pay. The required computations in determining total pay including overtime pay may be expressed by the following formula:

$$W = R_h \times H_s + R_o \times H_o$$

Wages equal regular rate per hour times the number of standard hours worked plus the overtime rate per hour times the number of overtime hours worked.

Example 1: James Callahan, an employee of the City of San Francisco, California, was paid \$2.25 per hour for a standard work week of 40 hr. and time and a half for overtime. Find his (*a*) overtime pay and (*b*) total pay for a week in which he worked 47 hr.

	$H_o = 47 - 40 =$ 7 overtime hours		
	$\$2.25 \times 40 =$	\$ 90.00	Pay for standard work week
(*a*)	$\$2.25 \times 1\frac{1}{2} \times 7 =$	23.625	Overtime pay
(*b*)	$W =$	\$113.625 = \$113.63	Total pay

Overtime Excess Pay. The required computations in determining total pay including overtime excess pay may be expressed by the following formula:

$$W = R_h \times H_w + R_e \times H_o$$

Wages equal regular rate per hour multiplied by total hours worked plus *excess* rate per hour for overtime hours multiplied by the number of overtime hours worked.

Example 2: Same problem as the preceding example except that it is required to find overtime *excess* pay (as distinguished from overtime pay) and total pay.

	$H_o = 47 - 40 =$ 7 overtime hours		
	$\$2.25 \times 47 =$	\$105.75	Pay at regular rate
(*a*)	$\$2.25 \times \frac{1}{2} \times 7 =$	7.875	Overtime excess pay
(*b*)	$W =$	\$113.625 = \$113.63	Total pay

The immediately preceding example of overtime excess pay illustrates the method most frequently used by private employers. In those states in which a workmen's compensation insurance law is in effect, the employer is required to carry workmen's compensation insurance (or post bond) so that, in the event an employee is injured on the job, the employee will receive disability compensation while unable to work.

Such compensation must be paid to the injured worker (including hospital and medical costs) regardless of whether negligence on the part of the employer or employee contributes to the disability. In some occupations, the basis for the employer's insurance premium is the total pay earned minus overtime *excess* pay. Thus it is necessary for such employers to compute earnings at the regular rate for the total hours worked and the bonus or overtime excess pay as distinguished from overtime pay illustrated in Example 1.

Not only do workmen's compensation insurance laws necessitate the employer's computing overtime excess pay, but also the provisions of the Wage and Hour Law (the Federal Fair Labor Standards Act) require for employees of concerns engaged in interstate commerce that earnings at the regular rate and overtime excess earnings be shown separately. Also, many states have enacted laws with similar provisions affecting intrastate commerce.

The keeping of payroll records by computing overtime excess pay rather than overtime pay may also be chosen by employers for the following two reasons: (1) the employer regards such pay as a direct reduction in net profit and a penalty payment for poor management or unavoidable circumstances, it being to his advantage to keep such excess pay at a minimum; and (2) some labor unions, particularly those whose dues are based on earnings at the regular rate, insist that the employer keep a separate account of such excess earnings.

EXERCISE 2

1. Workers at the Lakeside Bakery Company are paid a flat rate per hour. Find the weekly gross pay of Kenneth Hobbs who was paid $2.375 per hour and worked 9 hr. Monday, 8 hr. Tuesday, $6\frac{1}{2}$ hr. Wednesday, 10 hr. Thursday, and $10\frac{3}{4}$ hr. Friday.
2. John Herman received a weekly salary of $95; Donald Jensen received a biweekly salary of $185; Ruth Gavin received a semimonthly salary of $200; and Fred Kelly received a monthly salary of $410. For each worker, find earnings (*a*) per week, (*b*) per month, and (*c*) per year.
3. Luther Lyon, a carpenter, was paid $3.15 per hour. Find his gross pay for a week in which he worked 7 hr. Monday, 8 hr. Tuesday, 6 hr. Wednesday, 8 hr. Thursday, and $7\frac{1}{4}$ hr. Friday.
4. Michael Joseph, a salesclerk, was paid $2.75 per hour for a standard work week of $37\frac{1}{2}$ hr. and time and a half for overtime. During a week in which he worked 44 hr., find his (*a*) pay for the standard work week, (*b*) pay for the *overtime* hours, and (*c*) total gross pay.
5. Grover Klemmer, a construction supervisor, was paid $4.50 per hour for a standard work week of 40 hr. and time and a half for overtime. For a week in which he worked 46 hr., find his (*a*) pay for the standard work week, (*b*) pay for the *overtime* hours, and (*c*) total gross pay.

GADDY LUMBER COMPANY
Payroll for Week Ending Jan. 24, 19__

Employee number	S	M	T	W	T	F	S	Total time, hours	Overtime, hours	Reg. rate per hour	Earnings at reg. rate	Overtime excess earnings	Amount earned	Exemptions	Calif. U-D tax	F.I.C.A. tax	Inc. tax withhold.	Total deductions	Net amount paid
51		8	8	9	6	9	4	44	4	$2.20	$96.80	$4.40	$101.20	3	$1.01	$2.28	$11.50	$14.79	$86.41
52	6	8	9	9	9	9	5			1.80				1					
53		8	8	8	8	8	8			3.50				2					
54	9	9	7	8	8	8				1.96				0					
55		6	7	6	8	4				2.25				4					
56	4	8	8	8	10	8	6			3.30				6					
Total.										xxx				xx					

6. Arthur Cope is paid \$1.90 per hour with time and a half for overtime beyond the standard 8-hour day. If he worked 10 hours Monday, 8 hours Tuesday, 6 hours Wednesday, 11 hours Thursday, and 9 hours Friday, find (*a*) earnings at regular rate, (*b*) *overtime excess* earnings, and (*c*) total gross earnings.

7. Martha Scott, a fitter in a specialty shop, was paid \$1.95 per hour for a standard 7-hr. day and double time for overtime. For a day in which she worked $9\frac{3}{4}$ hr., find her (*a*) pay at the regular rate, (*b*) *overtime excess* pay, and (*c*) total gross pay.

8. Complete the payroll record of the Gaddy Lumber Company (see page 187). Time and a half is paid for more than 40 hr. per 7-day work week. Deduct a 1 per cent California unemployment-disability tax, a $2\frac{1}{4}$ per cent F.I.C.A. (old-age and survivors insurance) tax, and Federal income tax withholding in the amounts as indicated by the weekly wage-bracket withholding table, pages 178–179. Note that amount earned is computed by adding *overtime excess pay* to the earnings at the regular rate for the full number of hours worked.

UNIT 3. Piece-rate Basis for Wage Payments

Many plans have been devised to differentiate more accurately the value of the service rendered by the individual worker. All such plans are based on productivity, the more skillful and speedy workers receiving more pay than their less efficient coworkers.

The oldest form of incentive wage payment is known as *piece rate*, in which a fixed sum is paid per unit produced. Though the rate per piece may be established on some such basis as estimation or past production records, it is best established by a precise knowledge obtained through job analysis and motion and time study. Though innumerable variations may be made, following are the basic piece-rate plans.

Straight Piece-rate Plan. Workers under the straight piece-rate plan receive a fixed price per unit, and the total wages vary in direct ratio to the number of pieces produced.

$$W = R_p \times N_p$$

Wages equal the rate per piece times the number of pieces produced.

Example: Mrs Foster deWitt operates a power sewing machine in a necktie manufacturing company. For each necktie that she stitches, she receives \$0.032. Find her wage for a day in which she stitched 718 neckties.

$$W = \$0.032 \times 718 = \$22.976 = \$22.98$$

Standard Piece-rate Plus Bonus Piece-rate Plan. The standard piece-rate plus bonus piece-rate plan provides an excess rate of pay per piece for production beyond an established minimum (usually known as standard task).

$$W = R_s \times N_p + R_e \times N_{ep}$$

Wages equal the standard rate per piece multiplied by the number of pieces produced *plus* the excess rate per piece multiplied by the number of excess pieces produced beyond the standard task.

Example: Carton packers at the H. C. Lucas Company receive \$0.09 for each of the first 200 cartons packed per day (standard task) and bonus pay of \$0.03 for each carton packed in excess of 200. Find the wages per day of Ben Shaw who packed (*a*) 180 cartons on Monday and (*b*) 240 cartons on Tuesday.

(*a*) $W = \$0.09 \times 180 = \$16.20$

(*b*) $N_{ep} = 240 - 200 = 40$

$W = \$0.09 \times 240 = \$21.60$

$= \$0.03 \times 40 = 1.20$

$= \$22.80$

Taylor Differential Piece-rate Plan. One of the first and best-known incentive wage-payment plans, the Taylor differential piece-rate plan, consists of two piece rates for a given job. One rate applies to accomplishment below the standard performance that may be expected of the average worker; the other rate, to accomplishment at or above the standard performance of the average worker.

Below task, wages equal the lower rate per piece multiplied by the number of pieces produced.

$$W = R_l \times N_p$$

At or above task, wages equal the upper rate per piece multiplied by the number of pieces produced.

$$W = R_u \times N_p$$

Example: If task is 400 pieces, the rate below task is \$0.04 per piece, and the rate at or above task is \$0.05 per piece, find the wages of workers who produce (*a*) 320 pieces, (*b*) 399 pieces, (*c*) 400 pieces, and (*d*) 480 pieces.

(*a*) $W = \$0.04 \times 320 = \$12.80$

(*b*) $W = \$0.04 \times 399 = \$15.96$

(*c*) $W = \$0.05 \times 400 = \$20.00$

(*d*) $W = \$0.05 \times 480 = \$24.00$

Merrick Multiple Piece-rate Plan. An incentive wage-payment plan similar to that of the Taylor differential piece-rate plan, the Merrick multiple piece-rate plan offers at least three graded piece rates instead of two and in some instances as many as four or more graded piece rates. Thus the following:

Below minimum task, wages equal the lower rate per piece multiplied by the number of pieces produced.

$$W = R_l \times N_p$$

At or above each task but less than the next higher task, wages equal the task rate per piece multiplied by the number of pieces produced.

$$W = R_t \times N_p$$

At maximum task and above, wages equal the maximum rate per piece multiplied by the number of pieces produced.

$$W = R_m \times N_p$$

Example: The Walter Durst Electric Company pays assemblers of a certain type of transformer by the Merrick multiple piece-rate plan on the basis of the following differentials:

Articles assembled per week	*Rate per article*
79 or less	$1.10
80 (lowest task) to 89	1.20
90 (second task) to 99	1.30
100 (highest task) and above	1.40

During a week, employee A assembled 79 pieces, employee B assembled 80 pieces, employee C assembled 95 pieces, and employee D assembled 103 pieces. Find the weekly wages of each employee.

Employee A will earn $1.10 × 79 = $ 86.90
Employee B will earn $1.20 × 80 = $ 96.00
Employee C will earn $1.30 × 95 = $123.50
Employee D will earn $1.40 × 103 = $144.20

Take special note that under the Taylor differential piece-rate plan and the Merrick multiple piece-rate plan, workers achieving task or above are paid the stipulated rate for *each* article produced, not merely a bonus rate for articles produced *above* task as illustrated in the standard piece-rate plus bonus piece-rate plan (page 189).

EXERCISE 3

1. Eric Moeller worked on a straight piece-rate basis at $0.0225 per piece. Find his weekly gross pay if his production for the week was as follows: Monday, 519; Tuesday, 488; Wednesday, 543; Thursday, 602; and Friday, 626.
2. Valerie Phillips, a small-parts assembler, received $0.06 for each of the first 250 articles assembled per day and $0.0775 for each article assembled in excess of 250. Find her gross earnings (*a*) on Monday if she assembled 235 articles and (*b*) on Tuesday if she assembled 275 articles.
3. Walter Pickett, a tire mounter in an automobile tire sales agency, received a guaranteed minimum wage of $16.20 per day or $0.18 per tire mounted, whichever was higher. Find his total gross wages for a week in which his production of tire mountings was as follows: Monday, 112; Tuesday, 84; Wednesday, 98; Thursday, 90; Friday, 118; and Saturday, 137.
4. The Nelson Manufacturing Company paid its lathe operators on the Taylor differential piece-rate basis. For production of 129 articles or less per week, the rate was $0.65 per piece; for 130 articles or more per week, the rate was $0.75 per piece. Find for each the gross earnings during a week in which (*a*) Maurice Power produced 124 articles and (*b*) Herold Miller produced 136 articles.
5. Under the Taylor differential piece-rate plan with daily task set at 120 pieces, Robert Alder completed 118 pieces on Monday, 136 pieces on Tuesday, and 120 pieces on Wednesday. If the rate below task was $0.18 per piece, and at or above task was $0.22 per piece, find Alder's gross wages on (*a*) Monday, (*b*) Tuesday, and (*c*) Wednesday.
6. The Stoll Corporation paid its delivery department workers who furnished their own automobiles and expenses by the Merrick multiple piece-rate plan. For the number of packages delivered per week, the rates per package were as follows: less than 1,600, $0.045 per package; 1,600 to 1,799, $0.05 per package; 1,800 to 1,999, $0.055 per package; and 2,000 or more, $0.065 per package. Find the weekly gross pay of employees who delivered the following number of packages in one week: (*a*) 1,675 packages, (*b*) 2,103 packages, (*c*) 1,800 packages, and (*d*) 1,486 packages.
7. The Ross Company paid its employees on the Merrick multiple piece-rate basis. For the number of pieces produced per day the rates per piece were as follows: less than 60 pieces, $0.29; 60 to 69 pieces, $0.32; 70 or more pieces, $0.35. Find the weekly gross earnings of Alva McMillan who produced 64 pieces Monday, 75 pieces Tuesday, 58 pieces Wednesday, 66 pieces Thursday, and 80 pieces Friday.
8. Complete the following payroll record of the Sheldon Company. Deduct $1.20 from each employee's pay for group life insurance, $2\frac{3}{4}$ per cent F.I.C.A. tax, and Federal income tax withholding as computed by the percentage method income tax withholding table (page 180) based on each employee's *exact* gross earnings for the week and number of exemptions claimed.

SHELDON COMPANY
Payroll for Week Ending Jan. 24, 19__

Name	With-holding exemp-tions	Number produced					Total	Rate per piece	Gross earned	Deductions				Net pay
		M	T	W	T	F				Life ins.	F.I.C.A.	Inc. tax	Total ded.	
Kirby, D.	4	31	29	30	36	25	151	$0.80	$120.80	$1.20	$3.32	$12.38	$16.90	$103.90
Meyer, R.	1	23	18	26	20	23		0.90						
Soule, H.	0	55	56	59	71	48		0.45						
Tripp, A.	5	98	121	108	119	95		0.28						
Weber, V.	2	16	21	18	14	24		1.25						
Wells, N.	3	48	52	68	64	70		0.35						
Totals								xxxx						

UNIT 4. Task and Bonus and Gain-sharing Wage-payment Plans

In addition to the piece-rate basis for wage payments, a large number of other incentive wage-payment plans have been developed both in Europe and in the United States. All are combinations of the time basis and of piece work in varying ratios. Among such wage-payment plans now in effect, most are modifications of the following plans:

Gantt Task and Bonus Plan. The Gantt task and bonus plan guarantees a base rate plus a high bonus for superior productivity and incorporates many of the advantages of assured minimum pay combined with the incentive features of piece-rate plans.

Below task, wages equal the rate per hour multiplied by the hours worked.

$$W = R_h \times H_w$$

At or above task, wages equal 120 (up to 150) per cent times the rate per hour multiplied by the hours standard (the hours of work accomplished).

$$W = 1.20R_h \times H_s$$

Example: If the rate per hour is \$2.50, hours worked per day are 8, task 30 pieces per day, and at task and above the pay is 120 per cent times the rate per hour, find the gross wages of (*a*) Gerald Cresci who completed 26 pieces and (*b*) Everett Silvia who completed 30 pieces, and (*c*) James Hughes who completed 36 pieces.

(*a*) $W = \$2.50 \times 8 = \$20$

(*b*) $W = 1.20 \times \$2.50 \times 8 = \$24$

(*c*) $\text{Work accomplished} = 8 \times \frac{36}{32} = 9 \text{ hours standard}$

$$W = 1.20 \times \$2.50 \times 9 = \$27$$

The Halsey Premium Plan. The Halsey premium plan provides for fractions of the time saved, usually 25 to 75 per cent, to be paid to the worker at his wage rate. If the worker fails to save time, he is guaranteed a minimum pay. The Halsey plan is the first of the modern gain-sharing wage-payment plans. Task is usually set at approximately five-eighths to two-thirds of the normal accomplishment of efficient workers.

At or below task, wages equal the rate per hour multiplied by the hours worked.

$$W = R_h \times H_w$$

Above task, wages equal the rate per hour multiplied by the hours worked *plus* 25 (to 75) per cent of the rate per hour multiplied by the hours saved (hours standard accomplished less hours worked).

$$W = R_h \times H_w + .25R_h(H_s - H_w)$$

Example: If the rate per hour is \$2.40, the hours worked per week are 40, task is 180 pieces per week, and the premium is 50 per cent of the hours saved, find the gross earnings for a week in which (*a*) Charles Ohman completed 150 pieces and (*b*) Harold Friedman completed 198 pieces.

(*a*) $$W = \$2.40 \times 40 = \$96$$

(*b*) $$\text{Work accomplished} = 40 \times \frac{198}{180} = 44 \text{ hours standard}$$

$$\begin{aligned} W &= \$2.40 \times 40 + .50 \times \$2.40 \times (44 - 40) \\ &= \$96 + \$1.20 \times 4 \\ &= \$96 + \$4.80 = \$100.80 \end{aligned}$$

Haynes "Manit" Plan. In the Haynes plan, the standard of performance is set by time study in terms of *manits*, each manit representing four-fifths (usually) of the amount of work that a worker can normally be expected to produce in a minute of time without undue effort. Thus a manit is a unit of effort rather than a unit of work.

The Haynes plan is similar to the Halsey plan except that it uses a minute as a basis of measurement instead of an hour. The two plans differ primarily in that the Haynes plan recognizes supervision in the division of the premium for increased efficiency, the worker usually receiving five-sixths and the supervisory force receiving one-sixth of the savings, the company receiving its share of the gain in the decreased time.

At or below task, wages equal the rate per manit multiplied by the number of minutes worked.

$$W = R_m \times M_w$$

Above task, wages equal the rate per manit multiplied by the number of minutes worked *plus* $\frac{5}{6}$ of the rate per manit multiplied by the minutes saved (minutes standard accomplished less minutes worked).

$$W = R_m \times M_w + \frac{5}{6} R_m \times (M_s - M_w)$$

And at above task, the supervisory force would receive a premium of

$$\frac{1}{6} R_m \times (M_s - M_w)$$

Example: If the rate per manit is \$0.045 and the number of minutes worked is 480, find the gross earnings for a day in which (*a*) Lloyd Celli accomplished 425 manits, (*b*) Jack Cooper accomplished 544 manits, and (*c*) find the premium due the supervisory force for the work of Jack Cooper.

(*a*) $$W = \$.045 \times 480 = \$21.60$$

(*b*) $$\text{Minutes saved} = 544 - 480 = 64$$

$$\begin{aligned} W &= \$.045 \times 480 + \frac{5}{6} \times \$.045 \times 64 \\ &= \$21.60 + \$2.40 = \$24 \end{aligned}$$

(c) $$\text{Supervisory premium} = \frac{1}{6} \times \$.045 \times 64 = \$0.48$$

The Bedeaux Plan. In the Bedeaux plan, the standard of performance is the amount of work assigned to be accomplished in one minute with allowance made for rest, fatigue, and delay not controllable by the worker (and is thus similar to the Haynes manit plan). Each standard minute of work is termed a *point* or a "B," with 60 B's per hour the standard hour's work.

Similar again to the Haynes plan, the worker receives three-fourths of the earnings saved, the supervisory force receiving one-fourth of the savings and the company receiving its share of the gain in the decreased time.

At or below task, wages equal the rate per hour multiplied by the number of hours worked.

$$W = R_h \times H_w$$

Above task, wages equal the rate per hour multiplied by the hours worked *plus* $\frac{3}{4}$ of the rate per hour multiplied by the hours saved (hours standard accomplished less hours worked).

$$W = R_h \times H_w + \frac{3}{4} R_h \times (H_s - H_w)$$

And at above task, the supervisory force would receive a premium of

$$\frac{1}{4} R_h \times (H_s - H_a)$$

Example: If the rate per "B" is \$0.05 and the number of hours worked is 8, find the gross earnings for a day in which (a) James Barrett accomplished 439 B's, (b) Jack White accomplished 560 B's, and (c) find the premium due the supervisory force for the work of Jack White.

$$\text{Hourly rate} = \$.05 \times 60 = \$3$$
$$\text{8-hour task} = 60 \text{ B's} \times 8 = 480 \text{ B's}$$

(a) $$W = \$3 \times 8 = \$24$$

(b) $$\text{Hours saved} = \frac{560 - 480}{60} = \frac{80}{60} = 1\frac{1}{3}$$

$$W = \$3 \times 8 + \frac{3}{4} \times \$3 \times 1\frac{1}{3}$$
$$= \$24 + \$3 = \$27$$

(c) $$\text{Supervisory premium} = \frac{1}{4} \times \$3 \times 1\frac{1}{3} = \$1$$

The Emerson Plan. Workers under the Emerson plan are assured of a guaranteed wage plus a bonus for accomplishment at 67 per cent of efficiency and above that rapid increases as efficiency rises to 100 per cent of task and above.

The weekly or longer pay periods encourage the worker on each job performed since averaging of poor performances with good performances reduces the bonus the worker may have earned for his good performances.

For accomplishment to nearest per cent from 67 through 99 per cent, an arbitrary table of multipliers of the guaranteed wage is used to determine the bonus:

E or Emerson Bonus Rate Table

Efficiency per cent	Bonus multiplier	Efficiency per cent	Bonus multiplier	Efficiency per cent	Bonus multiplier
67	0.0001	78	0.0238	89	0.0911
68	.0004	79	.0280	90	.0991
69	.0011	80	.0327	91	.1074
70	.0022	81	.0378	92	.1162
71	.0037	82	.0433	93	.1256
72	.0055	83	.0492	94	.1352
73	.0076	84	.0553	95	.1453
74	.0102	85	.0617	96	.1557
75	.0131	86	.0684	97	.1662
76	.0164	87	.0756	98	.1770
77	.0199	88	.0832	99	.1881

To determine efficiency per cent, divide the standard time accomplished by the number of hours worked.

Example: Find the efficiency per cent of the following: (*a*) a worker who accomplishes 22.5 hours of standard time in a 40-hour work week; (*b*) a worker who accomplishes 218 hours of standard time in a 252-hour work month; and (*c*) a worker who accomplishes 94 hours of standard time in an 80-hour biweekly work period.

(*a*) $$\frac{22.5}{40} = .5625 = 56.25\%$$

(*b*) $$\frac{218}{252} = .865+ = 87\% \text{ (to nearest per cent)}$$

(*c*) $$\frac{94}{80} = 1.175 = 117.5\%$$

Thus in (*b*) the bonus multiplier for 87 per cent is .0756.

Three formulas are used in determining earnings:

Below 67 *per cent of task*, wages equal the rate per hour multiplied by the number of hours worked.

$$W = R_h \times H_w$$

At 67 *through* 99 *per cent of task,* wages equal the rate per hour multiplied by the number of hours worked *plus* the bonus multiplier E times the rate per hour multiplied by the number of hours worked.

$$W = R_h \times H_w + E \times R_h \times H_w$$

At 100 *per cent of task and above,* wages equal the rate per hour multiplied by the number of hours worked *plus* the rate per hour multiplied by the hours saved (standard time accomplished less hours worked) *plus* 20 per cent of the rate per hour multiplied by the hours worked.

$$W = R_h \times H_w + R_h \times (H_s - H_w) + .20R_h \times H_w$$

Example: Assuming that the rate per hour is \$2 in the immediately preceding example, find the gross earnings of (*a*), (*b*), and (*c*).

(*a*) The efficiency per cent is less than 67 per cent. Therefore,

$$W = \$2 \times 40 = \$80$$

(*b*) The efficiency per cent is 67 per cent or more, but less than 100 per cent. From the bonus rate table the bonus multiplier E for 87 per cent is .0756. Therefore,

$$\begin{aligned} W &= \$2 \times 252 + .0756 \times \$2 \times 252 \\ &= \$504 + \$38.10 = \$542.10 \end{aligned}$$

(*c*) The efficiency per cent is 100 per cent or more. Therefore,

$$\begin{aligned} W &= \$2 \times 80 + \$2 \times (94 - 80) + .20 \times \$2 \times 80 \\ &= \$160 + \$28 + \$32 = \$220 \end{aligned}$$

The Rowan Plan. The Rowan plan provides a guaranteed day wage for the less efficient workers. The premium or bonus for the workers who exceed task equals the product of the day rate and the time saved (hours standard accomplished less hours worked) divided by the hours standard accomplished. It should be noted that the premium may never be greater than the guaranteed day wage, that is, the worker's pay may never exceed twice his day rate.

At and below task, wages equal the rate per hour multiplied by the number of hours worked.

$$W = R_h \times H_w$$

Above task, wages equal the rate per hour multiplied by the hours worked *plus* the quotient of the hours saved (hours standard accomplished less hours worked) divided by the hours standard, times the rate per hour multiplied by the hours worked.

$$W = R_h \times H_w + \frac{(H_s - H_w)}{H_s} \times R_h \times H_w$$

Example: If the rate per hour is \$3 and the number of hours worked is 8, find the gross earnings for a day in which (*a*) Joe Carlstrom accomplished $7\frac{1}{2}$ hours of standard work and (*b*) Tom Meyer accomplished 12 hours of standard work.

(*a*) $$W = \$3 \times 8 = \$24$$

(*b*) $$W = \$3 \times 8 + \frac{(12 - 8)}{12} \times \$3 \times 8$$
$$= \$24 + \$8 = \$32$$

EXERCISE 4

1. The J. H. Cope Mfg. Co. paid its workers by the Gantt task and bonus plan using 130 per cent as the multiplier for work at or above task. If the rate per hour is \$2.75 and task is 66 pieces for an 8-hour day, find the gross earnings of (*a*) Fred Chopin who produced 61 pieces, (*b*) Edward Drohan who produced 66 pieces, and (*c*) Bill Delbrook who produced 72 pieces.

2. The Benson Company paid its workers by the Gantt task and bonus plan using 140 per cent as the multiplier for work at or above task. If the rate per hour is \$2.20 and weekly task is the completion of 120 articles for a 40-hour work week, find the gross weekly earnings of (*a*) Walter Durst who completed 118 articles, (*b*) Louis Fitzsimmons who completed 120 articles, and (*c*) John Paddock who completed 132 articles.

3. The Hand Iron Works paid its workers by the Halsey premium plan giving a bonus of 50 per cent for hours saved. If the rate per hour is \$2.60, find the gross earnings for a 40-hour work week by (*a*) Maury Franklin who accomplished 38.5 hours of standard work and (*b*) Maurice Green who accomplished 45 hours of standard work.

4. The Controlador Corp. paid its workers by the Halsey premium plan giving a bonus of 25 per cent for hours saved. If the rate per hour is \$2.125, find the gross earnings for a 36-hour work week by (*a*) Ben Giddings who accomplished 33 hours of standard work and (*b*) James Merritt who accomplished 42.4 hours of standard work.

5. The Haynes manit plan was used by the Huffman Machine Company in determining its employees' pay. If the rate per manit was \$0.055 and the number of minutes worked 480, find the gross earnings for a day in which (*a*) Edward Haley accomplished 469 manits, (*b*) Herbert Hart accomplished 534 manits, and (*c*) find the premium due the supervisory force for the work of Herbert Hart.

6. The Hutton Corporation paid its employees by the Haynes manit plan. If the rate per manit was \$0.048, find the gross earnings for a 40-hour work week in which (*a*) James Highland accomplished 2,369 manits, (*b*) Frank Herrick accomplished 2,860 manits, and (*c*) find the premium due the supervisory force for the work of Frank Herrick.

7. The Harkleroad Company used the Bedeaux plan in determining its employees' wages. If the rate per "B" was \$0.045 and the number of hours worked 10, find the gross earnings for a day in which (*a*) Kenneth Hanson accomplished 574 B's, (*b*) Charles Holstein accomplished 680 B's, and (*c*) find the premium due the supervisory force for the work of Charles Holstein.

8. The Bedeaux plan was adopted by the Fairmount Co., Inc., in paying its manufacturing personnel. If the rate per "B" was $0.0525 and the number of hours worked biweekly was 80, find the gross earnings for the period of (*a*) Templeton Johnson who accomplished 4,329 B's, (*b*) Roderick Stewart who accomplished 5,480 B's, and (*c*) find the premium due the supervisory force for the work of Roderick Stewart.

9. The Emerson wage payment plan was adopted by the Marston Company. If the hourly wage rate was $2.80, find the gross earnings for a 36-hour work week by (*a*) Arthur Kirk who accomplished 22.75 hours of standard time, (*b*) Harry Drew who accomplished 30 hours of standard time, and (*c*) Ralph Lucas who accomplished 43.6 hours of standard time.

10. The Raleigh Lage Company compensated its employees by the Emerson wage payment plan. If the hourly rate was $3.20, find the gross earnings for an 8-hour day by (*a*) Elwood Marshall who accomplished 5.2 hours of standard time, (*b*) Ben Steel who accomplished 6.8 hours of standard time, and (*c*) Willard Murdock who accomplished 10.4 hours of standard time.

11. The Lutkehaus Corporation paid its employees by the Rowan plan. If the rate per hour was $3.25 and number of hours worked 8, find the gross earnings for a day in which (*a*) Everett Stacy accomplished 7.75 hours of standard work and (*b*) Cleveland Linville accomplished 13.5 hours of standard work.

12. The Rowan plan of wage payment was used by the Winston Company. If the rate per hour was $2.875 and the number of hours worked during the week was 40, find the gross earnings for the week of (*a*) James Morrill who accomplished 32 hours of standard work and (*b*) Joseph Milliken who accomplished 54 hours of standard work.

UNIT 5. Commission Wage Payments

Employees whose productivity can be measured in terms of dollars or units of sales are often compensated for their efforts by means of commissions. Though many variations may be used, the following methods of computation are perhaps the most frequent:

1. Straight commission
2. Commission and bonus
3. Salary plus commission
4. Quota-bonus plan

Straight Commission. Workers paid on a straight commission basis have no guaranteed wages but are paid only commissions earned. Commissions are computed as a per cent of some base (usually sales), though sometimes they are a fixed number of dollars per item.

Example: William Fox, a salesman of vacuum cleaners, receives $32.50 for each cleaner sold plus 25 per cent commission for all accessories and supplies. Find his total income for a month in which he sells 14 cleaners and $237.40 worth of accessories and supplies.

$ 32.50 × 14	=	$455.00
237.40 × .25	=	59.35
Total earnings	=	$514.35

Commission and Bonus. Salesmen whose travel expenses are paid by their employers may be given a bonus in the form of higher commission rates for increased productivity. Since travel expenses do not increase necessarily with increased sales, the employer may be able to offer higher rates of commission for sales beyond certain fixed minimums.

Example: James Bryant, a salesman for Eli Walker Manufacturing Company, is compensated for all travel expenses, is allowed a drawing account of $600 per month, and receives a monthly commission of 2 per cent of his first $30,000 of sales, 2.5 per cent of the next $10,000 of sales, and 3 per cent for all sales in excess of $40,000. Find the amount due him for a month in which his travel expenses paid out of pocket total $332.75, his drawings are $600, and sales total $41,180.

$30,000 × .02	=	$ 600.00	
10,000 × .025	=	250.00	
1,180 × .03	=	35.40	
$41,180		$ 885.40	Commissions
		+332.75	Travel expense
Total due	=	$1,218.15	
Less drawing account	=	600.00	
Amount due	=	$ 618.15	

Salary Plus Commission. Sales employees, particularly in the retail trade, are often paid a salary plus a commission based on sales.

Example: Miss Anka Perisich worked as a salesclerk in the dress department of a specialty shop. She received $110 semimonthly salary plus a commission of 1 per cent of monthly sales. During the month of April, her sales were $3,680. Find her total earnings for the month.

Salary for month	=	$ 110 × 2	=	$220.00
Plus commission	=	3,680 × .01	=	36.80
Total earnings			=	$256.80

Quota-bonus Plan. A method frequently used by retail stores in computing the pay of sales employees is to pay a weekly salary plus a bonus (commission) on all sales in excess of a quarterly quota established on the basis of each employee's sales in the preceding quarter.

Example: Jack Brady, a men's clothing salesman, was paid by the quota-bonus plan. It was the store policy to pay its salesmen a guaranteed weekly wage for each 13-week period (quarter year). During the first quarter of the year, his sales had been $22,186, and this sum became his quota for the second quarter. His guaranteed pay for the second quarter was based on a 6 per cent rate of commission, and so his weekly wage was computed as follows:

$$\frac{\$22{,}186 \times .06}{13} = \frac{\$1{,}331.16}{13} = \$102.40 \text{ per week wage guarantee}$$

If his sales for the second quarter were $25,690, find (*a*) his bonus at 6 per cent of sales exceeding the quota, (*b*) his quota for the third quarter, and (*c*) his weekly wage guarantee during the third quarter.

(*a*) $(\$25{,}690 - \$22{,}186) \times .06 = \$3{,}504 \times .06 = \$210.24$ bonus
(*b*) $25,690 is quota for third quarter
(*c*) $\frac{\$25{,}690 \times .06}{13} = \frac{\$1{,}541.40}{13} = \$118.57$ per week wage guarantee

If the sales made by Jack Brady in the third quarter were less than $25,690, he would fail to earn a bonus, this lower sales figure would become his quota for the fourth quarter, and his weekly wage guarantee would be reduced. Thus if his sales in the third quarter totaled $23,980, this sum would become his quota for the fourth period, and his weekly wage guarantee during the fourth quarter would be computed as follows:

$$\frac{\$23{,}980 \times .06}{13} = \frac{\$1{,}438.80}{13} = \$110.68 \text{ per week wage guarantee}$$

EXERCISE 5

1. For making a 12-year lease at $320 per month on a piece of business property, a real-estate broker charged 4 per cent on the first 5 years' rental income and $3\frac{1}{4}$ per cent on the balance of the rental income. Find his total commission.
2. For obtaining an exclusive listing on property, a real-estate salesman received 15 per cent of half of the 5 per cent selling commission charged by the realty firm, and if he made the sale himself he was entitled to an additional half of the realty firm's commission charge. If he obtained an exclusive listing at $16,000, find (*a*) his listing commission if some other party made the sale and (*b*) the combined commissions total that he would receive if he made the sale.
3. A clothing salesman in a men's store was paid a commission of $7\frac{1}{2}$ per cent of his sales. If his sales were $188 on Monday, $316 on Tuesday, $284 on Wednesday, $308 on Thursday, $325 on Friday, and $507 on Saturday, find his total commissions for the week.
4. James McConnell, a salesman, was reimbursed for his travel expenses and received a commission of 11 per cent on his first $45,000 of sales, 13.5 per cent

GOULD'S MEN'S SHOP
Payroll for Week Ending Jan. 24, 19__

Name	Withholding exemptions	Net sales						Total sales	Com. rate	Total earned	Deductions				Net earned
		M	T	W	T	F	S				Union dues	F.I.C.A.	Inc. tax	Total ded.	
Austin, A.	2	$506	$365	$548	$146	$627	$921	$3,113	4%	$124.52	$1.10	$2.80	$17.40	$21.30	$103.22
Berman, L.	0		321	482	211	395	479		7%						
Cooper, L.	1	430		522	204	475	621		5%						
Dryden, B.	5	126	448		366	310	513		5%						
Hanson, R.	4	723	221	356		445	897		3%						
Jensen, M.	3	183	363	409	277		504		8%						
Totals									xx						

on the next $20,000 of sales, and 16 per cent on all sales above $65,000. If his travel expenses for the year were $8,212 and his sales were $80,062, find the total of his expenses and commissions.

5. Sam Smith, a salesman of orthopedic supplies, receives 10 per cent on sales up to and including $50,000, and 15 per cent on all sales above $50,000. He is compensated for his traveling expenses and is allowed a drawing account of $400 per month. During the past year his sales were $63,750 and his unreimbursed travel expenses were $1,280. He has withdrawn all of his drawing account. Find the gross amount due Mr. Smith.

6. Evelyn Kerkof, a saleswoman in the ready-to-wear section of a large department store, was paid a semimonthly salary of $105 and a commission of $2\frac{1}{4}$ per cent on all sales. Find her total gross earnings during a month in which her sales were $5,103.

7. Roger Ziegler, a shoe salesman in a woman's specialty store, was paid on the quota-bonus plan. His guaranteed weekly salary was $110 per week and his bonus was 8 per cent of all sales in excess of $17,875 during the 13-week quarter. If his sales were $19,012.50 for the quarter, find (*a*) his bonus, (*b*) his total earnings for the quarter, and (*c*) the weekly wage guarantee that he would receive in the following quarter based on 8 per cent of his sales of $19,012.50.

8. Complete the payroll record of the Gould's Men's Shop (page 202). Deduct $1.10 from each employee's pay for union dues, $2\frac{1}{4}$ per cent F.I.C.A. tax, and Federal income tax withholding in the amounts as indicated by the weekly wage-bracket withholding table (pages 178–179). Note that the per cent of commission on sales is variable.

UNIT 6. Commission Accounts

Sometimes it is impractical for manufacturers, wholesalers, retailers, and produce growers to assume all the selling or buying functions. Therefore they appoint others to act for them as selling or purchasing agents. The individuals or firms who act as the agents of others in selling or purchasing are known as commission merchants, agents, or brokers.

Account Sales. Many articles in daily use are not sold to wholesalers or retailers, but are delivered to them on consignment. When goods are "sold on consignment," the consignor (owner) retains title to the goods, can remove them at will, and merely delivers the goods to the consignee (wholesaler or retailer) who consummates the sale. When sold, the consignee pays the consignor for the goods, deducting a commission for selling and expenses such as freight, cartage, storage, insurance, etc. Most frequently sold under such an arrangement are food products, although manufacturers, wholesalers, and retailers of other types of goods will on occasion "sell" on a consignment basis.

As an example, a grower sends a carload of onions on consignment to a city commission merchant. The commission merchant pays the freight, cartage, storage, and other expenses, sells the goods for the highest obtainable price (gross proceeds), and after deducting these expenses and the agreed commission remits the net proceeds to the grower, together with an *account sales* in which all details of the transaction are recorded. An illustrative example of an account sales follows.

ACCOUNT SALES

February 24, 19__

GEORGE JOHNSON & SONS

Commission Merchants

St. Louis, Missouri

Sold for account of:

Sunkist Fruit Growers, Los Angeles, Calif.

19__					
Feb.	18	245 crates oranges	@ $7.20	$1,764.00	
	21	125 crates oranges	@ 6.95	868.75	
	23	130 crates oranges	@ 7.05	916.50	
		Gross proceeds			$3,549.25
		Charges:			
		Freight		$ 109.85	
		Cartage		27.50	
		Storage		42.40	
		Commission, 7% of $3,549.25		248.45	428.20
		Net proceeds			$3,121.05

Account Purchases. A second type of commission man buys for his client instead of selling for him. For example, if a large store wishes to secure a shipment of oriental rugs, it may commission an agent who will select and purchase the rugs, perhaps in Pakistan, send them by caravan to the nearest port, and then ship them by water and rail to the store. The agent will total his costs including freight, insurance, commission, etc., add this sum to the purchase price of the rugs and then bill the store accordingly for the gross cost in the form of an *account purchase.*

Commissions for this type of buying are based ordinarily on the purchase price (prime cost) of the goods, not on the purchase price plus expenses. The accompanying is an illustrative example of an account purchase.

ACCOUNT PURCHASE

June 15, 19__

FREYBERG & COMPANY
Commission Merchants
San Francisco, California

Bought for account of:

Wellman Black, Salt Lake City, Utah

19__				
June	14	1,500 lb. Hill Bros. coffee $1.18	$1,770.00	
		2,300 lb. Folger coffee 1.195	2,748.50	
		Prime cost		$4,518.50
		Charges:		
		Insured freight	$ 114.60	
		Commission, 2% of $4,518.50	90.37	204.97
		Gross cost		$4,723.47

EXERCISE 6

1. **Complete** the following account sales:

ACCOUNT SALES

May 10, 19__

BEN DRYDEN
Commission Merchant
San Francisco, Calif.

Sold for account of:

Acme Company, Chicago, Ill.

19__				
May	5	27 crates eggs @ $22.40		
	7	32 crates eggs @ 22.70		
	8	55 crates eggs @ 16.30		
	9	22 crates eggs @ 16.00		
		Gross proceeds		
		Charges:		
		Express	$64.45	
		Storage	15.75	
		Commission, 4%		
		Net proceeds		

2. Complete the following account sales:

ACCOUNT SALES

Sept. 7, 19__

PACIOTTI & SONS

Commission Merchants

Latonia, Ky.

Sold for account of:

Goldstone Company, Cincinnati, Ohio

19__				
Sept.	5	25 crates cauliflower @ $7.50		
	5	235 bundles celery @ 2.60		
	6	85 crates cauliflower @ 7.86		
	6	550 bundles celery @ 2.63		
		Gross proceeds		
		Charges:		
		Freight	$49.30	
		Storage	13.75	
		Commission, 3%		
		Net proceeds		

3. Complete the following account purchase:

ACCOUNT PURCHASE

Feb. 19, 19__

BEACH BAKER & COMPANY

Commission Merchants

Madison, Wisconsin

Bought for account of:

Independent Grocers Association, Los Angeles, Calif.

19__				
Feb.	16	7,500 lb. Wisconsin Swiss @ $0.97		
	16	1,575 lb. American cheddar @ 0.885		
	19	2,250 lb. domestic blue @ 1.13		
		Prime cost		
		Charges:		
		Freight	$248.60	
		Cartage	56.25	
		Commission, $1\frac{1}{2}$%		
		Gross cost		

4. Complete the following account purchase:

ACCOUNT PURCHASE

June 9, 19__

JAMES E. HENRY CO.

Commission Merchants

San Francisco, California

Bought for account of:

R. H. Green Company, Indianapolis, Ind.

19__				
June	8	5,800 lb. White Bros. coffee @ $1.06		
	8	600 crates tomatoes @ 1.97		
	8	275 crates #1 cling peaches @ 2.08		
	9	430 crates #2 avocadoes @ 3.52		
		Prime cost		
		Charges:		
		Freight, coffee	$186.80	
		Freight, refrigerator	334.50	
		Commission, 2%		
		Gross cost		

CHAPTER VI

PERSONAL AND BUSINESS INSURANCE

Insurance is a form of financial protection against loss or damage caused by a contingent or unforeseen event. Indemnification to the one suffering the loss is made by a carrier (usually a corporation) organized for the purpose of rendering the service of insurance.

The *insured* is the one who carries the insurance or financial protection against loss.

The *insurer* or *underwriter* is the carrier that assures payment of the stipulated loss according to contract provisions if the specified contingency occurs.

The *parties* to the usual insurance contract are the insurer and the insured.

The *policy* is the contract whereby the insurer agrees to indemnify (compensate) the insured for the loss, damage, or accident or injury arising within a given period of time from certain stipulated causes as provided by the policy.

The *premium* is the amount paid (usually at yearly intervals) by the insured for the protection provided by the policy.

The *risk* is the contemplated or unforeseen hazard for which the policy provides indemnification.

The *beneficiary* is the one to whom the proceeds of a policy are payable. This may be the insured himself or someone or several others whom the insured designates.

The *face* is the limit of the protection afforded for the one or several contingencies for which the policy provides.

Problems in insurance are solved by the principles of percentage: The face of the policy is equivalent to *base;* the rate of premium, usually quoted in terms of \$100, \$1,000, \$5,000, or \$10,000 units, is equivalent to *rate;* and the premium is equivalent to *percentage.*

Insurance is based on the principle of participation in or division of risk. If a loss to any one or several individuals is spread over a large number of individuals, the loss will not be an excessive burden on any one or several individuals. The larger the number of people participating, the greater will be the division of risk.

All insurance, whether it is life, health, fire, accident, public liability, or any of the hundreds of other types available, is based on the principle of division or distribution of risk. Premiums or charges for insurance are calculated upon the statistical probability of loss, the rate for a given face varying according to the varying likelihood of the specified loss occurring.

Insurance exists for the protection of the insured, not for the purpose of insuring at a profit if loss should occur. Therefore the amount paid cannot be greater than the loss, regardless of the face of the policy. Furthermore, if the loss is larger than the face of the policy, only the face will be paid, and the loss in excess of the face must be borne by the insured.

UNIT 1. Life Insurance

In most types of insurance, the underwriter makes payment upon the occurrence of a contingency which may or may not occur. In many instances, since losses do not occur, no payments are made; if losses do occur, they may be in an amount considerably less than the face of the policy. For example, a house may not burn, it may burn partially, or it may be a total loss.

It is obvious that life insurance is essentially different, for death of the insured and payment of the entire face of the policy by the insurer will eventually occur (provided, of course, the policy is in force at the time of the insured's death). The uncertainty in life insurance is not whether the contingency insured against will ultimately occur and the face of the policy must be paid in full but rather when this eventuality will occur. Furthermore, the risk increases progressively with the age of the insured. Also, the contract is not an indemnity contract but provides for payment as specified; that is, the economic value of the deceased is not material to the payment.

Additional Protection Available in Life-insurance Policies. A wide range of supplementary risks may be included in life-insurance contracts, each of course resulting in an increase in the amount of the premium. In comparing policies offered by different companies, among other considerations, it is necessary to consider the value of the additional protection that may be offered by some of the policies. Thus a policy for which the premiums seem to be lowest may be highest if the optional protection afforded by other policies is also purchased.

Some of the more commonly included additional protections are:

1. Double indemnity in event of death by accidental means
2. Waiver of premium in event of total disability
3. Periodic payments (usually monthly) in the event of total disability
4. Annuities or lump-sum payments upon attainment of a predetermined age or stipulated number of premium payments

Ownership of Life-insurance Companies. Ownership of life-insurance companies may be classified as of two kinds:

1. *Stock companies* are life-insurance companies owned by stockholders (just as in any corporation) who have supplied capital or purchased stock as an investment. Ordinarily, in companies of this type all earnings from investments, excess premium charges, and other savings belong to the stockholders. However, in some stock companies provision is made for limited participation in earnings by the policyholders.

2. *Mutual companies* are life-insurance companies owned by the policyholders. Earnings from investments, excess premium charges, and other savings belong to the policyholders and are used as additional reserves against possible future loss or are returned to the participating policyholders in the form of dividends. These dividends may be withdrawn by the insured, applied as part payment on the next premium, or left with the insurance company to purchase additional insurance or to pay up the policy.

Dividends from Life-insurance Policies. Insurance policies are commonly classified as to participation in earnings:

1. *Participating policies* entitle the holder to share in the earnings of the company.

2. *Nonparticipating policies* do not entitle the holder to share in the earnings of the company.

Premiums for life-insurance policies are based on actuarial tables, that is, tables of life expectancy. From these tables is determined the amount of premium (and/or number of premiums) that individuals of given ages must contribute in order to build funds equivalent to the face of the policies at the time of probable death of the insured.

Conservative practice among insurance companies is to charge higher rates than actuarial tables would indicate. This is particularly true in participating policies.

Therefore, in comparing the costs of participating and nonparticipating policies, it is necessary to consider the factor of dividends as a decrease in the gross cost of the participating policies. Thus the net cost of a participating policy in a company that has paid in the past (and probably will pay in the future) a comparatively high rate of dividend may be lower than the net cost of a participating policy with a company offering a lower annual premium but also a lower rate of dividend. And the net cost of a participating policy may be less than a nonparticipating policy the yearly premium of which is considerably smaller.

Kinds of Life-insurance Policies. Among the many available types of life-insurance policies, the most frequently selected, in order of premium cost from lowest to highest, are (1) term, (2) ordinary life (also known as straight life), (3) limited payment, (4) and endowment.

Term Insurance. Term life insurance is sold for a fixed term of years, usually for periods of 1, 5, 10, 15, or 20 years. It is usually nonparticipating and at maturity has no cash or paid-up value. Protection other than life insurance is rarely included, and no return is made by the insurer unless the insured dies within the specified term of years the contract is in force.

At the expiration of the term of the insurance, both premiums and insurance cease. Frequently, term insurance is convertible to other types of insurance, within a limited and specified period of time, by payment of higher premiums at the attained age.

Of all the life insurance available, term-insurance premiums are the lowest as they do not combine savings with protection.

Ordinary Life. Ordinary life policies are those in which the insured agrees to pay the insurer a specified premium each year until death, the insurer agreeing to pay the face of the policy to the estate of the insured or to the person or persons designated as beneficiaries.

In this type of policy, the insured combines a moderate amount of saving with protection. Excess of premiums over actual cost to the insurer builds for the insured a cash surrender value, a paid-up value, a borrowing collateral, or the right to purchase extended term insurance.

Limited Payment. Limited-payment policies are those in which the insured agrees to make premium payments for a specified number of years, usually 20, although 10-, 15-, and 30-year payments are not uncommon. They may also be purchased with maturity dates at some desired age of the insured, such as 55, 60, or 65 years.

In this type of policy the insured usually selects, as a specified number of years, the time during which his earnings will probably be the greatest and premium payments will be the easiest to meet without undue sacrifice.

Premiums are sufficiently higher than ordinary life premiums to accumulate a sum sufficient to mature the policy in the time specified. Upon completion of premium payments for the specified number of years, the premium ceases and the policy remains in force until death. Cash surrender value, paid-up value, borrowing collateral, and the amount of extended term insurance accumulate more rapidly than in ordinary life policies because of the higher premium rate.

Endowment. As in limited-payment policies, endowment policies are purchased with maturity dates of 10, 15, 20, 30, or even 35 years. They may also be purchased with maturity dates at some desired age of the insured, such as 55, 60, or 65 years.

If death occurs before the maturity date, the estate or beneficiaries receive the face of the policy. If the insured is alive at maturity date, the insured receives the face of the policy.

Premiums are considerably higher for this type of life insurance, for they must include not only protection but also an amount sufficient to create a fund during the maturing period that is equivalent to the face of the policy. Cash surrender value, paid-up value, borrowing value, and the amount of extended term insurance also accumulate rapidly.

Premiums. The following are excerpts from premium tables of large insurance companies. Rates vary slightly from company to company, and these given here are simply close approximations of those offered by most life-insurance companies.

Annual Premium Rates for $1,000 Policies in Companies A and B[1]

Age at issue	Co. A and Co. B 10-year term	Ordinary life		20-payment life		20-year endowment	
		Co. A participating	Co. B nonparticipating	Co. A participating	Co. B nonparticipating	Co. A participating	Co. B nonparticipating
18	$ 8.17	$18.44	$13.80	$28.53	$22.40	$48.18	$42.82
19	8.25	18.81	14.14	28.95	22.80	48.33	42.85
20	8.33	19.21	14.49	29.39	23.20	48.48	42.89
21	8.39	19.62	14.86	29.84	23.61	48.63	42.92
22	8.44	20.06	15.23	30.31	24.04	48.79	42.96
23	8.49	20.51	15.63	30.80	24.48	48.96	42.99
24	8.53	20.99	16.04	31.31	24.93	49.14	43.03
25	8.58	21.49	16.47	31.83	25.40	49.33	43.07
30	8.96	24.38	18.95	34.76	28.02	50.43	43.41
35	10.00	28.11	22.19	38.34	31.34	51.91	44.18
40	12.13	33.01	26.48	42.79	35.51	54.06	45.60
45	15.83	39.55	32.09	48.52	40.76	57.34	48.01
50	21.59	48.48	39.52	56.17	47.91	62.55	51.94
55	30.89	60.72	49.39	66.69	56.31	70.81	58.71
60	44.88	77.69	62.55	81.60	72.60	83.82	68.40

NOTE: Semiannual rate, 52% of annual; quarterly rate, 26.5% of annual; monthly rate, 8.875% of annual. These multipliers vary slightly between companies.

[1] This is a table for males. Because of their greater life expectancy, rates for females are approximately those of a male of 5 to 6 years younger.

To read the table, find in the first column the age of the insured to nearest birthday. The horizontal amount in dollars and cents is the annual premium on $1,000 units (for the age indicated in the first column) for the type of insurance specified at the head of each column.

Example 1: Mr. Arnold is 22 years old on his nearest birthday. What annual premium will he pay for $5,000 worth of (*a*) 10-year term, (*b*) Company A participating ordinary life, (*c*) Company B nonparticipating 20-payment life?

(*a*) Annual premium per $1,000, 10-year term = $ 8.44
Annual premium for $5,000 = $8.44 × 5 = $42.20
(*b*) Annual premium per $1,000, participating ordinary life = $20.06
Annual premium for $5,000 = $20.06 × 5 = $100.30
(*c*) Annual premium per $1,000, nonparticipating 20-pay life = $24.04
Annual premium for $5,000 = $24.04 × 5 = $120.20

Example 2: Mr. Beddow is 21 years of age on his nearest birthday. If he purchases $6,000 worth of Company B nonparticipating 20-year endowment insurance, what will be the (*a*) annual premium, (*b*) semiannual premium, (*c*) quarterly premium, (*d*) monthly premium?

Annual premium $1,000, nonparticipating, 20-year endowment = $42.92

(*a*) Annual premium for $6,000 = $42.92 × 6 = $257.52
(*b*) Semiannual premium for $6,000 = $257.52 × .52 = $133.91
(*c*) Quarterly premium for $6,000 = $257.52 × .265 = $68.24
(*d*) Monthly premium for $6,000 = $257.52 × .08875 = $22.85

EXERCISE 1

Use the table of annual premium rates for $1,000 policies (page 212) in solving the following problems:

1. If ages at issue are 21, 30, and 50, find the cost of the following $5,000 policies at each age: (*a*) 10-year term, (*b*) Company A participating ordinary life, (*c*) Company B nonparticipating ordinary life, (*d*) Company A participating 20-payment life, (*e*) Company B nonparticipating 20-payment life, (*f*) Company A participating 20-year endowment, and (*g*) Company B nonparticipating 20-year endowment.
2. Mr. Bedford will be 25 on next Oct. 15. On Mar. 4 he purchases Company A's $9,000 participating 20-year endowment policy. How much is his semiannual premium?
3. Mr. Ash, now 22 years of age, purchases Company B's $12,000 nonparticipating ordinary life policy on May 6. His next birthday will be Aug. 25. How much is his quarterly premium?
4. On June 17 Mr. King purchases Company A's $6,000 participating ordinary life policy. He will be 20 years of age on Nov. 5. How much is his monthly premium?
5. Mr. Newton purchased Company B's $35,000 nonparticipating 20-payment life policy at the age of 40. Find the (*a*) annual premium, (*b*) semiannual premium, (*c*) quarterly premium, and (*d*) monthly premium.
6. Mr. Palmer, aged 45, purchases $15,000 worth of 10-year term insurance and Company B's $10,000 nonparticipating 20-year endowment policy. What are his total payments each quarter?

7. On his twentieth birthday, Mr. Quinn purchases Company A's $2,000 participating ordinary life policy. How much will he save yearly if he pays his premiums semiannually instead of monthly?
8. Mr. Babcock, aged 55, purchases Company B's $25,000 nonparticipating 20-payment life policy. How much will he save over the 20-year period if he pays premiums annually instead of quarterly?
9. If Mr. Nixon, who was 21 on Jan. 17, purchases a $4,000 10-year term policy on July 8, what would be the (*a*) annual premiums (*b*) yearly cost of semiannual premiums, (*c*) yearly cost of quarterly premiums, and (*d*) yearly cost of monthly premiums?
10. Mr. Robert's birthday is Oct. 15. The first week in the April preceding his twenty-fifth birthday, he considers taking out Company A's participating 20-payment life policy for $8,000. How much will he save (*a*) on each annual premium and (*b*) over the 20-year period on annual premiums if he purchases the policy prior to Apr. 16?

UNIT 2. Privileges Attached to Most Life-insurance Policies

In casualty insurance, if the insured cancels his policy, he receives a refund.

In life insurance, each policyholder (except in term insurance) is theoretically accumulating with the insurer a fund sufficient in size to pay the beneficiary the face of the policy at the time of the insured's death or upon maturity of the policy. Because this fund does accumulate, life-insurance contracts (except in term insurance) ordinarily provide for reimbursement of the insured if he decides to discontinue his policy.

Because of selling costs, these values are ordinarily not considered as having accumulated until 2 or 3 years' premiums have been paid. However, this period of time varies between companies and policies, and in a few instances value is considered as having accumulated after payment of the first premium.

At the end of the specified time, insurance policies may be surrendered with the following optional privileges of the policyholders: (1) cash surrender value, (2) paid-up value, (3) or extended term insurance.

Cash surrender value is the amount of money the policyholder receives as a lump sum if he surrenders the policy. The amounts vary with the types of policies and amounts and numbers of premiums paid.

Paid-up value is the amount of the paid-up insurance for life the insured will receive if he surrenders the policy.

Extended term insurance is the length of time during which the face of the policy will continue as term insurance. If the policyholder allows his premiums to become in default, most insurance companies arbitrarily purchase extended term insurance unless state laws require otherwise.

An additional privilege attached to most insurance policies (but not usually to term insurance) is the right of the holder to borrow without surrendering the policy or the protection afforded by the policy.

Borrowing may be made by the policyholder in an amount up to but not in excess of the cash surrender value of the policy. The usual interest charge paid by the insured for borrowing is 5 or 6 per cent.

Cash Surrender Value. The following are excerpts from tables of certain large companies giving cash surrender values on ordinary life, 20-payment life, and 20-year endowment policies, both participating and nonparticipating. Term-insurance policies rarely have cash surrender values. Only ages 20, 25, 30, 35, and 40 for origin of the policies and cash surrender values after 5, 10, 15, and 20 years are included in these tables. The amounts given here will vary slightly from company to company, these being simply close approximations.

Cash Surrender Value, Ordinary Life, $1,000 Policies in Companies A and B

Age at issue	Premiums		Co. A participating				Co. B nonparticipating			
	Co. A participating	Co. B nonparticipating	5 yr.	10 yr.	15 yr.	20 yr.	5 yr.	10 yr.	15 yr.	20 yr.
20	$19.21	$14.49	$27	$ 71	$122	$192	$29	$ 77	$131	$192
25	21.49	16.47	35	88	150	230	36	94	157	230
30	24.38	18.95	44	108	183	276	44	114	190	276
35	28.11	22.19	54	131	221	327	54	138	229	328
40	33.01	26.48	66	159	264	383	67	167	273	383

Cash Surrender Value, 20-payment Life, $1,000 Policies in Companies A and B

Age at issue	Premiums		Co. A participating				Co. B nonparticipating			
	Co. A participating	Co. B nonparticipating	5 yr.	10 yr.	15 yr.	20 yr.	5 yr.	10 yr.	15 yr.	20 yr.
20	$29.39	$23.20	$ 69	$170	$297	$459	$ 70	$180	$307	$459
25	31.83	25.40	76	188	326	504	77	198	338	505
30	34.76	28.02	84	207	360	555	86	219	373	555
35	38.34	31.34	94	231	397	609	96	242	411	610
40	42.79	35.51	106	259	436	666	107	268	451	667

Cash Surrender Value, 20-year Endowment, $1,000 Policies in Companies A and B

Age at issue	Premiums		Co. A participating				Co. B nonparticipating			
	Co. A participating	Co. B nonparticipating	5 yr.	10 yr.	15 yr.	20 yr.	5 yr.	10 yr.	15 yr.	20 yr.
20	$48.48	$42.89	$161	$384	$652	$1,000	$157	$388	$666	$1,000
25	49.33	43.07	161	383	651	1,000	155	387	665	1,000
30	50.43	43.41	161	383	650	1,000	154	385	663	1,000
35	51.91	44.18	161	383	649	1,000	152	384	662	1,000
40	54.06	45.60	162	383	648	1,000	151	383	661	1,000

To find the net cost of a nonparticipating policy, the cash surrender value should be subtracted from the total premium cost.

$$\text{Net cost of nonparticipating policy} = \text{total premiums} - \text{cash surrender value}$$

To find the net cost of a participating policy, an additional factor, *dividends*, must also be deducted as well as cash surrender value from the total premium cost.

$$\text{Net cost of participating policy} = \text{total premiums} - \text{total dividends} - \text{cash surrender value}$$

Dividends. The following excerpts from the tables of Company A are used to illustrate cash surrender values of participating policies.

Accumulated Dividends on Company A, $1,000 Participating Policies

Age at issue	Ordinary life				20-payment life				20-year endowment			
	Premium	5 yr.	10 yr.	20 yr.	Premium	5 yr.	10 yr.	20 yr.	Premium	5 yr.	10 yr.	20 yr.
20	$19.21	$20.99	$53.94	$150.07	$29.39	$24.22	$64.91	$173.05	$48.48	$24.21	$67.68	$173.39
25	21.49	22.58	57.66	155.64	31.83	25.40	66.74	176.90	49.33	25.78	72.41	182.09
30	24.38	24.32	61.09	160.46	34.76	27.77	77.00	184.61	50.43	28.93	77.87	191.50
35	28.11	25.94	64.62	166.37	38.34	30.14	75.26	192.33	51.91	32.08	83.34	200.92
40	33.01	28.21	69.20	175.92	42.79	32.31	79.61	202.18	54.06	35.13	88.99	211.71

NOTE: Insurance underwriters have complete tables similar to this for all ages, all types of participating policies, and all dividend periods—both past and estimated in the future.

With information as to both cash surrender value of participating and nonparticipating policies and accumulated dividend payments on participating policies, it is possible to compare the net cost of participating and nonparticipating policies (assuming interest that might be earned on premiums is not considered).

Example: Mr. Peterson, 25 years old on his nearest birthday, wishes to compare the net cost (not including interest on premiums) of Company A participating and Company B nonparticipating ordinary life policies for $1,000 after a duration of 5 years.

From preceding tables, Company B nonparticipating policy for $1,000, age 25, is as follows:

Annual premium = $16.47		
5-year premium = $16.47 × 5	=	$82.35
Cash surrender value	=	−36.00
Net cost	=	$46.35

From preceding tables, Company A participating policy for $1,000, age 25, is as follows:

Annual premium = $21.49		
5-year premium = 21.49 × 5 =		$107.45
Cash surrender value =	$35.00	
Dividends for 5 years =	22.58	
Total deduction =		−57.58
Net cost =		$ 49.87

Paid-up and Extended Term Insurance. The table on page 218 shows the difference in cash surrender value and paid-up value. It also shows the extended term insurance for $1,000 that may be purchased at the option of the insured when he surrenders his policy.

Such tables are available for all kinds of policies (except term insurance). However, for purposes of illustration, only tables for $1,000 nonparticipating ordinary life policies issued at ages 20 and 30 are shown here. Cash surrender value, paid-up insurance value, and extended term insurance would of course be greater in limited-payment and endowment policies.

Example: Mr. Schulman purchased an $8,000 Company B nonparticipating ordinary life policy 6 years ago at the age of 20. What is (*a*) the cash surrender value, (*b*) the paid-up value, and (*c*) for how many days can he select extended term insurance at the same face?

(*a*) From the table:

Cash surrender value of \$1,000 policy after 6 years = \$38

Therefore

cash surrender value of \$8,000 policy = \$38 × 8 = \$304

(*b*) From the table:

Paid-up value of \$1,000 policy after 6 years = \$106

Therefore

paid-up value of \$8,000 policy = \$106 × 8 = \$848

(*c*) From the table:

Extended term insurance on \$1,000 after 6 years = 5 years 57 days

Therefore

extended term insurance on \$8,000 policy is also 5 years 57 days

When the insured defaults on premiums and fails to specify cash or paid-up insurance in some other form, the insurer usually elects extended term insurance at the same face as the original policy.

Cash Surrender Value, Paid-up Value, and Extended Term Insurance for Company B \$1,000 Nonparticipating Ordinary Life Policies (to Nearest Dollars)

Age 20, premiums \$14.49				End of policy year	Age 30, premiums \$18.95			
Cash surren-der value	Paid-up value	Extended term insurance			Cash surren-der value	Paid-up value	Extended term insurance	
		Years	Days				Years	Days
\$ 10	\$ 30	1	129	3	\$ 18	\$ 44	2	47
19	55	2	205	4	31	74	3	253
29	81	3	302	5	44	105	5	107
38	106	5	57	6	57	135	6	332
48	131	6	199	7	71	164	8	190
58	156	7	358	8	86	194	10	27
68	178	9	114	9	100	221	11	149
77	201	10	241	10	114	247	12	223
87	223	12	7	11	128	274	13	244
98	245	13	139	12	143	300	14	210
108	267	14	243	13	158	326	15	185
119	289	15	325	14	174	351	15	359
131	311	16	364	15	190	377	16	183
142	333	17	354	16	207	402	16	334
154	354	18	298	17	223	426	17	85
166	376	19	198	18	241	450	17	172
179	397	20	44	19	258	474	17	231
192	418	20	217	20	276	497	17	267

EXERCISE 2

1. Mr. Ziegler at the age of 20 purchases Company A's $7,000 participating ordinary life policy. What is the cash surrender value 5 years later?
2. At the age of 30, Mr. Lane purchased Company A's participating 20-payment life policy of $7,500. What cash surrender value does it have when he becomes 45?
3. If purchased at the age of 35, what is the cash surrender value at the age of 55 on the following Company A policies, each for $12,000: (*a*) participating ordinary life, (*b*) participating 20-payment life, (*c*) participating 20-year endowment?
4. Mr. Bell purchased Company A's $13,000 participating ordinary life policy 15 years ago, when he was 40. What is the maximum amount that he may now borrow on the policy?
5. Mr. Taylor, who is 30 years old on his nearest birthday, wishes to compare the net cost (not including interest on premiums) of a Company A participating and a Company B nonparticipating ordinary life policy for $8,000 after 10 years' time. What is (*a*) the net cost of the Company A participating policy and (*b*) the net cost of the Company B nonparticipating policy?
6. At the age of 30, Mr. Caldron purchased Company B's $5,000 nonparticipating 20-payment life policy. At the same time, Mr. Gates, also 30 years old, purchased Company A's $5,000 participating 20-payment life policy. After 5 years, what was the net cost (not including interest on premiums) of (*a*) Mr. Caldron's policy, (*b*) Mr. Gates's policy?
7. Mr. Irving, who is 20, is undecided between Company A's $3,000 participating and Company B's $3,000 nonparticipating 20-year endowment policies. After 20 years what would be the net cost or net return (not including interest on premiums) (*a*) of the participating policy, (*b*) of the nonparticipating policy?
8. Find the net cost or net return on the following (*a*) Company A participating and (*b*) Company B nonparticipating policies:

Face of policy	Age at issue	Kind of policy	Years in force
15,000	35	20-payment life	20
7,000	25	20-year endowment	20
5,000	30	Ordinary life	10

9. Mr. Foster purchased Company B's $7,500 nonparticipating ordinary life policy 12 years ago, when he was 20. Find (*a*) the cash surrender value, (*b*) the paid-up value, and (*c*) the period for which he may select extended term insurance of the same face.
10. Mr. Oberg purchased Company B's $24,000 nonparticipating ordinary life policy 18 years ago, when he was 30. Find (*a*) the cash surrender value, (*b*) the paid-up value, and (*c*) the period for which he may select extended term insurance of the same face.

UNIT 3. Monthly Old-age Benefits for Workers and Self-employed

The Social Security Act of 1935 and its amendments provide old-age, disability, and survivors insurance for all workers and self-employed people with the exception of certain specified services. It may be expected that future amendments to the act will change the scheduled taxes (see page 175) and benefits, and it is to the interest of each individual that he keeps himself informed of such revisions.

The Federal old-age, disability, and survivors insurance program is operated through the Federal Security Agency and the Treasury department. It is designed to furnish the average worker or self-employed person with disability insurance, retirement income, and income to dependents after his death.

Becoming Insured. The yardstick for measuring whether or not the individual is insured under the law is the *quarter of coverage.* A quarter of coverage is a calendar quarter (a 3-month period beginning Jan. 1, Apr. 1, July 1, or Oct. 1) in which the worker is paid $50 or more in wages covered by the law. For the self-employed, $100 of self-employed income credited during a calendar quarter constitutes a quarter of coverage; and $400 of such income credited for a full taxable year provides four quarters of coverage for that year.[1]

Quarters of coverage toward becoming insured may have been earned at any time after 1936. Once earned, credit for a quarter of coverage is never lost. Before 1951, if total wages in a year were $3,000 or more, a quarter of coverage was counted for the first quarter of the year in which $50 or more were earned and for each *later* quarter of the year. For 1951 through 1954, four quarters of coverage were counted for each calendar year in which total wages plus self-employment income were as much as $3,600. Beginning with 1955, four quarters of coverage have been counted for each calendar year in which total wages plus self-employment income have been as much as $4,200. (NOTE: As previously stated, only $400 of net income from self-employment is necessary to obtain four quarters of coverage for that year.)

Currently insured status is attained by the individual if he has at least 6 quarters of coverage within the 13 consecutive calendar quarters ending with the quarter in which he becomes entitled to monthly retirement payments or dies.

Fully insured status is attained by the individual if he has at least one quarter of coverage for each two calendar quarters that have passed since

[1] Special rules apply to farm income as an employer or employee. Full information may be obtained on request from local offices of the U.S. Social Security Administration.

1950 or at the time he reaches age 65 or dies. However, 6 quarters of coverage are established as minimum requirements, and 40 quarters of coverage after 1936 establishes coverage for life.

Table of Quarters of Coverage Needed for Fully Insured Status. The table that follows shows the number of quarters of coverage needed to be fully insured at 65 years of age. If age 65 is attained in the first 6 months of the year, the number of quarters of coverage needed to be fully insured is in the third column opposite the year of birth. If age 65 is attained in the last 6 months of the year, the number of quarters of coverage needed to be fully insured is in the fourth column opposite the year of birth.

Quarters of Coverage Needed for Fully Insured Status

Year of birth	The 65th year	Jan.–June	July–Dec.	Year of birth	The 65th year	Jan.–June	July–Dec.
1888 or earlier	1953 or earlier	6	6				
1889	1954	6	7	1898	1963	24	25
1890	1955	8	9	1899	1964	26	27
1891	1956	10	11	1900	1965	28	29
1892	1957	12	13	1901	1966	30	31
1893	1958	14	15	1902	1967	32	33
1894	1959	16	17	1903	1968	34	35
1895	1960	18	19	1904	1969	36	37
1896	1961	20	21	1905	1970	38	39
1897	1962	22	23	1906 or later	1971 or later	40	40

If enough quarters of coverage have not been attained by the sixty-fifth birthday, additional quarters of coverage may be earned after age 65.

Special Provision for Young People. For individuals under 22 years of age, months that are not part of a quarter of coverage (at least $50 in wages) are excluded. If insured status is attained after age 22, the whole period before age 22 is excluded if it reduces average monthly earnings.

Eligibility for Old-age Insurance. Old-age insurance may be paid to the retired worker or self-employed person if he meets the following conditions:

1. 65 years of age or older (age 62 if a woman, but with reduced benefits).
2. Is fully insured.
3. Makes an application for payments.

Between 65 and 72 years of age, it is not necessary to retire completely—see following section titled *Reduction of Payments.* Beginning with age 72 there are no limitations.

Reduction of Payments. Old-age or survivors insurance payments are made monthly unless certain events occur. Some events will stop the monthly payments for a period of one or more months, and some will end the right to receive payment.

A beneficiary (retired worker, dependent, or survivor) under age 72 can be paid old-age and survivors insurance checks for each month of a year after the year in which he first becomes entitled to benefits if his earnings during the year are not more than $1,200. Earnings from any source must be counted, whether or not the work is covered by the social security law. However, income from savings, property, investments, company pensions, annuities and other insurance does not affect the payments.

The following table shows the number of monthly benefits payable for different amounts of earnings (prior to age 72) for work in all months of the year:

Annual earnings	*Monthly benefits*	*Annual earnings*	*Monthly benefits*
$1,200 or less	12	$1,600.01 to $1,680	6
1,200.01 to $1,280	11	1,680.01 to 1,760	5
1,280.01 to 1,360	10	1,760.01 to 1,840	4
1,360.01 to 1,440	9	1,840.01 to 1,920	3
1,440.01 to 1,520	8	1,920.01 to 2,000	2
1,520.01 to 1,600	7	2,000.01 to 2,080	1

Regardless of the annual earnings, benefits are payable for any month in which a worker earns $80 or less in wages and does not render substantial services in self-employment. Whether substantial services in self-employment are performed is decided by the Social Security Administration.

Benefits are payable for the month in which age 72 is attained and the months afterwards without limitation on the amount of earnings.

Computing Benefits Based on Earnings after 1936. When average earnings since 1936 are equal to or higher than average earnings since 1950, the benefit is higher if it is based on average earnings since 1936.

For younger people and for most older people, average earnings since 1950 are larger than average earnings since 1936, and it is to their advantage to compute benefits by the *1954 Benefit Formula*. Since the methods of computation other than the *1954 Benefit Formula* are unlikely to be of interest to the users of this text, a presentation of such methods of computing has been omitted.

Determining Average Earnings After 1950. For those who attained age 65 after August, 1954, or who had at least 6 quarters of coverage after June, 1953, up to 4 calendar years (they need not be consecutive) *after* 1950 in which earnings were lowest or in which no earnings were made can be dropped in determining monthly average earnings. If at least 20 quarters of coverage have been acquired since 1936, an additional year (a total of any 5 calendar years) can be dropped in determining average earnings since 1950. In dropping low years, it may be necessary to keep at least 2 calendar years on which to base the average, for if fewer than 6 quarters (18 months) are left, the average earnings are found by dividing by 18.

When applying for benefits, the quarter in which application for and eligibility for benefits is attained because of age, disability, or death is excluded from the computations. In addition to the exclusion of the quarter of application, ordinarily, the two quarters (6 months) preceding the quarter of application, known as the *lag period*, are also excluded. If the lag period would increase the average monthly earnings and thus the monthly benefit, application can be made for recomputation in the second quarter following the original date of application, and the benefit will be recomputed.

Thus to compute average monthly earnings since 1950:

1. Drop up to 4 low earning years (or up to 5 low earning years if as many as 20 quarters of coverage have been attained).
2. Exclude the quarter of application and the two quarters preceding it (the lag period).
3. Add the remaining wages and self-employment income covered by the law, but not to exceed:
   (*a*) $3,600 for the years 1951, 1952, 1953, and 1954.
   (*b*) $4,200 for the years 1955 and following.
4. Divide the sum obtained in (3) by the number of months in the same period of time (quarters × 3) to determine average monthly earnings since 1950.
5. If this average should exceed $350, reduce it to $350, the maximum average permissible in computing benefits.
6. If the average monthly wage is not an exact multiple of $1, reduce it to the next lower multiple of $1; that is, drop any cents from the average. Thus an average of $137.87 is reduced to $137, $246.43 is reduced to $246, etc.

Example: On attaining his sixty-fifth birthday on Nov. 16, 1960, Joseph Smith retired and applied for a monthly old-age benefit. His monthly earnings were as follows: $250 per month earnings, 1951 through June 30, 1953; $325 per month earnings, July, 1953 through 1955; self-employment income of $2,175 in 1956; no earnings in 1957; $400 per month beginning Mar. 1, 1958 until date of retirement on Nov. 16, 1960. Compute his average monthly earnings (*a*) excluding the 6-month lag period and (*b*) including the 6-month lag period upon recomputation in April of 1961.

	Year			*Earnings*	*Allowable*	
	1951	$250 × 12		= $3,000	$3,000	
	1952	250 × 12		= 3,000	3,000	
	1953	250 × 6 + $325 × 6		= 3,450	3,450	
	1954	325 × 12		= 3,900	3,600	(maximum)
	1955	325 × 12		= 3,900	3,900	
	1956			= 2,175	2,175	
	1957			= none	none	
	1958	400 × 10		= 4,000	4,000	
	1959	400 × 12		= 4,800	4,200	(maximum)
(*a*) 3 mo.	1960	400 × 3	(lag excluded)	= 1,200	1,200	
(*b*) 9 mo.	1960	400 × 9	(lag included)	= 3,600	3,600	

Since Joseph Smith has 20 or more quarters of coverage, up to 5 calendar years of earnings may be omitted in computing. Therefore 1957, 1956, 1951, 1952, and 1953 are omitted. Earnings in 1960 are included for they exceed $350 per month (though not more than $4,200 could be counted for the year 1960) and thus serve to increase the average monthly earnings. Thus

(*a*)

	1954	$ 3,600
	1955	3,900
	1958	4,000
	1959	4,200
3 mo.	1960	1,200
Totals:	51 months =	$16,900

Average monthly earnings:

$$\frac{\$16,900}{51} = \$331.37$$

$331.37 is reduced to $331.

(*b*)

	1954	$ 3,600
	1955	3,900
	1958	4,000
	1959	4,200
9 mo.	1960	3,600
Totals:	57 months =	$19,300

Average monthly earnings:

$$\frac{\$19,300}{57} = \$338.60$$

$338.60 is reduced to $338.

Reduced Retirement Age for Women. Women qualified in their own right as workers or self-employed persons may choose to retire with reduced benefits at ages 62, 63, or 64 instead of waiting until age 65. Payments are reduced as follows:

Age 62: 80 per cent of what benefits would have been if age 65.

Age 63: $86\frac{2}{3}$ per cent of what benefits would have been if age 65.

Age 64: $93\frac{1}{3}$ per cent of what benefits would have been if age 65.

The wife of a man who is entitled to monthly old-age benefits may choose benefits at ages 62, 63, or 64 instead of waiting until age 65, but benefits are reduced as follows:

Age 62: 75 per cent of what benefits would have been if age 65.

Age 63: $83\frac{1}{3}$ per cent of what benefits would have been if age 65.

Age 64: $91\frac{2}{3}$ per cent of what benefits would have been if age 65.

With certain exceptions, women who choose reduced benefits continue to get the reduced amounts even after age 65.

Monthly benefits *are not reduced* to qualifying widows, or mothers of insured workers who die, even though benefits start at age 62, 63, or 64.

Disability Benefits. The Social Security Act as amended provides disability benefits to workers and self-employed persons who have a disability so severe that it prevents them from doing any substantial work and is expected to continue for an indefinite period. Monthly benefits are computed without any reduction for age as though the disabled person were 65 years of age or older. To qualify in their own right for monthly disability payments, workers must meet the following conditions:

1. Be 50 years of age or older
2. Have at least 20 quarters of coverage in the 40 quarters preceding the beginning date of the disability
3. Have at least 6 quarters of coverage in the 12 quarters preceding the beginning date of the disability

In addition to disability benefits of workers and self-employed, the law provides monthly insurance benefits for disabled children of any age if the disability began before 18 years of age and if either mother or father is receiving old-age insurance benefits or if the support of a qualified parent has been lost through death.

Computing by the 1954 Formula. Under the formula provided by the 1954 amendments to the Social Security Act, the monthly benefits for the retired worker or self-employed person are based on the average monthly earnings since 1950. The computation is made as follows:

1. If the average monthly wage is less than \$55, the monthly benefits are \$30, the minimum under the 1954 formula. (Note that a retired woman worker who chooses to retire at age 62 might receive as little as \$30 × .80 = \$24 monthly benefits.)
2. If the average wage is at least \$55 but not more than \$110:
   (*a*) Find 55 per cent of the average monthly wage.
   (*b*) If the benefit as computed in (*a*) is not a multiple of \$.10, raise it to the next higher multiple of \$.10. Thus \$47.85 would be raised to \$47.90, the next higher multiple of \$.10.
3. If the average wage is more than \$110 (but not more than the maximum of \$350):
   (*a*) Find 55 per cent of \$110 = \$60.50 always.
   (*b*) To \$60.50 add 20 per cent of the average monthly wage above \$110 (not to exceed 20 per cent of \$240 = \$48).

Example 1: Retired worker. Compute the monthly benefit of an eligible retired worker whose average monthly wages since 1950 were \$51.

Since the average monthly wage is less than \$55, the minimum monthly benefit of \$30 is paid the retired worker.

Example 2: Disabled worker. Compute the monthly benefit of an eligible disabled worker whose average monthly wages since 1950 were $89.96.

The cents are dropped and $89.96 is considered as $89. $89 × .55 = $48.95, raised to the next higher multiple of $.10 = $49 monthly benefit.

Example 3: Self-employed. Compute the monthly benefit of an eligible self-employed person whose average monthly earnings since 1950 were $308.75.

The cents are dropped and $308.75 is considered as $308.

$$\begin{array}{rl} \$308 & \\ \underline{-110} \times .55 = & \$60.50 \\ \$198 \times .20 = & \underline{+39.60} \\ & \$100.10 \quad \text{Monthly benefit} \end{array}$$

Example 4: Woman worker. Compute the monthly benefit of an eligible woman worker whose average monthly wages since 1950 were $54, if her age at retirement is (*a*) 65, (*b*) 62, (*c*) 63, and (*d*) 64.

(*a*) Since the average monthly wages are less than $55, the minimum benefit of $30 is paid to the retired woman worker.

(*b*) $\$30 \times .80 = \$24$, reduced monthly benefit starting at age 62

(*c*) $\$30 \times .86\frac{2}{3} = \$26$, reduced monthly benefit starting at age 63

(*d*) $\$30 \times .93\frac{1}{3} = \$28$, reduced monthly benefit starting at age 64

Example 5: Woman worker. Compute the monthly benefit of an eligible woman worker whose average monthly wages since 1950 were $350 if her age at retirement is (*a*) 65, (*b*) 62, (*c*) 63, and (*d*) 64.

(*a*)

$$\begin{array}{rl} \$350 & \\ \underline{-110} \times .55 = & \$60.50 \\ \$240 \times .20 = & \underline{+48.00} \\ & \$108.50 \quad \text{Maximum monthly benefit} \end{array}$$

(*b*) $\$108.50 \times .80 = \$86.80$, reduced monthly benefit starting at age 62

(*c*) $\$108.50 \times .86\frac{2}{3} = \$94.03$, raised to next higher multiple of $.10

$= \$94.10$, reduced monthly benefit starting at age 63

(*d*) $\$108.50 \times .93\frac{1}{3} = \$101.27$, raised to next higher multiple of $.10

$= \$101.30$, reduced monthly benefit starting at age 64

Example 6: Deceased worker; average monthly earnings and monthly base used in determining survivor benefits. James Henry had his twenty-second birthday on Jan. 2, 1954. Prior to age 22 he had been a student with maximum earnings in any year of $1,640. Following his twenty-second birthday his earnings were as follows: $1,850 in 1954; $200 per month in 1955; $250 per month in 1956; $250 per month in 1957; $260 per month in 1958; $260 per month in 1959; and $500 per month in 1960. On Jan. 17, 1961 he was killed in an automobile accident. Find his average monthly earnings (*a*) *excluding* the 6-month lag period, (*b*) *including* the 6-month lag period if recomputed in July of 1961, and (*c*) the monthly benefit computation that would be used as a base in determining survivor benefits.

Since his earnings prior to age 22 would reduce the monthly average, they are excluded from the computations:

	Year				*Earnings*	*Allowable*	
	1954			=	$1,850	$1,850	
	1955	$200 × 12		=	2,400	2,400	
	1956	$250 × 12		=	3,000	3,000	
	1957	$250 × 12		=	3,000	3,000	
	1958	$260 × 12		=	3,120	3,120	
	1959	$260 × 12		=	3,120	3,120	
6 mo.	1960	$500 × 6	(lag excluded)	=	3,000	3,000	
12 mo.	1960	$500 × 12	(lag included)	=	6,000	4,200	(maximum)

Since James Henry had 20 or more quarters of coverage, as many as 5 calendar years could be excluded in computing average monthly earnings. If you observe the allowable figures, it will be apparent that the entire 5-year period of 1954–1958 should be excluded.

(*a*)

	1959	$3,120
6 mo.	1960	3,000
Totals:	18 months =	$6,120

Average monthly earnings:

$$\frac{\$6,120}{18} = \$340$$

(*b*)

	1959	$3,120
12 mo.	1960	4,200
Totals:	24 months =	$7,320

Average monthly earnings:

$$\frac{\$7,320}{24} = \$305$$

(*c*) The monthly benefit would be computed on the average monthly earnings *excluding* the lag period since this would result in higher benefits.

$$\begin{array}{rl} \$340 & \\ -110 \times .55 = & \$60.50 \\ \hline \$230 \times .20 = & +46.00 \\ \hline & \$106.50 \end{array}$$ Base for computing survivor benefits

EXERCISE 3

Use the *1954 Benefit Formula* in solving the following problems in monthly old-age benefits. Assume that all earnings are covered by the law and that all persons are eligible to receive benefits.

1. Miss Hylda Knutsen averaged $43.76 monthly wages after 1950 until her retirement at age 65 in 1960. Find her monthly old-age benefit.
2. After 1950 and through 1960, Mr. Welburne Thomas had $107.35 of average monthly earnings. For what monthly old-age benefit was he eligible if his sixty-fifth birthday was Jan. 1, 1961?
3. Mr. Joseph Michael had average monthly earnings since 1950 of $276.59. To what monthly old-age benefit was he entitled?
4. Compute the monthly benefit of William James, an eligible disabled worker who had average monthly earnings since 1950 of $323.39.
5. Mr. Bernhardt Bjorseth, self-employed, had no covered earnings in 1951 through 1954. In 1955 his earnings from self-employment were $2,400. Beginning in 1956 through the date of his retirement at age 67 on June 18, 1961, his self-employment income had exceeded $4,200 per year. Find the monthly old-age benefit to which he was entitled.
6. Compute the monthly benefits of Mrs. Jeannette Nelson, whose monthly average earnings since 1950 had been $238.40, if her age at retirement was (*a*) 65, (*b*) 62, (*c*) 63, or (*d*) 64.
7. Compute the monthly benefits of Miss Edna Denhart, whose monthly average earnings since 1950 had been $94.82, if her age at retirement was (*a*) 65, (*b*) 62, (*c*) 63, or (*d*) 64.
8. Mr. Harold Ripley, a wage earner deceased on Aug. 28, 1960, had only the following yearly wage earnings under covered employment: 1951, $3,200; 1952, $4,435; 1953, $3,300; 1954, $4,100; 1955, no covered earnings; 1956, no covered earnings; 1957, no covered earnings; 1958, $1,860; 1959, $3,690. His earnings for the first six months of 1960 had been $3,150. Find the monthly benefit computation that would be used as a base in determining survivor benefits (*a*) *excluding* the lag period and (*b*) *including* the lag period.
9. Ronald Power's twenty-second birthday occurred on July 1, 1955. Prior to age 22 he had been a student with maximum earnings of $1,360 per year. Following his twenty-second birthday his earnings were as follows: $1,087 in 1955; $235 per month in 1956; $280 per month in 1957; no covered earnings in 1958; $105 per month in 1959; $375 per month in 1960; and $280 per month in 1961 until the date of his death on Dec. 4, 1961. Find the monthly benefit computation that would be used in determining survivor benefits (*a*) *excluding* the lag period and (*b*) *including* the lag period if recomputed in April of 1962.
10. Mr. William Hageman retired on Apr. 30, 1959 on his birthday at age 65. His earnings in covered employment had been as follows: $600 per month in 1951; $275 per month in 1952; $400 per month in 1953; $450 per month in 1954; $300 per month in 1955; $300 per month in 1956; $325 per month in 1957; $350 per month in 1958; $650 per month in 1959 until the date of his retirement. Find the monthly benefits to which he was entitled (*a*) *excluding* the lag period and (*b*) *including* the lag period when recomputed in October of 1959.

UNIT 4. Family and Survivors Benefits through Social Security

People approaching retirement age are likely to be interested not only in what they might receive if disabled or at retirement but also in benefits that might be received by their dependents or survivors. Younger people may look forward to retirement and plan their savings and insurance programs on the basis of expected retirement income to themselves and to their families through old-age benefits, but their primary concern is likely to be with the immediate protection to their families through survivors insurance.

Eligibility for Family or Survivor Benefits. In general, payments may be made to the spouse of an insured worker or self-employed person only if they were living together at the time the application was made for the insured's monthly benefits or at the time of the insured's death, if the insured is making regular contributions to the spouse, or if there is a court order requiring contributions.

If the child of a retired or deceased person is entitled to monthly payments, the child's mother may also be entitled to payments, regardless of her age, provided the child is in her care and she was living with the insured person or meets the other conditions described in the preceding paragraph.

The aged wife or husband of an old-age beneficiary can get monthly payments only after the marriage has been in effect for at least 3 years, unless the couple are parents of a child. The aged widow or widower of an insured person can get monthly payments only if the marriage had been in effect for at least 1 full year before the death of the husband or wife, unless the couple are parents of a child.

Payments to the dependent parents of a fully insured person who dies can be made only if no widow, widower, or child could qualify for payments.

An application for benefit payments must always be made before payments can begin.

Cessation of Payments. Annual earnings of $2,080.01 or more, except as previously noted (page 222), cause cessation of payments for that year.

The marriage of any person receiving monthly benefit payments as a dependent or as a survivor will end his or her payments.

If the wife or dependent husband of a retired insured worker is divorced, payments to the insured person's former spouse are ended.

If a woman under age 62 is receiving monthly benefits as the wife, widow, or divorced wife of an insured person, the payment may be made only while she has in her care a child who is also entitled to monthly payments.

When a child entitled to benefits reaches age 18 (except as provided for a disabled child if the disability was incurred under 18 years of age), or marries before reaching age 18, no more payments are made to the child.

If the child of a deceased insured is adopted by anyone except his stepparent, grandparent, aunt, or uncle, his payments end.

When any person receiving monthly benefits dies, his or her payments cease.

Insured Status as It Affects Payments. Payments to the insured and dependents depend in part on whether the status of the individual is that of one who is only currently insured, fully insured, or both fully and currently insured.

Retirement payments:	
Monthly payments to	*If worker's status is*
Retired worker	Fully insured
and to	
Wife 62 or over	Fully insured
Wife, regardless of age, if caring for child entitled to benefits	Fully insured
Child under 18	Fully insured
Dependent husband	Both fully and currently insured
Disability payments:	
Monthly payments to	*If worker's status is*
Worker if disabled and 50 years of age or older	Fully insured in 20 of past 40 quarters before disability and currently insured
and to	
Child if disabled and disability incurred under 18 years of age	Fully insured
Survivors payments:	
Lump-sum payment to	*If worker status at death was*
Widow or widower "living with" insured or to person who paid burial expenses (may be paid even though monthly benefits are also paid immediately)	Either fully or currently insured
Monthly payments to	
Widow 62 or over	Fully insured
Widow or dependent divorced wife (regardless of age) if caring for child entitled to benefits	Either fully or currently insured
Child under 18	Either fully or currently insured
Child if disabled and disability incurred under 18 years of age	Either fully or currently insured
Dependent widower 65 or over	Both fully and currently insured
Dependent parent 65 or over	Fully insured

Payments to members of the family are made only if they are considered dependents. In some cases this means the insured individual must have actually contributed to their support or have lived with them. In addition, the payments to the parent of an insured person are made only where no widow, widower, or child could qualify for payments.

Family Benefits. Based on the insured's monthly benefit computation, each eligible dependent's monthly payment is determined as follows:

Monthly payment to	*Is this part of insured's monthly benefit computation*
Wife	One-half
Child (when insured is retired)	One-half
Dependent husband	One-half
Widow	Three-fourths
Child (after death of insured)	Three-fourths to one child or, if more than one child, one-half to each child plus one-fourth divided equally among all children
Dependent widower	Three-fourths
Dependent parent	Three-fourths if no eligible widow or children

If the eligible dependent's benefit is not a multiple of \$.10, raise it to the next higher multiple of \$.10. Thus if the insured's monthly benefit is \$45.10: his wife, if eligible, would be entitled to $\$45.10 \times \frac{1}{2} = \$22.55$, raised to the next higher multiple of $\$.10 = \$22.60$; his widow, if eligible, would be entitled to $\$45.10 \times \frac{3}{4} = \$33.825$, raised to next higher multiple of $\$.10 = \$33.90$.

If a person is entitled to monthly benefits based on more than one account, the amount paid is the larger of the benefits. Thus a wife entitled to \$22.60 as in the preceding paragraph and to \$30 on her own account as an insured person would receive a single check for \$30; but as a widow entitled to \$33.90 she would receive two checks, one for \$30 and one for \$3.90 or a total of \$33.90.

Lump-sum Death Payments. After death, a lump sum of three times the insured's monthly benefit or \$255, *whichever is less*, is paid to the widow or widower if living with the insured at the time of his or her death, in addition to any monthly payments due the widow or widower. If there is no qualified widow or widower, the person who pays the expenses of burial is repaid up to the amount of the lump-sum but not to exceed the actual expense. If more than one such person pays the burial expenses, they are reimbursed pro rata.

Example 1: Lump-sum death benefit. Harriet Hart, a widow who had been living with her husband at the time of his death was entitled to what lump-sum death benefit if the husband's monthly benefit computation was \$78.50?

$$\$78.50 \times 3 = \$235.50 \quad \text{Lump-sum death benefit}$$

Example 2: Lump-sum death benefit. Roger Williams died leaving no widow eligible for lump-sum death benefits. If his monthly benefit computation was \$108.50 and two friends shared equally the cost of burial expenses totaling \$400, find the lump-sum death benefit reimbursement paid to each friend.

Payment is limited to $\$108.50 \times 3 = \$325.50$ or \$255, whichever is less.

Therefore the lump-sum death benefit is \$255 divided equally:

$$\frac{\$255}{2} = \$127.50 \quad \text{Reimbursement to each friend}$$

Limitations in Total Family Payments. The maximum total payments to a family (including the insured) or survivors may not exceed 80 per cent of the insured's average monthly earnings or \$200, *whichever is less.* If family payments as figured would be more than either of these amounts, each dependent's payments is reduced pro rata to bring the total down to the maximum amount payable.

However, the 80 per cent maximum of average monthly earnings cannot be applied to reduce the family benefit below \$50 or $1\frac{1}{2}$ times the worker's monthly benefit computation, *whichever is larger.* Note, however, that the preceding sentence does not mean that total family benefits may not be less than \$50. Thus, a retired worker entitled to \$30 on his own account and his eligible wife would receive a total monthly family benefit of $\$30 + \frac{1}{2} \times \$30 = \$30 + \$15 = \$45$.

Take special note that the minimum survivor benefit when there is *only one* person eligible (widow, child, or parent) may not be less than \$30 monthly.

Example 1: Reduced payments to wife. A retired worker received monthly old-age benefits of \$52.80. What monthly benefits was his wife eligible to receive if she applied for benefits beginning at ages (*a*) 65, (*b*) 62, (*c*) 63, and (*d*) 64? (See page 224 for multipliers.)

(*a*) $\$52.80 \times \frac{1}{2} = \$26.40$

(*b*) $\$26.40 \times .75 = \$19.80$

(*c*) $\$26.40 \times .83\frac{1}{3} = \$22.00$

(*d*) $\$26.40 \times .91\frac{2}{3} = \$24.20$

Example 2: Applying the \$50 limitation. A retired worker with average monthly earnings of \$40 received a monthly minimum benefit of \$30. If his wife and one child also received monthly benefits on his account, find (*a*) the maximum possible total family benefits and (*b*) monthly payments to each member of the family.

(*a*) $\$40 \times .80 = \$32$ theoretical maximum but the 80 per cent maximum rule may not be applied to reduce the family benefit below \$50 or $1\frac{1}{2}$ times the monthly benefit computation, whichever is larger.

$$\$30 \times 1\frac{1}{2} = \$45$$

Therefore \$50 is the maximum possible total family benefit.

(*b*) $\$30 \times \frac{1}{2} = \$15$, theoretically paid to wife and to child

Theoretical total payment to family:

To husband	=	\$30
wife	=	15
child	=	15
		\$60, but maximum payment is limited to \$50

\$50 − \$30 = \$20 to be divided equally between wife and child.

$$\frac{\$20}{2} = \$10$$

Actual payments to each member of the family:

To husband	=	\$30	Unreduced payment
wife	=	10	Reduced payment
child	=	10	Reduced payment
		\$50	Total payments to the family

Example 3: Applying the limitation of 80 per cent of insured's benefit. A retired worker with average monthly earnings of \$150 received a monthly old-age benefit of \$68.50. If his wife and child were also eligible for monthly benefits based on his account, find (*a*) the monthly payments to each member of the family and (*b*) the total family payments.

(*a*) $\$150 \times .80 = \$120$ Maximum family benefit

Wife and child are entitled to the following theoretical payments:

$\$68.50 \times \frac{1}{2} = \$34.25$, raised to next higher multiple of \$.10 = \$34.30

Theoretical total payments to the family:

To husband	=	\$ 68.50
wife	=	34.30
child	=	34.30
		\$137.10, but maximum is limited to \$120

\$120 − \$68.50 = \$51.50 to be divided equally between wife and child

$\frac{\$51.50}{2} = \$25.75$, raised to next higher multiple of \$.10 = \$25.80

Actual payments to each member of the family:

	To husband =	$ 68.50	Unreduced benefit
	wife =	25.80	Reduced benefit
	child =	25.80	Reduced benefit
(*b*)		$120.10	Total payments to the family

Note that the total of $120.10 exceeds the maximum of $120. This is caused by raising the individual payments to the wife and the child to the next-higher multiple of $.10 and actual payments would be made as illustrated.

Example 4: Applying the limitation of $1\frac{1}{2}$ times insured's benefit. A retired worker had average monthly earnings of $80 and a monthly old-age benefit of $44. Assuming his wife and two children were also eligible for monthly benefits, find (*a*) the total family benefits, (*b*) monthly payments to each member of the family, and (*c*) monthly payments after his death to the widow and to each child.

(*a*) $\$80 \times .80 = \$64$ Theoretical maximum

But the minimum family benefit may not be reduced below $50 or $1\frac{1}{2}$ times the monthly benefit computation, whichever is larger.

$$\$44 \times 1\frac{1}{2} = \$66$$

Therefore $66 is the total family benefit.

(*b*) $\$44 \times \frac{1}{2} = \$22$, theoretically paid to wife and to each child

Theoretical total payment to family:

To husband =	$ 44
wife =	22
1st child =	22
2d child =	22
	$110, but maximum payment is limited to $66

$66 − $44 = $22 to be divided equally between wife and each child.

$$\frac{\$22}{3} = \$7.33, \text{ raised to next higher multiple of } \$.10 = \$7.40$$

Actual payments to each member of the family:

To husband =	$44.00	Unreduced benefit
wife =	7.40	Reduced benefit
1st child =	7.40	Reduced benefit
2d child =	7.40	Reduced benefit
	$66.20	Total payments to the family

(*c*) $\$44 \times \frac{3}{4} = \$33$ Theoretical payment to the widow

Since there are two children, each child is entitled to one-half of the insured's monthly computation plus one-fourth divided equally. Thus

$$\frac{1}{2} + \frac{1}{4} \times \frac{1}{2} = \frac{1}{2} + \frac{1}{8} = \frac{5}{8}$$

$\$44 \times \frac{5}{8} = \$27.50$ Theoretical payment to each child

Theoretical total payment to family:

To widow	=	$33.00
1st child	=	27.50
2d child	=	27.50
		$88.00, but maximum payment is limited to $66

The widow and each child are to share $66 in the following ratios:

$$\frac{3}{4} : \frac{5}{8} : \frac{5}{8} = \frac{6}{8} : \frac{5}{8} : \frac{5}{8} = \text{the ratios of 6 to 5 to 5}$$

Thus 16 shares or 16 parts of $66 are to be so divided that the widow receives $\frac{6}{16}$ of $66 and each child receives $\frac{5}{16}$ of $66.

Actual payments to each member of the family:

To widow $\$66 \times \frac{6}{16}$	$= \$24.75$, raised to	$24.80	Reduced benefit
1st child $\$66 \times \frac{5}{16}$	$= \$20.625$, raised to	20.70	Reduced benefit
2d child $\$66 \times \frac{5}{16}$	$= \$20.625$, raised to	20.70	Reduced benefit
		$66.20	Total family payments

Note that in both (*b*) and (*c*) the total family payments are slightly above the maximum of $66. This is caused by raising individual payments to next-higher multiples of $.10 and actual payments would be made as illustrated.

Example 5: Applying the $200 limitation. A retired worker had average monthly earnings of $350 and a monthly old-age benefit of $108.50. Assuming his wife and three children were also eligible for monthly benefits, find (*a*) the maximum monthly benefits to the family, (*b*) monthly payments to each member of the family, and (*c*) monthly payments after his death to the widow and to each child.

(*a*) Maximum family benefits are $200 or 80% of $350, whichever is lower.

$\$350 \times .80 = \$280$
Maximum family benefit is therefore $200

(*b*) Theoretical payments to wife and each child:

$\$108.50 \times \frac{1}{2} = \$54.25$, raised to next higher multiple of $.10 = $54.30

Theoretical total payment to family:

To husband	$108.50
wife	54.30
1st child	54.30
2d child	54.30
3d child	54.30
	$325.70, but maximum payment is limited to $200

$\$200 - \$108.50 = \$91.50$ to be divided equally between wife and each child.

$$\frac{\$91.50}{4} = \$22.875, \text{ raised to next higher multiple of } \$.10 = \$22.90$$

Actual payments to each member of family:

To husband	=	$108.50	Unreduced benefit
wife	=	22.90	Reduced benefit
1st child	=	22.90	Reduced benefit
2d child	=	22.90	Reduced benefit
3d child	=	22.90	Reduced benefit
		$200.10	Total payments to the family

(*c*) $\$108.50 \times \frac{3}{4} = \$81.375$, raised to $81.40, theoretical payment to widow.

Since there are three children, each child is entitled to

$$\frac{1}{2} + \frac{1}{4} \times \frac{1}{3} = \frac{1}{2} + \frac{1}{12} = \frac{7}{12}$$

$\$108.50 \times \frac{7}{12} = \$63.29$, raised to $63.30, theoretical payment to each child.

Theoretical total payment to family:

To widow	=	$ 81.40
1st child	=	63.30
2d child	=	63.30
3d child	=	63.30
		$271.30, but maximum is limited to $200

The widow and each child are to share $200 in the following ratios:

$$\frac{3}{4}:\frac{7}{12}:\frac{7}{12}:\frac{7}{12} = \frac{9}{12}:\frac{7}{12}:\frac{7}{12}:\frac{7}{12} = 9:7:7:7$$

Thus 9 of 30 parts is the widow's share and 7 of 30 parts is each child's share. And the widow is entitled to $\frac{9}{30}$ of $200 and each child to $\frac{7}{30}$ of $200.

Actual payments to each member of the family:

To widow	$= \$200 \times \frac{9}{30} =$		\$ 60.00	Reduced benefit
1st child	$= \$200 \times \frac{7}{30} =$	\$46.67, raised to	46.70	Reduced benefit
2d child	$= \$200 \times \frac{7}{30} =$	\$46.67, raised to	46.70	Reduced benefit
3d child	$= \$200 \times \frac{7}{30} =$	\$46.67, raised to	46.70	Reduced benefit
			\$200.10	Total family payments

Note that in both (*b*) and (*c*) the total family payments are slightly higher than the maximum of \$200. This is caused by raising the individual payments to the next-higher multiple of \$.10, and actual payments would be made as illustrated.

EXERCISE 4

Solve the following problems in payments received by eligible dependents and survivors of individuals covered by Federal old-age, disability, and survivors insurance:

1. Golda Udell, a widow who had been living with her husband at the time of his death, was entitled to what lump-sum death benefit if the husband's monthly benefit computation was \$71.70?
2. Roger Cate died leaving no widow eligible for lump-sum death benefits. If his monthly benefit computation was \$106.50 and three friends shared equally the cost of burial expenses totaling \$485.35, find the lump-sum death benefit reimbursement paid to each friend.
3. A retired worker received monthly old-age benefits of \$90.90. What monthly benefit was his wife eligible to receive if she applied for benefits beginning at ages (*a*) 65, (*b*) 62, (*c*) 63, or (*d*) 64?
4. A husband had been retired for three years with a monthly old-age benefit of \$103.70. As the wife approached the age of 62, she considered whether she would prefer to apply for the old-age pension to which she would be entitled at age 62 on her husband's account or to wait until she was older. If she decided to wait until age 65, (*a*) what monthly benefit would she receive? If she chose to apply for the monthly benefit before she attained age 65, what monthly benefits would she receive at (*b*) age 62, (*c*) age 63, or (*d*) age 64?
5. A retired worker with average monthly earnings of \$52 received a monthly minimum benefit of \$30. If his wife and two children also receive monthly benefits on his account, find (*a*) the monthly payments to each dependent member of the family and (*b*) the total family benefits.
6. A deceased worker with average monthly earnings of \$58 would have been entitled to a monthly benefit computation of \$31.90. If his widow and one child were entitled to monthly benefits on his account, find (*a*) the separate monthly payments to the widow and child and (*b*) the total family benefits.

7. A retired worker with average monthly earnings of $162 received a monthly old-age benefit of $70.90. If his wife and one child also received monthly benefits on his account, find (*a*) monthly payment to each dependent member of the family and (*b*) the total family benefits.
8. A retired worker with average monthly earnings of $220 received a monthly old-age benefit of $82.50. If his wife and two children were also eligible for monthly benefits based on his account, find (*a*) the monthly payment to each dependent member of the family and (*b*) total family payments.
9. A retired worker had average monthly earnings of $88 and a monthly old-age benefit of $48.40. Assuming his wife and one child were also eligible for monthly benefits, find (*a*) the total family benefits, (*b*) monthly payments to each dependent member of the family, and (*c*) separate monthly payments after his death to the widow and to the child.
10. The average monthly earnings of a retired worker had been $64, and he received a monthly old-age benefit of $35.20. If his wife and two children were also eligible for monthly benefits, find (*a*) the total family benefits, (*b*) monthly payments to each dependent member of the family, and (*c*) monthly payments after his death to the widow and (*d*) to each child.
11. A retired worker had monthly average earnings of $345 and a monthly old-age benefit of $107.50. Assuming his wife and three children were also eligible for monthly benefits, find (*a*) the maximum monthly benefits to the family, (*b*) monthly payments to each dependent member of the family, and (*c*) monthly payments after his death to the widow and (*d*) to each child.
12. The average monthly earnings of a retired worker had been $280, and he received a monthly old-age benefit of $94.50. Assuming his wife and four children were also eligible for monthly benefits, find (*a*) the maximum monthly benefit to the family, (*b*) monthly payments to each dependent member of the family, and (*c*) monthly payments after his death to the widow and (*d*) to each child.

UNIT 5. Fire Insurance

Fire insurance insures against loss by fire and certain other damage that may result directly through attempts to extinguish the fire, such as loss caused by water and chemical extinguishers or by breakage of property by fire fighters. It may cover a wide range of items including damage to business properties, inventories, furniture, fixtures, homes, forests, lands, crops, automobiles, etc.

Fire protection for homes is a subject that should be of vital interest to you in the future, if not at present. Therefore the following discussion is devoted primarily to fire insurance for dwellings and their contents, although store buildings and their contents are also included.

Premium and Premium Rates. Premium rates are usually quoted in cents per $100 face, such as $.40 per $100, $.55 per $100, etc.

The basic period on which most companies quote rates is 1 *year*. When insurance is taken out for longer periods than 1 year and paid for in advance, the average cost per year is reduced. Thus:

Years	*Rate*
2	Annual rate $\times 1\frac{3}{4}$
3	Annual rate $\times 2\frac{1}{2}$
4	Annual rate $\times 3\frac{1}{4}$
5	Annual rate $\times$ 4

Example: If the annual rate of insurance on an apartment house is 30 cents per $100, what is the rate per $100 for (*a*) 2-year period, (*b*) 3-year period, (*c*) 4-year period, (*d*) 5-year period?

(*a*) 2-year period $= \$.30 \times 1\frac{3}{4} = \$0.525$

(*b*) 3-year period $= .30 \times 2\frac{1}{2} = 0.75$

(*c*) 4-year period $= .30 \times 3\frac{1}{4} = 0.975$

(*d*) 5-year period $= .30 \times 4 = 1.20$

Rates vary between urban and suburban areas and from community to community, depending on fire hazards, adequate fire-fighting protec-

Annual Rates for Fire Insurance on Buildings and Contents per $100 Units

Construction	Store building	Store contents	1-family bldg. and contents	2-family bldg. and contents	3- to 6-family bldg. and contents
Brick,[1] approved roof[2]...	$.16	$.22	$.14	$.18	$.26
Brick, shingle roof[3].....	.20	.26	.20	.24	.32
Frame,[4] approved roof..	.18	.24	.18	.22	.30
Frame, shingle roof.....	.26	.32	.24	.28	.36

[1] Brick includes hollow tile and hollow or solid concrete blocks.

[2] Approved by the Board of Fire Underwriters. Includes slate, tile, or composition shingles.

[3] Any roof not approved by the Board of Fire Underwriters.

[4] Frame includes stucco and brick veneer.

tion, past record of the community, and many other factors. The preceding sample table is one for a particular community and should not be construed as applying to all communities or areas. Furthermore, variance will occur among the different underwriters, although their rates tend to be much the same for any given area.

Example 1: Mr. Smith owns a one-family dwelling of hollow-tile construction with a shingle roof. He wishes to insure it for $6,000. What rate per $100 and what total premium would he pay for (*a*) 1 year, (*b*) 2 years, (*c*) 3 years, (*d*) 4 years, (*e*) 5 years?

$$\$100 \text{ is contained in } \$6{,}000\text{: } \frac{6{,}000}{100} = 60 \text{ times}$$

	Rate	*Premium*
(*a*)	$\$.20$	$\$.20 \times 60 = \$12$
(*b*)	$\$.20 \times 1\frac{3}{4} = \$.35$	$\$.35 \times 60 = \$21$
(*c*)	$\$.20 \times 2\frac{1}{2} = \$.50$	$\$.50 \times 60 = \$30$
(*d*)	$\$.20 \times 3\frac{1}{4} = \$.65$	$\$.65 \times 60 = \$39$
(*e*)	$\$.20 \times 4 = \$.80$	$\$.80 \times 60 = \$48$

Example 2: Mr. Smith also owns a store building of concrete with a tile roof, valued at $16,000, with contents valued at $7,000. What will be the total cost of 3-year premiums on both store and contents?

$$\$100 \text{ is contained in } \$16{,}000\text{: } \frac{16{,}000}{100} = 160$$

$$\text{3-year rate on building} = \$.16 \times 2\frac{1}{2} = \$0.40$$

$$\$100 \text{ is contained in } \$7{,}000\text{: } \frac{7{,}000}{100} = 70$$

$$\text{3-year rate on contents} = \$.22 \times 2\frac{1}{2} = \$0.55$$

Premium on building	$= \$.40 \times 160 =$	$ 64.00
Premium on contents	$= \$.55 \times 70 =$	38.50
Total premium cost for 3 years	$=$	$102.50

The large number of possible kinds of fire insurance is too complex for discussion in a course as necessarily brief as this. However, the methods of computing premiums are basically the same as has been illustrated.

In addition to fire insurance in its simplest form, additional hazards may be covered by endorsement for both homes and commercial properties. In the past several years, the cost of fire policies and additional coverages by endorsement has been considerably reduced in most areas in the United States, such reduction in cost being particularly true in the case of residences whether rented or occupied by the homeowner.

A number of years ago, it was common practice for owners of residences and commercial properties to add by endorsement certain separate coverages. Typical among the risk coverage on homes in addition to fire protection were and are what are known as extended coverage, additional extended coverage, earthquake, theft, personal property floaters, glass breakage, comprehensive personal liability, etc.—and for commercial properties most of these coverages plus separate policies for such risks as steam boilers, use and occupancy insurance, workmen's compensation insurance, water damage, etc.

Within the past few years, most fire and casualty underwriters have offered to homeowners so called "package policies" that combine many of the endorsements or separate coverages in one single policy. First of such offerings was what is designated as the *broad form,* and then followed what is called the *all physical loss* policy, both available for rented or owner-occupied residences. Even more extensive coverage than provided in the all physical loss policy is offered in homeowners' A, B, C, or comprehensive dwelling policies. On pages 242–243 is a summary of the coverages and also a comparison with certain separate contracts.

Short-term Policies and Cancellation. On occasion, the insured may find it desirable to purchase insurance for a period of less than 1 year; or he may desire to cancel a 1-year policy prior to its expiration and receive a refund for the period of time between cancellation date and expiration of the policy. In either event, the underwriter will short-rate the policy, that is, make a higher charge than an exact pro rata of the annual premium for the period that the policy is in force (see table on page 244).

In other instances, the insured may wish to cancel a policy on which he originally paid the full premium in advance for 2, 3, 4, or 5 years.

If the insurance has been in force less than 1 year, the insuring company may retain the stated per cent of the *full annual* premium for the number of days the insurance has been in force. If the insurance has been in force more than 1 year, the insuring company may retain from the premium paid one *full annual* premium plus pro rata of the remainder of the policy premium for the number of days in excess of 12 months that the insurance has been in force.

Package Risk Policies for Homeowners[1]

Property & extensions	Ordinary fire policy	Homeowners A	Homeowners B	Homeowners C	Comprehensive dwelling
Your dwelling, including building equipment and fixtures and outdoor equipment while on premises	No minimum limit	$8,000 minimum	$8,000 minimum	$15,000 minimum	No minimum, but should be at least 80% of value
Your garage, and other private structures on your premises	10% of dwelling (optional insurance)	10% of dwelling (additional insurance)	10% of dwelling (additional insurance)	10% of dwelling (additional insurance)	10% of dwelling (optional insurance)
Additional living expenses (the extra cost of living if home is uninhabitable due to insured hazard)	Not included	10% of amount on dwelling	20% of amount on dwelling	20% of amount on dwelling	10% of amount on home (20% of contents if tenant form)
Replacement cost coverage, buildings only (losses paid without deduction for depreciation if proper insurance-to-value is carried)	Not included	Yes, where permitted	Yes, where permitted	Yes, where permitted	Yes, under broad and special forms; otherwise, by endorsement
Trees, shrubs, plants (perils are named; wind and hail excluded in most areas)	Not included	No	No	5% of amount on dwelling	5% of amount on dwelling under broad and special forms
Personal property on premises	You specify amount; no coverage on cash or securities	40% of amount on home (may be raised); $100 cash; $500 securities	40% of amount on home (may be raised); $100 cash; $500 securities	50% of amount on home (may be raised); $100 cash; $500 securities	You specify (should be at least 80% of value); no cash or securities
Personal property off premises	10% of amount on premises (North America)	10% of amount on premises; $1,000 minimum (worldwide)	10% of amount on premises; $1,000 minimum (worldwide)	Same amount as on premises (worldwide)	10% of amount on premises (North America, worldwide; floater opt.)

[1] From brochure #1113.15 of the Insurance Pictorial Visual Selling Service, The Rough Notes Company, Inc., Indianapolis, Ind.

Package Risk Policies for Homeowners—(*Continued*)

Hazards covered	Separate coverages	Homeowners A	Homeowners B	Homeowners C	Comprehensive dwelling
Fire and extended coverage (fire, lightning, wind, hail, explosion, riot, vehicle damage, aircraft damage, smoke from heating or cooking unit)	Fire policy with extended coverage endorsement	Yes	Yes	Yes	Yes
Additional perils (water damage, rupture of steam or hot water system, vandalism, falling trees or objects, freezing, glass breakage, collapse, landslide)	Additional extended coverage ($50 deductible)	Vandalism only (no deductible)	Yes ($50 deductible. Vandalism covered in full)	Yes (deductible applies to water, glass, fall of trees, freezing)	Yes (no deductible)
Crime hazards (burglary, robbery, theft)	Personal theft policy	Yes	Yes	Yes	Yes
Mysterious disappearance	Broad personal theft policy	No	No	Yes	Yes
Theft from unlocked car		No	No	Yes	Yes
All risks—home, outbuildings (covers everything except perils specifically excluded; flood and surface waters usually excluded)	Dwelling special form	No	May be endorsed	Yes	Under the special form
All risks personal property (covers everything except perils specifically excluded; flood and earthquake covered)	Personal property floater	No	No	Yes	No, may be added
Glass breakage	Residence glass endorsement	No, may be endorsed	$50 deductible on building glass; full coverage by endorsement	$50 deductible on building glass; full coverage by endorsement	No deductible on building glass; specific items may be insured
Personal liability (sums for which you are liable because of bodily injury or damage to property of others arising from premises accidents or family activities)	Comprehensive personal liability policy	$10,000 minimum, $250 medical payments	$10,000 minimum, $250 medical payments	$25,000 minimum, $500 medical payments	$10,000 minimum, $250 medical payments

Fire or Casualty Short-rate Table

Days policy in force	Per cent of premium earned	Days policy in force	Per cent of premium earned	Days policy in force	Per cent of premium earned
1	5	88–91	35	201–205	65
2	6	92–94	36	206–209	66
3–4	7	95–98	37	210–214	67
5–6	8	99–102	38	215–218	68
7–8	9	103–105	39	219–223	69
9–10	10	106–109	40	224–228	70
11–12	11	110–113	41	229–232	71
13–14	12	114–116	42	233–237	72
15–16	13	117–120	43	238–241	73
17–18	14	121–124	44	242–246	74
19–20	15	125–127	45	247–250	75
21–22	16	128–131	46	251–255	76
23–25	17	132–135	47	256–260	77
26–29	18	136–138	48	261–264	78
30–32	19	139–142	49	265–269	79
33–36	20	143–146	50	270–273	80
37–40	21	147–149	51	274–278	81
41–43	22	150–153	52	279–282	82
44–47	23	154–156	53	283–287	83
48–51	24	157–160	54	288–291	84
52–54	25	161–164	55	292–296	85
55–58	26	165–167	56	297–301	86
59–62	27	168–171	57	302–305	87
63–65	28	172–175	58	306–310	88
66–69	29	176–178	59	311–314	89
70–73	30	179–182	60	315–319	90
74–76	31	183–187	61	320–323	91
77–80	32	188–191	62	324–328	92
81–83	33	192–196	63	329–332	93
84–87	34	197–200	64	333–337	94
				338–342	95
				343–346	96
				347–351	97
				352–355	98
				356–360	99
				361–365	100

Example 1: Short-term policy. Mr. Brown wants a 15-day policy on a store building of brick with an approved roof, valued at $30,000. What will be the premium?

Annual premium = $.16 × 300 = $48
15-day short rate = 13% of annual premium
15-day premium = $48 × .13 = $6.24

Example 2: Cancellation by insured. Mr. Harris notifies his underwriters that he has sold his home and that he wants to cancel his fire-insurance policy on Sept. 22. If the date of the policy was Apr. 15 and the 1-year premium paid by Mr. Harris was $18, find (*a*) net cost of the policy and (*b*) refund due Mr. Harris.

Apr. 15 to Sept. 22 by exact time = 160 da.
160-day short rate = 54%
(*a*) 160-day premium = $18 × .54 = $9.72
(*b*) Refund due = $18 − $9.72 = $8.28

Example 3: Cancellation by insured. Mr. Marsh insured his home for 3 years on July 1, 1956, at a cost of $65. On Nov. 24, 1958, he canceled the policy. Find (*a*) net cost of the policy and (*b*) refund due Mr. Marsh.

July 1, 1956, to Nov. 24, 1958 = 2 yr. 146 da.

(*a*) Premium for 1st yr. $= \frac{\$65}{2.5} = \$26$

Premium for 2d yr. + 3d yr., or 730 da. = $65 − $26 = $39
Days in excess of 12 months = 1 yr. + 146 da. = 511 da.

Pro rata of premium for 2d yr. + 3d yr. $= \$39 \times \frac{511}{730} = \$27.30$

Net cost of policy = $26 + $27.30 = $53.30
(*b*) Refund due = $65 − $53.30 = $11.70

Cancellation by Insurer. Fire and casualty underwriters include in their policies the right of cancellation by the insurer as well as by the insured. Ordinarily the insurer will give notice of cancellation of not less than 5 days in order that the insured may have time to secure other insurance, either with the same insurer or some other underwriter.

If the policy is canceled by the insurance company before expiration of the term, the company is obligated by law to retain not more than an exact pro rata of the premium for the length of time the policy has been in force. Thus if an insurer cancels a 1-year policy after 172 days (exact time) during which the policy has been in effect, the insurer retains $\frac{172}{365}$ of the premium. If the insurer cancels a 3-year policy after it has been in force 1 year and 17 days (365 + 17 = 382 days), the insurer retains $\frac{382}{1095}$ of the premium.

Note that in determining the prorata portion of the premium that may be retained, it is usual to count the actual number of days for both numerator and denominator, although some companies count each policy year as 360 days and use 30-day-month time to determine the number of days that the policy has been in force.

Example: Cancellation by insurer. On Apr. 30, 1957, Mr. Herman purchased a 2-year fire-insurance policy on his store building, paying a premium of \$132. On July 12, 1958 the insurer canceled the policy. Find (*a*) the premium retained by the insurer and (*b*) the refund paid to Mr. Herman.

Policy is for 2 yr. = 730 da.
Apr. 30, 1957, to July 12, 1958 = 365 da. + 73 da. = 438 da.

(*a*) $\$132 \times \frac{438}{730} = \$79.20$

(*b*) $\$132 - \$79.20 = \$52.80$

EXERCISE 5

A. Find the missing quantities in the following table of fire-insurance rates:

	Annual rate per \$100	2-yr. rate per \$100	3-yr. rate per \$100	4-yr. rate per \$100	5-yr. rate per \$100
1	\$.11	\$	\$	\$	\$
2		.28			
3			.45		
4				1.43	
5					1.20

B. Use the table of annual rates on buildings and contents, page 239, in solving the following problems on fire insurance:

1. Mr. Nourse owns a one-family dwelling of frame construction with an approved roof. He insures it for \$7,500. What premium does he pay for (*a*) 1 year, (*b*) 2 years, (*c*) 3 years, (*d*) 4 years, and (*e*) 5 years?

2. Mr. Winthrop owns a house of wood-and-plaster construction with a shingle roof. The house is valued at \$9,000 and contents at \$2,500. He wishes to insure both house and contents. Find the total premiums he will be required to pay for (*a*) 1 year, (*b*) 2 years, (*c*) 3 years, (*d*) 4 years, and (*e*) 5 years.

3. Mr. Allen owns a store building constructed of concrete with an approved roof. He insures it with Company A for \$10,000, Company B for \$4,500, and Company C for \$7,500. What premium does he pay each company for a 2-year policy, and what is the total cost of the premiums?

4. Mr. Livingstone owns the following property which he desires to insure:

House of wood construction with shingle roof, value	$ 5,000
House of brick construction with shingle roof, value	7,200
Two-family flat of frame construction, tile roof, value	11,000
Six-family apartment of concrete with slate roof, value	24,000
Store building of brick with an approved roof, value	34,500
Store contents valued at	13,400

Find the total insurance premiums he will be required to pay for policies of (*a*) 1 year, (*b*) 2 years, (*c*) 3 years, (*d*) 4 years, and (*e*) 5 years.

C. Use the table of annual rates on buildings and contents, page 239, and the short-rate table, page 244, in solving the following problems in fire insurance:

1. On June 1, Mr. Bennett insured his house and contents with policies totaling $9,500. If the policy is only for the period to Oct. 1 of the same year, find the premium if the house is of frame construction with a shingle roof.
2. On Feb. 4, Mr. Morrison agrees to sell his drugstore as of May 16. He has a policy of $15,000 on the building and $12,500 on the stock which expires on Feb. 27. The building is of brick with an approved roof. Find the total premiums he will have to pay on the store and contents for short-term policies to cover the time up to transfer.
3. Mr. Bergen insured his brick and tile-roof house for 3 years with a $12,000 policy on Aug. 5, 1960. On Oct. 17, 1961, he canceled the policy. Find the refund due Mr. Bergen.
4. Mr. Cameron insured his frame and approved roof, 4-family apartments with a 3-year, $35,000 fire policy on Apr. 27, 1960. On Dec. 2, 1962, he canceled the policy. Find (*a*) the net cost of the policy and (*b*) the refund due to Mr. Cameron.
5. On Mar. 1, 1962, Mr. Burton took out a 1-year, $31,000 fire policy on his 2-family brick building with approved roof. On Dec. 1, the policy was canceled by the fire underwriter. What refund did Mr. Burton receive?
6. Mr. Allen insured his frame house with a shingle roof on Feb. 16, 1961, with a 3-year fire-insurance policy in a face of $18,000. On Nov. 8, 1963, the insurer canceled the policy. Find the refund received by Mr. Allen.

UNIT 6. Two or More Fire Underwriters Insuring the Same Property; Coinsurance

On occasions, more than one fire underwriter insures the same piece of property. This may occur for a number of reasons: the value of the property may be so large that no one company wishes to assume all of the risk; a lending agency holding a mortgage on the property may require more than one insurer; the insured may wish to divide his policies among two or more friendly agents or brokers; or the insurance agent transfers from one company to another and the insured, when raising the total amount of his insurance because of increased value of the property, may prefer to retain the same agent for all his policies.

Whenever more than one underwriter insures the same property, if a loss occurs, each company pays the prorata share that its policy bears to the total insurance carried. Thus if Company A's policy is 50 per cent, Company B's policy is 30 per cent, and Company C's policy is 20 per cent of the total insurance carried by the insured, the total of any loss to be paid by the three insurers is ascertained as follows: Company A will pay 50 per cent; Company B will pay 30 per cent; and Company C will pay 20 per cent. Loss is limited to the value of the property damaged, but in no case will the loss paid be in excess of the face of the policies.

Expressed as a formula:

$$\text{Each insurer's share of loss} = \underbrace{\text{loss}}_{\substack{\text{Actual loss or total faces of}\\ \text{policies, whichever is smaller}}} \times \frac{\text{the face of its policy}}{\text{total insurance carried}}$$

Example: The Georgetown Corporation carries the following fire-insurance policies: Aetna Insurance Co., $30,000; Fireman's Fund Insurance Co., $20,000; Phoenix Insurance Co., $15,000; Southwestern Insurance Co., $10,000. A loss through fire occurs amounting to $27,000. What is the amount of loss borne by each company?

Insurer	*Face of policy*
Aetna	$30,000
Fireman's Fund	20,000
Phoenix	15,000
Southwestern	10,000
Total insurance	$75,000

$$\text{Loss sustained by Aetna} = \$27{,}000 \times \frac{30{,}000}{75{,}000} = \$10{,}800$$

$$\text{Loss sustained by Fireman's Fund} = \$27{,}000 \times \frac{20{,}000}{75{,}000} = \$\ 7{,}200$$

$$\text{Loss sustained by Phoenix} = \$27{,}000 \times \frac{15{,}000}{75{,}000} = \$\ 5{,}400$$

$$\text{Loss sustained by Southwestern} = \$27{,}000 \times \frac{10{,}000}{75{,}000} = \$\ 3{,}600$$

COINSURANCE

Since few fires result in total loss of the insured property, many owners of large properties insure their holdings for only a fractional part of their value. To adjust fire-insurance costs equitably for those property owners who desire less than full coverage, the principle of *coinsurance* has been developed. In coinsurance, the insured agrees to carry insurance to cover a stated per cent of the value of the property—frequently 80 per cent, although this per cent varies.

If the insured fails to carry insurance equivalent to the stated per cent, he is considered a coinsurer for the difference between the per cent he carries and the stated per cent of the policy. If a loss is sustained, the insured is reimbursed in full up to the face value of his policy if his insurance is at least the stipulated per cent of the value of the property at the time of the loss. The insurance usually need not be taken wholly with one company, but the total or aggregate insurance must equal or exceed the required amount. If the total insurance is less than the required amount, the insured shares pro rata with the insurers in any loss sustained. Regardless of the amount of total loss, in no case will the loss paid be in excess of the actual loss or of the face of the policies.

Coinsurance clauses become inoperative if the loss is equal to or exceeds the stipulated percentage of value. Thus if the insurance required is $8,000, the insurance taken $2,000, and the loss $8,000 or more, the insurer pays the loss in the ratio that $2,000 bears to $8,000 times the loss, or to the extent of $2,000. The formula for computing the insurer's share of the loss may be stated as follows:

$$\underbrace{\text{Insurer's share of loss}}_{\substack{\text{Not to exceed actual loss or face} \\ \text{of policy, whichever is smaller}}} = \text{loss} \times \frac{\text{insurance carried}}{\text{insurance required}}$$

Example 1: Mr. Abbott carried $10,000 insurance with an 80 per cent coinsurance clause on the stock of his men's clothing store. At a time when his inventory showed $15,000 as the value of his merchandise at cost, a fire destroyed $3,600 worth of the goods. How much insurance settlement did Mr. Abbott receive?

$$80\% \text{ insurance required} = \$15{,}000 \times .80 = \$12{,}000$$

But Mr. Abbott carried only $10,000 insurance

$$\text{Therefore settlement} = \$3{,}600 \times \frac{10{,}000}{12{,}000} = \$3{,}000$$

Example 2: Mr. Plaskett carries $18,000 insurance with a 90 per cent coinsurance clause on a stock of hardware. At a time when his inventory shows $19,000 as the value of his merchandise at cost, a fire completely destroys the store and contents. How much insurance settlement will Mr. Plaskett receive?

90% insurance required = $19,000 × .90 = $17,100
Mr. Plaskett carries $18,000 insurance
Therefore the settlement = face of policy = $18,000

Example 3: Mr. Pribble carries $12,000 insurance with an 80 per cent coinsurance clause on his stock of merchandise. At a time when the value of the merchandise is $20,000, a fire destroys $18,000 worth of the stock. How much insurance settlement will Mr. Pribble receive?

80% insurance required = $20,000 × .80 = $16,000
Mr. Pribble carries only $12,000 insurance

$$\text{Therefore settlement} = \$18,000 \times \frac{12,000}{16,000} = \$13,500$$

but loss is limited to face of policy = $12,000

EXERCISE 6

A. Solve the following:

1. A loss of $27,500 occurred on an apartment building. The insurance was carried by three companies, A for $20,000, B for $13,500, and C for $7,750. How much did each company have to pay to the insured?
2. Fire-insurance policies for $15,000, $12,000, and $9,000 were carried with Companies A, B, and C, respectively. The insured building, valued at $35,000, was completely destroyed by fire. What loss was assumed by each company?
3. Mr. Mitchell carries $12,000 insurance with a 90 per cent coinsurance clause on his stock of electrical appliances. At a time when his inventory shows $13,000 as the value of the merchandise at cost, a fire completely destroys the store and contents. What insurance settlement does Mr. Mitchell receive?
4. Mr. Hart carries $15,000 insurance with an 80 per cent coinsurance clause on the stock of his grocery store. At a time when his inventory shows $20,000 as the value of the merchandise at cost, a fire destroys $5,800 worth of the goods. What insurance settlement does Mr. Hart receive?
5. A factory was valued at $500,000. The insurance with 80 per cent coinsurance clauses was carried by four companies. Company A carried $150,000; B, $90,000; C, $100,000; and D, $80,000. A loss of $290,000 occurred. How much did each company pay?
6. A fire loss of $125,000 occurred. Four companies had sold policies with 80 per cent coinsurance clauses. A held $50,000, B held $70,000, C held $85,000, and

D held $110,000. The building was valued at $450,000. How much did each pay?

Find the fire insurance settlement in each of the following:

	Face of policy	Coinsurance clause, %	Value at time of loss	Actual loss sustained
1	$ 10,000	80	$ 12,000	$ 4,000
2	35,000	90	40,000	40,000
3	5,600	60	8,000	6,000
4	7,200	80	10,000	7,500
5	900,000	80	1,200,000	230,000
6	78,000	90	85,000	85,000

UNIT 7. Automobile Insurance

Of general interest to almost everyone is the subject of automobile surance, a topic that deserves much more time and space than may be lotted in this text. As with other kinds of insurance, premiums are ased on the risk experience of the underwriter. Most automobile insurnce policies are for a one-year term though a number of companies sell olicies on a semiannual or quarterly basis and in some instances on a onthly premium basis.

Automobile insurance coverage may be divided roughly into two oups: (1) to insure against loss to the insured's automobile; and (2) to sure the driver and/or insured against liability arising from damage to hers' property or person.

Insuring the Automobile. Fire, theft, windstorm, earthquake, and milar risks may be insured against separately but are usually covered nder a so-called *comprehensive* policy (excluding collision). To this omprehensive group may be added *collision* insurance protecting the vner in part or in full for the cost of repairs arising through collision or pset damage to the automobile.

When an automobile is purchased through a finance company, bank, or her lending agency, the lender retains legal ownership of the automoile until the loan with interest has been paid in full. To protect their an, the lending agencies require usually that the borrower purchase both comprehensive and collision insurance. Collision insurance may b full coverage in which the insurer pays 100 per cent of any loss but i more frequently a modified coverage in which the insured bears a portio of the loss.

Typical of the modified collision coverages available are deductibl policies in which the insured pays the first $50, $100, $150, etc., of th loss in any one collision, the insurer paying any excess up to the rate value of the automobile. A number of underwriters specialize in a forr of collision insurance in which the insured pays 20 per cent of any colli sion repair bills, limited usually to not more than $50 by the insured, an the insurer pays 80 per cent of the remaining repair cost (up to $200), th total cost in excess of $250 being paid in full by the insurer.

Insuring against Liability. Insuring against liability arising from dam age to others' property or person is usually an optional form of insuranc though some states have "driver responsibility laws" that stipulate th minimum coverages that should be provided.

Insuring against responsibility arising out of civil suits for damage because of bodily injury or death incurred through the negligence (nc necessarily criminal negligence) of the driver and/or registered owner i known as *public liability* or *bodily injury liability* insurance.

Insuring against responsibility arising out of damage to other person property is known as *property damage liability* insurance.

Though ordinarily an optional form of insurance, every driver of a automobile should have this type of insurance protection. Insofar as th automobile itself is concerned, the maximum loss that can be sustaine is the value of the automobile. But damage to others' property or pe son may result in liability far in excess of the value of the automobil liability judgments often being in tens of thousands of dollars and som times in hundreds of thousands of dollars.

The minimum face for bodily injury policies is usually $5,000/$10,00 meaning that the insurer is liable for damage up to $5,000 arising out bodily injury to one person and not to exceed $10,000 for two or mo persons. Property damage policies usually have a minimum face $5,000. Increased liability limits may be obtained for slightly high cost, many individuals choosing to carry as much as or more tha $100,000 bodily injury and $25,000 property damage policies.

Incidental Coverages. In addition to comprehensive, collision, bodil injury, and property damage policies, insurance may be purchased fc such incidental coverages as medical payments, towing, emergency roa service, disability or death, use of other automobiles, etc. Many these risks are now insured by a combined package form known a "family auto policies."

Private Passenger Automobile Driver Classification. Drivers and automobiles may be classified as follows:

Class 1: nonbusiness use, no male operator under age 25.
- 1A. Not customarily used to or from work.
- 1B. To or from work less than 10 road miles one way.
- 1C. To or from work 10 or more road miles one way.

Class 2: business and nonbusiness use, any male operator under age 25.
- 2A. Business and nonbusiness use and the male operators under 25 are not owners or principal operators or the male owners and operators under 25 are married.
- 2C. Business and nonbusiness use and the male operators under 25 are owners or principal operators and are not married.

Class 3: business and nonbusiness use, individually owned, no male operator under age 25 and no unmarried female operator under age 25 who is an owner or principal operator—and not individual-owned but owned by corporations, copartnerships or unincorporated associations, without age qualification of operator.

Territorial Definitions for Comprehensive and Collision Premiums. Though each underwriter may have differing definitions in any given area, the various areas in each state carry differing rates for comprehensive and collision insurance based upon past experience of the insurers and subject to constant revision. Since the state of California has the largest number of private passenger automobiles, it will perhaps best serve to illustrate territorial segregations with a recent schedule of one of the major underwriters in that state:

Territorial definitions	*Comprehensive*	*Collision*	*Territorial definitions*	*Comprehensive*	*Collision*
Alameda county	B—B	3	Sacramento county	C—C	4
Contra Costa county	C—C	4	San Diego county	D—D	2
Fresno county	D—D	4	San Francisco county	E—E	6
Humboldt county	D—D	7	San Joaquin county	C—C	5
Imperial county	G—G	7	San Mateo county	B—B	1
Kern county	F—F	3	Santa Clara county	A—A	3
Los Angeles county	D—D	2			
Marin county	B—B	4	Remainder of state	D—D	5

Territorial Definitions for Bodily Injury and Property Damage Premiums. As with comprehensive and collision premiums, the varying areas in each state carry differing ratings for bodily injury and property damage insurance based upon past experience of the insurers and subject to constant revision. Again, the state of California is used to illustrate recent territorial segregations by one of the major underwriters:

Areas classified	*Territories*
Antioch	2
Bakersfield	7
Berkeley, see Oakland	
Eureka	8
Fresno city	7
Fullerton	5
Half Moon Bay, Montara	8
Hayward	2
Imperial county, see Remainder of state	
Los Altos, Cupertino, Sunnyvale, Los Gatos	4
Los Angeles city	3
Los Angeles county, see Remainder of state	
Los Angeles suburban	5
Modesto	8
Mountain View, Palo Alto, Redwood City, San Jose, Santa Clara	4
Oakland	2
Ontario	5
Redlands	5
Richmond	2
Riverside, San Bernardino cities	5
Sacramento city	7
Salinas	8
San Diego city	6
San Francisco city	1
San Francisco suburban	4
San Leandro	2
Santa Ana	5
Santa Barbara city	8
Santa Cruz city	8
Santa Rosa	8
Stockton	7
Vallejo	2
Walnut Creek	2
Watts	3
West Covina	5
Remainder of state	8

Determining Automobile Age Classification. The year model (age) of the automobile affects the cost of comprehensive and collision premiums. Age groupings are determined usually as follows:

Age group	*Automobiles purchased new prior to date insurance attaches*
1	Not more than 6 months
2	More than 6 months, not more than 18 months
3	More than 18 months, not more than 30 months
4	More than 30 months

If original date of purchase cannot be ascertained, use May 1 of the model year.

Determining Automobile Value for Insurance. Value for insurance is customarily based on the manufacturer's factory price plus Federal tax. Symbols for all makes, models, and body types by model years are listed in order of increasing cost beginning with A, B, C, D, etc., on up to Z for the higher-priced automobiles manufactured in the United States and foreign countries. Following is a very brief excerpt from a recent list, 19-a representing the earliest year and 19-c representing the current year.

Symbol Information in Determining Value for Comprehensive and Collision Premiums

Buick, Model 50:				*Cadillac, Model 62:*			
Year model	19-c	19-b	19-a	Year model	19-c	19-b	19-a
Sed 4Dr	K	K	K	Sed 4Dr	M	M	M
Cpe Conv	L	K	L	Cpe Conv	N	N	N
Cpe Riviera	J	J	J	Cpe de Ville	O	N	M
Chevrolet 8-cyl. Bel Air				*Ford 8-cyl. Custom line*			
Year model	19-c	19-b	19-a	Year model	19-c	19-b	19-a
Sed 4Dr	H	H	G	Sed Tud	H	H	G
Cpe Spt	I	I	H	Sed For	H	H	H
Cpe Conv	J	J	I	Sed Country	J	I	I
Mercury Custom				*Plymouth 8-cyl. Belv'd*			
Year model	19-c	19-b	19-a	Year model	19-c	19-b	19-a
Cpe Spt	K	J	J	Sed Clb	I	H	G
Sed 2Dr	J	I	I	Sed 4Dr	J	I	H
Sed 4Dr	I	I	I	Cpe Spt	K	J	J

Premium Rates for Comprehensive and Collision Policies. Again using the state of California and the charges for one-year policies by a major underwriters, the tables on pages 256 and 257 are excerpts from territories 2 and 3, and 7 of the seven territories into which California was divided for purposes of determining comprehensive and collision premiums for private passenger automobiles in a recent listing.

Premium Rates for Bodily Injury and Property Damage Policies. Again using the state of California and the charges for one-year policies by one of the major underwriters, the table on page 258 is an excerpt from a recent listing of the eight territories into which California was divided for purposes of determining bodily injury and property damage premiums for private passenger automobiles:

Example 1 of automobile insurance: Mr. Beach Baker, a casualty insurance broker, sold an automobile insurance policy to Mr. James Moore, a resident of Oakland, Alameda county. Mr. Moore's automobile was a 32-month-old Buick, model 50, 4-door sedan, year model 19-a. There were no male operators under 25 years of age in Mr. Moore's household, but he customarily drove the automobile to his work, a distance of less than 10 road miles one way. The following coverages were obtained: (*a*) comprehensive, (*b*) $100 deductible collision,

Comprehensive and Collision Premiums

Symbols	Age groups	Comprehensive					Collision premiums—territory schs. 2, 3											
		Terr. schedules					$50 ded.			$100 ded.			$150 ded.			$250 ded.		
							Class			Class			Class			Class		
		A—A B—B	C—C D—D	E—E	F—F	G—G	1	2	3	1	2	3	1	2	3	1	2	3
A, B, C	1	$8	$10	$11	$12	$19	$25	$36	$31	$10	$15	$13	$8	$12	$10	$6	$9	$8
	2	7	9	10	11	17	24	34	29	10	14	12	8	11	10	6	9	8
	3	6	7	8	9	14	23	32	28	9	14	12	7	11	9	5	8	7
	4	5	6	7	7	11	21	31	26	9	13	11	7	10	9	5	8	7
D, E	1	9	12	13	14	22	31	45	39	13	18	16	10	15	13	8	12	10
	2	8	10	12	13	20	29	43	37	12	17	15	10	14	12	8	11	10
	3	7	9	10	11	16	28	41	35	12	16	14	9	14	12	7	11	9
	4	5	7	8	8	13	26	38	33	11	15	14	9	13	11	7	10	9
F	1	10	13	15	16	25	37	53	46	17	24	21	14	20	17	10	15	13
	2	9	12	13	15	23	35	50	44	16	23	20	13	19	16	10	14	12
	3	8	10	11	12	19	33	48	41	15	22	19	13	18	15	9	14	12
	4	6	8	9	10	15	31	45	39	14	20	18	12	17	14	9	13	11
G	1	12	15	17	18	28	42	60	52	19	28	24	15	22	19	11	16	14
	2	10	13	15	16	25	40	57	49	18	27	23	14	21	18	10	15	13
	3	9	11	12	14	21	38	54	47	17	25	22	14	20	17	10	14	13
	4	7	9	10	11	17	36	51	44	16	24	20	13	19	16	9	14	12
H	1	13	17	18	20	31	45	64	56	22	32	28	18	25	22	14	20	17
	2	12	15	17	18	28	43	61	53	21	30	27	17	24	21	13	19	16
	3	10	12	14	15	23	41	58	50	20	29	25	16	23	20	13	18	15
	4	8	10	11	12	19	38	54	48	19	27	24	15	21	19	12	17	14
I	1	14	18	20	22	34	49	70	61	26	38	33	21	30	26	16	23	20
	2	13	16	18	20	31	47	67	58	25	26	31	20	29	25	15	22	19
	3	11	14	15	17	26	44	63	55	23	34	30	19	27	23	14	21	18
	4	8	11	12	13	21	42	60	52	22	32	28	18	26	22	14	20	17
J	1	16	20	23	25	38	54	78	68	30	44	38	24	35	30	18	26	23
	2	14	18	20	22	35	51	74	65	29	42	36	23	33	29	17	25	22
	3	12	15	17	19	29	49	70	61	27	40	34	22	32	27	16	23	21
	4	9	12	14	15	23	46	66	58	26	37	32	20	30	26	15	22	20
K, L	1	18	23	26	28	44	59	85	74	35	51	44	28	40	35	21	30	26
	2	16	21	23	26	40	56	81	70	33	48	42	27	38	33	20	29	25
	3	14	17	19	21	33	53	77	67	32	46	40	25	36	32	19	27	23
	4	11	14	16	17	26	50	72	63	30	43	37	24	34	30	18	26	22
M	1	21	27	30	33	51	61	87	76	36	52	45	29	41	36	22	31	27
	2	19	24	27	30	46	58	83	72	34	49	43	28	39	34	21	29	26
	3	16	20	22	25	38	55	78	68	32	47	41	26	37	32	20	28	24
	4	13	16	18	20	30	52	74	65	31	44	38	25	35	31	19	26	23
N	1	24	31	35	38	59	62	90	78	37	53	46	30	43	37	22	32	28
	2	22	28	31	34	53	59	86	74	35	50	44	29	41	35	21	30	27
	3	18	23	26	29	44	56	81	70	33	48	41	27	39	33	20	29	25
	4	15	19	21	23	35	53	77	66	31	45	39	26	37	31	19	27	24
O	1	27	35	39	43	67	64	92	80	38	55	48	30	44	38	23	33	29
	2	25	32	35	39	60	61	87	76	36	52	46	29	42	36	22	31	28
	3	21	26	29	32	50	58	83	72	34	50	43	27	40	34	21	30	26
	4	16	21	24	26	40	54	78	68	32	47	41	26	37	32	20	28	25
P	1	29	38	42	46	71	65	93	81	39	56	49	31	45	39	23	33	29
	2	26	34	38	42	64	62	88	77	37	53	47	29	43	37	22	31	28
	3	22	28	32	35	54	59	84	73	35	50	44	28	41	35	21	30	26
	4	18	23	25	28	43	55	79	69	33	48	42	26	38	33	20	28	25

Collision Premiums

Symbols	Age groups	Collision premiums—territory sch. 7											
		$50 ded.			$100 ded.			$150 ded.			$250 ded.		
		Class			Class			Class			Class		
		1	2	3	1	2	3	1	2	3	1	2	3
A, B, C	1	$42	$61	$53	$18	$25	$22	$14	$21	$18	$10	$15	$13
	2	40	58	50	17	24	21	13	20	17	10	14	12
	3	38	55	48	16	23	20	13	19	16	9	14	12
	4	36	52	45	15	21	19	12	18	15	9	13	11
D, E	1	54	77	67	22	31	27	18	25	22	13	18	16
	2	51	73	64	21	29	26	17	24	21	12	17	15
	3	49	69	60	20	28	24	16	23	20	12	16	14
	4	46	65	57	19	26	23	15	21	19	11	15	14
F	1	63	91	79	27	39	34	22	31	27	16	23	20
	2	60	86	75	26	37	32	21	29	26	15	22	19
	3	57	82	71	24	35	31	20	28	24	14	21	18
	4	54	77	67	23	33	29	19	26	23	14	20	17
G	1	70	101	88	33	47	41	26	38	33	20	29	25
	2	67	96	84	31	45	39	25	36	31	19	28	24
	3	63	91	79	30	42	37	23	34	30	18	26	23
	4	60	86	75	28	40	35	22	32	28	17	25	21
H	1	77	110	96	38	54	47	30	44	38	22	32	28
	2	73	105	91	36	51	45	29	42	36	21	30	27
	3	69	99	86	34	49	42	27	40	34	20	29	25
	4	65	94	82	32	46	40	26	37	32	19	27	24
I	1	84	121	105	43	62	54	34	49	43	26	37	32
	2	80	115	100	41	59	51	32	47	41	25	35	30
	3	76	109	95	39	56	49	31	44	39	23	33	29
	4	71	103	89	37	53	46	29	42	37	22	31	27
J	1	93	133	116	50	71	62	40	58	50	30	43	37
	2	88	126	110	48	67	59	38	55	48	29	41	35
	3	84	120	104	45	64	56	36	52	45	27	39	33
	4	79	113	99	43	60	53	34	49	43	26	37	31
K, L	1	102	146	127	57	82	71	46	66	57	34	49	43
	2	97	139	121	54	78	67	44	63	54	32	47	41
	3	92	131	114	51	74	64	41	59	51	31	44	39
	4	87	124	108	48	70	60	39	56	48	29	42	37
M	1	104	150	130	58	84	73	46	67	58	35	51	44
	2	99	143	124	55	80	69	44	64	55	33	48	42
	3	94	135	117	52	76	66	41	60	52	32	46	40
	4	88	128	111	49	71	62	39	57	49	30	43	37
N	1	106	153	133	60	86	75	48	69	60	36	52	45
	2	101	145	126	57	82	71	46	66	57	34	49	43
	3	95	138	120	54	77	68	43	62	54	32	47	41
	4	90	130	113	51	73	64	41	59	51	31	44	38
O	1	110	158	137	61	87	76	49	70	61	37	53	46
	2	105	150	130	58	83	72	47	67	58	35	50	44
	3	99	142	123	55	78	68	44	63	55	33	48	41
	4	94	134	116	52	74	65	42	60	52	31	45	39
P	1	110	159	138	62	90	78	50	71	62	38	54	47
	2	105	151	131	59	86	74	48	67	59	36	51	45
	3	99	143	124	56	81	70	45	64	56	34	49	42
	4	94	135	117	53	77	66	43	60	53	32	46	40

Premiums for Bodily Injury and Property Damage

Terr.	Class	Bodily injury in thousands								Property damage		
		5/10	10/20	15/30	20/40	25/50	50/100	100/100	100/300	5,000	10,000	25,000
1	1A	$38.00	$45.60	$48.64	$50.54	$51.68	$55.10	$55.86	$58.52	$22.00	$24.20	$26.40
	1B	45.00	54.00	57.60	59.85	61.20	65.25	66.15	69.30	25.00	27.50	30.00
	1C	54.00	64.80	69.12	71.82	73.44	78.30	79.38	83.16	31.00	34.10	37.20
	2A	70.00	84.00	89.60	93.10	95.20	101.50	102.90	107.80	40.00	44.00	48.00
	2C	96.00	115.20	122.88	127.68	130.56	139.20	141.12	147.84	54.00	59.40	64.80
	3	64.00	76.80	81.92	85.12	87.04	92.80	94.08	98.56	36.00	39.60	43.20
2	1A	28.00	33.60	35.84	37.24	38.08	40.60	41.16	43.12	16.00	17.60	19.20
	1B	33.00	39.60	42.24	43.89	44.88	47.85	48.51	50.82	19.00	20.90	22.80
	1C	40.00	48.00	51.20	53.20	54.40	58.00	58.80	61.60	23.00	25.30	27.60
	2A	52.00	62.40	66.56	69.16	70.72	75.40	76.44	80.08	30.00	33.00	36.00
	2C	71.00	85.20	90.88	94.43	96.56	102.95	104.37	109.34	41.00	45.10	49.20
	3	47.00	56.40	60.16	62.51	63.92	68.15	69.09	72.38	27.00	29.70	32.40
3	1A	25.00	30.00	32.00	33.25	34.00	36.25	36.75	38.50	18.00	19.80	21.60
	1B	29.00	34.80	37.12	38.57	39.44	42.05	42.63	44.66	21.00	23.10	25.20
	1C	35.00	42.00	44.80	46.55	47.60	50.75	51.45	53.90	26.00	28.60	31.20
	2A	46.00	55.20	58.88	61.18	62.56	66.70	67.62	70.84	33.00	36.30	39.60
	2C	62.00	74.40	79.36	82.46	84.32	89.90	91.14	95.48	45.00	49.50	54.00
	3	41.00	49.20	52.48	54.53	55.76	59.45	60.27	63.14	30.00	33.00	36.00
4	1A	28.00	33.60	35.84	37.24	38.08	40.60	41.16	43.12	16.00	17.60	19.20
	1B	28.00	33.60	35.84	37.24	38.08	40.60	41.16	43.12	16.00	17.60	19.20
	1C	40.00	48.00	51.20	53.20	54.40	58.00	58.80	61.60	23.00	25.30	27.60
	2A	52.00	62.40	66.56	69.16	70.72	75.40	76.44	80.08	30.00	33.00	36.00
	2C	71.00	85.20	90.88	94.43	96.56	102.95	104.37	109.34	41.00	45.10	49.20
	3	47.00	56.40	60.16	62.51	63.92	68.15	69.09	72.38	27.00	29.70	32.40
5	1A	18.00	21.60	23.04	23.94	24.48	26.10	26.46	27.72	14.00	15.40	16.80
	1B	22.00	26.40	28.16	29.26	29.92	31.90	32.34	33.88	16.00	17.60	19.20
	1C	26.00	31.20	33.28	34.58	35.36	37.70	38.22	40.04	20.00	22.00	24.00
	2A	33.00	39.60	42.24	43.89	44.88	47.85	48.51	50.82	25.00	27.50	30.00
	2C	46.00	55.20	58.88	61.18	62.56	66.70	67.62	70.84	35.00	38.50	42.00
	3	31.00	37.20	39.68	41.23	42.16	44.95	45.57	47.74	23.00	25.30	27.60
6	1A	17.00	20.40	21.76	22.61	23.12	24.65	24.99	26.18	14.00	15.40	16.80
	1B	20.00	24.00	25.60	26.60	27.20	29.00	29.40	30.80	16.00	17.60	19.20
	1C	25.00	30.00	32.00	33.25	34.00	36.25	36.75	38.50	20.00	22.00	24.00
	2A	32.00	38.40	40.96	42.56	43.52	46.40	47.04	49.28	25.00	27.50	30.00
	2C	44.00	52.80	56.32	58.52	59.84	63.80	64.68	67.76	35.00	38.50	42.00
	3	29.00	34.80	37.12	38.57	39.44	42.05	42.63	44.66	23.00	25.30	27.60
7	1A	22.00	26.40	28.16	29.26	29.92	31.90	32.34	33.88	14.00	15.40	16.80
	1B	26.00	31.20	33.28	34.58	35.36	37.70	38.22	40.04	17.00	18.70	20.40
	1C	31.00	37.20	39.68	41.23	42.16	44.95	45.57	47.74	20.00	22.00	24.00
	2A	41.00	49.20	52.48	54.53	55.76	59.45	60.27	63.14	26.00	28.60	31.20
	2C	56.00	67.20	71.68	74.48	76.16	81.20	82.32	86.24	36.00	39.60	43.20
	3	37.00	44.40	47.36	49.21	50.32	53.65	54.39	56.98	24.00	26.40	28.80
8	1A	20.00	24.00	25.60	26.60	27.20	29.00	29.40	30.80	14.00	15.40	16.80
	1B	20.00	24.00	25.60	26.60	27.20	29.00	29.40	30.80	14.00	15.40	16.80
	1C	29.00	34.80	37.12	38.57	39.44	42.05	42.63	44.66	20.00	22.00	24.00
	2A	37.00	44.40	47.36	49.21	50.32	53.65	54.39	56.98	25.00	27.50	30.00
	2C	51.00	61.20	65.28	67.83	69.36	73.95	74.97	78.54	35.00	38.50	42.00
	3	34.00	40.80	43.52	45.22	46.24	49.30	49.98	52.36	23.00	25.30	27.60

(*c*) 50/100 thousand dollars bodily injury, and (*d*) $10,000 property damage. Find the premium cost of each coverage and the total premium.

Driver classification (page 253) is 1B.
Territorial classification (page 253) for comprehensive is B—B, for collision is 3.
Territorial classification (page 254) for bodily injury and property damage is 2.
Automobile age classification (page 254) is age group 4.
Automobile value for insurance (page 255) symbol is K.

(*a*) comprehensive, symbol K, age group 4, territory B—B (page 256) premium is	$ 11.00
(*b*) $100 deductible collision, symbol K, age group 4, territory 3, driver class 1 (page 256) premium is	30.00
(*c*) $50,000/$100,000 bodily injury, territory 2, driver class 1B (page 258) premium is	47.85
(*d*) $10,000 property damage, territory 2, driver class 1B (page 258) premium is	20.90
Total premium	$109.75

Example 2 of automobile insurance: Harry Shaw, a 22-year old student residing in Imperial county, owned and operated a 4-month old Plymouth, 8-cylinder Belvedere club sedan, year model 19-a. The lending agency from whom he financed the purchase of the automobile required that he carry (*a*) comprehensive and (*b*) $50 deductible collision insurance. To meet possible minimum obligations under the California state driver responsibility code, he purchased (*c*) $10,000/$20,000 bodily injury and (*d*) $5,000 property damage coverages. Find the cost of each coverage and the total premium.

Driver classification (page 253) is 2C.
Territorial classification (page 253) for comprehensive is G—G, for collision is 7.
Territorial classification (page 254) for bodily injury and property damage is 8.
Automobile age classification (page 254) is age group 1.
Automobile value for insurance (page 255) symbol is I.

(*a*) comprehensive, symbol I, age group 1, territory G—G (page 256) premium is	$ 34.00
(*b*) $50 deductible collision, symbol I, age group 1, territory 7, driver class 2 (page 257) premium is	121.00
(*c*) $10,000/$20,000 bodily injury, territory 8, driver class 2C (page 258) premium is	61.20
(*d*) $5,000 property damage, territory 8, driver class 2C (page 258) premium is	35.00
Total premium	$251.20

Cancellation by Insurer or by Insured. As with fire and other casualty insurance policies, automobile insurance may be canceled by the insurer or by the insured.

If the policy is canceled by the insurance company before expiration of the term, the company is obligated by law to retain not more than an exact pro rata of the premium for the length of time the policy has been in force. Thus, if the insurer cancels a 1-year policy after it has been in force 181 days, the insurer may retain $\frac{181}{365}$ of the premium.

But if the insured cancels the policy before expiration of the term, the company may apply a short-rate table to determine the premium that it will retain. For most 1-year policies, underwriters use the same short-rate table used for fire insurance (see page 244) and compute the refund due the policyholder in the same manner as illustrated by example 2, page 245.

Example of cancellation of an automobile policy: Assume that in the preceding Example 2, (*a*) Harry Shaw sold his automobile and canceled his policy 219 days after the policy became effective or (*b*) that a series of minor collision claims caused the insurer to cancel the policy 219 days after the effective date of the policy. In each instance, find the premium retained by the insurer and the refund paid to Harry Shaw.

(*a*) from the short-rate table (page 244) the insurer retained 69 per cent of the premium.

$$\$251.20 \times .69 = \$173.33 \text{ retained by the insurer}$$
$$\$251.20 - \$173.33 = \$77.87 \text{ refunded to Harry Shaw}$$

(*b*) the insurer retains an exact pro rata of the premium for the time the policy was in force.

$$\$251.20 \times \frac{219}{365} = \$150.72 \text{ retained by the insurer}$$
$$\$251.20 - \$150.72 = \$100.48 \text{ refunded to Harry Shaw}$$

EXERCISE 7

Solve the following problems in automobile insurance using the necessary classifications and tables as provided in Unit 7:

1. Nonbusiness use automobile, no male operators under age 25, not customarily used to or from work. Principal place of garaging: Bakersfield, Kern county. Chevrolet 8-cylinder Bel Air, coupe convertible, new car on date insurance attaches, year model 19-c. Insurance purchased: (*a*) comprehensive but no collision insurance, (*b*) 100/300 thousand bodily injury, (*c*) $25,000 property damage. Find premium cost for each coverage and (*d*) total premium cost.
2. Nonbusiness use automobile, no male operators under age 25, customarily driven to and from work more than 10 road miles one way. Principal place

of garaging: Los Angeles City in the county of Los Angeles. Cadillac, model 62 coupe de Ville, 15-months old, year model 19-b. Insurance purchased: (*a*) comprehensive but no collision insurance, (*b*) 100/100 thousand bodily injury, (*c*) $10,000 property damage. Find the premium cost for each coverage and (*d*) total premium cost.

3. Business and nonbusiness use automobile, male operators under age 25 are not owners or principal operators. Principal place of garaging: Eureka, Humboldt county. Mercury custom, 4-door sedan, 32-months old, year model 19-a. Insurance purchased: (*a*) $250 deductible collision insurance but no comprehensive, (*b*) $15,000/$30,000 bodily injury, (*c*) $5,000 property damage. Find the premium cost for, each coverage and (*d*) total premium cost.
4. Business and nonbusiness use automobile, owned and operated by 23-year old college student residing in Berkeley, Alameda county. Ford 8-cylinder, 2-door sedan, 5 months old, year model 19-c. Insurance purchased: (*a*) $100 deductible collision insurance but no comprehensive, (*b*) 20/40 thousand bodily injury, (*c*) $10,000 property damage. Find the premium cost for each coverage and (*d*) total premium cost.
5. Business and nonbusiness use automobile, individually owned, no male operator under age 25 and no unmarried female operator under age 25 who is an owner or principal operator. Principal place of garaging: El Centro, Imperial county. Cadillac, model 62, convertible coupe, 27-months old, year model 19-a. Insurance purchased: (*a*) comprehensive, (*b*) $50 deductible collision, (*c*) 100/300 thousand bodily injury, (*d*) $25,000 property damage. Find the premium cost for each coverage and (*e*) total premium cost.
6. Nonbusiness use automobile, no male operator under age 25, customarily driven to or from work but less than 10 road miles one way. Principal place of garaging: San Jose, Santa Clara county. Buick, model 50, Riviera coupe, 9-months old, year model 19-b. Insurance purchased: (*a*) comprehensive, (*b*) $150 deductible collision, (*c*) $50,000/$100,000 bodily injury, (*d*) $5,000 property damage. Find the premium cost for each coverage and (*e*) total premium cost.
7. An automobile policy with an annual premium of $122.75 is canceled by the insured after 71 days in force. Find (*a*) the premium retained by the insurer and (*b*) the refund due the insured.
8. After 180 days of being in force, a one-year automobile policy with a premium of $201.35 was canceled by the insured. Find (*a*) the premium retained by the insurer and (*b*) the refund paid the insured.
9. After a number of insurance claims indicating that the insured was "accident-prone," the insurer canceled a policy that had been in effect 195 days. If the one-year premium was $219.73, find (*a*) the premium retained by the insurer and (*b*) the refund due the insured.
10. Three collision claims arising out of an insured's negligence caused his insuring company to cancel his one-year policy after 146 days had elapsed. If the premium cost was $184.25, find (*a*) the premium retained by the insurer and (*b*) the refund due the insured.

UNIT 8. Business Insurance

A great number of business risks in addition to the possibility of loss through fire need to be protected against by the businessman. Some of these are purely for his own protection, others are for the protection of his employees and may be provided, among other reasons, as a contribution by the employer to the well-being of his working force or to increase their loyalty and efficiency.

Use and Occupancy Insurance. This form of insurance is a means of protecting a business from the losses that would occur if an event such as fire, tornado, or earthquake should interrupt the normal activities of the business.

Use and occupancy insurance provides indemnity for expenses that will continue and for the net profit that would have been made during the suspension of business. Among the expenses that may continue in whole or in part are taxes, insurance, interest, advertising, leaseholds, utilities, and the wages and salaries of key employees who must be retained.

Example: For a given month, net sales of a business are estimated to be $60,000, cost of sales $38,000, and expenses $15,000. Find the estimated amount of use and occupancy insurance that needs to be carried for each working day if the average of working days each month is 25 and expenses that must continue during suspension of business are $11,000 per month.

Net sales	$60,000
Less cost of sales	−38,000
Gross profit	$22,000
Less expenses	−15,000
Net profit	$ 7,000
Add expenses that must continue	11,000
Use and occupancy value for month	$18,000

$$\text{Use and occupancy insurance value per day} = \frac{\$18{,}000}{25} = \$720$$

Workmen's Compensation Insurance. This form of insurance provides financial protection for the loss of earnings by the worker due to accidental or occupational sickness incurred while on duty.

Workmen's compensation insurance policies may be purchased from casualty insurance companies, although a few states also have their own workmen's compensation insurance funds that provide insurance protection for the employer (and employee). Such policies usually include death benefits as well as wage compensation in limited amounts per pay period.

Rates vary with the occupational hazards of the differing types of work covered. Premiums are then determined by the number of dollars of wages at regular rates (overtime excess pay is not usually considered) paid by the employer.

Example 1: If the workmen's compensation insurance rate for clerical workers was $.93 per $100 of wages, find the total premium paid by an employer whose clerical staff earned $8,765.

$8,765 = 87.65 (hundreds of dollars)
$.93 × 87.65 = $81.51 Premium

Example 2: A deposit of $200 on his workmen's compensation insurance premium was made by a painting contractor to cover expected wage payments during a 3-month period. If the rate was $2.25 per $100 of wages and the total wages paid for the period was $9,340, find the amount owed or the refund due on the policy.

$9,340 = 93.40 (hundreds of dollars)
$2.25 × 93.40 = $210.14 Premium
Amount owed on policy = $210.14 − $200 = $10.14

Health and Accident Insurance. This form of insurance is provided to compensate employees for loss of earnings due to sickness and accidents not covered by workmen's compensation insurance. The costs of health and accident insurance plans are usually paid in part by the employees, though in some businesses the employer pays all the costs. Contributions by employees are limited to a small charge which is deducted from wages. In some states, health and accident insurance for nonoccupational illnesses or accidents is provided through disability insurance funds contributed to by both employer and employee.

In most instances, length of service by the employee is a major factor in determining the amount that he may receive.

Example 1: The Eaton Company disability plan provided that workers with less than 1 year of service received no benefits; 1 but less than 5 years received 4 weeks full pay plus half-pay for the next 6 weeks; 5 but less than 10 years received 8 weeks full pay plus half-pay for the next 8 weeks; 10 years and over received 13 weeks full pay plus half-pay for the next 13 weeks. Find the maximum disability benefits to which an employee with 7 years' service was entitled if his weekly wage was $65.50.

Full pay for 8 weeks = $65.50 × 8 = $524

$$\text{Half-pay for 8 weeks} = \frac{\$65.50}{2} \times 8 = \$262$$

Maximum disability benefits = $524 + $262 = $786

Example 2: The Hicks Company health and accident plan provided 50 per cent of wages to employees in service up to 5 years, and 75 per cent of wages to employees in service more than 5 years, and maximum benefit of \$55 per week for 26 weeks. Mr. Robert Merritt who had been employed for 3 years at \$65 per week became incapacitated for 30 weeks. Find his total benefit.

$\$65 \times .50 = \$32.50$ Per week benefit
$\$32.50 \times 26 = \$845$ Total benefit (maximum time, 26 weeks)

Group Life Insurance. Such insurance provides the worker with low-cost life insurance (usually term insurance with no accumulating values), for a portion of the premium is paid by the employer. If the employee leaves the services of the particular employer, the insurance usually ceases although some group life insurance plans provide that the employee may in such case optionally convert his group policy to an ordinary life-insurance policy without medical examination.

The simplest form of group life insurance is for a fixed face (for example, \$1,000) provided to all employees for a small monthly payment. In other instances the face of the policy increases with any increase in the employee's annual income. In this latter case, the monthly contribution by the employee usually increases pro rata both with any increased coverage and with his increasing age.

Example: Employees of the Halsey Corporation earning less than \$2,000 per year are required to carry \$1,000 of life insurance. For workers earning more than \$2,000 per year, an additional \$300 of life insurance is required for each additional \$500 or fraction thereof of earnings. The contribution schedule by the employees per \$1,000 of insurance is based on age. If Mr. Henry Cook, age 36, whose yearly earnings are \$4,200, has a contribution schedule rate of \$.70 per month per \$1,000 of insurance, find the monthly deductions that will be made from his salary for life insurance.

Excess earnings over \$2,000 $= \$4,200 - \$2,000 = \$2,200$
Insurance required in addition to the base of \$1,000 is:

$$\frac{\$2,200}{\$500} = 4+, \text{ or 5 additional units of \$300 each}$$

Total insurance $= \$1,000 + (\$300 \times 5) = \$1,000 + \$1,500 = \$2,500$
Monthly deduction $= \$.70 \times 2.5 = \$1.75$

EXERCISE 8

Solve the following:

1. A retail business had average monthly sales of \$125,000, cost of goods sold of \$68,000, and expenses of \$43,000. If fire should cause a complete suspension of business, find the estimated amount of use and occupancy insurance that should be carried for each working day if the average number of working days per month is 25 and the expenses that will continue are \$23,750 per month.

2. Assuming that it would require 152 working days to reconstruct the Morris Manufacturing Co. plant in the event of complete loss from fire, from the planned data for the period that follows compute the use and occupancy insurance required (*a*) in total amount, (*b*) per work day, and (*c*) the 3-year insurance premium if the rate is $.65 per $100 for a 3-year policy. Beginning inventory, $85,652; ending inventory, $86,305; manufacturing costs and operating expenses, $1,745,868; net sales, $1,820,500. Fixed expenses that will continue: administrative salaries, $28,625; interest, $8,900; taxes, $12,434; insurance, $5,040; salaries of office help, supervisors, and foremen that must be retained, $108,475; and miscellaneous expenses, $15,923.
3. Mr. Walter Pickett planned to build a summer and week-end cabin for his own use. In conformance with the state law he deposited $100 on a workmen's compensation insurance premium. Upon completion of the cabin, his labor costs and insurance rates per $100 of wages paid were as follows: carpenters, $1,285 at $4.09; electricians, $132 at $2.10; plumbers, $318 at $2.25; painters, $204 at $2.75; miscellaneous labor, $83.50 at $1.75. Find the additional premium or refund due on his policy.
4. A deposit of $300 was made on a workmen's compensation insurance policy. The payroll audit showed the following wage payments and insurance rates per $100 of wages paid: $9,085 at $1.28; $6,071 at $.83; $2,344 at $3.20; and $5,983 at $1.09. Find the additional premium or refund due on the policy.
5. The Merchant Company group health and accident insurance plan provided the following benefits for employees who became incapacitated through non-occupational sickness or accident: 6 months but less than 2 years of service, 35 per cent of wages, maximum of $25 for 8 weeks; 2 but less than 5 years of service, 50 per cent of wages, maximum of $40 for 16 weeks; 5 but less than 10 years of service, 65 per cent of wages, maximum of $55 for 24 weeks; and 10 or more years of service, 80 per cent of wages, maximum $70 for 32 weeks. Find the total benefits received by (*a*) Ralph Stocker, employed 6 years with average earnings of $72 per week and ill for 15 weeks; (*b*) Helen Forbes, employed 9 months with average earnings of $40 per week and ill for 12 weeks; (*c*) Ben Fitzsimmons, employed 19 years with average earnings of $110 per week and ill for 28 weeks.
6. The health and accident insurance plan of the Philip's Manufacturing Corporation provided benefits as follows: 1 but less than 10 years of service, full pay for 4 weeks, half-pay for the next 8 weeks, and one-fourth pay for the next 12 weeks; more than 10 years of service, full pay for 6 weeks, three-fourths pay for the next 12 weeks, and half-pay for the next 18 weeks. Find the benefits received by the following employees: (*a*) Mr. Harvey Wayne, employed 4 years and earning $72.50 per week who was incapacitated for 15 weeks; (*b*) Mrs. Sara Alden, employed 11 years and earning $51.60 per week who was incapacitated for 23 weeks.
7. Group life insurance provided without charge to all employees of the Raymond Specialty Company was 1 month's salary for each year of service with a maximum of 12 months' salary or $6,000, whichever was lower. Find the insurance provided for (*a*) John Spear, employed 3 years at $3,900 per year, (*b*) Ruth Clay, employed 11 years at $5,100 per year, (*c*) Helene McGovern,

employed 5 years at $4,980 per year, (*d*) Fred Foultz, employed 9 years at $10,800 per year.

8. The General Manufacturing Corporation group life-insurance plan for all employees determined the face of the policies as follows: earnings of $2,500 per year or less, $2,000 of insurance; earnings of more than $2,500 per year, $2,000 of insurance plus $50 of insurance for each full $100 of earnings in excess of $2,500 per year. Employee contributions per month per $100 of insurance were computed by age groups as follows: under 30 years, $.06; 30 but under 40 years, $.07; 40 but under 50 years, $.085; 50 but under 60 years, $.105; 60 years and over, $.13. Find the monthly insurance contributions by (*a*) employee A, age 38, and earning $4,380 per year, (*b*) employee B, age 68, and earning $5,900 per year, (*c*) employee C, age 48, and earning $12,750 per year.

CHAPTER VII

SALES AND PROPERTY TAXES; DEPRECIATION

UNIT 1. Sales Taxes and Property Taxes

A sum of money assessed by government authority for any public use or service such as for the support of municipal, state, or Federal undertakings or for the support of government is a *tax*.

Taxes on tobacco, liquor, luxuries, transportation, imports, communication, etc., are *indirect taxes*. Taxes on the person, property, or income of an individual are *direct taxes*.

Deductions from employees' gross earnings for Federal old-age and survivors insurance, state unemployment or disability taxes, and Federal income taxes have already been discussed (see pages 174 to 181). Among other important taxes paid by most individuals are sales taxes and property taxes.

SALES TAXES

Many state, county, and/or municipal governments now levy taxes on the sale of merchandise, known as *sales taxes*. Usually a per cent of the amount of the transaction is charged the purchaser by the seller who acts as an agent, periodically turning over such collections to the state, county, and/or municipal governments.

To avoid charges of fractional cents, sales taxes are usually assessed in arbitrary amounts on sales involving fractional parts of a dollar, although in some states more accurate collections are made through the issuance of stamps or tokens representing fractions of a cent.

Following are a typical schedule of arbitrary rates of sales tax charged by a state government and a combined schedule of arbitrary rates of sales tax that includes a 1 per cent charge by a municipality in the same state.

State 3% sales tax schedule for sales involving fractional parts of a dollar	*State 3% and municipality 1% combined sales tax schedule for sales involving fractional parts of a dollar*
\$0.00 to \$0.14 = none	\$0.00 to \$0.14 = none
0.15 to 0.42 = \$0.01	0.15 to 0.28 = \$0.01
0.43 to 0.73 = 0.02	0.29 to 0.54 = 0.02
0.74 to 1.00 = 0.03	0.55 to 0.80 = 0.03
	0.81 to 1.00 = 0.04
Plus 3% of the number of full dollars involved in the transaction	Plus 4% of the number of full dollars involved in the transaction

Purchases made in the municipality and taken by the customer (known as "cash take" and "charge take") or delivered within the municipality bear the 4 per cent charge. Purchases delivered within the state but outside the municipality bear the 3 per cent charge. Purchases delivered outside the state are free of sales tax.

Example. Using the preceding tax schedules, find the sales taxes paid by John Edens on the following purchases made in the municipality: (*a*) \$10.00 cash take, (*b*) \$32.29 delivered to his home in the municipality, (*c*) \$8.73 delivered outside the municipality but within the state, and (*d*) \$15.50 delivered outside the state.

(*a*) \$10.00 × .04 = \$0.40

(*b*) \$32.00 × .04 = \$1.28
Tax on \$0.29 = .02
\$1.30

(*c*) \$8.00 × .03 = \$0.24
Tax on \$0.73 = .02
\$0.26

(*d*) No tax on delivery outside state

PROPERTY TAXES

Real- and personal-property taxes are imposed by state, county, and/or municipal governments for the operation and maintenance of their services and institutions. Real-property taxes are levied against land and fixed improvements thereon, such as buildings; personal-property taxes are levied against all other property, tangible or intangible, such as cash, radios, television sets, household furnishings, etc.

Although real- and personal-property taxes vary from state to state, county to county, and incorporated municipality to incorporated municipality, the method of computation is the same.

Three factors are involved: (1) assessed valuation, an arbitrary value placed on property for tax purposes; (2) the tax rate applied by the state, county, and/or municipality expressed as a per cent, in mills (tenths of a cent) and fractions thereof, or in dollars-and-cents and fractions thereof; (3) the tax itself. Note that assessed valuations (arbitrary values) made by state, county, and/or municipality may be the same or different. In some states, real- and personal-property taxes are collected only by counties and/or municipalities.

The formulas for property tax computations are

$$\text{Tax rate} = \frac{\text{tax}}{\text{assessed valuation}}$$

$$\text{Tax} = \text{assessed valuation} \times \text{tax rate}$$

$$\text{Assessed valuation} = \frac{\text{tax}}{\text{tax rate}}$$

To determine the amount of tax that must be raised to pay the expenses of a municipality, the general procedure is for the various divisions or departments to prepare a budget. This budget of estimated expenses is then subject to inspection and analysis by the legally authorized representatives of the citizens of the municipality. Upon acceptance or upon modification and subsequent acceptance, the property tax for the municipality is determined. To this must be added the municipality's share of county and state taxes. Thus:

$$\text{Total tax} = \text{municipal tax} + \text{county tax} + \text{state tax}$$

Assessed valuation is determined by an appointed or elected representative of the citizens. The assessor or assessors places a valuation known as "assessed valuation" on the various real properties contained within the areas of the municipality. This valuation varies between communities, but it is usually 25 to 60 per cent of the current market valuation of the real properties. Within a community, the assessed valuation is supposedly calculated on the previously agreed upon per cent. Thus if a 50 per cent assessed valuation is to be used, a $10,000 piece of property would be valued at $5,000, a $15,000 property at $7,500, and an $8,000 property at $4,000.

Residents of unincorporated municipalities do not pay a municipal tax, their tax being the sum of the county and state taxes, if any.

To Find Tax Rate. When the total assessed valuation and the tax budget are known:

$$\text{Tax rate} = \frac{\text{tax}}{\text{assessed valuation}}$$

Custom varies as to the number of decimal places of accuracy used in setting the tax rate, *but in no instance is even the smallest fraction rounded off*, the practice being to raise the final digit. Thus if computations indicate the necessary tax rate to be .043521+, the rate might be set and expressed as $4.3522 per $100, $4.353 per $100, or $4.36 per $100.

Example: The assessed valuation of the taxable property in a certain municipality is \$52,384,600, and the taxes to be raised are \$123,475 by the state, \$931,442.75 by the county, and \$319,878 by the municipality. If the county collects the taxes and then reimburses the state and the municipality, find the combined tax rate if expressed (*a*) to thousandths per cent, (*b*) in mills (tenths of a cent) per \$1 of assessed value, (*c*) to cents per \$100 of assessed value, and (*d*) to mills per \$1,000 of assessed value.

$$\text{Total tax} = \$123{,}475 + \$931{,}442.75 + \$319{,}878 = \$1{,}374{,}795.75$$

$$\frac{\$1{,}374{,}795.75}{\$52{,}384{,}600} = .0262442+$$

(*a*) To thousandths per cent = 2.625%
(*b*) In mills per \$1 of assessed value = 27 mills (or \$.027)
(*c*) To cents per \$100 of assessed value = \$ 2.63
(*d*) To mills per \$1,000 of assessed value = \$26.245

Note in each instance that the final digit retained is raised, no matter how small the remainder.

To Find Tax. When the assessed valuation and the tax rate are known:

$$\text{Tax} = \text{assessed valuation} \times \text{tax rate}$$

Example 1: Mr. Smith owns a home with an assessed value of \$3,250. On Nov. 10 the tax rate for the fiscal year beginning Feb. 1 is announced as 2.351 per cent. What tax will he be required to pay?

$$2.351\% = \$.02351 \text{ per dollar of assessed valuation}$$
$$\$3{,}250 \times .02351 = \$76.4075 = \$76.41$$
$$\text{or } 2.351\% = \$2.351 \text{ per } \$100 \text{ of assessed valuation}$$
$$\text{and } \$3{,}250 = 32.5 \text{ hundreds}$$
$$\$2.351 \times 32.5 = \$76.4075 = \$76.41$$

Sometimes a collector's fee, usually a per cent of the tax itself, is added to the tax payment collected.

Example 2: Mr. Rose owned a store with an assessed valuation of \$6,640. The tax rate was \$3.87 per \$100, and the collector charged 2 per cent of the tax for collecting. What was the total amount paid by Mr. Rose?

$$\$6{,}640 = 66.4 \text{ hundreds}$$
$$\text{Tax} = \$3.87 \times 66.4 = \$256.97$$
$$\text{Collector's fee} = \$256.97 \times .02 = 5.14$$
$$\text{Total amount paid} = \$262.11$$

Usually, failure to pay property taxes when they are due subjects the owner to interest charges and sometimes to other penalties. Ordinarily, if taxes on property are in default for a stipulated period of years, the property is sold under court order; and the accumulated taxes, interest, penalties, and costs are deducted, with the remainder, if any, remitted to the owner. In practice, the selling price is unlikely to exceed the obligation, and tax-defaulted property often brings no return to the owner.

To Find Assessed Valuation. When the total tax budget and the tax rate are known:

$$\text{Assessed valuation} = \frac{\text{tax}}{\text{tax rate}}$$

Example 1: A city has a municipal, county, and state tax budget totaling $2,455,335. The tax rate is comprised of a state tax of $.52 per $100, a county tax of $.31 per $100, and a municipal tax of $1.42 per $100. What is the total assessed valuation?

$$\text{Total tax rate} = \$.52 + \$.31 + \$1.42 = \$2.25 \text{ per } \$100$$
$$\$2.25 \text{ per } \$100 = 2.25\% = .0225$$
$$\frac{\$2{,}455{,}335}{.0225} = \$109{,}126{,}000 \text{ Total assessed valuation}$$

Example 2: Mr. Eyre pays a tax and collector's fee totaling $70.62 on his home. What is the assessed valuation if the tax rate is 2.432 per cent and a collection fee of 1 per cent of the tax is charged?

$$\text{Tax} + 1\% \text{ collector's fee} = \$70.62$$
$$100\% \text{ tax} + 1\% \text{ tax} = \$70.62$$
$$101\% \text{ or } 1.01 \text{ tax} = \$70.62$$
$$\text{Therefore, tax} = \frac{\$70.62}{1.01} = \$69.92$$
$$2.432\% = .02432$$
$$\frac{\$69.92}{.02432} = \$2{,}875 \text{ Assessed valuation}$$

EXERCISE 1

A. Solve the following problems in computing sales taxes, using the arbitrary schedules shown on page 268:

1. Orlan Kindorf made a purchase of $23.45 in an unincorporated area. Find the state sales tax that he paid.
2. Oletta Johnson bought a $238.50 dining-room table in the municipality and had it delivered outside the municipality but within the state. Find the sales tax paid.

3. Karen Malloch purchased a $189.75 cloth coat in the municipality and had it delivered to her home in the municipality. Find the sales tax paid.
4. Find the sales taxes paid by John O'Shaughnessy on the following purchases made in the municipality: (*a*) $19.75 cash take; (*b*) $49.25 topcoat delivered to his office in the municipality; (*c*) $3,806.40 automobile delivered to his home outside the municipality but within the state; and (*d*) a gift costing $38.25 and delivered outside the state.

B. Solve the following problems in property taxes:

1. The assessed valuation of the taxable property in a certain municipality is $28,454,000. If planned expenditures require that $723,000 be raised through property taxes, find the tax rate to cents per $100 of assessed value. (REMINDER: in establishing a tax rate, raise the last digit retained if there is any remainder, regardless of how small the remainder may be.)
2. The assessed valuation of the taxable property in a certain county is $48,546,000, and annual property taxes to be raised are $356,718 for the state and $208,512 for the county. Find the combined tax rate (*a*) if quoted in per cent to thousandths or (*b*) if quoted to cents per $1,000 of assessed value.
3. The assessed valuation of the taxable property in a certain incorporated municipality is $135,640,780. The property taxes to be raised are $575,423 for the state, $362,400 for the county, and $2,875,625 for the municipality. Find the combined tax rate if quoted (*a*) in per cent to thousandths, (*b*) to hundredths of a mill per dollar of assessed value, (*c*) to tenths of a cent per $100 of assessed value, and (*d*) to cents per $1,000 of assessed value.
4. Mr. Daly's home has an assessed value of $3,100, and the tax rate is $.0261 per dollar of assessed value. What annual property tax is Mr. Daly required to pay?
5. Mrs. Chesley has a home with an assessed valuation of 40 per cent of its cost of $14,000. If the tax rate is $3.65 per $100 of assessed value, find the annual property tax that she must pay.
6. Mr. Ainsworth owns a store building with an assessed valuation of $36,500. If the tax rate is $41.05 per $1,000 of assessed value and a collector's fee of 1 per cent of the tax is charged, what total annual property tax and collector's fee does he pay?
7. A city has a combined municipal, county, and state property-tax budget totaling $1,375,600. Per $100 of assessed value, the municipal tax rate is $1.75, the county tax rate is $.27, and the state tax rate is $.63. Find the total assessed valuation of the taxable property in the city.
8. If the total annual tax payment on a building lot including a collector's charge of $1\frac{1}{2}$ per cent of the property tax is $79.17 and the tax rate is 39 mills per dollar of assessed value, find the assessed value of the lot.
9. Mr. Fremont pays an annual total of $432.48 tax on his apartment house, a sum determined by a tax rate of 3.2 per cent of assessed value plus a collector's fee of 2 per cent of the tax. Find the assessed valuation of the apartment house.

UNIT 2. Depreciation

A decrease in the value of property that is not restored by current maintenance is *depreciation.*

Business properties such as buildings, fixtures, equipment, machinery, etc., ultimately must be retired from use because of wear and tear, decay, inadequacy, and obsolescence.

The Federal Bureau of Internal Revenue recognizes the loss in value that may occur because of depreciation and allows the taxpayer to recover over the useful life of the property the capital invested by permitting the taxpayer to charge such loss against current taxable income. However, such tax allowance is permitted only where property is used in a trade or business or is used for earning income, such as rents and royalties.

An estimated useful life of the property must be determined, for it is during this period of time that depreciation allowances must be taken. This may be done on the basis of equal annual installments or in accordance with any recognized trade practices. Often equipment used in business will have a *trade-in value* when it must be replaced or a *scrap value* at the end of its estimated life. Final disposal of the property at more than trade-in or scrap value is treated as a gain; final disposal of the property at less than trade-in or scrap value is treated as a loss.

Three of the commonly used methods of determining depreciation are:

1. The straight-line method
2. The declining-balance method
3. The sum-of-the-years'-digits method

The Straight-line Method of Computing Depreciation. Probably the most frequently used of all methods of computing depreciation is the *straight-line method.*

Cost or cost less estimated scrap value is the base. Annual depreciation is found by dividing the base thus established by the estimated life (in years). If the assumptions are correct, the actual trade-in value (or scrap value at the end of the useful life) will be equivalent to the remaining cost or cost less scrap value not yet recovered through depreciation.

Example 1: Straight-line method. Find the depreciation schedule by the straight-line method at the end of each year for a machine acquired Jan. 1, 1956, that cost $10,000 with estimated life of 5 years.

$$\text{Annual depreciation} = \frac{\$10{,}000}{5} = \$2{,}000$$

$$\text{or } \$10{,}000 \times \frac{1}{5} \text{ (or } 20\%) = \$2{,}000$$

(1) End of year	(2) Date acquired	(3) Cost or other basis (excluding value of land or other nondepreciable property)	(4) Depreciation allowed (or allowable) in prior years	(5) Remaining cost or other basis to be recovered	(6) Life used in accumulating depreciation	(7) Estimated life from beginning of year	(8) Depreciation allowable this year
12/31/56	1/1/56	$10,000.00	None	$10,000.00	5 yr.	5 yr.	$2,000.00
12/31/57	1/1/56	10,000.00	$2,000.00	8,000.00	5 yr.	4 yr.	2,000.00
12/31/58	1/1/56	10,000.00	4,000.00	6,000.00	5 yr.	3 yr.	2,000.00
12/31/59	1/1/56	10,000.00	6,000.00	4,000.00	5 yr.	2 yr.	2,000.00
12/31/60	1/1/56	10,000.00	8,000.00	2,000.00	5 yr.	1 yr.	2,000.00

Depreciation allowable in 1961 and thereafter = none

The assumption in Example 1 is that trade-in value at the *beginning* of each year is indicated in column 5, Remaining cost or other basis to be recovered, and that there is no scrap value at the end of the year 1960. Had a scrap value of $500 been assumed, the yearly depreciation would have been based on 20 per cent of $9,500 = $1,900 per year, the remaining cost to be recovered *after* 1960 being $500 through trade-in or sale as scrap.

The Declining-balance Method of Computing Depreciation. Computing depreciation on the basis of the decreasing value of the property is known as the *declining-balance method.*

Scrap value is not considered in determining the original base, the original cost being used. The annual fixed rate or per cent of depreciation taken as permitted by present tax laws may not be more than in excess of twice the rate that would be used were the allowance computed under the straight-line method. Thus the maximum rate allowable is 2 times the fractional part that 1 year is of the estimated life in years. In accounting practice, as at present, the usual rate is the fractional part that 1 year is of the estimated life in years. However, this usual rate may now be doubled and this is acceptable for tax purposes, the intention being when so doubled to obtain a higher depreciation in the earlier years in the life of the asset.

Thus the maximum rate allowable for a machine with an estimated life of 10 years would be $\frac{1}{10} \times 2 = \frac{1}{5}$ or 20 per cent, and the maximum rate allowable for a piece of equipment with an estimated life of 8 years would be $\frac{1}{8} \times 2 = \frac{1}{4}$ or 25 per cent.

The rate so established is then applied year by year against the remaining values not yet recovered to determine the annually reducing amount of depreciation. The values not yet recovered presumably will be equivalent to the trade-in or scrap value at the end of any given period of time.

Example 2: Declining-balance method. Same as Example 1, but computed by the maximum rate allowable under the declining-balance method.

$$\text{Annual depreciation rate} = \frac{1}{5} \times 2 = \frac{2}{5} \text{ or } 40\%$$

(1) End of year	(2) Date acquired	(3) Cost or other basis (excluding value of land or other nondepreciable property)	(4) Depreciation allowed (or allowable) in prior years	(5) Remaining cost or other basis to be recovered	(6) Life used in accumulating depreciation	(7) Estimated life from beginning of year	(8) Depreciation allowable this year
12/31/56	1/1/56	$10,000.00	None	$10,000.00	5 yr.	5 yr.	$4,000.00
12/31/57	1/1/56	10,000.00	$4,000.00	6,000.00	5 yr.	4 yr.	2,400.00
12/31/58	1/1/56	10,000.00	6,400.00	4,600.00	5 yr.	3 yr.	1,840.00
12/31/59	1/1/56	10,000.00	8,240.00	1,760.00	5 yr.	2 yr.	704.00
12/31/60	1/1/56	10,000.00	8,944.00	1,056.00	5 yr.	1 yr.	422.40

The remaining cost of $1,056 − $422.40 = $633.60 [or $10,000 − ($8,944 + $422.40) = $633.60] may be depreciated at the 40 per cent rate per annum until traded in or sold as scrap.

The Sum-of-the-years'-digits Method of Computing Depreciation. The use of a fraction of decreasing value in computing depreciation is known as the *sum-of-the-years'-digits method.*

As with the straight-line method, cost or cost less estimated scrap value is the base, and it is assumed that actual trade-in value (or scrap value at the end of the useful life) will be equivalent to the remaining cost or cost less scrap value not yet recovered through depreciation.

In the sum-of-the-years'-digits method the constant denominator of the fraction used is the sum of all the remaining years of life, beginning with the first day of the first year of life. The declining numerator of the fraction is one smaller each year, beginning with the original number of years of estimated life. Thus if the estimated life is 4 years, the denominator is $4 + 3 + 2 + 1 = 10$, and the numerators will be 4, 3, 2, and 1 for each of the successive 4 years of life.

Example 3: Sum-of-the-years'-digits method. Same as Example 1, but computed by the sum-of-the-years'-digits method.

The constant denominator $= 5 + 4 + 3 + 2 + 1 = 15$
The declining numerators $=$ 5, 4, 3, 2, and 1
The fractional parts of the original value used in computing at the end of the first, second, third, fourth, and fifth years will be, respectively, $\frac{5}{15}$, $\frac{4}{15}$, $\frac{3}{15}$, $\frac{2}{15}$, $\frac{1}{15}$.

(1) End of year	(2) Date acquired	(3) Cost or other basis (excluding value of land or other non-depreciable property)	(4) Depreciation allowed (or allowable) in prior years	(5) Remaining cost or other basis to be recovered	(6) Life used in accumulating depreciation	(7) Estimated life from beginning of year	(8) Depreciation allowable this year
12/31/56	1/1/56	$10,000.00	None	$10,000.00	5 yr.	5 yr.	$3,333.33
12/31/57	1/1/56	10,000.00	$3,333.33	6,666.67	5 yr.	4 yr.	2,666.67
12/31/58	1/1/56	10,000.00	6,000.00	4,000.00	5 yr.	3 yr.	2,000.00
12/31/59	1/1/56	10,000.00	8,000.00	2,000.00	5 yr.	2 yr.	1,333.33
12/31/60	1/1/56	10,000.00	9,333.33	666.67	5 yr.	1 yr.	666.67

Depreciation allowable in 1961 and thereafter = none

The sum-of-the-years'-digits method results in high depreciation in the early years of life as does the declining-balance method. Its choice in preference to the straight-line method or declining-balance method is likely to be determined on the basis of possible income tax advantages to the user.

EXERCISE 2

1. John Fawcett, a traveling salesman, used his automobile entirely for business. He purchased the car on July 1, 1958, at a cost of $2,800 and claimed depreciation as a deductible business expense. If he estimated the life of the car to be 4 years and he computed by the straight-line method, find (*a*) depreciation allowable for the year 1958 and (*b*) depreciation allowable for the year 1959.
2. The Scott Manufacturing Company depreciated its equipment at the maximum rate allowable by the declining-balance method. For a new machine that cost $750 on Jan. 1, 1959, and had an estimated life of 10 years, find the depreciation allowable for (*a*) the year 1959 and (*b*) the year 1960.
3. The Snepp Transfer Company depreciated its trucks by the sum-of-the-years'-digits method. For a new truck that cost $12,600 on Jan. 1, 1960, and had an estimated life of 6 years, find the depreciation allowable for (*a*) the year 1960 and (*b*) the year 1961.
4. Follow the procedure shown by Example 1, pages 273–274, and set up a complete depreciation schedule by the straight-line method at the end of each of

the years 1958 through 1965 for a used machine acquired Jan. 1, 1958, at a cost of $7,164, with an estimated life of 8 years ending without trade-in or scrap value.

5. Follow the procedure shown by Example 2, page 275, and set up (*a*) a complete depreciation schedule at the maximum rate allowable by the declining-balance method at the end of each of the years 1958 through 1963 for new equipment acquired Jan. 1, 1958, at a cost of $6,561 with an estimated life of 6 years. Find (*b*) the remaining cost that might be depreciated in 1964.

6. Follow the procedure shown by Example 3, pages 275–276, and set up a complete depreciation schedule by the sum-of-the-years'-digits method at the end of each of the years 1959 through 1962 for a new electric pump acquired Jan. 1, 1959, at a cost of $3,108.60 with an estimated life of 4 years ending without trade-in or scrap value.

CHAPTER VIII

PURCHASE DISCOUNTS AND MARKUP

Intelligent business management requires an analysis of past operations and a shrewd forecasting of future business conditions. The methods of accomplishing this analysis and forecast are not within the province of this discussion, as our concern is with certain mathematical calculations necessary in the operation of most business enterprises.

It is obvious that the businessman must know the cost of the goods or services that he sells as well as the selling price that he must obtain if he is to pay his expenses and make a satisfactory profit.

UNIT 1. Trade Discounts

Manufacturers and wholesalers distribute their goods largely through the agency of salesmen who call on customers and sell the various products by means of published catalogues containing accurate descriptions, illustrations, and prices of the products.

These catalogues are frequently large, bulky, and costly, sometimes numbering several thousands of pages of closely printed matter.

Products are also sold by the placing of catalogues in the hands of retailers who are thus able to continue ordering even in the absence of the salesmen.

When catalogues were not so large, different sections were printed and bound together in one volume. When a line was discontinued or added or when other changes were made, it was necessary to reprint an entire section of the catalogue.

Today, with the loose-leaf system of binding, the making of changes has become much simpler. Single pages are sent for replacement or as additions to the catalogues and are inserted by the retailers or salesmen within the loose-leaf binders of the catalogues.

Prices quoted in the catalogues are not prices at which the goods are sold to the retailers. They are arbitrary prices, often suggested retail prices, from which discounts are taken in order to arrive at the actual net cost to the retailers. Rather than change pages in the catalogue every time a price change takes place, the accepted practice is to mail mimeographed, multigraphed, or printed sheets to the retailers, which give the new lists of discounts that are to be taken on the prices quoted in the catalogues.

Extra discounts are often given for purchases in quantities or to secure the business of particularly desirable accounts. Frequently as many as a half-dozen discounts are given. When the price rises, a discount is reduced or dropped from the series; when the price goes down, a discount is increased or added to the series.

List or *catalogue price* is the price quoted in the catalogue.

Net price is the price after deduction of the trade discounts. This price is also known as *seller's selling price,* the *purchaser's cost,* the *purchase price,* or the *cost price.*

Series or *chain discounts* are comprised of two or more discounts.

Trade-discount problems are solved by the same principles that you learned in your study of percentage. When more than one discount is allowed, each succeeding discount is taken from the remainder of the preceding discount.

Thus, if 30 per cent, 15 per cent, and 5 per cent (commonly written as 30/15/5) are to be taken on a bill, 30 per cent is deducted from the list price, 15 per cent is deducted from this remainder, and 5 per cent is then deducted from the second remainder. However, the order in which the discounts are taken is immaterial, for the result (net price) will be the same.

Note that you *cannot* add the discounts and then make the deduction. 30%/15%/5% is *not* equivalent to a 50 per cent discount.

CALCULATING CHAIN DISCOUNTS

Computing the net price may be accomplished by either of two general methods:

1. By direct application of the discount series against the list price.
2. By determining the complement of the decimal equivalent of the several discounts and then applying this single equivalent against the list price.

When only one bill is to be discounted, either method may be used. When a number of bills have the same series of discounts, the second method (see pages 282–283) is much quicker and therefore preferable.

Examples: Discounting directly against the list price. Glassware with a list price of $1,500 is subject to trade discounts of 25/20/10. What is the net price?

(*a*) Multiplying by the decimal equivalent of each rate of discount and subtracting:

```
$1500
 ×.25 (25%)
 7500          $1500
3000            −375
375.00          1125          $1125
                 ×.20 (20%)    −225
                225.00          900            $900
                                ×.10 (10%)      −90
                               90.00           $810 = net price
```

(*b*) Aliquot-parts method:

$4\overline{)1500}\ \left(25\% = \frac{1}{4}\right)$
-375

$5\overline{)1125}\ \left(20\% = \frac{1}{5}\right)$
-225

$10\overline{)900}\ \left(10\% = \frac{1}{10}\right)$
-90

$810 = net price

Multiplying by (*c*) decimal complements, and (*d*) common-fraction complements of each rate of discount:

(*c*) *Using decimals:*

```
  $1500
  × .75 (complement of 25%)
   7500
 10500
1125.00
  ×.80     (complement of 20%)
 900.00
  ×.90     (complement of 10%)
$810.00 = net price
```

(*d*) *Using common fractions:*

Complement of 25% = 75% = $\frac{3}{4}$

Complement of 20% = 80% = $\frac{4}{5}$

Complement of 10% = 90% = $\frac{9}{10}$

$\overset{30}{\cancel{\overset{150}{\cancel{\$1500}}}} \times \frac{3}{\cancel{4}} \times \frac{\cancel{4}}{\cancel{5}} \times \frac{9}{\cancel{10}} = \$810$ = net price

EXERCISE 1

A. Discount directly against the list price and solve each problem by the following methods: (*a*) multiplying by the decimal equivalent of each rate of discount and subtraction, (*b*) by the use of aliquot parts, (*c*) multiplying by decimal complement of each rate of discount, and (*d*) multiplying by the common-fraction complement of each rate of discount. NOTE: Answers for (*a*), (*b*), (*c*), and (*d*) in each problem will check, for the methods will obtain the same answers.

1. A furniture dealer orders a dozen armchairs listed at $15 each less discounts of 20 per cent, 5 per cent, and 10 per cent. What is the net price of the entire bill?
2. A millinery shop orders 4 gross of hats at $22.50 per dozen, less discounts of 25/20/5. What is the net price of the entire bill? NOTE: A gross is 12 dozen.

B. **Discount** directly against the list price in solving the following problems in trade discount. Solve by any method or combination of methods desired.

1. An electric refrigerator is offered at $275, less discounts of $33\frac{1}{3}$ per cent, 25 per cent, and 5 per cent. What is the net price?
2. A manufacturer of hosiery offers to ship 2,000 pairs of women's silk stockings to a retailer at $1.25 per pair, less discounts of 25/20/10/5. What would be the net cost of the entire shipment to the retailer?
3. A wholesaler offers a job lot of hardware with listed prices totaling $1,240 at discounts of $33\frac{1}{3}$ per cent, 25 per cent, 20 per cent, and 10 per cent. What is the net price?
4. A nationally famous line of cosmetics is sold to retailers by the manufacturer at discounts of $33\frac{1}{3}$ per cent, 5 per cent, and 2 per cent. Find the net price to the retailer on a purchase listed at $2,675.50 by the manufacturer.
5. A manufacturer of furniture, who regularly sells his furniture to retailers at discounts of 40 per cent and 15 per cent, offers an additional discount of 20 per cent on some dining-room sets with a list price of $495. Find (*a*) the regular net price and (*b*) the special net price at the additional discount of 20 per cent.
6. Two radio manufacturers offer comparable instruments at prices as follows: X Company quotes $150 less $33\frac{1}{3}$ per cent, 25 per cent, and $6\frac{1}{4}$ per cent. Y Company quotes $160 less 40 per cent, 20 per cent, and 10 per cent. Which company has the lower net price and by how many dollars?

UNIT 2. Trade Discount Equivalents

As suggested on page 279, the net price of an invoice may be computed by discounting directly against the list price and also by determining the complement of the decimal or fractional equivalent of the several discounts and then applying this single equivalent against the list price. When a number of invoices have the same series of discounts or when it is desirable or necessary to know the net cost of individual items comprising an invoice or several invoices, the use of the complement of the single equivalent of the discount series is by far the better method.

Examples: Determining net price by applying the complement of the single equivalent of the discount series. Glassware with a list price of $1,500 is subject to trade discounts of 25/20/10. Find the net price (note that this is the same problem as that illustrated on pages 279–280).

(*a*) Multiplying $1 by each rate of discount and subtracting:

```
$1.00
×.25 (25%)     $1.00
.2500          −.25
                .75              $.75
               ×.20 (20%)        −.15
               .1500              .60                 $.60
                                 ×.10 (10%)           −.06
                                  .06                 $.54 = net price on $1 list
                                                             (decimal equivalent)

                    $1500
                     ×.54
                     6000
                    7500
                  $810.00 = net price on $1,500
```

(*b*) Aliquot-parts method (using $1 as base):

$$4)\underline{1.00} \quad \left(25\% = \frac{1}{4}\right)$$
$$-.25$$
$$5)\underline{.75} \quad \left(20\% = \frac{1}{5}\right)$$
$$-.15$$
$$10)\underline{.60} \quad \left(10\% = \frac{1}{10}\right)$$
$$-.06$$

Net price on $1 list = $.54 (or decimal equivalent)

Multiplying $1 by (*c*) the decimal complements, and (*d*) the common-fraction complements of each rate of discount:

(*c*) *Using decimals:*

$1.00
×.75 (complement of 25%)
.7500

(*d*) *Using common fractions:*

Complement of 25% = 75% = $\frac{3}{4}$

$$\begin{array}{rl} \times .80 & \text{(complement of 20\%)} \\ \hline .6000 & \\ \times .90 & \text{(complement of 10\%)} \\ \hline \$.5400 & \end{array}$$

$$\text{Complement of } 20\% = 80\% = \frac{4}{5}$$

$$\text{Complement of } 10\% = 90\% = \frac{9}{10}$$

$$\$1 \times \frac{3}{4} \times \frac{4}{5} \times \frac{9}{10} = \frac{27}{50} = \$.54$$

Net price on \$1 list = \$.54 (or decimal equivalent)

In (*b*), (*c*), and (*d*) preceding, the net price on a bill for \$1,500 is determined just as in (*a*); \$1,500 × .54 = \$810.

To Find the Single-discount Equivalent of a Series of Discounts. If it is desired to find the single-discount equivalent of a series of discounts, first find the decimal equivalent of the net price and then subtract this figure from 1.00 (100%).

Example: In Examples *a, b, c,* and *d*, .54 was found to be the decimal equivalent of the net price. That is, .54 was the complement of the single decimal equivalent of the discounts 25 per cent, 20 per cent, and 10 per cent. Therefore the single-discount equivalent of 25 per cent, 20 per cent, and 10 per cent is

$$1.00 - .54 = .46 = 46\%$$

The single-discount equivalent of two trade discounts also may be found directly by subtracting the product of the two discounts from the sum of the two discounts. Thus:

$$20\% \text{ and } 10\% = (.20 + .10) - (.20 \times .10) = .28$$
$$30\% \text{ and } 20\% = (.30 + .20) - (.30 \times .20) = .44$$

If there are more than two trade discounts and it is desired to use this method of finding the single-discount equivalent, it is necessary to find first the discount equivalent of any two of the discounts, then to find the discount equivalent of this first discount equivalent and a third discount, and so on. Thus, to find the single-discount equivalent of 25 per cent, 20 per cent, and 10 per cent:

$$25\% \text{ and } 20\% = (.25 + .20) - (.25 \times .20) = .40 = 40\%$$
$$40\% \text{ and } 10\% = (.40 + .10) - (.40 \times .10) = .46 = 46\%$$

To Find List Price If Given Net Price and the Series of Discounts. The problem of finding list price if given net price and the series of trade discounts is a so-called "reverse operation." It may be solved (1) by dividing the net price by the complement of one of the discounts, dividing this obtained quotient by the complement of one of the other discounts, and continuing this division of obtained quotients by complements of the discounts until a final quotient is obtained which will be the list price (reversing Examples *c* and *d*, page 280); or (2) by dividing the net price by the decimal equivalent of the net price on $1 list.

Example 1: Glassware priced at $810 net has been subject to discounts of 25/20/10. Find the list price.

Using decimals

Complement of 25% = .75

Complement of 20% = .80

Complement of 10% = .90

$ 810 ÷ .90 = $ 900
$ 900 ÷ .80 = $1,125
$1,125 ÷ .75 = $1,500

Using common fractions

Complement of 25% $= \frac{3}{4}$

Complement of 20% $= \frac{4}{5}$

Complement of 10% $= \frac{9}{10}$

Since division by fractions may be accomplished by inverting the terms of the divisor and multiplying,

$$\$810 \div \frac{3}{4} \div \frac{4}{5} \div \frac{9}{10} =$$

$$\overset{\overset{30}{\cancel{90}}}{\$\cancel{810}} \times \frac{\cancel{4}}{\cancel{3}} \times \frac{5}{\cancel{4}} \times \frac{10}{\cancel{9}} = \$1,500$$

Example 2: By any of the methods used in the examples, pages 282–283, the decimal equivalent of the net price on $1 list was found to be .54. Thus

$810 ÷ .54 = $1,500

Ordinarily, credit on a partial payment (on an invoice subject to trade discounts) would not be a problem of this type, for the net price of the entire invoice would be determined and the partial payment would be applied against this net price to reduce the balance. However, if it were desired to find the list valuation of a partial payment, any of the immediately preceding methods could be used.

Do Not Drop or Round Off Decimal Places in Equivalents. In solving for decimal equivalents *do not* drop or round off any decimal places or fractional endings of decimal places either during the calculations or in the obtained decimal equivalents.

Tables of Net Cost Factors. When certain combinations of trade discounts are frequently repeated, it is customary to tabulate the net cost factors equivalent to the cost of $1.00 list after deducting the trade discounts. Following is an excerpt from such a table.

Net Cost of $1.00 List Less Trade Discounts

Trade discounts, %	Trade discounts in addition to series listed in first column			
	None	$33\frac{1}{3}$%	20%	15%
Net	None	0.666 667	0.800 000	0.850 000
10	0.900 000	0.600 000	0.720 000	0.765 000
10, 5	0.855 000	0.570 000	0.684 000	0.726 750
20	0.800 000	0.533 333	0.640 000	0.680 000
20, 10	0.720 000	0.480 000	0.576 000	0.612 000
20, 10, 5	0.684 000	0.456 000	0.547 200	0.581 400
$2\frac{1}{2}$	0.975 000	0.650 000	0.780 000	0.828 750
10, $2\frac{1}{2}$	0.877 500	0.585 000	0.702 000	0.745 875
10, 5, $2\frac{1}{2}$	0.833 625	0.555 750	0.666 900	0.708 581

Example 1: Find the net cost of an invoice of $565.43 list less trade discounts of 20/20/10/5.

$$\$565.43 \times .547200 = \$308.86$$

Example 2: Find the list price of an invoice if the net price is $478.80 and the trade discounts allowed are $33\frac{1}{3}$%, 10%, and 5%.

$$\frac{\$478.80}{.570000} = \$840$$

EXERCISE 2

A. Express decimally the net cost of $1.00 list price less the following trade discounts. Do not drop any decimal places and show any repetends as fractional endings reduced to lowest terms.

1. 40% and 25% **2.** $33\frac{1}{3}$%, 15%, and 25% **3.** 40/5/15/10

B. Express decimally the single discount equivalents of the following trade discounts. Do not drop any decimal places and show any repetends as fractional endings reduced to lowest terms.

1. 15% and 5% **2.** 40/25/20 **3.** $33\frac{1}{3}/12\frac{1}{2}/16\frac{2}{3}/2$

C. Find the per cent of discount of each of the following:

1. Baseball glove listed at $15.75, net price $9.45.
2. Radio listed at $195, net price $105.30.
3. Refrigerator listed at $246, net price $143.91.

D. Find in each of the following (*a*) present net price, (*b*) additional discount in per cent that must be granted if the desired new net price is allowed, and (*c*) the new discount chain in per cents.

1. List price \$80; present discounts $33\frac{1}{3}\%$, 25%; desired new net price \$34.
2. List price \$150; present discounts 30%, 20%; desired new net price \$63.
3. List price \$450; present discounts 35%, 20%, 10%; desired new net price \$200.07.

E. Find the decimal equivalent of the net cost of \$1 list in solving the following:

1. A merchant made several purchases from a manufacturer whose list prices were subject to trade discounts of 25%, 20%, 10%, and $16\frac{2}{3}\%$. Find the net price of each item if the list prices were (*a*) \$1.36, (*b*) \$40.04, and (*c*) \$223.64.
2. The buyer of a stationery department in a large store purchased several items at trade discounts of $33\frac{1}{3}\%$, $7\frac{1}{2}\%$, 20%, and 5%. Find the net price of each item if the list prices were (*a*) \$68.50, (*b*) \$3.75, and (*c*) \$274.

F. Find the list price of the following:

1. The net price of an invoice was \$684. If the trade discounts were $33\frac{1}{3}\%$, 25%, and 5%, find the list price.
2. The net price on four invoices subjected to trade discounts of 20%, 15%, and $7\frac{1}{2}\%$ were (*a*) \$28.43, (*b*) \$2,176.34, and (*c*) \$752.16. Find the list price of each invoice. (SUGGESTION: In solving, find the decimal equivalent of the net cost of \$1 list.)

G. Use the table of net cost of \$1 list less trade discounts from page 285 in solving the following:

1. Find the net price of each of the following invoices: (*a*) \$29.50 list, trade discounts 15%, 10%, and 5%, (*b*) \$108.75 list, trade discounts 20%, 10%, and 5%, and (*c*) \$850 list, trade discounts $33\frac{1}{3}\%$ and 10%.
2. Find the list price of each of the following invoices: (*a*) \$49.02 net, trade discounts $33\frac{1}{3}\%$, 10%, and 5%, (*b*) \$76.17 net, trade discounts 20%, 10%, and $2\frac{1}{2}\%$, and (*c*) \$711.36 net, trade discounts $33\frac{1}{3}\%$, 10%, 5%, and $2\frac{1}{2}\%$.

UNIT 3. Cash Discounts

Practically all lines of merchandise are purchased with cash discount rates, such discounts ordinarily ranging between 1 and 10 per cent.

Cash discounts are stipulated in the *terms of sale* included in the heading of an invoice. As you already know, a trade discount may be given on a catalogue or list price, and this trade discount is deducted to determine the net price. This net price or a directly quoted net price is usually subject to a cash discount.

Although the term "cash discount" implies that it is granted only upon the immediate payment of cash, this is not true in general business practice, as a period of several days from the date of the invoice or the receipt of the goods is usually granted within which period the stipulated per cent of discount may be taken if a payment is made in full or in part. The exception to this statement is C.O.D. dating, which indicates that the purchaser must make payment in full upon delivery of the goods.

Theoretically, cash discounts are given as an incentive to prompt payment. In practice, cash discounts vary greatly and the variance cannot be explained as simply a greater or lesser incentive to prompt payment. Whether the discount is 1 per cent or 10 per cent, it is imperative that the purchaser who wishes to resell the goods at a competitive price take advantage of the cash discount.

Custom within certain industries seems to be the determinant of the cash discount granted, although in general it may be said that rates of discount tend to be highest for lines of merchandise in which style risk or perishability is greatest.

Terms of Sale and Their Meaning. Since there are various means of symbolizing cash discounts and various methods of calculating the time period within which the discount may be taken, the following examples are given as illustrative of the more common types of cash discounts found in the *terms of sale.*

Ordinary dating: 2/10,n/30. Also written as 2/10, net 30. The first digit is the discount rate of 2 per cent. The second group of digits stipulates the number of days within which the discount may be taken, or 10-days. Thus if the invoice is paid in full within 10 days of the date of shipment, which corresponds to the date of the invoice, a 2 per cent cash discount may be taken. After 10 days and up to 30 days, the full amount of the invoice is due. *N*/30 or net 30 means that the invoice must be paid within *exactly* 30 days from the date of the invoice (not 30-day-month time) and that it will be considered overdue after 30 days and may from that time be considered as subject to an interest charge.

Example 1: What payments are indicated on a \$100 invoice shipped Nov. 16 with terms of 3/10,n/30?

(*a*) If paid on or before Nov. 26:
\$100 less 3% = \$100 − \$3 = \$97
(*b*) If paid on or between Nov. 27–Dec. 16:
The full amount of \$100 is due
(*c*) If paid Dec. 17 or later:
The bill is past due and may be subject to an interest charge

Example 2: What payments are indicated on a \$450 invoice dated Oct. 28 with terms of 2/10,n/60?

(a) If paid on or before Nov. 7:
$450 less 2% = $450 − $9 = $441
(b) If paid on or between Nov. 8 through Dec. 27:
The full amount of $450 is due
(c) If paid Dec. 28 or later:
The bill is past due and may be subject to an interest charge

A similar type of cash discount occurs with such terms of sale as 5/10, 2/30, 1/60, n/90. This would signify 5 per cent discount if paid within 10 days of the date of the invoice, 2 per cent discount if paid within 11 to 30 days, 1 per cent discount if paid within 31 to 60 days, net if paid within 61 to 90 days, and overdue and subject to an interest charge if paid on the 91st day or thereafter.

Advance or Postdating. When the terms allow more time than the date of the shipment and the time numerals (as 10 days in terms of 2/10) in the terms would indicate, the terms are said to be advance dated or postdated. In advance dating or postdating the invoice carries a later date than the actual date of the shipment, and the payment does not need to be made until the time indicated by both the terms and the advanced date of the invoice. Thus goods shipped on Aug. 18 may be accompanied by an invoice dated Aug. 18 as of Oct. 1, with terms of 3/10, net 30. The cash discount may be earned by payment made on or before Oct. 11, or the payment of the net invoice may be delayed until Oct. 31.

End-of-month Dating. "E.O.M." is the abbreviation or symbol used to express end-of-month dating, which means that the days for allowing discount are counted from the end of the month following the date of the invoice, not from the date of the invoice.

Thus if an invoice dated Mar. 17 has terms of 8/10 E.O.M., the discount of 8 per cent is available up to and including the first 10 days of April, or through Apr. 10. Business practice is also to grant a month's extension of time on E.O.M. terms if the invoice dating is on or after the 26th of the month. For example, a bill dated May 26 with terms of 4/10 E.O.M. is subject to discount up to and including July 10.

After the cash discount period has elapsed, bills with E.O.M. dating are considered generally as having a 20-day net period following the cash discount period and thereafter being overdue and subject to an interest charge.

Proximo Dating. "Prox." is the abbreviation or symbol used to express proximo, defined as the next month after the present. Invoices with proximo dating are treated in the same manner as though they had E.O.M. dating.

Thus if an invoice dated Aug. 24 has terms of 2/10, prox., the discount of 2 per cent is available up to and including Sept. 10. As with E.O.M.

dating, invoices dated on or after the 26th of a month are considered as being dated in the following month. For example, a bill dated Dec. 28 with terms of 5/10, prox. is subject to discount up to and including Feb. 10.

Again as with E.O.M. dating, bills with proximo dating are considered generally as having a 20-day net period following the cash discount period and thereafter being overdue and subject to an interest charge.

Receipt-of-goods Dating. "R.O.G." is the abbreviation or symbol used to express receipt-of-goods dating, which means that the days for allowing discount are counted after receipt of the goods and not after the invoice date.

This type of dating is particularly useful when the time required for transportation is apt to be in excess of the number of days allowed in the discount period or when the time in transit is likely to be indefinite, as in shipments by water through the Canal Zone that may take 30 to 60 or more days depending upon the frequency of the ship's ports of call.

Thus on an invoice dated Apr. 4, with terms of 5/10 R.O.G. and received on Apr. 16, the discount of 5 per cent is available up to and including Apr. 26. On an invoice dated Sept. 26, with terms of 3/10 R.O.G. and received on Oct. 26, the discount of 3 per cent is available up to and including Nov. 5.

When the net period is not stipulated, as is usual with R.O.G. terms, it may be assumed as being the 20 days following the cash discount period, and thereafter the invoice is overdue and subject to an interest charge.

Extra Dating. "Extra," "ex." or "X," meaning extra dating, indicates that the discount is available for a period of time in addition to the number of days first specified in the terms. Thus 2/10–60X, or 2/10–60 extra, indicates 10 plus 60 or a total of 70 days from the date of the invoice as the period during which a 2 per cent cash discount may be taken. In a bill the terms of which are 3/10–90 extra and the invoice date is June 7, 3 per cent discount may be taken if payment is made on or before 100 days after June 7, or to and including Sept. 15.

When the net period is not stipulated, as is usual with extra dating, it may be assumed as being the 20 days following the cash discount period, and thereafter the invoice is overdue and subject to an interest charge.

This type of dating is found most frequently in industries in which sales are likely to be seasonal. For example, if a manufacturer of heating equipment wishes to induce purchase in May or June, he is likely to offer extra dating with the final date for discount falling due in the normal fall selling season for heating equipment.

When Final Date of Discount Period Is a Nonbusiness Day. If the last day of the discount period falls on a Sunday (or a Saturday in some states) or a legal holiday, the final date of allowable discount is extended to the first business day following.

Example of an invoice with both trade and cash discounts:

CARRIGAN & HAYDEN
WHOLESALE HARDWARE
Kansas and Division Telephone UNderhill 1-3400
SAN FRANCISCO 8, CALIFORNIA

SOLD TO

Harry K. Jensen
Contractor and Builder
1025—44th. Avenue
Oakland 1, California

INVOICE NO. B 29015
DATE 7-27-58
CUSTOMER'S NO. 3c6235

TERMS: 2/10, n/30

Quantity	Description	Unit price	Amount
12	Rolls felt paper #60	$3.85	$ 46.20
8	Plumb hammers #14-16	2.75	22.00
150 ft.	Manila rope, $\frac{1}{4}$	.08$\frac{1}{3}$	12.50
2	Disston saws, 26-12, #107	5.40	10.80
4	Disston saws, 26-8, #114	6.65	26.60
	TOTAL LIST		$118.10
	Less 25% and 10%		38.38
	NET INVOICE		$ 79.72

If Harry K. Jensen, Contractor and Builder, pays this invoice in full within 10 days following July 27 (not later than Aug. 6), he will deduct 2 per cent from the net invoice of $79.72. Thus

Net invoice $79.72
1.59 Cash discount ($79.72 × .02 = $1.59)
$78.13 Remittance necessary to pay invoice in full

If payment is made Aug. 7 through Aug. 26, a remittance of $79.72 will be required to pay the net invoice in full. In accordance with general business practice, it would be understood by both buyer and seller that any payments made *after* Aug. 26 would be subject to an additional charge for interest at the "going rate," usually 6 per cent.

Partial Payment on Account. On occasions, the purchaser may make only a partial payment on account. If this payment is made within the discount period, the purchaser is entitled to a discount on the portion of the bill paid.

As may be seen readily, if terms are 2 per cent 10 days, every $.98 paid within the 10-day period entitles the purchaser to a credit of $1. If terms are 3 per cent 10 days, a payment of $.97 within the 10-day period entitles the purchaser to a credit of $1.

To find credit on a partial payment entitled to cash discount, divide the payment by the complement of the cash discount per cent.

Cash discount earned on a partial payment equals the amount credited less the amount paid.

Example 1: On a net invoice of $235 with terms of 4/10, E.O.M., dated May 22, a partial payment of $144 is made on June 10. Find (*a*) amount credited to the purchaser by the seller, (*b*) cash discount earned, and (*c*) balance due.

(*a*) Cash discount is earned on $144 payment made on June 10

$100\% - 4\% = 96\% = .96$

Amount credited $= \$144 \div .96 = \$150$

(*b*) Cash discount earned $= \$150 - 144 = \$6$

(*c*) Balance due $= \$235 - 150 = \$85$

Example 2: A net invoice of $463.50 dated Aug. 6 has terms of 5/10 R.O.G. The goods are received Sept. 10, and payment of $265 is made on Sept. 20. Find (*a*) amount credited to the purchaser by the seller, (*b*) cash discount earned, and (*c*) balance due.

(*a*) Cash discount is earned on $265 payment made on Sept. 20

$100\% - 5\% = 95\% = .95$

Amount credited $= \$265 \div .95 = \$278.95$

(*b*) Cash discount earned $= \$278.95 - \$265 = \$13.95$

(*c*) Balance due $= \$463.50 - \$278.95 = \$184.55$

EXERCISE 3A

A. Solve the following:

1. An invoice for $295 has cash terms of 3/15, net 60 and is dated May 25. Find (*a*) the final date on which the cash discount may be taken and (*b*) the amount necessary to pay in full if the discount is earned.
2. An invoice for $1,750 is dated July 15 and has cash terms of 3/30, 2/60, 1/90, n/120. Find the amount necessary to pay in full on Aug. 15.
3. If cash terms are 4/10, net 60 as of Oct. 1, the net invoice is for $365.50, and the date of the invoice is July 14, find (*a*) the final date on which the discount may be taken, (*b*) the amount of the cash discount that may be taken, if earned, and (*c*) the amount necessary to pay in full if the cash discount is earned.

4. An invoice for \$660 is dated Feb. 15 and has cash terms of 8/10, E.O.M. Find (*a*) the final date on which the cash discount may be taken and (*b*) the amount necessary to pay in full if the cash discount is earned.
5. If an invoice for \$1,870 is dated Oct. 1 and has cash terms of 3/10, proximo, how much should be remitted by the purchaser to the seller if paid in full on Nov. 10?
6. An invoice for \$136 is dated Jan. 12 and has cash terms of 6/10–60 ex. Find (*a*) the final date on which the cash discount may be taken, (*b*) the cash discount if paid in full on Mar. 25, and (*c*) the amount necessary to pay the invoice in full on Feb. 24.

B. Find (*a*) the cash discounts, if earned, assuming that cash discounts are allowed on partial payments as well as on payments in full, (*b*) the amounts remitted by purchaser, (*c*) the amounts credited by seller to purchaser, and (*d*) the balance due, if any. Assume that anticipation is not permitted.

Invoice no.	Date of invoice	Net invoice	Terms	Receipt of goods	Amount paid	Date of payment
1	Jan. 9	\$ 240.50	2/10, n/30		In full	Jan. 19
2	June 28	2,620.00	4/10, net 60		\$1,400	July 8
3	July 15	22.50	3/10, 2/30-n/60		In full	Aug. 5
4	Sept. 28	133.50	6/30, 3/60, net/120		\$75	Oct. 28
5	May 27	127.65	1/30, n/60 as of Aug. 15		In full	Sept. 14
6	Nov. 12	458.75	2/10, 1/30 as of Apr. 1		\$300	May 1
7	Mar. 26	912.30	8/10, E.O.M.		In full	May 10
8	Aug. 16	825.00	5/10, E.O.M.		\$600	Sept. 10
9	Feb. 2	47.16	3/10, prox.		In full	Mar. 10
10	Dec. 27	356.25	2/10, proximo		\$250	Feb. 10
11	May 7	288.20	3/10-R.O.G.	July 6	\$100	July 16
12	Oct. 29	3.63	4/10, R.O.G.	Dec. 15	In full	Dec. 26
13	Mar. 31	406.40	2/30, 60 extra		In full	June 29
14	Sept. 14	334.26	3/10-45 X		\$200	Nov. 8

Bank Discount or Interest Rate Equivalents of Cash Discounts. A comparison of cash discount rates with corresponding bank discount and interest rates will further emphasize the necessity of the businessman's taking advantage of cash discounts permitted in the terms of sale. In the following, d is the bank discount rate per annum, and i is the interest rate (true discount rate) per annum.

$$d = \frac{\text{cash discount rate} \times 365}{\text{days in net period}}$$

$$i = \frac{\text{cash discount rate} \times 365}{(1 - \text{cash discount rate})\ \text{days in net period}}$$

Example 1: For terms of 2/10, net 60 compute to nearest $\frac{1}{10}$ per cent the equivalent (*a*) bank discount rate and (*b*) interest rate.

NOTE: The net period following the 10-day cash discount period is 50 days.

(a) $d = \dfrac{.02 \times 365}{50} = .146 = 14.6\%$

(b) $i = \dfrac{.02 \times 365}{(1 - .02)50} = \dfrac{.02 \times 365}{.98 \times 50} = .149 = 14.9\%$

Example 2: For terms of 5/10, E.O.M. compute to nearest $\frac{1}{10}$ per cent the equivalent (a) bank discount rate and (b) interest rate.

NOTE: When net period is not stipulated as in E.O.M. proximo, or extra dating, the net period is assumed to be 20 days.

(a) $d = \dfrac{.05 \times 365}{20} = .913 = 91.3\%$

(b) $i = \dfrac{.05 \times 365}{(1 - .05)20} = \dfrac{.05 \times 365}{.95 \times 20} = .961 = 96.1\%$

EXERCISE 3B

1. By comparison with the cash discount allowed, find to the nearest $\frac{1}{10}$ per cent the equivalent (a) bank discount rate and (b) interest rate on an invoice with terms of 4/10, proximo.
2. For terms of 3/10, net 90, compute in comparison with the cash discount allowed to nearest $\frac{1}{10}$ per cent the equivalent (a) bank discount rate and (b) interest rate.
3. An invoice of $176.50 net, dated May 16, has terms of 3/10, 2/30, 1/60, net 90. Find the amount remitted by the purchaser if payment in full is made on (a) May 26, (b) June 15, (c) July 15, and (d) Aug. 14.
4. A job lot of sport coats priced at $942 has terms of 8/10, prox. If the invoice is dated May 28, find (a) final date on which cash discount is earnable, (b) cash discount allowable, and (c) amount remitted by purchaser if the invoice is paid in full and the cash discount is earned.
5. Rose and Company, manufacturers, offer neckwear at $18 per dozen with terms of 6/10, E.O.M. A department store buyer is required to obtain terms of 10/10, E.O.M. on all purchases. What must be the adjusted price per dozen if Rose and Company is not to lose and the buyer's required terms of 10/10, E.O.M. are allowed?
6. An invoice to Kramer and Jones, men's furnishers, is dated June 24 and itemizes $3\frac{1}{2}$ dozen hats at $72 per dozen list less trade discounts of 40% and 10% with cash terms of 4/10, net 60. If payment in full is made on July 5, find the amount remitted by Kramer and Jones.
7. An invoice dated May 18 for some merchandise is received on July 21 by the Crown-Imperial Company. The list price totals $1,842.60 with allowed trade discounts of $33\frac{1}{3}$%, 25%, and 10%. If the terms of sale are 5/15, R.O.G., find the amount necessary to pay in full on Aug. 5.
8. Find the net price balance due from a purchaser who remits $288 on Oct. 11 on an invoice of $920 dated June 8 and subject to trade discounts of 25% and 20% with terms of 4/10, net 30 as of Oct. 1.

9. On Aug. 23, a partial payment of $400 is made on a net invoice of $952.81 with terms of 3/10, 2/30, 1/60, net 90, and dated Aug. 13. Find the additional payment required to pay in full on Sept. 12.

10. On the following invoice, find (*a*) extensions, (*b*) total list, (*c*) trade discount, (*d*) net invoice due, including prepaid freight, (*e*) net cost per unit not considering cash discount and prepaid freight, (*f*) cash discount if paid in full on July 2, and (*g*) amount necessary to pay in full on July 2. (NOTE: A cash discount is not allowed on the prepaid freight.)

BOOHER ELECTRIC CORPORATION
717 Sound Street
Seattle, Washington

SOLD TO		INVOICE	4X-715
Stephen F. Shorb		DATE	June 2, 1956
11 Sequoia Ave.			
San Francisco 6, Calif.		SHIPPED VIA	Prepaid freight
CUSTOMER ORDER	5-17-83	TERMS	2/30, n/60, F.O.B., Seattle

Quantity	Description	Unit Price	Amount
1	Receiver 214-21	$345.00	$
2	Receiver 218-24	475.00	
15	Receiver 50-5X	39.50	
9	Receiver 50-5Y	44.75	
1	Coil 802	3.95	
6	Condenser AY-43	1.80	
	LIST TOTAL		$
	Less 40/10 trade discount		
	NET TOTAL		$
	Plus prepaid freight		165.45
	NET INVOICE DUE		$

UNIT 4. Anticipation

In certain industries it is customary to deduct interest on accounts paid before the final due date. This deduction, known as "anticipation" (actually the equivalent of bank discount), is based on the prevailing rates of interest, sometimes 5 per cent but usually 6 per cent per annum. Anticipation is taken in lieu of a cash discount when the terms of sale are net and is added to or taken in addition to any cash discount that may be permitted in the terms of sale.

In the examples that follow, note that anticipation is a per cent per annum computed by counting the actual number of days (exact time) of prepayment and the use of a 360-day year as the base (denominator). When both a cash discount and anticipation are taken, count *only* the remaining days in which the cash discount per cent earned is allowable.

The practice of taking anticipation is encouraged by many vendors, who feel the additional discount for prompt payment to be justified. Anticipation is computed in two ways:

1. Based on the net invoice *before* cash discounts have been taken.
2. Based on the net invoice *after* cash discounts have been taken.

It is obvious that, when the former method is used, the amount of anticipation will be slightly in excess of the latter method.

Example 1: Based on net invoice. What is (*a*) the anticipation at 5 per cent on an invoice of $500 dated June 10, terms of 90 days net if paid in full on July 16, and (*b*) the amount remitted by the purchaser?

Anticipation is for the 54 days prepayment of the final date of the net period.

$$(a)\ \$500 \times \frac{54}{360} \times \frac{5}{100} = \$3.75$$

$$(b)\ \$500 - \$3.75 = \$496.25$$

Example 2: Based on net invoice. What is (*a*) the cash discount earned, (*b*) the anticipation at 6 per cent, and (*c*) the amount remitted by the purchaser if payment in full is made on Mar. 8 on an invoice for $240 if the terms of sale are 2/30, 1/60, net 90, and the date of the invoice is Feb. 26?

Payment is made 10 days after date; therefore the 2 per cent cash discount is earned and anticipation is for 20 days.

$$(a)\ \$240 \times .02 = \$4.80$$

$$(b)\ \$240 \times \frac{20}{360} \times \frac{6}{100} = \$.80$$

$$(c)\ \$240 - (\$4.80 + \$.80) = \$240 - \$5.60 = \$234.40$$

Note that (*c*) may be solved directly by combining both (*a*) and (*b*) as per cents. Thus:

$$\text{Cash discount} = 2\% = .02$$

$$\text{Anticipation} = \frac{20}{360} \times \frac{6}{100} = .00\tfrac{1}{3}$$

$$\text{Cash discount} + \text{anticipation} = .02\tfrac{1}{3}$$

$$\text{and } \$240 \times .02\tfrac{1}{3} = \$5.60$$

$$\$240 - \$5.60 = \$234.40$$

Example 3: Based on net invoice less cash discount. Same problem as Example 2 except that anticipation is based on net invoice *after* cash discount has been taken.

$$(a)\ \$240 \times .02 = \$4.80$$
$$(b)\ \$240 - \$4.80 = \$235.20$$
$$\text{and } \$235.20 \times \frac{20}{360} \times \frac{6}{100} = \$.78$$
$$(c)\ \$235.20 - \$.78 = \$234.42$$

Note that (*c*) may be solved directly by treating (*a*) and (*b*) as though they were chain discounts (which, in fact, they are).

Since anticipation is for 20 days, then $\frac{20}{360} \times \frac{6}{100} = .00\frac{1}{3}$. And 2% and $\frac{1}{3}$% in series discount equal a single discount factor of $2.32\frac{2}{3}$% or a single cost equivalent of $97.67\frac{1}{3}$% by any of the methods used in computing chain discounts (see pages 282–284), then

$$\$240 \times .0232\frac{2}{3} = \$5.58$$
$$\$240 - \$5.58 = \$234.42$$
$$\text{or } \$240 \times .9767\frac{1}{3} = \$234.42$$

Anticipation on Partial Payments. On partial payments there may be anticipation as well as cash discount to consider. If so, an additional calculation must be made. It is apparent that if anticipation is equivalent to $\frac{1}{2}$ per cent, then every $\$.99\frac{1}{2}$ paid entitles the purchaser to a credit of $1.00 *before* computing the credit on a partial payment entitled to cash discount.

If only anticipation is to be considered (no cash discount being granted or earned), the steps in solution are as follows:

1. Find the decimal or fractional equivalent of the anticipation at the stipulated rate (usually 6 per cent) for the number of days that anticipation is earned. Thus:

$$6\% \text{ anticipation for 45 days} = \frac{6}{100} \times \frac{45}{360} = \frac{3}{400} = \frac{3}{4}\% = .0075$$

2. Divide the partial payment by the complement of the decimal of fractional equivalent. Thus to find the complement:

$$\text{Complement of } \frac{3}{400} = \frac{397}{400} \quad \text{or} \quad \text{of } .0075 = .9925$$

Example 1: Considering only anticipation. A partial payment of $400 is made on a net invoice of $745. If no cash discount is granted but anticipation at 6 per cent is allowed, find the amount credited to the purchaser by the seller if 36 days anticipation is earned.

$$36 \text{ days at } 6\% = \frac{36}{360} \times \frac{6}{100} = \frac{6}{1000} = .006$$

$$\text{Complement} = 1.000 - .006 = .994$$

$$\text{Amount credited} = \frac{\$400}{.994} = \$402.41$$

Proof: $402.41 × .994 = $400

When both anticipation and cash discount are to be considered, the amount credited on a partial payment will vary, depending upon whether anticipation is based (*a*) upon the net invoice before the cash discount has been taken or (*b*) upon the net invoice less the cash discount.

If anticipation is based on the net invoice before the cash discount has been taken, the steps in solution may be as follows:

1. Find the sum of the decimal or fractional equivalent of the per cent of cash discount and per cent of anticipation earned.
2. Divide the partial payment by the complement of this obtained sum.

Example 2: Considering anticipation as based upon the net invoice before the cash discount has been taken. A net invoice of $937.50 dated July 7 has terms of 3/10/E.O.M. A partial payment of $500 is made on July 11. If allowed anticipation of 6 per cent is based upon the net invoice before the cash discount has been taken, find the amount credited to the purchaser by the seller.

Anticipation is 30 days

$$30 \text{ days at } 6\% = \frac{30}{360} \times \frac{6}{100} = \frac{5}{1000} = .005$$

Cash discount earned is 3% = .03

$$\text{Anticipation} + \text{discount} = .005 + .03 = .035$$

$$\text{Complement} = 1.00 - .035 = .965$$

$$\text{Amount credited} = \frac{\$500}{.965} = \$518.13$$

Proof: $518.13 × .965 = $500

If anticipation is based upon the net invoice less the cash discount, the problem of finding the amount credited is somewhat more difficult. The solution may be obtained as follows:

1. Divide the partial payment by the complement of the decimal or fractional equivalent of the anticipation earned.
2. Divide this obtained quotient by the complement of the decimal or fractional equivalent of the cash discount earned.

Example 3: Considering anticipation as based upon the net invoice less the cash discount. A net invoice of $500 dated June 20 has terms of 2/15–50 extra. A partial payment of $200 is made on June 25. If anticipation at 6 per cent based on the net invoice less the cash discount is allowed, find the amount credited to the purchaser by the seller.

Anticipation is 60 days

$$60 \text{ days at } 6\% = \frac{60}{360} \times \frac{6}{100} = \frac{1}{100} = .01$$

$$\text{Complement} = 1.00 - .01 = .99 \quad (\text{or } 100\% - 1\% = 99\%)$$

$$\text{Credit before cash discount is considered} = \frac{\$200}{.99} = \$202.02$$

Therefore anticipation is earned on $202.02

$$\text{Cash discount complement} = 100\% - 2\% = 98\% = .98$$

$$\text{Amount credited} = \frac{\$202.02}{.98} = \$206.14$$

Proof: $\$206.14 \times .98 = \$202.02$; and $\$202.02 \times .99 = \$200$

Example 3 may also be solved by treating the cash discount per cent and the anticipation per cent earned as though they were chain discounts. Thus by any of the methods used in computing the single equivalent of chain discounts (see pages 282–284):

The single discount equivalent of 1% and 2% = 2.98%
The single cost equivalent of 1% and 2% = 97.02%

$$\text{and } \frac{\$200}{.9702} = \$206.14$$

EXERCISE 4

1. Find (*a*) the anticipation taken at 6 per cent and (*b*) the amount remitted by the purchaser on an invoice of $506.85 dated June 3 with terms of net 10–60 extra if payment in full is made on June 13.
2. On an invoice of $342.75 with terms of net 10 days as of Mar. 1, find (*a*) the anticipation allowed at 5 per cent and (*b*) the amount remitted by the purchaser if the date of the invoice is Jan. 14 and payment in full is made on Jan. 25.
3. On an invoice of $95.72 with terms of 4/10, 60 extra, dated Mar. 27, anticipation at 5 per cent based on the net invoice is allowed. If payment in full is made on Mar. 31, find (*a*) the cash discount earned, (*b*) the anticipation earned, and (*c*) the amount received by the seller from the purchaser.
4. Based on the net invoice, if anticipation at 6 per cent is allowed, find if paid in full (*a*) the cash discount earned, (*b*) the anticipation earned, and (*c*) the amount remitted by the purchaser to the seller on each of the following: Invoice No. 1, date Mar. 28, net price $85.36, terms 5/10, 90 extra, payment made on date; Invoice No. 2, date Sept. 2, net price $7,450.50, terms 3/30, net 60, payment made Sept. 5; Invoice No. 3, date July 27, net price $1,009.82, terms 6/10, E.O.M., payment made Aug. 11.
5. Based on the net invoice *less* the cash discount, if anticipation at 6 per cent is

allowed, find for the invoices in Problem 4 (*a*) the cash discount earned, (*b*) the anticipation earned, and (*c*) the amount received by the seller from the purchaser.

6. An invoice with trade discounts of 25, 10, and $33\frac{1}{3}$ per cent has a total list of $1,948.71. Cash terms are net 10 days as of July 1. If the date of the invoice is Apr. 8, $540 is paid on Apr. 27, and anticipation at 6 per cent is allowed, find the balance due to the seller.

7. Mr. Marston, proprietor of a novelty store, purchases some goods at a net price of $2,653.50 on terms of 2/10/E.O.M. with anticipation at 6 per cent based on net invoice allowed. If the invoice is dated Mar. 11 and Mr. Marston makes a partial payment of $1,000 on Mar. 26, find the amount of credit that he receives.

8. On an invoice of $8,300 with terms of 2/10, 1/30, n/60, dated May 17, a partial payment of $5,000 is made on June 7. If anticipation of 6 per cent based on net invoice *less* cash discount is granted, compute the amount credited. NOTE: Anticipate only for the remaining number of days in which the cash discount per cent earned is allowable.

UNIT 5. Markup Per Cents Based on Cost and on Selling Price; Basic Markup Equations

The successful operation of any business depends in large part upon the proper pricing of its goods (or services). This requires that to the cost is added a markup sufficiently high so that the selling price will be large enough to pay the original cost plus all expenses incurred in making the final sale and still leave a satisfactory operating profit.

Markup or markon is the difference between cost and selling price.[1]

Per Cents Based on Cost. Since most manufacturers, many wholesalers, and some retailers take inventories at cost, such concerns are likely to compare sales, markup, expenses, profit or loss, etc., with cost.

Such businesses find that the records of their operations can be kept most easily and expressed best by means of what are known as "cost accounting systems." When a manufacturer quotes per cents it may be assumed that the base is cost, not net sales. Since wholesalers and jobbers may use either cost or sales as a base, it is necessary to know whether per cent comparisons refer to cost or sales. Among retailers, the use of cost as a base for per cent comparisons is found most commonly in

[1] In this text, the terms "markup" and "markon" are synonymous. In common usage, the terms "selling price," "sales," and "retail" have the same meaning.

such establishments as furniture stores and jewelry stores in which stock is limited in variety and number of pieces, thus simplifying the problem of keeping a cost inventory, and also in those establishments (notably jewelry stores) in which extremely wide variations in the per cent of markup of individual items are likely to occur, causing serious discrepancies in the valuation of stocks if the retail base is used.

Per Cents Based on Retail. Since most retailers find that it is much simpler for them to take inventories at retail (selling price), such concerns are most likely to compare cost, markup, expenses, profit or loss, etc., with net sales.

In such retail establishments, the use of cost as a base for comparisons in per cent would require that inventories be taken at cost, thus necessitating the coding of all price tickets or reference to original invoices, either method being slow and costly. Furthermore, among retailers, many expense items are determined by net sales, not by the cost of goods purchased or sold. As examples, salesmen are paid frequently by salary and/or commission or bonus based on net sales, administrative officers often receive salaries and/or bonuses based on net sales, and rental contracts often vary directly with net sales volume. Thus it is reasonable to assume that when a retailer quotes per cents, the comparison is with net sales and is not based on cost.

The Basic Equation in All Markup Problems. The solution of all problems in markup whether based on cost or on sales is dependent on an understanding of the following basic equation:

$$\begin{array}{rcl} \textit{Cost} + \textit{markup} & = & \textit{selling price} \\ \$32 + \quad \$8 & = & \\ + \quad \$8 & = & \$40 \\ \$32 + \qquad & = & \$40 \end{array}$$

The method of finding the missing quantity in each of the foregoing equations is, of course, obvious to you. When cost is the base or 100 per cent, the markup and the selling price *as per cents of cost* are found as follows:

$$\text{Markup per cent} = \frac{\text{markup}}{\text{cost}} = \frac{\$8}{\$32} = .25 = 25\%$$

$$\text{Selling price per cent} = \frac{\text{selling price}}{\text{cost}} = \frac{\$40}{\$32} = 1.25 = 125\%$$

When selling price is the base or 100 per cent, the markup and the cost *as per cents of selling price* are found as follows:

$$\text{Markup per cent} = \frac{\text{markup}}{\text{selling price}} = \frac{\$8}{\$40} = .20 = 20\%$$

$$\text{Cost per cent} = \frac{\text{cost}}{\text{selling price}} = \frac{\$32}{\$40} = .80 = 80\%$$

Using the preceding per cents and the basic equation, the following becomes apparent:

	Cost + *markup* = *selling price*
As per cents of cost	100% + 25% = 125%
As per cents of sales	80% + 20% = 100%

If one of the per cents in the foregoing equations was missing, you would have little difficulty in solving for it.

Assuming that you have carefully studied and understand the preceding equations and their solutions, you need learn only three more solutions based on cost and three more solutions based on selling price which combined with the preceding equations will enable you to solve every conceivable basic markup problem.

When Cost Is Base or 100 Per Cent

Example 1: To find markup if given cost and markup as a per cent of cost. If cost is \$32 and markup is 25 per cent of cost, find the markup.

$$\text{Markup} = \text{cost} \times \text{markup per cent} = \$32 \times .25 = \$8$$

Example 2: To find cost if given markup and markup as a per cent of cost. If markup is \$8 and is 25 per cent of cost, find the cost.

$$\text{Cost} = \frac{\text{markup}}{\text{markup per cent}} = \frac{\$8}{.25} = \$32$$

Example 3: To find cost if given selling price and selling price as a per cent of cost. If the selling price is \$40 and is 125 per cent of cost, find the cost.

$$\text{Cost} = \frac{\text{selling price}}{\text{selling price per cent}} = \frac{\$40}{1.25} = \$32$$

EXERCISE 5A

Solve the following problems in which cost is the base or 100 per cent:

1. A furniture store put a markup of \$8.75 on some end tables that cost \$25. Find (*a*) the selling price, (*b*) the markup per cent on cost, and (*c*) the selling price as a per cent of cost.

2. A jewelry store priced a set of silver-plated flatware at \$70. If the cost was \$40, find (*a*) the markup, (*b*) the markup as a per cent of cost, and (*c*) the selling price as a per cent of cost.

3. A manufacturer had a markup of \$5.83 on some handbags that he sold for \$27.83. Find (*a*) the cost, (*b*) the markup per cent on cost, and (*c*) the selling price as a per cent of cost.

4. A wholesaler put a markup of 26 per cent on cost on some goods for which he paid \$4.50. Find (*a*) markup, (*b*) selling price, and (*c*) the selling price as a per cent of cost.

5. A manufacturer of games sold some novelty playing cards that cost him \$7.36 per dozen decks to produce at a selling price that was 225 per cent of his cost. Per dozen, find (*a*) the selling price, (*b*) the markup, and (*c*) the markup per cent on cost.
6. A jobbing house sold toys at a markup of 35 per cent on cost. For a toy on which the markup was \$1.75, find (*a*) the cost, (*b*) the selling price, and (*c*) the selling price as a per cent of cost.
7. A manufacturer of automobile accessories sold rear-view mirrors at a selling price that was 132 per cent of the cost. If the markup was \$1.20, find (*a*) the markup per cent on cost, (*b*) the cost, and (*c*) the selling price.
8. A manufacturer of leather goods priced overnight bags at \$22.26, which was 127.2 per cent of his cost. Find (*a*) the cost, (*b*) the markup, and (*c*) the markup as a per cent of cost.
9. A wholesale house marked up wash dresses 27.5 per cent on cost. If the selling price was \$19.38 per dozen, find per dozen (*a*) the selling price as a per cent of cost, (*b*) the cost, and (*c*) the markup.
10. A wholesaler purchased 800 sweaters for \$2,640. If he sold 240 of the sweaters at \$4.75 each, 150 at \$4.20 each, 180 at \$4.00 each, 122 at \$4.50 each, and the remainder as a job lot for \$274.20, find (*a*) the total selling price, (*b*) the total markup, and (*c*) the markup per cent on cost to nearest tenth per cent.

When Selling Price Is Base or 100 Per Cent

Example 1: To find markup if given selling price and markup as a per cent of selling price. If the selling price is \$40 and markup is 20 per cent of selling price, find markup.

$$\text{Markup} = \text{selling price} \times \text{markup per cent} = \$40 \times .20 = \$8$$

Example 2: To find selling price if given markup and markup as a per cent of selling price. If the markup is \$8 and is 20 per cent of selling price, find the selling price.

$$\text{Selling price} = \frac{\text{markup}}{\text{markup per cent}} = \frac{\$8}{.20} = \$40$$

Example 3: To find selling price if given cost and cost as a per cent of selling price. If the cost is \$32 and is 80 per cent of selling price, find the selling price.

$$\text{Selling price} = \frac{\text{cost}}{\text{cost per cent}} = \frac{\$32}{.80} = \$40$$

EXERCISE 5B

Solve the following problems in which the selling price is the base or 100 per cent:

1. A merchant put a markup of \$1.76 on some goods that cost \$3.74. Find (*a*) the selling price, (*b*) the markup per cent on selling price, and (*c*) the cost as a per cent of the selling price.
2. A wholesaler of plumbing supplies priced a faucet at \$14.75. If the cost was

$12.39, find (*a*) the markup, (*b*) the markup as a per cent of selling price, and (*c*) the cost as a per cent of the selling price.

3. A retailer put a markup of $25.50 on a suit that he sold at $60. Find (*a*) the cost, (*b*) the markup per cent on the selling price, and (*c*) the cost as a per cent of selling price.
4. A buyer in a store put a markup of 37.6 per cent of the selling price on some women's coats that he sold at $47.50. Find (*a*) the markup, (*b*) the cost, and (*c*) the cost as a per cent of the selling price.
5. A men's shop placed a selling price of $8.75 on hats that cost 68 per cent of the selling price. Find (*a*) the cost, (*b*) the markup, and (*c*) the markup as a per cent of selling price.
6. A drugstore sold a line of cosmetics at a markup of 36 per cent on the selling price. For a bottle of lotion on which the markup was $1.62, find (*a*) the selling price, (*b*) the cost, and (*c*) the cost as a per cent of selling price.
7. A sporting-goods store sold golf balls at a markup of $1.98 per dozen. If the cost was 64 per cent of the selling price, find (*a*) the markup as a per cent of selling price, (*b*) the selling price per dozen, and (*c*) the cost per dozen.
8. A buyer of men's clothes paid $44.40 each for a group of suits. If the cost was 59.2 per cent of the selling price, find per suit (*a*) the selling price, (*b*) the markup, and (*c*) the markup as a per cent of selling price.
9. A store paid $27.60 for table radios. If the markup was 26.4 per cent of the selling price, find (*a*) the cost as a per cent of selling price, (*b*) the selling price, and (*c*) the markup.
10. A buyer purchased a job lot of 279 linen tablecloths for $1,845. If he sold 33 of the cloths at $12 each, 90 at $11.50 each, 108 at $10.75 each, and the remainder at $8.50 each, find (*a*) the total selling price, (*b*) the total markup, and (*c*) the markup per cent (to tenths) on selling price.

UNIT 6. Relating Markup Based on Cost to Markup Based on Selling Price

In business, it is desirable frequently to convert from a cost base to a selling-price base—or from a selling-price base to a cost base. Manufacturers who think in terms of a cost base for their own businesses find it necessary to understand the use of selling price as a base by those retailers and wholesalers who are their customers and who prefer to think in terms of a selling-price base. In like manner, it is helpful to such retailers and wholesalers to understand and to compare readily their operations with those of manufacturers who think in terms of and who use a cost base.

To Convert Markup Per Cent on Cost to Selling Price, or on Selling Price to Cost. An article costing $2 and marked up $1 to a selling price (sales or retail) of \$3 has a markup on cost of \$1 ÷ \$2 = $\frac{1}{2}$ = .50 = 50 per cent, and a markup on selling price of \$1 ÷ \$3 = $\frac{1}{3}$ = .33$\frac{1}{3}$ = 33$\frac{1}{3}$ per cent. Thus a markup of 50 per cent on cost is equivalent to a markup of 33$\frac{1}{3}$ per cent on selling price.

The relationship between markup based on cost and markup based on selling price may be seen readily in the following:

Markup based on cost		*Markup based on sales*
$\frac{1}{3}$	=	$\frac{1}{4}$
$\frac{1}{4}$	=	$\frac{1}{5}$
$\frac{1}{5}$	=	$\frac{1}{6}$
$\frac{2}{3}$	=	$\frac{2}{5}$
$\frac{3}{4}$	=	$\frac{3}{7}$

If you will observe the preceding fractions, you will see that the numerators in the equivalents are the same, only the denominators varying. Furthermore, you will notice that the *denominator* of each markup on sales equals the *sum of the numerator and denominator* of the equivalent cost fraction. Thus a markup of $\frac{1}{8}$ on cost equals a markup of $\frac{1}{9}$ on selling price, $\frac{3}{5}$ markup on cost equals a markup of $\frac{3}{8}$ on retail, etc.

You will also observe that the *denominator* of each markup on cost equals the *difference in the numerator and denominator* of the equivalent sales fraction. Thus a markup of $\frac{1}{7}$ on selling price equals a markup of $\frac{1}{6}$ on cost, $\frac{3}{5}$ markup on retail equals a markup of $\frac{3}{2}$ (or 1$\frac{1}{2}$ times) on cost, etc.

Per cent markups may be converted to their equivalents in the same manner.

Markup Per Cents

Given per cent based on cost		*To find per cent based on sales*	*Given per cent based on sales*		*To find per cent based on cost*
50% or $\frac{50}{100}$	=	$\frac{50}{150}$ or $33\frac{1}{3}$%	50% or $\frac{50}{100}$	=	$\frac{50}{50}$ or 100%
25% or $\frac{25}{100}$	=	$\frac{25}{125}$ or 20%	25% or $\frac{25}{100}$	=	$\frac{25}{75}$ or $33\frac{1}{3}$%
150% or $\frac{150}{100}$	=	$\frac{150}{250}$ or 60%	80% or $\frac{80}{100}$	=	$\frac{80}{20}$ or 400%

As you know, the solution of all problems in markup is dependent upon an understanding of the basic equation:

$$\text{Cost} + \text{markup} = \text{selling price}$$

From this basic equation, it is apparent that the following may be derived:

$$\text{Selling price} - \text{markup} = \text{cost}$$
$$\text{Selling price} - \text{cost} = \text{markup}$$

Since each of these terms may be stated in dollars, as per cents of cost, or as per cents of sales, there are three possible ways of stating the basic equation. If C = cost, M = markup, and S = selling price (or sales, or retail), then

1. Expressed in dollars: $\$C + \$M = \$S$
2. As per cents of cost: $100\%\,C + M\%\text{ of }C = S\%\text{ of }C$
3. As per cents of selling price: $C\%\text{ of }S + M\%\text{ of }S = 100\%\,S$

Note that when the basic equation is stated as a per cent of cost as in 2, cost is 100 per cent; and that when the basic equation is stated as a per cent of selling price as in 3, selling price is 100%. When solving problems expressing cost, markup, or selling price as per cents, it is essential that it be *first determined* whether cost or selling price is the base (100 per cent).

The following examples will further illustrate the changing base.

Example 1:

Basic equation:	*Cost*	+	*markup*	=	*selling price*
1. Example in dollars	\$60	+	\$15	=	\$75
2. As per cents of cost	$\frac{60}{60}$ or 100%	+	$\frac{15}{60}$ or 25%	=	$\frac{75}{60}$ or 125%
3. As per cents of sales	$\frac{60}{75}$ or 80%	+	$\frac{15}{75}$ or 20%	=	$\frac{75}{75}$ or 100%

Example 2:

Basic equation:	*Cost*	+	*markup*	=	*selling price*
1. Example in dollars	\$120	+	\$80	=	\$200
2. As per cents of cost	$\frac{120}{120}$ or 100%	+	$\frac{80}{120}$ or $66\frac{2}{3}$ %	=	$\frac{200}{120}$ or $166\frac{2}{3}$ %
3. As per cents of sales	$\frac{120}{200}$ or 60%	+	$\frac{80}{200}$ or 40%	=	$\frac{200}{200}$ or 100%

EXERCISE 6

A. Find markup based on sales, expressing as a fraction in lowest terms, when the markup based on cost is:

1. $\frac{1}{9}$ 2. $\frac{3}{5}$ 3. $\frac{2}{3}$ 4. $1\frac{5}{18}$

B. Find markup based on cost expressing as a fraction in lowest terms, when the markup based on sales is:

1. $\frac{3}{8}$ 2. $\frac{2}{5}$ 3. $\frac{9}{10}$ 4. $\frac{5}{7}$

C. Find markup based on sales to nearest hundredth per cent, when the markup based on cost is:

1. 54% 2. 35% 3. 150% 4. 115%

D. Find markup based on cost to nearest hundredth per cent, when the markup based on sales is:

1. 52% 2. 35% 3. 63% 4. 48%

E. Complete the following equations. Give dollar-and-cents answers to nearest cents, and per cent answers to nearest hundredth per cent.

	Cost	+ *markup*	= *sales*
1.	$ 120.00	+ $______	= $______
	100%	+ ______%	= ______%
	60.00%	+ ______%	= 100%
2.	$ 12.50	+ $______	= $______
	100%	+ 70.00%	= ______%
	______%	+ ______%	= 100%
3.	$ 1.86	+ $______	= $______
	100%	+ ______%	= ______%
	______%	+ 36.90%	= 100%
4.	$ 1.25	+ $______	= $______
	100%	+ ______%	= 156.00%
	______%	+ ______%	= 100%
5.	$______	+ $ 1.70	= $______
	100%	+ ______%	= ______%
	56.96%	+ ______%	= 100%
6.	$______	+ $ 7.45	= $______
	100%	+ 59.60%	= ______%
	______%	+ ______%	= 100%
7.	$______	+ $ .85	= $______
	100%	+ ______%	= ______%
	______%	+ 42.50%	= 100%
8.	$______	+ $ 80.00	= $______
	100%	+ ______%	= 184.21%
	______%	+ ______%	= 100%
9.	$______	+ $______	= $ 189.50
	100%	+ ______%	= ______%
	62.00%	+ ______%	= 100%
10.	$______	+ $______	= $ 22.50
	100%	+ 55.17%	= ______%
	______%	+ ______%	= ______%
11.	$______	+ $______	= $ 1.39
	100%	+ ______%	= ______%
	______%	+ 46.04%	= 100%
12.	$______	+ $______	= $ 45.00
	100%	+ ______%	= 163.64%
	______%	+ ______%	= 100%

CHAPTER IX

PROBLEMS IN RETAILING

Much of Chapter VIII, Purchase Discounts and Markup, was an introduction to the subject of retail-store mathematics, and it is suggested that you refresh your memory, if necessary, with a few minutes review of that chapter before attempting work in Chapter IX.

Terminology of Retailing. To continue with the subject of retailing, it is necessary that you become acquainted with the terms that follow. The definitions for each of these terms, though some are perhaps difficult to understand at first reading, will be fully explained in this chapter.

Net cost is the price paid by the retailer to the manufacturer or distributor after trade discounts, cash discounts if earned, and anticipation if taken have been deducted from the invoice.

Net delivered cost is net cost plus transportation charges.

Gross delivered cost is the cost after trade discounts have been taken plus transportation charges, but *does not include* cash discounts earned or anticipation taken. Some stores do not treat cash discounts earned and anticipation taken as part of the store operating statement but classify them as "other income earned" thus adding them to the store operating statement in determining a total profit or loss statement of the business.

Original retail price is the first price placed on merchandise. It may be reduced by means of markdowns or increased by means of additional markons. NOTE: In this text, the terms "markon" and "markup" are synonymous.

Retail or *selling price* is the price of the merchandise at any given time; or after a sale has been completed, it is the net selling price.

Initial markup is the difference between the gross delivered cost and the original retail price. Expressed in dollars, it is ordinarily used in reference to a single purchase rather than a series of purchases. Expressed in per cent, it is a predetermined optimum markup per cent that the retailer attempts to secure on all purchases.

Cumulative markup is the difference between the total of the beginning inventory at cost plus the gross delivered cost of purchases less purchase returns at cost and the total of the beginning inventory at retail plus the purchases at retail less the purchase returns at retail plus any net additional markups.

Gross margin or *gross profit* is the difference between net sales and the cost of goods sold. It is equal to the maintained markup plus cash discounts earned and minus alteration costs.

Maintained markup is equal to the gross margin less cash discounts earned and plus alteration costs. It is equivalent to the initial markup in dollars less markdowns and shortages.

Markdown is a reduction in price below the original selling price. It is the difference between the original price and the reduced price.

Gross markdown is the total of one or a series of markdowns in the original selling price.

Markdown cancellation is a revision of a reduced price upward to, but not above, the original price.

Net markdown is the final amount of the markdown. It reflects the net downward change in the original selling price and is expressed in dollars or as a per cent of net sales.

Additional markup is an increase above the original selling price. It is the difference between the original price and the increased price.

Additional markup cancellation is a revision of an increased price downward to, but not below, the original price.

Net additional markup is the final amount of the increase in the original selling price. It reflects the net upward change in the original selling price and is expressed in dollars or as a per cent of net sales.

Shortages are losses at retail that occur through breakage, unrecorded markdowns and allowances, theft, or mysterious disappearance.

Reductions include both markdowns and shortages at retail.

Deductions include net sales, markdowns, and shortages at retail.

Inventory at retail is expressed either as a book inventory or as a physical inventory. The book inventory at retail is equivalent to merchandise available for sale at retail less net sales, less markdowns, less anticipated shortages. The physical inventory at retail is determined by an actual count of the goods in stock.

Inventory at cost is expressed either as a book inventory or as a physical inventory. It is found by multiplying the inventory at retail by the complement of the cumulative markup per cent.

UNIT 1. Markup Based on Retail and the Use of Complements

Standard practice among retailers is to base the markup per cent on retail. Therefore whenever markup per cent quoted by a retailer is given without a statement as to whether it is based on cost or on selling price, it is justifiable to assume that the markup per cent is based on selling price.

The term "markup" may refer to an individual item, a group of items, or even an entire inventory of stock. Thus an item selling for $2 with a markup of $.80 and an inventory at retail of $500,000 with a markup of $200,000 may both be referred to as having a markup of 40 per cent.

Use of Complements in Retail Calculations. Since retailers consider the selling price as 100 per cent and since cost plus markup equals the selling price, then the cost per cent and the markup per cent total 100 per cent and are complementary. Thus:

Markup 35%, cost is 65%	Cost 80%, markup is 20%
Markup 40%, cost is 60%	Cost $66\frac{2}{3}$%, markup is $33\frac{1}{3}$%
Markup 25%, cost is 75%	Cost 58%, markup is 42%
Markup 55%, cost is 45%	Cost 47%, markup is 53%

Therefore, if markup per cent for a given inventory at retail is known, cost in dollars is readily found by multiplying the value of the inventory at retail by the decimal equivalent of the cost per cent (complement of markup per cent).

Example: What is the cost in dollars of $230,000 worth of stock at retail if the markup is 30 per cent of retail?

$$100\% - 30\% = 70\%$$
$$70\% = .70$$
$$\$230{,}000 \times .70 = \$161{,}000 \text{ Cost}$$

If the cost per cent on a given inventory at retail is known, the markup in dollars is found by multiplying the value of the inventory at retail by the decimal equivalent of the markup per cent (complement of cost per cent).

Example: What is the markup in dollars on $230,000 worth of stock at retail if the cost is 70 per cent of retail?

$$100\% - 70\% = 30\%$$
$$30\% = .30$$
$$\$230{,}000 \times .30 = \$69{,}000 \text{ Markup}$$

Finding the Values of Retail, Cost, and Markup. Whether determining dollars or per cents, the following equation is basic:

$$\text{Retail} = \text{cost} + \text{markup}$$

From this equation the following are derived:

$$\text{Cost} = \text{retail} - \text{markup}$$
$$\text{Markup} = \text{retail} - \text{cost}$$

When any two of the values in dollars or per cents are known, it is apparent that the third value is found readily. Perhaps the simplest form in which the problem of determining all three elements (in dollars and as per cents of retail) may be presented is when any two are known in dollars. Thus in the following the missing dollar value is obvious:

$$\begin{aligned} \textit{Retail} &= \textit{cost} + \textit{markup} \\ R &= \$120 + \$80 \\ \$200 &= C + \$80 \\ \$200 &= \$120 + M \end{aligned}$$

Once all three dollar values are known, the per cent equivalents of retail may then be found as follows:

$$\textit{Retail} = \textit{Cost} + \textit{markup}$$

As per cents of retail: $\frac{200}{200}$ of $100\% = \frac{120}{200}$ or $60\% + \frac{80}{200}$ or 40%

If only one of the elements (retail, or cost, or markup) is known in dollars and a retail per cent equivalent of the cost or of the markup is known, then the solution for one of missing dollar figures may be found as follows:

Given retail of \$200:

(*a*) and *cost* is 60 per cent of retail

$$C = \$200 \times .60 = \$120$$

(*b*) and *markup* is 40 per cent of retail

$$M = \$200 \times .40 = \$80$$

Given cost of \$120:

(*a*) and *cost* is 60 per cent of retail

$$60\% \text{ of } R = \$120$$
$$R = \frac{\$120}{.60} = \$200$$

(*b*) and *markup* is 40 per cent of retail

$$C = 100\% - 40\% = 60\% \text{ of retail}$$
$$60\% \text{ of } R = \$120$$
$$R = \frac{\$120}{.60} = \$200$$

Given markup of \$80:

(*a*) and *cost* is 60 per cent of retail

$$M = 100\% - 60\% = 40\% \text{ of retail}$$
$$40\% \text{ of } R = \$80$$
$$R = \frac{\$80}{.40} = \$200$$

(*b*) and *markup* is 40 per cent of retail

$$40\% \text{ of } R = \$80$$
$$R = \frac{\$80}{.40} = \$200$$

EXERCISE 1

A. Complete the following equations. Give dollar-and-cents answers to nearest cents, and per cent answers to nearest hundredth per cent.

	Retail	=	*cost*	+ *markup*		*Retail*	=	*cost*	+ *markup*
1.	\$ 125.00	=	\$______	+ \$______	2.	\$ 375.00	=	\$______	+ \$______
	100%	=	61.08%	+ ______%		100%	=	______%	+ 40.76%
3.	\$______	=	\$ 60.42	+ \$______	4.	\$______	=	\$ 2.30	+ \$______
	100%	=	71.25%	+ ______%		100%	=	______%	+ 42.50%
5.	\$______	=	\$______	+ \$ 26.65	6.	\$______	=	\$______	+ \$ 143.85
	100%	=	57.36%	+ ______%		100%	=	______%	+ 32.88%

B. Solve the following, finding required per cents to nearest hundredths. Unless stipulated otherwise, assume that per cents are based on retail in this and all following exercises in this chapter.

1. A manufacturer of women's handbags wishes to obtain a profit of 5 per cent on cost on some handbags that cost him \$9.60 to produce. If he allows cash terms of 4/10 E.O.M., what price will he ask?
2. A buyer wishes to purchase sport coats to retail at \$19.75. If he is required to obtain a minimum markup of 40 per cent, what is the maximum price that he can pay for each coat?
3. A buyer purchases a group of shirts at \$1.12 each. If the cost is 57.44 per cent, what is his planned selling price per shirt?
4. A buyer purchases some dresses at \$25. (*a*) At what price must he mark the dresses to obtain a markup of 41 per cent? (*b*) What would be the markup

per cent if the dresses are priced at $39.50? (*c*) What would be the markup per cent if the dresses are priced at $44.50?

5. A buyer of men's furnishings paid $19.20 per dozen for some wool neckties. If his markup was 36 per cent, what was the selling price per necktie?

6. If the markup on a chair was $60.45 and the cost was 51.64 per cent find (*a*) retail and (*b*) cost.

7. A buyer purchases a job lot of 120 scarfs for $192. If she prices 50 of them at $1.69 each, 40 at $1.95 each, and the remainder at $2.50 each, what markup per cent does she obtain on the entire job lot?

8. A merchant purchases a job lot of 80 robes on which he plans to obtain a markup of 42 per cent. If he intends to retail 30 of them at $19.50 each, 25 at $15 each, and the remainder at $10 each, what is the maximum total price that he can afford to pay for the 80 robes?

UNIT 2. Cumulative Markup[1]

The retail method of determining inventory at cost (and then cost of goods sold) is found by multiplying the inventory at retail by the complement of the cumulative markup per cent. The cumulative markup *in dollars* is found by determining the difference between the total of the beginning inventory at cost plus the gross delivered cost of purchases and the total of the beginning inventory at retail plus the purchases at retail plus the net additional markups. Additional markups are increases in original selling prices.

The cumulative markup *per cent* is found by dividing the cumulative markup in dollars by the value of the merchandise at retail.

Note particularly that the markup of a beginning inventory is the cumulative markup of the immediately preceding ending inventory. Note also that while net additional markups *are* taken into account in computing cumulative markup, earned cash discounts, markdowns, shortages, and alteration costs *are not* considered in computing cumulative markup.

The method used in determining cumulative markup in dollars and in per cent will be apparent from the following examples.

Example 1: If the Jan. 1 inventory at retail is $48,000 and its valuation at cost is $30,000, what is the cumulative markup (*a*) in dollars and (*b*) in per cent (to nearest hundredths) on Jan. 31, if purchases during the month cost $25,000 and were priced at $40,000 and net additional markups were $2,000?

[1] It should be specially noted that cumulative markup at the end of any given period of time is thought of as initial markup (markup of beginning inventory) at the beginning of the next period of time.

	Cost	*Retail*
Jan. 1 inventory	$30,000	$48,000
Plus gross purchases	25,000	40,000
Plus net additional markups		2,000
Total merchandise available	$55,000	$90,000

(*a*) $90,000 − $55,000 = $35,000

(*b*) $\frac{35,000}{90,000} = .3889 = 38.89\%$

The cost valuation of inventory at any time may be determined by multiplying the inventory at retail by the complement of the cumulative markup per cent. (The cost of goods sold at any time may be determined by subtracting the ending inventory at cost from the cost valuation of the total merchandise available.) This complement is also known as the cost equivalent and may be obtained directly. Thus in Example 1:

Complement of cumulative markup per cent or cost equivalent $= 1.0000 - .3889 = .6111 = 61.11\%$

or, directly $= \frac{55,000}{90,000} = .6111 = 61.11\%$

The cumulative markup per cent $= 1.0000 - .6111 = .3889 = 38.89\%$

Example 2: Stock on hand Mar. 1 is $100,000 at retail with a markup of 40 per cent (the cumulative markup on Feb. 28), purchases during the month amount to $37,700 at cost with an average markup of 35 per cent, net additional markons total $4,000, and the ending inventory on Mar. 31 is $96,500 at retail. Find (*a*) the cumulative markup in dollars, (*b*) the cumulative markup per cent, (*c*) the cost valuation of the ending inventory, (*d*) the deductions at retail, and (*e*) the cost of goods sold.

Decimal equivalent of cost of beginning inventory = 1.00 − .40 = .60
Decimal equivalent of cost of purchases = 1.00 − .35 = .65

	Cost		*Retail*
Beginning inventory = $100,000 × .60 =	$60,000		$100,000
Plus gross purchases	37,700	$\frac{37,700}{.65} =$	58,000
Plus net additional markup			4,000
Total merchandise available	$97,700		$162,000
Ending inventory			96,500

(*a*) $162,000 − $97,700 = $64,300

(*b*) $\frac{64,300}{162,000} = .39691358 = 39.69+\%$

(*c*) Cost equivalent $= 1.00000000 - .39691358 = .60308642$

If found directly $= \frac{97,700}{162,000} = .60308642$

$96,500 × .60308642 = $58,197.84

(*d*) $162,000 − $96,500 = $65,500

(*e*) $97,700 − $58,197.84 = $39,502.16

In the example preceding, note the use of eight decimal places in applying the cost equivalent (the complement of the cumulative markup) in determining the cost valuation of the ending inventory and thence the cost of goods sold. Since such is the practice of many retailers, use the same degree of accuracy (though it may not be justified mathematically) in solving for cost valuation of ending inventory and then finding the cost of goods sold, unless specified otherwise, in the exercises that follow in this chapter.

In solving problems requiring determination of the cost valuation of ending inventory or cost of goods sold, it is suggested that the use of a "set-up form" similar to the following will be helpful to you.

	Cost	*Retail*			
Beginning inventory	$....	$....			
Purchases gross	....	....			
		....	Net additional markups		
Total goods available	$....	$....			
Less ending inventory	....	....			
				net sales	$....
Cost of goods sold	$....	$....	Deductions =	markdowns	....
				shortages	....

Note that the word *deductions* refers to the sum of the net sales, the markdowns, and the shortages. The word *reductions* (not appearing in the "set-up form") refers to the sum of the markdowns and shortages.

EXERCISE 2

In the following exercise, assume that purchases means *gross* purchases. Unless stipulated otherwise, assume that per cents are based on retail in this and all following exercises in this chapter.

1. On June 1, inventory at retail is $65,000 and its valuation at cost is $40,000. If purchases during the month cost $22,000 and are priced at $36,000 and net additional markups are $2,000, what will be the cumulative markup per cent (to nearest hundredths) on June 30?
2. Beginning inventory on Sept. 1 is $55,000 at retail with a markup of 41.6 per cent. Purchases during the month total $73,200 and are marked up 33.4 per cent. What is the cumulative markup per cent (to nearest hundredths) on Sept. 30?
3. On May 1, beginning inventory is $37,500 at cost with a markup of 43.7 per cent. NOTE: This is the cumulative markup per cent for Apr. 30. Purchases during the month are marked up 39.3 per cent and total $52,500 at retail. Find the cumulative markup per cent (to nearest hundredths) on May 31.

4. On Nov. 1 inventory at retail of $27,260 had a cost valuation of $15,885. Purchases during November cost $14,325 and were priced to retail at $21,000. During the month, net additional markups were $3,100. Deductions (sales + markdowns + shortages) were $28,974. What was the cost valuation of the ending inventory? (In solving, compute the decimal equivalent of the cumulative markup or its complement to eight decimal places.)
5. The records of the bedding department of the Benjamin Department Store contain the following information for the period from Oct. 1 to Dec. 31: beginning inventory was $7,550 at cost, $12,500 at retail; purchases were $20,000 at cost, $33,800 at retail; gross additional markups were $1,500 at retail and additional markup cancellations were $300; deductions (sales + markdowns + shortages) totaled $33,600. Find (*a*) the ending inventory at cost and (*b*) the cost of goods sold.
6. On Jan. 1, stock at retail is $128,500 with cumulative markup on that date of 39.32 per cent. Purchases at retail during the following quarter total $276,000 with a markup of 43.75 per cent. Net additional markups during the quarter are $5,500. On Mar. 31, inventory at retail is $139,400. Find (*a*) the deductions at retail, (*b*) the cost valuation of the ending inventory, and (*c*) the cost of goods sold. (In solving, compute the decimal equivalent of the cumulative markup on Mar. 31 or its complement to eight decimal places.)
7. On Aug. 1, the inventory at retail of the Reidy Dress Shop was $6,785.60, with a cumulative markup of 42.5 per cent. Purchases during August totaled $4,362.75 at retail, with an average markup of 46.8 per cent. Deductions were $9,380.50. What was the cost valuation of the ending inventory? (In solving, compute the decimal equivalent of the cumulative markup or its complement to seven decimal places.)
8. If beginning inventory of $119,600 was valued at $68,300, deductions totaled $82,500, and ending inventory of $106,600 was valued at $65,026, find the markup per cent (to nearest hundredths) on purchases.

UNIT 3. Initial Markup; Averaging Markup

Unless the original or initial markup (M_i), the difference between cost and original price, is sufficiently high to cover planned expenses and planned operating profit, a business will not be profitable. Thus if planned expenses are 30 per cent and planned operating profit is 5 per cent, the markup would need to be 35 per cent.

Thus initial markup per cent ($M_i\%$) expressed as a formula would be

$$M_i\% = \frac{\text{expenses} + \text{planned profits}}{\text{sales}}$$

Example 1: If expenses are estimated as 32 per cent and planned operating profit is 6 per cent, what should be the initial markup per cent?

$$M_i\% = \frac{32 + 6}{100} = \frac{38}{100} = 38\%$$

Example 2: If expenses are estimated at $27,500, planned operating profit at $5,000, and net sales at $92,500, what should be the initial markup per cent?

$$M_i\% = \frac{\$27,500 + \$5,000}{\$92,000} = \frac{\$32,500}{\$92,500} = 35.14\%$$

Furthermore, certain other elements must be considered, for they also will affect the gross margin required. These are markdowns, shortages, alteration expenses, and cash discounts earned.

Past experience enables the merchant to predetermine the amount of markdowns, shortages, and alteration costs that will probably occur on any given group of merchandise. These must be added to the probable expenses and desired operating profit in determining a profitable selling price. Since markdowns and stock shortages also constitute a deduction from the original price as well as increasing the margin required, they must be added to the probable net selling price.

Because cash discounts from vendors (on purchases) are deducted from the cost of merchandise, the lowered cost increases the margin between cost and selling price. In calculating the initial markup, it is therefore necessary to subtract the amount of the cash discounts.

With these adjustments, the initial markup equation becomes

$$M_i\% = \frac{\text{expenses} + \text{planned profit} + \text{markdowns} + \text{stock shortages} + \text{alteration cost} - \text{purchase discounts}}{\text{net sales} + \text{markdowns} + \text{stock shortages}}$$

Example 1: What should be the initial markup per cent if expenses are estimated at 30 per cent, operating profit desired 5 per cent, markdowns 9 per cent, shortages 3 per cent, alteration expenses 2 per cent, and cash discounts earned 4.2 per cent?

$$M_i\% = \frac{30 + 5 + 9 + 3 + 2 - 4.2}{100 + 9 + 3} = .40 = 40\%$$

Example 2: What should be the initial markup per cent on sales of $200,000 if expenses are estimated at $56,000, markdowns at $15,000, shortages at $5,000, alteration cost at $2,500, and cash discounts earned from vendors at $4,500, if an operating profit of $12,000 is desired?

$$M_i\% = \frac{\$56,000 + \$15,000 + \$12,000 + \$5,000 + \$2,500 - \$4,500}{\$200,000 + \$15,000 + \$5,000}$$

$$= .3909 = 39.09\%$$

Averaging Markup. Merchants frequently have the opportunity of purchasing, at a low average cost, groups of merchandise that should be marked at two retail prices because of the varying grades of quality within the assortment.

The problem confronting the merchant is to determine the numbers of units that should be placed at the lower price and at the higher price in order to maintain an average required initial markup.

Example 1: Assume that a buyer for a dress department has the opportunity of purchasing a group of dresses at \$6.75 that can be assorted into two groups to retail at \$10.50 and \$12.75. If the initial markup desired is 40 per cent, what ratio of the dresses should be marked at each price?

$$\text{Average markup} = 40\%$$
$$C = R - M$$
$$= 100\% - 40\% = 60\%$$
$$60\%\ R = \$6.75$$
$$R = \frac{\$6.75}{.60} = \$11.25$$

Retail prices to be	\$10.50	\$12.75
Average retail	11.25	11.25
Loss or gain	−\$ .75	+\$ 1.50

Since \$.75 is lost on each sale at \$10.50 and \$1.50 is gained on each sale at \$12.75, 150 dresses may be marked for sale at \$10.50 for each 75 dresses priced at \$12.75 and still maintain an average initial markup of 40 per cent. Reduced to simplest terms, this is a ratio of 2 dresses at \$10.50 to 1 dress at \$12.75.

Example 2: A buyer purchases 100 hats at \$3.25 each, 25 of which he marks at \$6. What is the minimum retail price that the buyer may place on the remainder if the average initial markup is to be 35 per cent?

$$\text{Total cost} = \$3.25 \times 100 = \$325$$
$$C = R - M$$
$$= 100\% - 35\% = 65\%$$
$$65\%\ R = \$325$$
$$R = \frac{\$325}{.65} = \$500$$

25 hats priced at \$6	= \$150
Remainder must bring	\$350

$$\text{Remainder} = 100 - 25 = 75$$
$$75 \text{ hats} = \$350$$
$$1 \text{ hat} = \frac{\$350}{75} = \$4.67$$

Therefore the remainder must be priced at \$4.67 or higher to maintain an average initial markup of 35 per cent.

A second type of averaging the markup is necessitated when a merchant wishes to buy at two costs and to sell at one retail price. In this case the problem is to determine the ratio of items that must be purchased at each cost in order to maintain the average initial markup desired.

Example 1: Wholesale costs are \$5.25 and \$6.50; retail selling price is \$10. What ratio of items at each price must be purchased if an average initial markup of 40 per cent is desired?

If retail is \$10 and average initial markup is 40 per cent, then average cost should be 60 per cent of \$10, or \$6.

Average cost	=	\$6	\$6
Actual cost	=	5.25	6.50
Gain or loss	=	+\$ .75	−\$ .50

Therefore for every 50 hats purchased at \$5.25, 75 hats may be purchased at \$6.50, a ratio of 2 hats at \$5.25 for every 3 at \$6.50.

Example 2: A merchant has a cumulative inventory at retail of \$18,600 with a markup of $33\frac{1}{3}$ per cent. His planned purchases during the month are \$9,000 at cost. What average initial markup must he place on the purchases if he wishes to increase his cumulative markup to 35 per cent?

The inventory at cost would be $100\% - 33\frac{1}{3}\% = 66\frac{2}{3}\%$

$$\$18{,}600 \times 66\frac{2}{3}\% = \$12{,}400$$

Inventory at cost	=	\$12,400
Purchases	=	9,000
Total merchandise	=	\$21,400

If average planned markup is 35 per cent, then average cost would be

$$100\% - 35\% = 65\%$$
$$65\% = \$21{,}400$$
$$\text{Total retail} = \frac{\$21{,}400}{.65} = \$32{,}923.08$$

Less inventory at retail	=	18,600
Purchases at retail	=	\$14,323.08
Less purchases at cost	=	9,000
Markup in dollars	=	\$ 5,323.08

$$\text{Purchases } M\% = \frac{\$5{,}323.08}{\$14{,}323.08} = 37.16\%$$

EXERCISE 3

In solving, find per cents to nearest hundredths.

1. If planned net sales are $73,654, estimated expenses are $27,345, and desired operating profit is $7,200, what should be the initial markup per cent?
2. If planned net sales are $19,672, estimated expenses are $6,350, and desired operating profit is $1,750, what should be the initial markup per cent?
3. What should be the initial markup per cent if expenses are estimated at 28 per cent, operating profit desired 7 per cent, markdowns 8 per cent, shortages 2.5 per cent, alteration expenses 1.25 per cent, and cash discounts 3.2 per cent?
4. What should be the initial markup per cent on net sales of $42,000 if expenses are estimated at $12,500, markdowns $3,500, shortages $900, alteration costs $400, cash discounts $1,400, and a profit of $2,500 is desired?
5. A buyer has planned net sales totaling $120,000. If estimated expenses are $36,000, markdowns $12,000, shortages $2,000, alteration costs $2,600, and cash discounts $3,000, what initial markup should be obtained if a 5 per cent profit is desired?
6. A buyer has the opportunity of purchasing at $3.75 each a job lot of sweaters that can be assorted into two groups retailing at $5.50 and $7.50. If the initial markup desired is 40 per cent, what ratio of the sweaters should be marked (*a*) $5.50 and (*b*) $7.50?
7. A buyer purchases 275 blankets at $5.50 each, 125 of which the buyer prices at $7.70. What is the minimum price the buyer must place on the remainder of the blankets if he wishes the average initial markup to be at least 37.5 per cent?
8. Wholesale prices are $2.10 and $2.80, retail selling price $3.75. What is the ratio of items at (*a*) $2.10 and (*b*) $2.80 that must be purchased if an average initial markup of 36 per cent is desired?
9. A buyer's Mar. 1 inventory at retail is $6,800, with a cumulative markup of 44 per cent. Planned purchases for March are $4,200 at cost. What average initial markup per cent must be placed on the purchases if he wishes to reduce his cumulative markup to 41 per cent?

UNIT 4. Maintained Markup and Gross Margin

Frequently, original retail prices are lowered to induce the sale of slow-moving merchandise or to attract customers into the store through sales promotions at lowered prices. Regardless of the reason for such reductions (known as markdowns), the result is a smaller margin between cost and selling price.

Maintained markup (M_m) is the margin after all reductions (including shortages as well as markdowns) have occurred.

It represents the final difference between the *gross cost*[1] and the actual selling price. By formula, the maintained markup in dollars may be found:

$$M_m = \text{initial selling price} - \text{reductions} - \text{gross cost}$$

Ordinarily, maintained markup is expressed as a per cent of the net sales and, if the initial selling price, reductions, and gross cost in dollars are known, may be found as follows:

$$M_m\% = \frac{\text{initial selling price} - \text{reductions} - \text{gross cost}}{\text{initial selling price} - \text{reductions}}$$

Example 1: If goods with gross cost of \$75 and priced at \$125 are marked down \$10, find (*a*) the initial markup per cent and (*b*) the maintained markup per cent.

(*a*) $$M_i\% = \frac{\$125 - \$75}{\$125} = \frac{\$50}{\$125} = .40 = 40\%$$

(*b*) $$M_m\% = \frac{\$125 - \$10 - \$75}{\$125 - \$10} = \frac{\$40}{\$115} = .3478 = 34.78\%$$

Example 2: If gross cost is \$55, actual selling price \$85, and markdowns of \$5 already taken, find (*a*) the maintained markup per cent and (*b*) the initial markup per cent.

(*a*) $$M_m\% = \frac{\$85 - \$55}{\$85} = \frac{\$30}{\$85} = .3529 = 35.29\%$$

(*b*) $$M_i\% = \frac{\$85 + \$5 - \$55}{\$85 + \$5} = \frac{\$35}{\$90} = .3889 = 38.89\%$$

When the *initial markup per cent* (or *cumulative markup per cent*) and the reduction per cent (expressed as a per cent of the net sales) are known or may be found, the maintained markup per cent may be computed readily through the use of the following equation:

$$M_m\% = {}_{Mi}\% - (\text{reduction }\% \times \text{complement of } M_i\%)$$

Example: If initial markup (or cumulative markup) is 38 per cent and markdowns are 7 per cent, find the maintained markup per cent.

$$\text{Complement of initial markup per cent} = 100\% - 38\% = 62\% = .62$$
$$M_m\% = .38 - (.07 \times .62) = .38 - .0434 = .3366 = 33.66\%$$

[1] *Gross cost* is the cost computed without consideration of the following two elements: cash discounts earned on purchases, which decrease the actual cost; and alterations or workrooms, which usually operate at a loss and thus increase the actual cost.

If the markdowns or shortages do not occur, then the margin or markup remains constant and is the same for the initial markup and the maintained markup.

Maintained markup in dollars is equivalent to gross margin, less cash discounts earned on purchases, plus alteration or workroom costs. Thus:

$$M_m = \text{gross margin} - \text{cash discounts} + \text{alteration costs}$$

Example: If gross margin is \$45, cash discounts from vendors \$2.70, and alteration costs \$1, what is the maintained markup?

$$M_m = \$45 - \$2.70 + \$1.00 = \$43.30$$

Gross margin (M_g), or the difference between net sales and the cost of goods sold, is the same as maintained markup except for cash discounts earned on purchases and alteration costs.

Cash discounts earned increase the size of the gross margin, alteration or workroom costs decrease it. Since cash discounts are almost always larger than alteration costs, gross margin usually exceeds maintained markup. The cost of goods sold (complement of the gross margin) is accordingly smaller than the gross cost of goods sold (complement of the maintained markup). Thus:

$$M_m = \text{net sales} - \text{gross cost of goods sold}$$
$$M_g = \text{net sales} - \text{cost of goods sold}$$
$$M_m\% = \frac{\text{net sales} - \text{gross cost of goods sold}}{\text{net sales}}$$
$$M_g\% = \frac{\text{net sales} - \text{cost of goods sold}}{\text{net sales}}$$

The distinction between "gross cost of goods sold" and "cost of goods sold" will be apparent by the following equations:

$$C\ of\ GS = gross\ C\ of\ GS - \text{cash disc.} + \text{alteration costs}$$
$$Gross\ C\ of\ GS = C\ of\ GS + \text{cash disc.} - \text{alteration costs}$$

The difference between maintained markup and gross margin may also be observed in the following equations:

$$M_m = \text{gross margin} - \text{cash disc.} + \text{alteration costs}$$
$$M_g = \text{maintained markup} + \text{cash disc.} - \text{alteration costs}$$
$$M_m = \text{net sales} - (C\ of\ GS + \text{cash disc.} - \text{alteration costs})$$
$$M_g = \text{net sales} - (gross\ C\ of\ GS - \text{cash disc.} + \text{alteration costs})$$

Example 1: If gross margin is \$3,660, cash discounts earned \$126, and alteration costs \$75, what is the maintained markup?

$$M_m = \$3,660 - \$126 + \$75 = \$3,609$$

Example 2: If maintained markup is \$2,320, vendors' discounts \$130, and alteration costs \$60, what is the gross margin?

$$M_g = \$2{,}320 + \$130 - \$60 = \$2{,}390$$

Example 3: If sales are \$2,500, gross cost of sales \$1,500, cash discounts earned on purchases \$50, and alteration costs \$20, find (*a*) the maintained markup in dollars, (*b*) the maintained markup per cent, (*c*) the gross margin in dollars, and (*d*) the gross margin per cent.

(*a*) $M_m = \$2{,}500 - \$1{,}500 = \$1{,}000$

(*b*) $M_m\% = \frac{1000}{2500} = .4000 = 40.00\%$

(*c*) $M_g = \$2{,}500 - (\$1{,}500 - \$50 + \$20) = \$1{,}030$

(*d*) $M_g\% = \frac{1030}{2500} = .4120 = 41.20\%$

Example 4: If sales are \$3,200, cost of goods sold \$1,800, cash discounts from vendors \$115, and alteration costs \$65, find (*a*) the maintained markup in dollars, (*b*) the maintained markup per cent, (*c*) the gross margin in dollars, and (*d*) the gross margin per cent.

(*a*) $M_m = \$3{,}200 - (\$1{,}800 + \$115 - \$65) = \$1{,}350$

(*b*) $M_m\% = \frac{1350}{3200} = .4219 = 42.19\%$

(*c*) $M_g = \$3{,}200 - \$1{,}800 = \$1{,}400$

(*d*) $M_g\% = \frac{1400}{3200} = .4375 = 43.75\%$

The primary reason for distinguishing between maintained markup per cent and gross margin per cent is the fact that some retailers do and some retailers do not consider cash discounts earned in computing gross margin in dollars and thus the gross margin per cent. Since maintained markup per cent does not consider cash discounts earned (and alteration costs) in its determination, all retailers may directly compare the maintained markup per cent of their own stores with the maintained markup per cent of similar stores on the basis of figures available through statistics furnished by the Federal Reserve system and member stores of groups with which they may be affiliated. Comparisons of gross margin per cents would be invalid unless all stores compared used the same accounting systems in determining gross margin per cent.

EXERCISE 4

It is suggested that in solving Problems 5 and 6 of this exercise you make use of the "set-up form" immediately preceding Exercise 2 of this chapter, page 314. Find all required per cents to nearest hundredths.

1. Goods with gross cost of $130 and priced at $225 are marked down $30. Find (*a*) the initial markup per cent and (*b*) the maintained markup per cent.
2. If gross cost is 57 per cent of the original retail and reductions are 9 per cent, what is the maintained markup per cent?
3. If gross cost is $27.50, actual selling price $39.50, and markdowns of $5.50 have already been taken, find (*a*) the maintained markup per cent and (*b*) the initial markup per cent.
4. If gross margin is $135, cash discounts earned from vendors $7.50, and alteration costs $2, what is the maintained markup in dollars?
5. Find the maintained markup per cent from the following data: beginning inventory $6,400 at cost, $12,500 at retail; purchases $24,600 at gross cost, $37,500 at retail; ending inventory $7,130 at cost; markdowns and shortages 10 per cent (of net sales). Since there are neither alteration or workroom costs nor cash discounts in this problem, maintained markup is the same as gross margin, and gross cost of goods sold is the same as cost of goods sold.
6. Find the maintained markup per cent from the following data: beginning inventory $3,600 at cost, markup 40 per cent; purchases $5,516 at gross cost, markup 44 per cent; ending inventory $5,520.96 at cost; markdowns and shortages $400. Since there are neither alteration or workroom costs nor cash discounts in this problem, maintained markup is the same as gross margin, and gross cost of goods sold is the same as cost of goods sold.
7. If maintained markup is $5,670, vendors' discounts earned $252, and alteration costs $175, find the gross margin in dollars.
8. If sales are $19,650, gross cost of goods sold $11,600, cash discounts earned on purchases $325, and alteration costs $125, find (*a*) the maintained markup per cent and (*b*) the gross margin per cent.
9. If sales are $5,300, cost of goods sold $2,900, cash discounts earned $125, and workroom and alteration costs $80, find (*a*) the maintained markup per cent and (*b*) the gross margin per cent.
10. If gross margin is $4,445, gross cost of goods sold is $8,572.50, cash discounts earned are $508, and alteration costs are $190.50, find (*a*) the maintained markup per cent and (*b*) the gross margin per cent.

UNIT 5. Markdown and Additional Markup

In every retail business, reduction in the selling price of some of the merchandise is necessary to stimulate the sale of slow-selling merchandise, to meet competitors' prices, and to attract customers to the store.

Such reduction in the original retail price is known as *gross markdown*. If the original price is restored or partially restored, the change is recorded as a *markdown cancellation.* The final amount of markdown is the *net markdown.*

Markdowns (M_d) may be expressed either in dollars or as a per cent. Retail accounting practice is to base markdown per cent on net sales, not as a per cent of the original retail.

Example 1: An item originally priced $2.25 is marked down and sold at $2.00. Find (*a*) the markdown and (*b*) the per cent of markdown.

$$(a)\ M_d = \$2.25 - \$2.00 = \$0.25$$

$$(b)\ M_d\% = \frac{.25}{2} = .125 = 12.5\%$$

Example 2: An item originally priced at $6.75 is reduced to $4.50 for the duration of a sale and is then re-marked and finally sold at $5.50. Find (*a*) the gross markdowns in dollars, (*b*) the markdown cancellation in dollars, and (*c*) the net markdowns in dollars and in per cent.

$$(a)\ \text{Gross } M_d = \$6.75 - \$4.50 = \$2.25$$

$$(b)\ M_d \text{ cancellation} = \$5.50 - \$4.50 = \$1.00$$

$$(c)\ \text{Net } M_d = \$2.25 - \$1.00 = \$1.25$$

$$\text{Net } M_d\% = \frac{1.25}{5.50} = .2273 = 22.73\%$$

In some instances merchandise already in stock is re-marked upward in price. Such upward revision in price may occur because of increased cost of replacement, errors in original pricing, or in order that purposely low-priced sale merchandise may be restored to normal selling price.

Such increase in the original retail price is known as *gross additional markup.* If the original price is restored or partially restored, the change is recorded as an *additional markup cancellation.* The final amount of additional markup is known as *net additional markup.*

Additional markups (M_a) may be expressed either in dollars or as a per cent. Additional markup per cent is based on net sales rather than as a per cent of original retail.

Example 1: An item originally priced $2.25 is marked up and sold at $2.50. Find (*a*) the additional markup and (*b*) the per cent of additional markup.

$$(a)\ M_a = \$2.50 - \$2.25 = \$0.25$$

$$(b)\ M_a\% = \frac{.25}{2.50} = .10 = 10\%$$

Example 2: An item originally sale priced at $9.00 is marked up to the regular selling price of $12.00 and is later reduced and sold at $10.00. Find (*a*) the gross additional markup in dollars, (*b*) the additional markup cancellation in dollars, and (*c*) the net additional markup in dollars and in per cent.

(*a*) Gross M_a = \$12.00 − \$9.00 = \$3.00
(*b*) Additional M_a cancellation = \$12.00 − \$10.00 = \$2.00
(*c*) Net M_a = \$3.00 − \$2.00 = \$1.00

$$\text{Net } M_a\% = \frac{1.00}{10.00} = .10 = 10\%$$

Take special note that additional markup cancellation is a revision of price downward to, but not below, the original selling price. Any further reduction constitutes a markdown. Likewise, markdown cancellation is a revision of price upward to, but not above, the original selling price. Any further increase in price is an additional markup.

As you already know (pages 319–322), maintained markup in dollars equals the original markup in dollars less the reductions (markdowns and shortages) in dollars. If the initial markup per cent and the reduction per cent on net sales are known, maintained markup per cent can be determined readily by subtracting from the initial markup per cent the product of the complement of the initial markup per cent and the reduction per cent. Repeating the equation,

$$M_m\% = M_i\% - (\text{reduction } \% \times \text{complement of } M_i\%)$$

Example: If the initial markup is 40 per cent, markdowns 9 per cent, and shortages 1 per cent, what is the maintained markup per cent?

Complement of initial markup per cent = 100% − 40% = 60%
Reduction per cent = 9% + 1% = 10%

$$M_m\% = .40 - (.10 \times .60) = .40 - .06 = .34 = 34\%$$

When it is desired to know the reduction per cent on sales that may be taken on a given initial markup to yield a desired maintained markup per cent, the solution may be obtained readily by the use of the following equation:

$$\text{Reduction } \% = \frac{M_i\% - M_m\%}{\text{complement of } M_i\%}$$

Example 1: Initial markup is 40 per cent and desired maintained markup is 34 per cent. Find the reduction (markdowns plus shortages) per cent on sales that may be taken.

Complement of initial markup per cent = 100% − 40% = 60%

$$\text{Reduction } \% = \frac{.40 - .34}{.60} = \frac{.06}{.60} = .10 = 10\%$$

Example 2: Initial markup is 35 per cent, and desired maintained markup is 29.15 per cent. Find the per cent of reduction on sales that may be taken.

Complement of initial markup per cent = 100% − 35% = 65%

$$\text{Reduction } \% = \frac{.35 - .2915}{.65} = \frac{.0585}{.65} = .09 = 9\%$$

EXERCISE 5

In solving, find all per cents to nearest hundredths.

1. A buyer reduces 100 coats from $27.50 to $19.75 for a sale. After the sale, the 40 coats remaining are marked back to the original price and sold at $27.50. Find (*a*) the markdown cancellation in dollars and (*b*) the net markdown per cent.
2. A buyer marks down 260 robes from $10 to $7.50 for a sale during which 145 robes are sold at the reduced price. Those remaining after the sale are re-marked at the original price of $10. Two months later, 39 robes remaining are priced for clearance and sold at $5.95. What were the net markdowns (*a*) in dollars and (*b*) in per cent?
3. A special purchase of 60 lamps that would have been marked regularly at $12.50 were priced at $9.95 for an anniversary sale. After the sale the 21 lamps that remained were re-marked and sold at their regular price. Find (*a*) the additional markup in dollars and (*b*) the net additional markup per cent.
4. Of a group of 108 sweaters sale-priced at $6.75, 84 were sold and the remainder marked up to $8.75. Two months later, eight sweaters still in stock were reduced to $7.50 and sold. Find (*a*) the additional markup cancellation in dollars and (*b*) the net additional markup per cent.
5. Twenty dozen pairs of wool socks were specially priced at $1.50 per pair. One hundred sixty pairs were sold and the remainder marked up to $2.00. At a later date, 30 pairs remaining in stock were reduced to $.65 and sold in a month-end clearance. Find (*a*) the net additional markup per cent and (*b*) the net markdown per cent.
6. If the initial markup was 33 per cent, markdowns are 5.5 per cent, and shortages are .5 per cent, what is the maintained markup per cent?
7. In the men's furnishing department, the average initial markup for the season has been 38.5 per cent. What is the maximum markdown per cent that can be taken in order to end the season with a desired maintained markup of 35 per cent?
8. The initial markup on a group of sweaters was $371, equaling 35 per cent. If a maintained markup of 29.8 per cent was desired on the sweaters, find the maximum markdown that could be made (*a*) in per cent and (*b*) in dollars.

UNIT 6. Retail Operating Statements[1]

In business, the primary purpose of an operating statement is to show the profit or loss for a given period of time.

[1] See operating statement of the Carter Clothing Store on pp. 330–331 for a complete operating statement and a summary of the methods of computing the various items in dollars and in per cents.

In mercantile establishments, if there is to be a profit, it is apparent that sales must be in excess of cost of the merchandise plus the expenses of operating. If sales are less than merchandise cost plus operating expenses, then the store will have operated at a loss. The equation is

$$\text{Profit or loss} = \text{sales} - (\text{cost of goods sold} + \text{expenses})$$

This equation may be restated as follows:

$$\text{Sales} = \text{cost of goods sold} + \text{expenses} + \text{profit (or} - \text{loss)}$$

In an operating statement, the main elements are (1) net sales, (2) cost of goods sold, (3) gross margin, (4) expenses, (5) operating profit or loss.

Example:

ABBOTT SPECIALTY STORE

Operating Statement for Year Ending Jan. 31, 19—

Gross sales	$27,500	
Less sales returns and allowances	−3,500	
Net sales		$24,000
Less cost of goods sold		−17,500
Gross margin		$ 6,500
Less expenses		− 4,200
Operating profit		$ 2,300

Net sales represent the actual dollars of income. *Gross sales* less merchandise returns, allowances to customers, and any discounts granted to customers equal net sales.

Example: If gross sales are $102,673.50, merchandise returns $8,674.20, customer allowances $975.38, and discounts granted to customers $1,238.14, what are net sales?

Gross sales		$102,673.50
Less:		
Merchandise returns	$8,674.20	
Customer allowances	975.38	
Customer discounts allowed	1,238.14	
		−10,887.72
Net sales		$ 91,785.78

Cost of goods sold is the sum of the beginning inventory at cost plus billed cost of purchases plus freight or express in, less the cash discounts earned on purchases, plus workroom or alteration costs, less final inventory at cost.

Example: If the beginning inventory is $42,682.34 at cost, purchases $75,614 at billed cost with an average earned cash discount of 2 per cent from vendors, freight in $3,842, alteration costs $1,000, and final inventory $38,675.53 at cost, what is the cost of goods sold?

Beginning inventory		$ 42,682.34
Plus net cost of purchases:		
Net purchases	$75,614.00	
Freight in	3,842.00	
Gross cost of purchases	$79,456.00	
Less 2% of net purchases	−1,512.28	
Net cost of purchases		77,943.72
Plus alteration costs		1,000.00
Merchandise available for sale		$121,626.06
Less ending inventory		−38,675.53
Cost of goods sold		$ 82,950.53

Gross margin (or gross profit) is the difference between net sales and cost of goods sold. It is also the sum of the expenses plus operating profit or minus operating loss.

Example: If net sales are $32,398 and cost of goods sold is $24,865, what is the gross margin?

Net sales	$32,398
Less cost of goods sold	−24,865
Gross margin	$ 7,533

Expenses are the cost of operating the business and must be paid out of gross margin. If they exceed the gross margin, there is an operating loss; if they are less than the gross margin, there is an operating profit.

Operating profit or loss is the remainder after expenses have been subtracted (or paid for) from the gross margin.

Example 1: If expenses are $8,534 and gross margin is $9,096, what is the operating profit or loss?

Gross margin	$9,096
Less expenses	−8,534
Operating profit	$ 562

Example 2: If expenses are $5,852 and operating loss is $938, what is the gross margin?

Expenses	$5,852
Less operating loss	−938
Gross margin	$4,914

EXERCISE 6

1. If gross sales are $129,672.50, merchandise returns $7,342.14, customer allowances $1,145.80, and cash discounts granted customers $1,678.57, what are net sales?

2. Customer returns and allowances total $4,372.85, cash discounts granted customers are $1,131.40, and net sales are $85,617.19. What are gross sales?
3. Beginning inventory is $33,675.93 at cost, purchases are $83,740 at billed cost with an average earned discount of 3 per cent, freight in is $4,513.75, and final inventory is $29,723.10 at cost. What is the cost of goods sold?
4. Beginning inventory was $21,381.75 at cost; purchases $37,680 at billed cost with an average earned discount of 2.5 per cent; freight in $1,931.18; and cost of goods sold $42,371.82. What was the ending inventory at cost?
5. Net sales are $72,541.73, purchases are $45,672 at billed cost with an average earned discount from vendors of 1.5 per cent, freight in is $2,781.50, workroom and alteration costs are $1,381.93, beginning inventory at cost is $21,678.43, and ending inventory at cost is $19,842.37. What is the gross margin in dollars?
6. Gross sales are $25,619.13; customer returns, allowances, and discounts $2,791.32; beginning inventory at cost $6,348.90; purchases at billed cost $12,585; freight in $932.45; workroom cost $351.85; cash discounts earned from vendors average 2 per cent; and ending inventory at cost $7,535.25. What is the gross margin in dollars?
7. Gross sales are $32,529.38, customer returns and allowances are $3,769, total merchandise available for sale is $42,173 at cost, ending inventory at cost is $25,630.75, and expenses are $10,971.10. What is the operating profit or loss in dollars?
8. Gross sales are $135,672, returns and allowances are $15,680, cash discounts granted customers are $2,785, beginning inventory at cost is $43,732, workroom and alteration costs are $3,576, cash discounts earned from vendors are $4,381, freight in is $5,673, purchases at billed cost are $78,362, ending inventory at cost is $35,688, and expenses are $20,605. What is the operating profit or loss in dollars?

UNIT 7. Average Inventory and Stock Turnover

The speed with which the average merchandise in a department or store is sold is a common criterion used by retailers to determine efficiency of operations.

If the stock is maintained at a minimum, less capital is required to operate the department or store, and the risk of carrying unseasonable merchandise that will require a high per cent of markdown is greatly reduced.

Average inventory is determined by dividing the sum of the inventories by the number of times the inventory has been taken. Thus if inventory

An Operating Statement Showing How Each Item is Computed

CARTER CLOTHING STORE

Operating Statement, Year Ending Jan. 31, 19—

		Cost		*Per cents of net sales*	*Retail*	
Gross sales			$113,670	113.67		
Deduct returned sales and allowances			13,670	13.67		(12.03% of gross sales)
Net sales			$100,000	100.00		
Deduct merchandise sold:						
Beginning inventory		$16,128			$ 24,200	
Add net delivered cost of purchases:						
Purchases	$66,768					
Deduct returns and allowances	2,960					
Net purchases	$63,808					
Add freight and cartage in	4,736					
Gross cost of purchases	$68,544				126,000	
Less earned cash discounts	2,500					
Net delivered cost of purchases		66,044				
Add alteration costs		1,396		1.40	1,000	(Add additional markup)
Total goods available for sale		$83,568			$151,200	
Deduct ending inventory		23,520			42,000	
Less cost of goods sold			60,048		$109,200	(Deductions)
Gross margin			$ 39,952	39.95	100,000	(Net sales)
					$ 9,200	(This is the sum of the net markdowns and shortages)
Deduct expenses:						
Administration		$ 5,650		5.65		
Occupancy		8,930		8.93		
Publicity		4,300		4.30		
Buying		4,120		4.12		
Selling		7,300		7.30		
Delivery		800		.80		
Total expenses			31,100	31.10		
Operating profit			$ 8,852	8.85		

Computing Certain Frequently Used Per Cents

Markup of beginning inventory $= \dfrac{\$24,200 - \$16,128}{\$24,200} = 33.36\%$ (This is cumulative markup per cent of 33.3553719% at end of preceding year)

Markup on purchases (gross cost) $= \dfrac{\$126,000 - \$68,544}{\$126,000} = 45.60\%$

Earned cash discount on purchases (net) $= \dfrac{\$2,500}{\$63,808} = 3.92\%$

Additional markup $= \dfrac{\$1,000}{\$100,000} = 1.00\%$ (Note that additional markup is not canceled by markdowns. It is included in cumulative markup base)

Net markdowns (from markdown records) $= \dfrac{\$8,000}{\$100,000} = 8.00\%$

Shortages ($9,200 − $8,000 = $1,200) $= \dfrac{\$1,200}{\$100,000} = 1.20\%$

(Reductions totaling $9,200 are 9.20% of net sales and are deductions from stock in addition to net sales)

Cumulative markup $= \dfrac{\$151,200 - (\$16,128 + \$68,544)}{\$151,200} = 44.00\%$ (Note that $151,200 includes additional markup of $1,000)

Maintained markup $= \dfrac{\$39,952 - \$2,500 + \$1,396}{\$100,000} = 38.85\%$ (If there were neither earned cash discounts on purchases nor alteration costs, M_m would equal M_g)

Computing Average Inventory and Stock Turnover

Average inventory at retail $= \dfrac{\$24,200 + \$42,000}{2} = \$33,100$

Stock turnover at retail $= \dfrac{\$100,000}{\$33,100} = 3.02$ times (Stock turnover expressed as a decimal, not as a per cent)

Average inventory at cost $= \dfrac{\$16,128 + \$23,520}{2} = \$19,824$

Stock turnover at cost $= \dfrac{\$60,048}{\$19,824} = 3.03$ times (Stock turnover expressed as a decimal, not as a per cent)

is taken for 1 month, that is, on the first and the last days of the month, the average inventory is found by dividing the sum of the two inventories by 2.

If the average inventory is to be found for 12 months, with inventories taken on the first day of each month and the final day of the last month, the average inventory is obtained by dividing the sum of the inventories by 13, the number of times inventory has been taken. The formula is

$$\text{Average inventory} = \frac{\text{sum of the inventories}}{\text{number of inventories taken}}$$

Example 1: Inventory at retail in a shoe department was \$12,600 on Jan. 1 and \$14,732 on Jan. 31. What was the average inventory?

$$\text{Average inventory at retail} = \frac{\$12{,}600 + \$14{,}732}{2} = \$13{,}666$$

Example 2: Inventory at cost in the lingerie department was \$6,076 on Apr. 1, \$5,031.50 on May 1, \$5,256.50 on June 1, and \$5,805 on June 30. What was the average inventory at cost for the 3-month period?

$$\text{Av. inv. at cost} = \frac{\$6{,}076 + \$5{,}031.50 + \$5{,}256.50 + \$5{,}805}{4} = \$5{,}542.25$$

The *rate of stock turnover* (or stock turn) indicates the number of times the average stock has been sold for a given period. Usually this period of time is for a year.

The rate of stock turnover may be determined at retail or at cost by the following formulas:

$$\text{Stock turnover at retail} = \frac{\text{sales}}{\text{average inventory at retail}}$$

$$\text{Stock turnover at cost} = \frac{\text{cost of goods sold}}{\text{average inventory at cost}}$$

Example: At retail. If sales are \$86,234 and average inventory is \$22,560 at retail, what is the rate of stock turnover?

$$\text{Stock turnover at retail} = \frac{\$86{,}234}{\$22{,}560} = 3.82$$

Example: At cost. If cost of goods sold is \$28,672 and average inventory at cost is \$11,593, what is the rate of stock turnover?

$$\text{Stock turnover at cost} = \frac{\$28{,}672}{\$11{,}593} = 2.47$$

Stock turnover at retail or at cost will be the same only if there are neither markdowns nor shortages. The greatest use of the rate of stock turnover is to compare department to department or store to store.

Provided the same method is used, the comparative figures will express a true relationship.

Since the accepted store practice is to use the retail method rather than the cost method, the retail method is preferred. The fact that it is also slightly more conservative makes it more desirable from the viewpoint of most accountants.

Example: Sales in a store are \$125,681. Inventory Jan. 1 is \$46,634 at retail; inventory on June 30 is \$28,260 at cost. The cumulative markup is 40 per cent. What is the rate of stock turnover for the 6-month period at retail?

$$\text{Inventory at retail June 30} = \frac{\$28{,}260}{.60} = \$47{,}100$$

$$\text{Average inventory} = \frac{\$46{,}634 + \$47{,}100}{2} = \$46{,}867$$

$$\text{Stock turnover at retail} = \frac{\$125{,}681}{\$46{,}867} = 2.68$$

EXERCISE 7

1. Stock at retail in a shoe department was as follows: July 1, \$6,782; Aug. 1, \$7,324; Sept. 1, \$7,765; and Sept. 30, \$7,537. What was the average inventory at retail?
2. Cost valuation of inventories in a men's clothing shop was as follows: \$10,342 on Jan. 1; \$13,678 on Apr. 1; \$11,349 on July 1; \$15,621 on Oct. 1; and \$10,525 on Dec. 31. What was the average inventory at cost?
3. Inventory on June 1 was \$16,380 at retail, with a cumulative markup of 42 per cent. Inventory on June 30 was \$14,325 at retail with a cumulative markup of 41 per cent. What was average inventory (*a*) at retail and (*b*) at cost?
4. Sales were \$39,545 and average inventory at retail was \$15,260. What was the rate of stock turnover at retail, to nearest hundredths?
5. Cost of goods sold was \$23,268 and average inventory at cost was \$8,561. What was the rate of stock turnover at cost, to nearest hundredths?
6. Sales for the quarter were \$129,287. Inventory at retail was as follows: Jan. 1, \$35,672; Feb. 1, \$40,923; Mar. 1, \$43,754; and Mar. 31, \$47,893. What was the rate of stock turnover at retail for the quarter, to nearest hundredths?
7. Cost of goods sold for the quarter was \$63,960. Inventory at cost was as follows: July 1, \$29,725; Aug. 1, \$32,330; Sept. 1, \$37,825; and Sept. 30, \$40,028. What was the rate of stock turnover at cost for the period, to nearest hundredths?
8. In solving this problem, it is suggested that you refer to the operating statement of the Carter Clothing Store, pages 330–331. Find (*a*) reductions (markdowns + shortages) in dollars and as a per cent of net sales, (*b*) markup per cent of beginning inventory, (*c*) markup per cent on gross cost of purchases, (*d*) cumulative markup per cent (compute it or its complement to eight

decimal places in determining ending inventory at cost), (*e*) gross margin in dollars and as a per cent of net sales, (*f*) maintained markup per cent, (*g*) average inventory at retail, (*h*) average inventory at cost, (*i*) stock turnover at retail, and (*j*) stock turnover at cost. (Give all answers to nearest hundredths.)

		Cost	*Retail*	
Beginning inventory		$24,800	$35,000	
Purchases gross	$66,000		98,600	
Less earned cash discounts	2,640			
Net purchases		......		
			2,400	Net additional markup
Plus alteration costs		1,700		
Total goods available		$......	$......	
Less ending inventory		......	42,000	
Cost of goods sold		$......	$......	Deductions = { net sales $85,000; reductions .... }

UNIT 8. Per Cent of Return on Investment; Stock Sales Ratio; Open-to-buy

Computing Per Cent of Return on Investment. A prime motive in operating most retail establishments, as well as other businesses, is to earn as large a profit as possible on the money invested. To understand further some of the problems that confront the merchant and the decisions that he must make correctly if he is to earn the maximum profit on his investment, consider the following equations:

(1) Profit = sales × per cent of profit on sales

$$(a)\ \text{Sales} = \frac{\text{profit}}{\text{per cent of profit on sales}}$$

$$(b)\ \text{Per cent of profit on sales} = \frac{\text{profit}}{\text{sales}}$$

$$(2)\ \text{Capital turnover} = \frac{\text{sales}}{\text{investment}}$$

(*a*) Sales = investment × capital turnover

$$(b)\ \text{Investment} = \frac{\text{sales}}{\text{capital turnover}}$$

The basic equation is

$$(3)\ \text{Per cent return on investment} = \frac{\text{profit}}{\text{investment}}$$

$$(a)\ \text{Profit} = \text{investment} \times \text{per cent return on investment}$$

$$(b)\ \text{Investment} = \frac{\text{profit}}{\text{per cent return on investment}}$$

A higher rate of stock turnover will result in a larger sales volume even though there is no increase in investment (in inventory). If the per cent of profit on sales remains constant, the net result will be a greater earning per dollar invested.

A higher rate of stock turnover with constant sales volume and per cent of profit on sales will result in a smaller required investment (in inventory) and thus in a greater earning per dollar invested.

Finally, a higher per cent of profit on sales with constant sales, stock turnover, and investment will result in a greater earning per dollar invested.

Example: Sales of a store are \$100,000, net merchandise profit 6 per cent and capital investment \$25,000. Find (*a*) dollar profit, (*b*) capital turnover, and (*c*) per cent of return on investment.

$$(a)\ \text{Profit} = \$100{,}000 \times .06 = \$6{,}000$$

$$(b)\ \text{Capital turnover} = \frac{100{,}000}{25{,}000} = 4$$

$$(c)\ \text{Per cent return on investment} = \frac{6{,}000}{25{,}000} = .24 = 24\%$$

If, in the example, turnover were increased to 5, the results would be (*a*) sales, \$25,000 × 5 = \$125,000; profit, \$125,000 × .06 = \$7,500; and per cent return on investment, 7,500 ÷ 25,000 = 30 per cent; or (*b*) if sales remained constant, then the investment would be reduced to \$100,000 ÷ 5 = \$20,000; profit constant at \$6,000; and per cent of return on investment, 6,000 ÷ 20,000 = 30 per cent.

The conclusions made in the preceding example were based on the assumption that the rate of profit on sales would remain constant. In actual practice, this is rarely true. Thus a major merchandising problem arises from the tendency of the rate of profit to decrease with increase in stock turnover, since the increase is often brought about by lower prices or greater promotion expenses, or both. When inventory is purposely reduced in order to increase the rate of stock turnover, the profit rate tends to rise, but sales frequently will be less, because a lower inventory usually means less selection and consequent loss of sales. It is the problem of the merchant to determine an optimum rate of turnover for his business that will provide him with the most profitable dollar return.

Computing Stock Sales Ratios. The successful management of a retail store necessitates not only careful estimation of future sales but also determination of the minimum inventories required to make planned future sales an accomplished fact. Estimates are usually made for each month, and the relationship between the beginning inventory (B.I.) and the planned sales for a particular month is known as the *stock sales ratio.*

Stock sales ratio is computed by dividing the beginning of the month (B.O.M.) inventory *at retail* by the planned sales for the month.

$$\text{Stock sales ratio} = \frac{\text{B.O.M. inventory}}{\text{planned sales}}$$

It is apparent that the larger the planned sales and the smaller the B.O.M. inventory, the smaller will be the stock sales ratio. Unlike stock turnover, in which a high ratio is ordinarily desirable, stock sales ratio is preferably as low as possible without causing a loss in sales because of insufficient inventories of goods. Estimations of future business conditions together with records of past experience enable the retailer to determine, for each month of the year, the stock sales ratio that will probably prove most profitable.

From the preceding equation, the following may be derived:

$$(a)\quad \text{B.O.M. inventory} = \text{planned sales} \times \text{stock sales ratio}$$

$$(b)\quad \text{Planned sales} = \frac{\text{B.O.M. inventory}}{\text{stock sales ratio}}$$

Example 1: Planned sales for November are $28,000, and planned retail stock on Nov. 1 is $43,400. Find B.O.M. stock sales ratio.

$$\text{Stock sales ratio} = \frac{43{,}400}{28{,}000} = 1.55$$

Example 2: Planned sales for June are $15,000 and the planned B.O.M. stock sales ratio is 2.5. What should be the B.O.M. stock on June 1?

$$\text{B.O.M. inventory} = \$15{,}000 \times 2.5 = \$37{,}500$$

Example 3: Planned B.O.M. inventory for April is $32,000. What are the planned sales for April if the desired stock sales ratio is .4?

$$\text{Planned sales} = \frac{\$32{,}000}{.4} = \$80{,}000$$

Computing Open-to-buy. Profits in retailing are determined largely by the maintenance of a proper balance between inventories and sales. As you know, stock turnover and stock sales ratios are helpful guides in making a merchandise plan. However, actual sales and stock do vary from plan, and these variances necessitate adjustments in future purchases in order to keep the desired ratio between stock and sales.

The original monthly appropriations for purchases must be readjusted constantly with fluctuations in sales, for an increase in sales over planned figures results in a lowered inventory on hand, while a decrease in sales results in a larger than planned inventory.

Actual purchases at the end of any period of time may be found as follows:

$$\text{Purchases} = (\text{ending inventory} + \text{sales} + \text{markdowns}) - (\text{beginning inventory} + \text{purchases on order})$$

Open-to-buy (O.T.B.), or planned purchases for a period of time to follow, is determined as follows:

$$\text{O.T.B.} = (\text{planned ending inventory} + \text{planned sales} + \text{planned markdowns}) - (\text{beginning inventory} + \text{purchases on order})$$

Example 1: Find O.T.B. if planned ending inventory is \$12,000, planned sales \$25,000, planned markdowns \$1,000, beginning inventory \$9,000, and purchases on order \$5,000.

$$\begin{aligned} \text{O.T.B.} &= (\$12{,}000 + \$25{,}000 + \$1{,}000) - (\$9{,}000 + \$5{,}000) \\ &= \$38{,}000 - \$14{,}000 = \$24{,}000 \end{aligned}$$

Note that all of the figures in the above example and O.T.B. are at retail. To determine planned purchases at cost, multiply O.T.B. at retail by the decimal complement of the planned initial markup per cent on purchases. Thus, in this example, if the planned markup on purchases were 40 per cent, planned purchases at cost would be

$$\$24{,}000 \times .60 = \$14{,}400$$

The use of the stock sales ratio in determining open-to-buy is made apparent in the following:

Example 2: Planned sales for a department with an initial markup of 35 per cent are \$10,000 for May and \$12,000 for June. If the desired B.O.M. stock-sales ratio for May is 2 and for June is 1.5, what will be the May O.T.B. at cost?

B.O.M. stock for May: \$10,000 × 2	=	\$20,000
B.O.M. stock for June: \$12,000 × 1.5	=	\$18,000
Therefore E.O.M. stock for May		\$18,000
Plus planned sales for May	+	10,000
		\$28,000
Deduct B.O.M. stock for May	−	20,000
May O.T.B. at retail		\$ 8,000

Or stated as an equation:

$$\text{May O.T.B. at retail} = (\$18{,}000 + \$10{,}000) - \$20{,}000 = \$8{,}000$$

If initial markup = 35%, then cost = 65% of O.T.B. at retail

May O.T.B. at cost = $8,000 × .65 = $5,200

Purchases on order and planned markdowns are not included in this illustration. However, any purchases on order (at retail) would be added to the B.O.M. stock for May, and any planned markdowns would be added to planned sales for May. Note that B.O.M. stock for any month is the E.O.M. stock (or ending inventory) for the preceding month. Thus in Example 2, B.O.M. stock for June is also the ending inventory for May.

Example 3: Same problem as Example 2 but with purchases on order at retail of $2,500 and planned markdowns for May of $600.

B.O.M. stock for May:	$10,000 × 2 = $20,000	
Plus purchases on order:	+ 2,500 =	$22,500
B.O.M. stock for June:	$12,000 × 1.5	= $18,000
Therefore E.O.M. stock for May		$18,000
Plus: planned sales for May	$10,000	
planned markdowns for May	+ 600 =	+ 10,600
		$28,600
Deduct B.O.M. stock for May plus purchases on order		− 22,500
May O.T.B. at retail		$ 6,100

May O.T.B. at cost: $6,100 × .65 = $3,965

EXERCISE 8

Unless stipulated otherwise, *given figures are at retail.*

1. A store's sales are $75,000, net merchandise profit 0.5 per cent, capital turnover five times on an investment of $15,000. Find (*a*) per cent of return on the investment. If sales and profit in dollars remained constant and capital turnover was reduced to 3, find (*b*) the amount of the investment and (*c*) the per cent of return on the investment. If the investment and rate of profit remained constant and the capital turnover was 6, find (*d*) the sales and (*e*) the per cent of return on the investment.
2. Planned sales for May are $35,750; planned retail stock on May 1 is $22,675. Find the planned B.O.M. stock sales ratio, to nearest hundredths.
3. Planned sales for November are $68,400; planned B.O.M. stock sales ratio is 1.75. What should be the B.O.M. stock on Nov. 1?
4. Planned stock for June 1 is $47,300. If the desired stock sales ratio is 0.5, what are the planned sales for June?
5. If a stock sales ratio of 1.3 for March is desired and if planned B.O.M. stock for March is $29,640, what are the planned sales for March?
6. If planned sales for August are $18,650 and the desired B.O.M. stock sales ratio is 0.8, what should be the planned B.O.M. stock for August?

7. Beginning inventory is $24,200, planned ending inventory is $21,600, planned sales are $38,500, planned markdowns are 9 per cent, and purchases on order are $7,800. What is the O.T.B. at retail?
8. What is the O.T.B. for May at cost if planned initial markup on purchases is 36 per cent, beginning inventory is $7,452, planned sales are $8,500, planned markdowns are $530, purchases on order at retail are $1,260, and planned ending inventory is $7,100?
9. Planned sales are $128,000, planned markdowns are 12.4 per cent, planned ending inventory is $86,800, purchases on order at retail are $11,684, and beginning inventory is $71,492. What is the O.T.B. at cost if planned initial markup on purchases is 43.5 per cent?
10. Planned sales for a department with an initial markup of 40.6 per cent is $19,000 for March and $23,000 for April. The desired stock sales ratio for March is 1.3 and for April is 1.8. What will be the March O.T.B. (*a*) at retail and (*b*) at cost?
11. A department with an initial markup of 46 per cent has planned sales of $9,800 for July and $11,500 for August. Purchases on order at retail on July 1 are $1,920, and planned markdowns are 6.5 per cent of planned July sales. The desired B.O.M. stock sales ratio is 0.95 for July and 0.82 for August. Find O.T.B. for July (*a*) at retail and (*b*) at cost.

CHAPTER X

DISTRIBUTION OF OWNERSHIP AND PROFITS

UNIT 1. Determination of Net Worth and Distribution of Ownership

The ownership of business enterprises may be classified in three general groupings: (1) sole proprietorships, (2) partnerships, and (3) corporations.

A business in which a single individual supplies all the capital, assumes all the liabilities, and receives all the profits or bears all the losses is known as a *sole proprietorship* or as an *individual enterprise.* The limitation in capital and management that could be supplied by one individual led to the formation of a type of business enterprise known as a partnership.

A business owned by two or more individuals who together supply the capital, assume jointly and separately all the liabilities, and share in the profits and losses is known as a *partnership.* Unless formed in states where liability may be limited, partnerships place complete responsibility for the acts and debts of the partnership upon each partner; that is, the partners may be held responsible separately or jointly for all liabilities incurred by the partnership. Limitation of capital, legal liabilities for debt, dissolution through death, and the difficulties that often arose in withdrawing from a partnership without excessive loss led to the creation of a third form of business organization known as a corporation.

A business organization authorized by law to act as a single entity conducting an enterprise with the ownership consisting of transferable shares (stock) is known as a *corporation.* Liability is limited usually to what has been invested in the corporation by the shareholders, and neither creditors nor the corporation itself may make additional assessments on the shareholders. Earnings belong to the shareholders in the ratio that their shares bear to the total outstanding shares of the same class of stock (e.g., preferred, class A common, class B common, etc.).

DETERMINATION OF NET WORTH

The net worth of any form of business enterprise may be found by subtracting the sum of its liabilities (amounts owed) from the sum of its assets (gross amounts owned).

$$\textit{Net worth} = \textit{assets} - \textit{liabilities}$$

Example: The Smith Drug Store is a sole proprietorship with the following assets: building and land valued at $36,000, furniture and fixtures valued at $12,000, merchandise at cost $23,500, accounts receivable (money owed by customers) of $3,675, and cash $3,150. Liabilities are: mortgage owed on the building and land of $14,250, a note owed to the bank for $1,820, and accounts payable (money owed to suppliers) of $6,085. Find the net worth of the Smith Drug Store.

Assets		*Liabilities*	
Cash	$ 3,150	Note to bank	$ 1,820
Merchandise	23,500	Accounts payable	6,085
Accounts receivable	3,675	Mortgage	14,250
Furniture and fixtures	12,000		
Building and land	36,000		
Total assets	$78,325	Total liabilities	$22,155

$$\text{Net worth} = \$78{,}325 - \$22{,}155 = \$56{,}170$$

DISTRIBUTION OF OWNERSHIP

In a sole proprietorship, the entire net worth of the business belongs to the individual owner.

In a partnership, all partners are considered equal owners of the business in the absence of an agreement, usually written, that divides the net worth of the business in some other manner among the partners.

In a corporation, the net worth of the business belongs to the stockholders in the ratio that each stockholder's shares bear to the total number of shares issued.

Example 1: In the preceding example of the Smith Drug Store, what is the net worth belonging to Mr. Harvey Smith, owner?

Since this is a sole proprietorship, the entire net worth of $56,170 belongs to Mr. Harvey Smith, owner.

Example 2: Mr. Hill and Mr. Latham enter into a partnership investing $30,000 and $15,000, respectively. Four years later the partnership is sold for $39,000. How much does each partner receive?

Since there is no agreement otherwise, each partner is an equal partner and each receives

$$\frac{\$39{,}000}{2} = \$19{,}500$$

Example 3: If in Example 2 there had been a written agreement that in the event of dissolution of the partnership each partner should receive a share of the net worth (selling price) in the ratio that his original investment bore to the total original investment of the partners, what would each partner receive?

Investment by Mr. Hill	=	$30,000
Investment by Mr. Latham	=	15,000
Total investment	=	$45,000

$$\text{Mr. Hill's share} = \frac{30{,}000}{45{,}000} \times \$39{,}000 = \$26{,}000$$

$$\text{Mr. Latham's share} = \frac{15{,}000}{45{,}000} \times \$39{,}000 = \$13{,}000$$

Example 4: The Universal Corporation with 500,000 issued shares of stock had a net worth of $3,200,000. Mr. Brugh owned 200 shares of stock. What was Mr. Brugh's share of the net worth of the company?

$$\frac{200}{500{,}000} \times \$3{,}200{,}000 = \$1{,}280$$

EXERCISE 1

A. Find the missing quantities in the following:

	Net worth	=	*assets*	−	*liabilities*		*Net worth*	=	*assets*	−	*liabilities*
1.	$____	=	$ 8,670	−	$ 5,371	**2.**	$ 31,380	=	$ 76,740	−	$____
3.	4,811	=	____	−	2,399	**4.**	____	=	14,658	−	14,308
5.	623	=	1,151	−	____	**6.**	12,392	=	____	−	9,085

B. Solve the following:

1. Mr. Hopkins owns a drugstore. The building is valued at $15,000, fixtures are valued at $2,700, and the stock at cost is $5,360. There is a $4,600 mortgage on the building, $1,735 is owed on the fixtures, a note of $300 is owed to the bank, and $675 is owed to manufacturers and wholesalers. What is the net worth of Mr. Hopkins's proprietorship in the drugstore and building?
2. Mr. Crowell is the sole owner of a small manufacturing concern. The building and land, valued at $35,000, have a $13,000 mortgage. The machinery and equipment are valued at $9,300; the inventory includes $2,100 worth of raw materials at cost and $5,850 worth of finished products at cost; and accounts receivable (money owed by customers) total $1,720. Accounts payable (money owed to suppliers) total $3,640, and the bank holds Mr. Crowell's note for $1,000. What is Mr. Crowell's proprietorship (net worth) in the manufacturing company?
3. Mr. Jones, Mr. Smith, and Mr. Brown formed a partnership with investments of $3,600, $4,200, and $6,500, respectively. After 3 years of operation, the partnership had a net worth of $12,600. What was the value of each partner's share in the business if it was agreed that each partner's share should be in the ratio that his original investment bore to the total investment of the partners?
4. Mr. Lombard, Mr. Flood, Mr. Green, and Mr. Thompson formed a partnership with investments of $1,800, $2,400, $1,500, and $1,200, respectively, each partner's share in the ownership to be in the ratio that his original investment

bore to the total investment of the partners. Mr. Green died 10 years later, automatically dissolving the partnership. At that time, the capital worth (net worth) of the partnership was $33,000. What share in the net worth belonged to the estate of Mr. Green, to Mr. Lombard, to Mr. Flood, and to Mr. Thompson?

5. Mr. Ball, Mr. Hanson, and Mr. Magee formed a partnership with the agreement that each partner's share in the ownership should be in the ratio that his original investment bore to the total investment of the partners and also that, if any one of the partners withdrew, the remaining partners were privileged to purchase the withdrawing partner's share in such amount that the remaining partners' shares would be equal. The original investments were $5,000, $6,000, and $7,500, respectively. After 2 years, Mr. Ball decided to withdraw. Assets at that time were $39,600 and liabilities $8,400. Mr. Hanson and Mr. Magee purchased Mr. Ball's share in amounts according to the agreement, which made them equal owners of the business. How much did Mr. Ball receive (*a*) from Mr. Hanson, (*b*) from Mr. Magee?
6. The Madden Corporation with 600,000 issued shares of stock had a net worth of $4,800,000. Mr. Flood owned 260 shares of stock. What was his share of the net worth of the company?
7. The Mason Company with 36,000 issued shares of stock had assets of $1,220-, 000 and liabilities of $878,000. Mr. Ancker owned 335 shares. Find (*a*) the net worth of the company and (*b*) the net worth of Mr. Ancker's shares.
8. The Reidy Corporation had a net worth of $4,842,600. Of this sum, first claim to ownership of the net worth was reserved for the preferred stock in an amount of $1,263,850. The balance of the net worth belonged to 57,260 shares of common stock of which Mr. Hillsman owned 225 shares. What was the net worth of Mr. Hillsman's shares of common stock?

UNIT 2. Distribution of Profit and Loss in a Partnership

Unless the partnership contract specifies otherwise, profits and losses are shared equally by the partners, regardless of how disproportionate may be the capital invested or the time or the value of the services rendered by the individual partners.

The division of future profits or losses is usually agreed upon at the time of formation of the partnership, and any method of distribution mutually satisfactory to the partners may be used. Several of the more common methods are illustrated in the following examples:

Example 1: Shared equally. Foster and Seldon enter into a partnership, investing $6,000 and $4,000, respectively. It is agreed in writing that they are to be equal partners. The first year they lose \$3,000, the second year they gain \$6,500. Find each partner's share of gain or loss (*a*) the first year and (*b*) the second year.

Since they are to share gains and losses equally:

(*a*) $\frac{\$3,000}{2} = \$1,500$ Loss by each partner

(*b*) $\frac{\$6,500}{2} = \$3,250$ Gain by each partner

Example 2: According to original investment. A and B enter into a partnership, investing \$5,000 and \$4,000, respectively. Profits are to be shared in the ratio that each partner's original investment bears to the total original capital. Profits are \$2,250 for the first year and \$3,375 for the second year. A withdraws his entire share of the profits both years. B withdraws his share of the profits only in the second year. Find the profit to which each partner is entitled (*a*) the first year and (*b*) the second year.

(*a*) Original capital = \$5,000 + \$4,000 = \$9,000

$$\text{A's share} = \frac{5,000}{9,000} \times \$2,250 = \$1,250$$

$$\text{B's share} = \frac{4,000}{9,000} \times \$2,250 = \$1,000$$

(*b*) Notice that B's ratio the second year remains the same and does not equal A's, even though his total investment is then \$4,000 + \$1,000, equivalent to A's original investment of \$5,000.

$$\text{A's share} = \frac{5,000}{9,000} \times \$3,375 = \$1,875$$

$$\text{B's share} = \frac{4,000}{9,000} \times \$3,375 = \$1,500$$

Example 3: According to investment at beginning of each year. A and B enter into a partnership, investing \$8,000 and \$6,000, respectively. Profits and losses are to be shared in the ratio that each partner's investment at the beginning of each year bears to the total investment at that time. Profits the first year are \$10,500, A withdrawing his entire share, B withdrawing only \$1,500. Profits the second year are \$3,400, each partner withdrawing his full share. The third year a loss of \$2,550 occurs. Find the profit or loss of each partner (*a*) the first year, (*b*) the second year, and (*c*) the third year.

(*a*) 1st year investment = \$8,000 + \$6,000 = \$14,000

$$\text{A's share} = \frac{8,000}{14,000} \times \$10,500 = \$6,000$$

$$\text{B's share} = \frac{6,000}{14,000} \times \$10,500 = \$4,500$$

(*b*) Since B withdraws only \$1,500, investing the remainder, or \$3,000: 2d year investment = \$8,000 + \$6,000 + \$3,000 = \$17,000

$$\text{A's share} = \frac{8{,}000}{17{,}000} \times \$3{,}400 = \$1{,}600$$

$$\text{B's share} = \frac{6{,}000 + 3{,}000}{17{,}000} \times \$3{,}400 = \frac{9{,}000}{17{,}000} \times \$3{,}400 = \$1{,}800$$

(*c*) Since each partner withdrew his entire share of the profits the second year, the share of each in the loss for the third year is in the same ratio as was the share of each in the profit for the second year:

$$\text{A's loss} = \frac{8{,}000}{17{,}000} \times \$2{,}550 = \$1{,}200$$

$$\text{B's loss} = \frac{9{,}000}{17{,}000} \times \$2{,}550 = \$1{,}350$$

Example 4: According to average investment. A and B enter into partnership, agreeing to share profits in ratio to their share in the average capital invested. A invests \$5,000 on Jan. 1, \$1,000 on Apr. 1, and \$3,000 on June 1. B invests \$6,000 on Jan. 1, deducts \$2,000 on Apr. 1, and invests \$4,000 on Sept. 1. If the profits for the calendar year are \$4,800, what is each partner's share?

Method a:

A invests:

\$5,000 for 12 mo.	=	\$60,000 for 1 mo.
1,000 for 9 mo.	=	9,000 for 1 mo.
3,000 for 7 mo.	=	21,000 for 1 mo.
		\$90,000 for 1 mo.

B invests:

\$6,000 for 12 mo.	=	\$72,000 for 1 mo.
4,000 for 4 mo.	=	16,000 for 1 mo.
		\$88,000 for 1 mo.
Less \$2,000 for 9 mo.	=	−18,000 for 1 mo.
		\$70,000 for 1 mo.

Total dollar-month investment of partners = \$90,000 + \$70,000 = \$160,000

$$\text{A's share} = \frac{90{,}000}{160{,}000} \times \$4{,}800 = \$2{,}700$$

$$\text{B's share} = \frac{70{,}000}{160{,}000} \times \$4{,}800 = \$2{,}100$$

Method b:

A invests:

\$5,000 for 3 mo.	=	\$15,000 for 1 mo.	
6,000 for 2 mo.	=	12,000 for 1 mo.	(\$5,000 + \$1,000 = \$6,000)
9,000 for 7 mo.	=	63,000 for 1 mo.	(\$6,000 + \$3,000 = \$9,000)
		\$90,000 for 1 mo.	

B invests:

$6,000 for 3 mo. = $18,000 for 1 mo.
4,000 for 5 mo. = 20,000 for 1 mo. ($6,000 − $2,000 = $4,000)
8,000 for 4 mo. = 32,000 for 1 mo. ($4,000 + $4,000 = $8,000)
$70,000 for 1 mo.

The solution is then obtained in the same manner as in method *a*.

Example 5: Shared equally with interest on his investment paid to each partner before division of profit or loss. A invests $10,000 and B $6,000 in a partnership. Interest at 6 per cent on his invested capital is to be paid each partner, the remaining profit or loss to be shared equally. Find each partner's share including interest on his investment if, before payment of interest, (*a*) profits the first year are $4,200 and (*b*) profits the second year are $400.

A's interest = $10,000 × .06 = $600
B's interest = $6,000 × .06 = $360
Total interest = $960

(*a*) Profit exceeds interest due. Therefore after payment of interest,

$4,200 − $960 = $3,240

the net profit to be divided.

$$\frac{\$3{,}240}{2} = \$1{,}620$$

A's share = $600 + $1,620 = $2,220
B's share = $360 + $1,620 = $1,980

(*b*) Profit is less than interest due. Therefore if interest is to be paid,

$960 − $400 = $560

the net loss to be divided.

$$\frac{\$560}{2} = \$280$$

A's share = $600 − $280 = $320
B's share = $360 − $280 = $ 80

As is obvious from these five examples, the number of ways by which profits in a partnership may be divided is almost unlimited. Combinations of these methods may be used, or entirely different arrangements may be made. The important point is that whatever method is used should be mutually decided and agreed upon in writing at the time the partnership is formed. Unless otherwise specified, it may be assumed that partners share equally in the ownership and in all profit or loss.

EXERCISE 2

1. Mr. Cate and Mr. Stout enter into a partnership, investing $8,000 and $6,000, respectively. Profits are to be shared in the ratio that each partner's original investment bears to the total original capital. Profits the first year are $3,600, the second year $4,500. Mr. Cate withdraws his entire share of profits both years, Mr. Stout withdrawing his share of profits only the second year. What is the profit earned by each partner (*a*) the first year, (*b*) the second year?
2. If profits in Problem 1 were shared equally, regardless of investment, what would each partner be entitled to receive as profits (*a*) the first year, (*b*) the second year?
3. If profits in Problem 1 were shared according to investment at the beginning of each year, what would each partner receive (*a*) the first year, (*b*) the second year?
4. If profits in the partnership formed in Problem 1 were shared equally with interest at 6 per cent on his total investment remaining in the partnership paid to each partner before division of profits, what would each partner be entitled to (*a*) the first year and (*b*) the second year if Mr. Stout withdraws only interest the first year and Mr. Cate withdraws both interest and profit the first year?
5. Mr. James and Mr. Evans enter into a partnership, investing $12,500 and $12,800, respectively. Profits or losses are to be shared in the ratio that each partner's investment at the beginning of each year bears to the total investment at that time. Profits the first year are $10,120, Mr. James withdrawing his full share and Mr. Evans only $2,920. The second year, a loss of $5,500 occurs. What is the profit or loss of each partner (*a*) the first year, and (*b*) the second year?
6. Mr. Hoge and Mr. Jensen enter into a partnership, agreeing to share profits in ratio to their share in the average capital invested. Mr. Hoge invests $7,500 on Jan. 1, $3,200 on Mar. 1, $1,500 on June 1, and $3,500 on Oct. 1. Mr. Jensen invests $10,000 on Jan. 1, deducts $1,000 on Mar. 1, invests $2,000 on June 1 and $4,500 on Sept. 1, and deducts $5,000 on Oct. 1. If the profits for the calendar year are $8,154, what is each partner's share?
7. On Jan. 1, Mr. Kilham invested $8,200 and Mr. Reed invested $9,400 in a partnership, mutually agreeing that interest at 5 per cent per annum is to be paid to each partner on his invested capital, the remaining profit or loss to be divided equally. On May 1, Mr. Kilham invested an additional $1,500. At the end of the year, profits before payment of interest are $1,750. What should each partner receive?
8. Mr. Stewart, Mr. Frustuck, and Mr. Buttimer enter into a partnership agreeing that interest at 6 per cent per annum is to be allowed to each partner on his invested capital, the remaining profit or loss to be divided equally. On Jan. 1, each partner invests $6,000; on Mar. 1, Mr. Frustuck invests an additional $3,000; on July 1, Mr. Stewart withdraws $2,000. At the end of the year, profits before payment of interest are $600. What should each partner receive?

UNIT 3. Corporate Ownership

A *corporation* is authorized by law to operate and act as a single entity in conducting a specified enterprise, the ownership or capital consisting of transferable shares.

Legal authority to organize a corporation is conferred by the state in which the charter or certificate of organization is granted. Ordinarily, this charter will include the name under which the enterprise will operate, the business in which it is to engage, the quantity and kind of capital stock that it is authorized to issue, and the life of the charter.

Shareholders of the corporation participate in the ownership and in any profits earned by the business in the ratio that their shares are to the total capital stock issued. Ordinarily, liability is limited to what has been invested in such stock, and neither creditors nor the corporation itself may make additional assessments on the stockholders. Further, the shares may be sold or transferred at any time without affecting the organization of the company, and the value of each share is ordinarily low enough to allow ready sale to a large number of people, whereas in a partnership the value of any partner's holding may be so large as to limit the number of prospective purchasers.

Finally, since the value per share is usually low, a great number of people may participate in the ownership, and these accumulated savings allow the formation of capital investments far exceeding in size the capital investment possible in an individual enterprise or in a partnership.

STOCKS

The capital stock of a corporation is the number of shares of stock that the corporation is authorized to issue. However, the corporation is not required to issue or sell all of the stock authorized by its charter. The issued stock certificates represent the ownership of the company.

Certificates of stock are usually issued for each 100 shares or fraction thereof.

Authorized stock is the number of shares of stock that the corporation's charter entitles it to issue.

Outstanding stock is the number of shares of stock issued (also known as "issued stock").

Treasury stock is stock issued and reacquired. It remains within the company and does not share in the earnings, nor does it have voting power.

Surplus is an excess portion of the net assets of a business not accounted for in the statement of nominal values of the issued capital stock.

Deficit is the amount by which the sum of the liabilities and the statement of nominal values of the issued capital stock exceed the gross assets of a business.

Par value is the nominal value placed by the issuing corporation on its stock. It usually gives no true indication of the real worth of the stock.

The *book value* of a share of stock is its prorata part in the tangible net assets (net worth) of the corporation. Ordinarily, the book value of a par-value preferred share is its par value. If the net assets are less than the total par of the preferred, the book value of a preferred share may be found by dividing the net assets by the number of outstanding shares of preferred. The book value per share of the common stock is found by dividing the net assets *less* the total par of any outstanding preferred shares by the number of outstanding shares of common stock.

Fig. 6. Example of a stock certificate.

The *market value* of a share of stock is the price at which the stock may be purchased or sold on the open market or in a stock exchange. It is the current price, usually fluctuating, and it may be more or less than either the par value or the book value.

Common Stock. Stock without preference as to dividends or to assets in the event of dissolution of the corporation, each share usually entitling its holder to one vote in the election of directors of the corporation, is known as *common stock.* Expenses, interest on bonds or notes, and dividends to preferred stock must be paid before any dividends may be declared on the common stock.

No-par (or *nonpar*) *common* stock is issued without any nominal value.

Par-value common stock is issued with a nominal value placed on it by the authority of the state in which the corporation is chartered. It may be assumed that the par value of a common stock has no real significance in so far as the real value of the stock is concerned.

Thus, a $50 par-value common stock might be valueless or might be worth $1, $1,000, or any amount. A no-par common stock might likewise be worthless or valuable.

Because par valuation had a tendency to confuse some investors, it became common practice to issue no-par common stock. However, among other reasons, since the Federal government and some states arbitrarily consider no-par stock to have a $100 valuation for certain tax charges, the issuance of low-par common stocks with a nominal valuation of less than $10 is now a frequent practice.

Preferred Stock. Stock that has certain preferences over the common stock, as stipulated in the charter granted to the corporation or on the certificate of stock, is known as *preferred stock.* These preferences usually take the form of a fixed rate of dividends per annum on the specified par value or a fixed rate of dividends per annum in dollars per share. Also, preferred stock usually has prior rights over the common stock to the assets of the company in the event of dissolution, usually limited to the par value (if any). Ordinarily, preferred stock is nonvoting and does not share in earnings in excess of the stipulated fixed dividends. However, both of these privileges and many others may be granted to preferred shares.

Surplus. When the net assets of a corporation exceed the nominal value of the common stock, there is established what is known as a *surplus.* If created by the accumulation of undistributing earnings of the corporation, it is an *earned* surplus. If created by some other means such as the sale of stock by the corporation at more than par value or by gift, it is an *unearned* surplus.

As previously stated, ordinarily the book value per share of a preferred stock is its par value, if any. The book value per share of a common stock is determined by dividing the net worth of the corporation less the book values belonging to the outstanding preferred stock by the number of outstanding shares of common stock. Thus the total book value of a common stock is the sum of its nominal value and the surplus, if any.

The Street Corporation

Statement of Capital Stock and Surplus

Capital stock:		
30,000 issued shares of $50 par, 6% preferred stock	$1,500,000	
219,000 issued shares of $1 par common stock	219,000	
Total capital stock		$1,719,000
Surplus:		
Unearned surplus (from stock sales above par value)	$1,752,000	
Earned surplus (undistributed earnings)	3,860,000	
Total surplus		5,612,000
Net worth (total capital stock plus total surplus)		$7,331,000

Example 1: Book value of preferred and common stock. From the accompanying statement of capital stock and surplus of The Street Corporation, determine (*a*) the share of the net worth (total book value) belonging to the total issued preferred stock, (*b*) the book value (net worth) per share of the preferred stock, (*c*) the share of the net worth (total book value) belonging to the total issued common stock, and (*d*) the book value (net worth) per share of the common stock.

(*a*) Net worth belonging to outstanding preferred stock = \$1,500,000
(*b*) Book value per share of preferred stock is its par value = \$50

$$\text{Or, book value per share} = \frac{\$1{,}500{,}000}{30{,}000} = \$50$$

(*c*) Net worth belong to outstanding common stock = \$7,331,000 − \$1,500,000 = \$5,831,000

Or, \$219,000 + \$5,612,000 = \$5,831,000

$$(d)\ \text{Book value per share of common stock} = \frac{\$5{,}831{,}000}{219{,}000} = \$26.63$$

Example 2: To determine book value per share. The Jones Company has 500 shares of \$5 par-value common stock outstanding. Its balance sheet of date shows assets of \$125,000 and liabilities of \$50,000. Find (*a*) net worth, (*b*) total par of stock, (*c*) surplus, and (*d*) book value per share of the stock.

(*a*) Net worth = \$125,000 − \$50,000 = \$75,000
(*b*) Par value = \$5 × 500 = \$2,500
(*c*) Surplus = \$75,000 − \$2,500 = \$72,500

$$(d)\ \text{Book value per share} = \frac{\$75{,}000}{500} = \$150$$

Example 3: To determine book value per share. The Brown Manufacturing Company in its statement of proprietorship indicates that it has \$20,000 worth of \$100 par-value preferred shares with a total capital stock including \$50 par-value common of \$80,000, and a surplus of \$30,000. Find (*a*) number of shares of preferred stock, (*b*) number of shares of common stock, (*c*) book value per share of preferred, and (*d*) book value per share of common.

$$(a)\ \frac{\$20{,}000}{\$100} = 200 \text{ Shares of preferred}$$

(*b*) \$80,000 − \$20,000 = \$60,000 Total par value of common

$$\frac{\$60{,}000}{\$50} = 1{,}200 \text{ Shares of common}$$

(*c*) Book value per share of preferred equals its par value = \$100

$$(d)\ \text{Book value per share of common} = \frac{\$60{,}000 + \$30{,}000}{1{,}200} = \$75$$

Example 4: To determine surplus, net worth, and total assets. The Benny Company with liabilities of $109,500 has 2,400 shares of $25 par cumulative preferred, 1,000 shares of $100 par noncumulative preferred, and 30,000 shares of $1 par common with a book value of $1.75 per share. Find (*a*) total book value (par value) of cumulative preferred, (*b*) total book value (par value) of noncumulative preferred, (*c*) total par value of the common stock, (*d*) surplus, (*e*) net worth of the company, and (*f*) total assets.

(*a*) $\$25 \times 2{,}400 = \$60{,}000$
(*b*) $\$100 \times 1{,}000 = \$100{,}000$
(*c*) $\$1 \times 30{,}000 = \$30{,}000$
(*d*) $(\$1.75 \times 30{,}000) - \$30{,}000 = \$52{,}500 - \$30{,}000 = \$22{,}500$
(*e*) $\$60{,}000 + \$100{,}000 + \$30{,}000 + \$22{,}500 = \$212{,}500$
Or $\$60{,}000 + \$100{,}000 + \$52{,}500 = \$212{,}500$
(*f*) $\$109{,}500 + \$212{,}500 = \$322{,}000$

EXERCISE 3

1. The Slade Manufacturing Company has 800 shares of $50 par-value stock outstanding. Its balance sheet shows assets of $75,000 and liabilities of $42,500. What is (*a*) the net worth of the company and (*b*) the book value per share of stock?
2. The balance sheet of the White Company shows the following items: cash, $5,600; notes receivable, $6,750; accounts receivable, $7,830; furniture and fixtures, $4,750; inventory at cost, $34,670; land and buildings, $45,000; notes payable, $9,840; accounts payable, $16,720; mortgage on land and buildings, $24,000. The company has issued 2,500 shares of $2 par-value stock. What is (*a*) the net worth of the company and (*b*) the book value per share of stock?
3. The Davis Manufacturing Company in its statement of proprietorship indicates that it has 350 issued shares of $100 par-value preferred stock and 4,500 issued shares of non-par-value common stock and that its total net worth is $175,000. Find (*a*) the book value of the total preferred and (*b*) the book value per share of common.
4. The Myerson Dry Goods Company has issued $30,000 worth of $50 par-value preferred shares and a total capital stock, including $20 par-value common, of $60,000, and has a surplus of $12,500. Find (*a*) the number of shares of preferred, (*b*) the number of shares of common, (*c*) the book value per share of the preferred, and (*d*) the book value per share of the common stock.
5. The Howard Company has the following assets and liabilities: cash, $16,000; notes receivable, $18,300; accounts payable, $27,550; notes payable, $14,820; land and buildings, $89,700; raw inventory, $8,200; inventory of goods in process of manufacture, $3,250; finished inventory at cost, $6,380; mortgages owed, $25,000; equipment, $4,620; accounts receivable, $13,300. Outstanding are 200 shares of $100 par-value preferred and 1,200 shares of $10 par-value common. What are (*a*) the net worth of the outstanding common stock and (*b*) the book value of the common stock per share?
6. The Murray Company with liabilities of $326,000 has 8,000 issued shares of

$20 par cumulative preferred, 3,000 issued shares of $10 par noncumulative preferred, and 37,500 issued shares of $1 par common with a book value of $3.26. Find (*a*) total book value of cumulative preferred, (*b*) total book value of noncumulative preferred, (*c*) total par value of common, (*d*) total book value of common, (*e*) surplus, (*f*) net worth of the company, and (*g*) total assets.

7. The Shaw Wholesale Company has outstanding 2,000 shares of $100 par-value preferred stock and 15,400 shares of $5 par-value common stock with a book value per share of $12.60. If total liabilities are $245,000 what are (*a*) the surplus and (*b*) the total assets?

UNIT 4. Allocation of Corporate Dividends

When the board of directors of a corporation declare a dividend to the shareholders, the first monies set aside for such a purpose must be allocated to the owners of the preferred stock. Dividends in excess of the amount required to meet the rights to earnings by the preferred stock may then be allocated to the owners of the common stock.

Preferred stock frequently has a specified par of $100, although $25, $50, and other par valuations are not unusual. Thus a 5 per cent, $100 par preferred would be expected to pay dividends of $5 per share each year; a 6 per cent, $25 par preferred would be expected to pay dividends of $1.50 per share each year; etc. If the preferred stock has no par valuation, then the amount of the yearly dividends per share that may be expected will be stated in dollars, as $6, $3.50, or $5 preferred.

Cumulative preferred stocks are stocks the unpaid dividends of which are accumulated and must be paid in full before any dividends may be declared to the common stock. Thus if a 6 per cent cumulative preferred stock with par value of $50 had failed to pay dividends for 3 years, an accumulated dividend of $12 would have to be paid at the end of the fourth year before any dividend to the common stock could be paid.

Noncumulative preferred stocks are stocks the unpaid dividends of which do not accumulate and payment of the dividend for any year permits the declaration of a dividend to the common stock. Thus, if a 7 per cent, $20 par-value, noncumulative stock failed to receive dividends for 3 years, a dividend of $1.40 at the end of the fourth year to each share of the noncumulative preferred would permit the payment of a dividend at that time to the common stock.

Example 1: Allocation of dividends. The ABC company's capital consisted of 2,000 shares of no-par common and 1,000 shares of 6 per cent cumulative preferred with a par value of $100. During 1960, 1961, and 1962 no dividends were declared. At the end of the year 1963, the directors determined to distribute $20,000 in earnings. How much was received (*a*) by each share of preferred stock and (*b*) by each share of common stock?

(*a*) Par value of 1,000 pfd. shares = $100 × 1,000 = $100,000
Dividends due yearly = $100,000 × .06 = $6,000
Accumulated 1960 through 1963 = $6,000 × 4 = $24,000

Since only $20,000 in dividends was declared, the cumulative preferred received it all.

$$\text{Each preferred share received } \frac{\$20{,}000}{1{,}000} = \$20 \text{ per share}$$

(*b*) Since there were no remaining dividends, common stockholders received nothing; and there remained a cumulative balance of

$$\$24{,}000 - \$20{,}000 = \$4{,}000$$

still due the preferred stockholders which had to be paid before the common stockholders could receive dividends.

Example 2: Allocation of dividends. Same problem as Example 1, except that preferred stock is noncumulative.

(*a*) Par value of 1,000 pfd. shares = $100 × 1,000 = $100,000
Dividends due yearly = $100,000 × .06 = $6,000
1960–1962 not paid but noncumulative

Dividends declared	$20,000
To preferred shares	6,000
To common shares	$14,000

$$\text{Each preferred share received } \frac{\$6{,}000}{1{,}000} = \$6 \text{ per share}$$

(*b*) Since 2,000 common shares received $14,000, each share received

$$\frac{\$14{,}000}{2{,}000} = \$7 \text{ per share}$$

EXERCISE 4

1. The Pederson Company capital consisted of 3,240 shares of no-par common stock and 1,500 shares of 5 per cent cumulative preferred stock with a par

value of $100. During 1957 and 1958 no dividends were declared. At the end of 1959 the directors distributed $18,750 in dividends. What was received by each share (*a*) of preferred stock? (*b*) of common stock?

2. The George Manufacturing Company directors announce yearly dividends of $52,013.75. There are issued 2,670 shares of $50 par-value, 6 per cent cumulative preferred stock, and 5,875 shares of $25 par-value common stock. Assuming that no dividends have been passed (are not in default, not in arrears) on the preferred stock, what dividends will be received by each share (*a*) of preferred stock? (*b*) of common stock?
3. The Heath Manufacturing Company had a capital stock of $120,000 consisting of $40,000 of $100 par-value, $5\frac{1}{2}$ per cent cumulative preferred stock, and $80,000 of $10 par-value common stock. In 1956, dividends of $1,100 had been paid. At the end of 1957, dividends totaling $11,300 were distributed. How much was received by each share (*a*) of preferred stock? (*b*) of common stock?
4. The De Voss Company's capital stock consisted of 3,800 shares of $25 par-value common stock and 1,250 shares of $100 par-value 7 per cent noncumulative preferred stock. During 1960, 1961, and 1962 no dividends were declared. At the end of 1963 the directors distributed $42,000 in dividends. What dividends were received by each share (*a*) of preferred stock? (*b*) of common stock?
5. The West Manufacturing Company, Inc., had a capital consisting of $60,000 total of $50 par-value, 6 per cent noncumulative preferred stock, and $84,000 total of $8 par-value common stock. Dividends of $1.50 were declared to each preferred share in 1958 and 1959. At the end of 1960, dividends of $12,630 were declared. How much was received for 1960 by each share (*a*) of preferred stock? (*b*) of common stock?
6. The Frazier Company had a capital consisting of 3,000 shares of $100 par-value 5 per cent cumulative preferred; 2,000 shares of $100 par-value 6 per cent noncumulative preferred; and 45,000 shares of $5 par-value common stock. In 1958 full dividends were paid to the cumulative preferred, but not to the noncumulative preferred or common stock. In 1959 a $2.50 dividend was paid to each share of the cumulative preferred. In 1960, a dividend of $44,850 was declared. How much was received for 1960 by each share (*a*) of cumulative preferred? (*b*) of noncumulative preferred? (*c*) of common stock?
7. The Lyon Company had the following number of outstanding shares, each with a par value of $20: 75,000 shares of 5 per cent cumulative preferred; 42,000 shares of 7 per cent noncumulative preferred; and 136,000 shares of common. During the year ending Dec. 31, 1959, the Lyon Company earned a profit of $83,800, but no dividends were declared. At the year ending Dec. 31, 1960, the board of directors declared a dividend of 12 per cent of its par value to the common stock. For 1960, what *total* dividends were received by (*a*) the cumulative preferred, (*b*) the noncumulative preferred, and (*c*) the common stock? If the $83,800 profit earned in 1959 were added to the profit earned in 1960, (*d*) what amount of profit was necessary in 1960 to cover the dividends?

UNIT 5. Trading on the Equity by Individuals, Partnerships, and Corporations

Individual businessmen and partnerships borrow money frequently by means of notes or mortgages so that they may expand their businesses with the thought that the borrowed capital will increase earnings by more than it costs in interest. In so borrowing, the assets of the business are usually pledged as security to the lender to insure payment of interest and principal when due.

In like manner, to increase net earnings, corporations borrow money by means of notes, mortgages, and bonds. A *bond* is a written promise to pay a specified sum of money at maturity and interest at specified times.

The essential distinction between stocks and bonds is simply that stocks represent ownership, while bonds represent a particular kind of debt incurred. A stockholder is a part owner; a bondholder is a creditor.

Because of the many types of so-called "compromise securities," it is sometimes difficult to distinguish certain types of stocks from certain types of bonds. For example, preferred stocks sometimes carry conditions of preference that in many respects make them more like a bond than like a common stock.

A *note* is usually the term applied to a written promise to pay if its duration is less than 10 years.

As the above definitions indicate, notes and bonds are quite similar in nature, the difference largely being the length of time from date of origin to maturity. Bonds are usually issued in $1,000 denominations, although other denominations, such as $10,000, $5,000, $2,000, $500, $100, $25, are not uncommon.

Interest payments on both bonds and notes must be made when due, regardless of earnings. Since bonds ordinarily have a prior lien over preferred or common stocks to the assets of a business, failure to meet fixed charges (interest due on bonds) may result in insolvency proceedings being forced in court by the bondholders, followed by liquidation (sale of the assets in order to meet the claims of the bondholders).

Since this risk occurs, the question naturally arises as to why corporation bonds are issued. The answer is to be found in the principle of *trading on the equity*. It is advantageous for a corporation (or individual) to borrow if the average rate of earnings on the borrowed capital is in excess of the interest charges for the use of the borrowed capital.

The issuance of preferred stock by a corporation offers common stockholders the opportunity to gain by trading on the equity without the risk of borrowing through notes, mortgages, or bonds, for payment of dividends even to cumulative preferred may be indefinitely delayed at the discretion of the board of directors of the corporation. However, the amount of gain will usually be somewhat less, for preferred dividends ordinarily must be at a higher rate to induce investor's capital than the rates of interest necessary to induce the more secure investments offered by notes, mortgages, and bonds.

Example 1: Gain in dollars. John Harney, owner of a small variety store, earns 12 per cent on his investment of $35,000. If additional capital of $15,000 that he can borrow at 5 per cent interest will earn 14 per cent before payment of interest, find the yearly increase in income.

14% − 5% = 9% Net gain on borrowed capital
$15,000 × .09 = $1,350 Net increase in income

Or, solve:

$15,000 × .14 = $2,100 Gross gain
$15,000 × .05 = 750 Less interest cost
$1,350 Net increase in income

Example 2: Per cent of increase in earnings and per cent of return on original capital. The Lang-Grant Electrical Suppliers, a partnership, earns $35,200 on a capital investment of $220,000. The partners estimate that they can make the same rate of gain on an additional investment of $80,000. If this $80,000 is borrowed at 5½ per cent, find (*a*) the expected per cent of increase in income, and (*b*) the expected per cent of return on their original capital investment.

$\frac{\$35{,}200}{\$220{,}000} = .16 = 16\%$ Original rate of return

16% − 5.5% = 10.5% Net gain in per cent on borrowed capital
$80,000 × .105 = $8,400 Net gain in dollars

(*a*) $\frac{\$8{,}400}{\$35{,}200} = .2386 = 23.86\%$ Per cent increase in income

(*b*) $\frac{\$35{,}200 + \$8{,}400}{\$220{,}000} = \frac{\$43{,}600}{\$220{,}000} = .1982 = 19.82\%$ Per cent return on original capital

Example 3: Dollar and per cent gains from trading on the equity. The Barlow Company, Inc., has a capital of $400,000 all financed by common stock. Its present earnings are 9 per cent on the investment. The board of directors believe that an additional investment of $120,000 would earn 12 per cent. If their estimate is true and the additional capital is raised by means of a 4 per cent bond issue, find (*a*) original earnings, (*b*) dollar gain in net earnings, (*c*) total net earnings, including the increase, (*d*) per cent of gain in earnings, and (*e*) new per cent of return on the original capital investment.

(*a*) $400,000 × .09 = $36,000 Original earnings
(*b*) 12% − 4% = 8% Net gain in per cent on borrowed capital
$120,000 × .08 = $9,600 Dollar gain in net earnings
(*c*) $36,000 + $9,600 = $45,600 Total net earnings, including increase

(*d*) $\frac{\$9{,}600}{\$36{,}000} = .2667 = 26.67\%$ Per cent gain in earnings

(*e*) $\frac{\$45{,}600}{\$400{,}000} = .1140 = 11.40\%$ New return in per cent on original capital

There are two main classifications for bonds: (1) bonds secured by property and (2) bonds issued on the strength of the general credit of the corporation.

Bonds secured by property may take the form of mortgages on the real property or equipment of the issuing company, or they may be secured by the deposit of other securities, such as stocks and bonds, which are pledged as collateral.

Both interest rate and date of maturity are used frequently to describe particular bond issues. As an example: Bell Telephone of Pennsylvania debenture bonds bearing interest at 3 per cent and maturing in 1974 may be known as "Bell Telephone of Pa. Deb. 3s'74," "Bell Tel. of Pa. Deb. 3's," or as "Bell Tel. of Pa. 74's," (the ticker tape symbol is "BLP 3's"), or any other simple contraction of the complete name that will distinguish the bonds from other companies' bonds or other bonds issued by the same company.

The terminology of bonds is complex, but following are a few of the more common expressions and definitions with which you may wish to be familiar.

Registered bonds are carried on the books of the registrar or trustee in the name of the bond owner so that loss of the bond itself will not mean loss of the investment. Payment of interest is made to the registered holder.

Coupon bonds, which are the more frequent, are rarely registered but carry a separate coupon for each interest payment, and each coupon when detached entitles the bearer to the interest when due. Loss of the bond, unless it is recovered, means loss of the investment.

Mortgage bonds are secured by real property, equipment, or collateral. They may be issued as first mortgage, second mortgage, etc., the first-mortgage bonds having prior lien over the later issues.

Debentures are bonds secured solely by the general credit of the issuing company. This does not necessarily mean that they are undesirable, for a debenture in a strong company is preferable to a first-mortgage bond in a weak company.

Convertible bonds may be converted to stocks within a specified period of time. The speculative element created by this privilege may help in the original sale of the bonds by the issuing company.

Collateral trust bonds are secured not by tangible physical property but by the securities of other corporations pledged as collateral. This type of bond is most frequently issued by holding corporations.

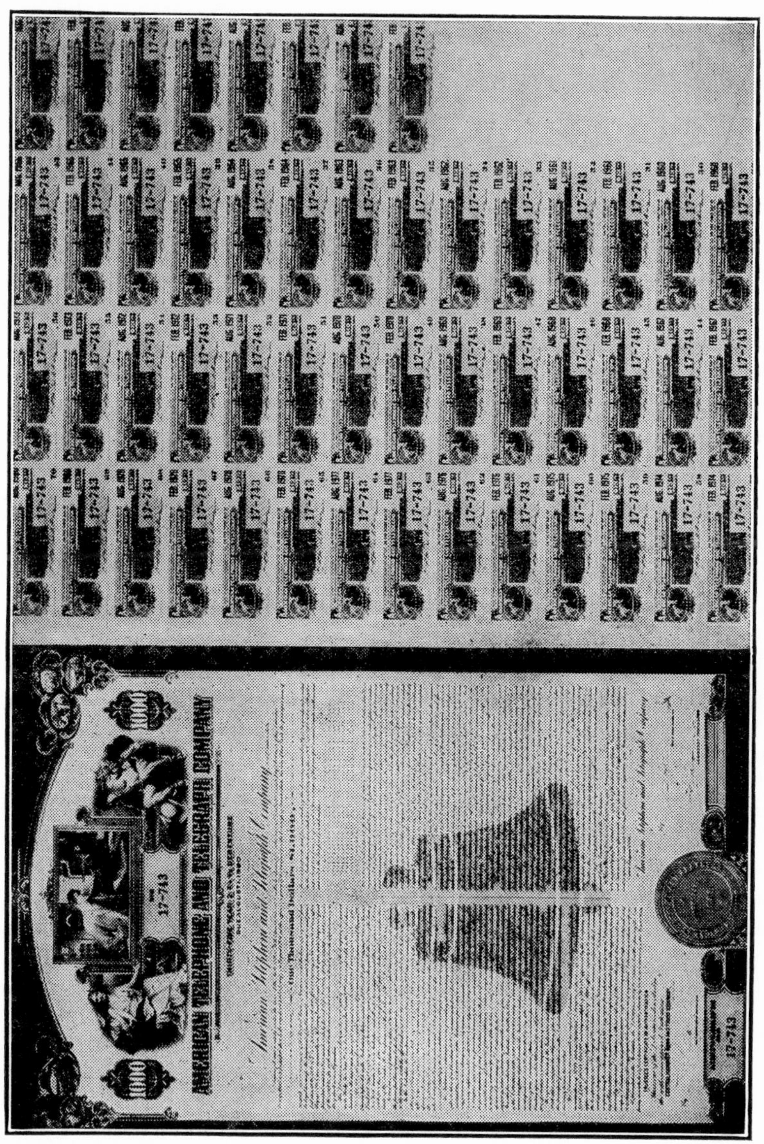

AMERICAN TELEPHONE AND TELEGRAPH COMPANY

1000

17-743

Fig. 7. Example of a corporate bond.

Income bonds are ordinarily undesirable, for they are not required to pay interest at stated periods but pay only if earnings are sufficient to meet the interest charges. They are issued often by companies that have gone through insolvency proceedings, and in such instances the bond interest payment is frequently in default.

EXERCISE 5

Solve the following. Find all per cent answers to nearest hundredths.

1. Mr. Weaver owns a service station that cost him $12,000 and that earns an average yearly net profit of $1,500. He estimates that improvements costing $5,000 will bring an additional return at the same rate of profit. If his estimate is correct and he borrows the $5,000 from his bank at 6 per cent interest, find (*a*) the net annual increase in income that he would make in dollars, (*b*) his per cent of increase in income, and (*c*) his new per cent of return on his original investment.
2. Mr. Johnson and Mr. Evans have a partnership in which profits are divided in the ratio that each partner's original investment bears to their total original investment. Mr. Johnson's investment is $7,500; Mr. Evans's, $6,200. Earnings have been 12 per cent on the total investment. If the same per cent of earnings could be made on an additional investment of $4,500, find (*a*) the yearly increase in income that each partner would make if $4,500 is borrowed by the partnership at 7 per cent interest, (*b*) the per cent of increase in income by the partnership, and (*c*) the new per cent of profit that the partnership would make yearly on the original investment.
3. The Madden Company with capital of $500,000, all financed by the sale of $25 par-value common stock, earns 9 per cent on the investment. It is estimated that an additional capital of $200,000 would earn 8 per cent. If this estimate is correct and this additional capital can be raised by the sale of 4 per cent interest bearing bonds, find (*a*) the net increase in dollars of yearly income that would be earned by each share of common stock, (*b*) the per cent of increase in earnings by the common stock, and (*c*) the per cent of profit the common stock would then earn annually on the par value.
4. The Coulter Corporation capital consists of $300,000 of $50 par-value, 6 per cent preferred stock and 60,000 shares of $10 par-value common stock. Earnings on the common stock are 10 per cent on the par value. It is estimated that $400,000 in additional capital will earn the same rate of return as does the entire present capital investment. If this additional capital is raised by the sale of bonds bearing interest at $4\frac{1}{2}$ per cent, find (*a*) the expected increase in dollars of yearly income (to nearest cents) that would be earned by each share of common stock, (*b*) the expected per cent of increase in earnings by the common stock, and (*c*) the expected per cent of profit that the common stock would earn annually on its par value.
5. The Woerner Manufacturing Company's capital stock consists of 20,000 shares of $50 par-value common stock and 4,000 shares of $7 cumulative preferred

stock. Bonded indebtedness consists of $200,000 at par of $3\frac{1}{2}$ per cent interest-bearing bonds. Earnings by the common stock are $6 per share. If additional capital of $400,000 raised by the sale of 5 per cent interest-bearing bonds will earn 8 per cent before payment of interest in addition to the present earnings of the company, find (*a*) what the total annual earnings would be per share of common stock, (*b*) the per cent of increase in annual earnings by the common stock, and (*c*) the per cent of earnings the common stock would then be making on its par value.

6. The Hall Company's capital consisted of 60,000 shares of $5 par-value common stock. Earnings were $22,500 per year. Then 1,500 shares of $100 par-value 6 per cent cumulative preferred shares are sold. Earnings increase to $30,000 per year before payment of dividends to the preferred stock. Find the per-year (*a*) original earnings in dollars per share of common stock, (*b*) present earnings in dollars per share of common stock, (*c*) original per cent of earnings by common stock on par value, and (*d*) present per cent of earnings by common stock on par value.

7. Silvia and Company, Inc., has a capital of $540,000, all financed by common stock. Its present earnings are 8 per cent on the investment. The board of directors believes that an additional investment of $180,000 would earn 12 per cent. If their estimate is true and the additional capital is raised by means of a $4\frac{1}{2}$ per cent bond issue, find (*a*) original earnings, (*b*) dollar gain in net earnings, (*c*) total net earnings including the increase, (*d*) per cent of gain in earnings, and (*e*) new per cent of return on the original capital investment.

8. The Edward Corporation earned 12.5 per cent on its capital of $450,000. After borrowing $150,000 at 5 per cent interest, earnings before payment of interest are $59,250. Find (*a*) the net gain or loss in earnings, (*b*) the new per cent of earnings on the original capital, and (*c*) the per cent of gain or loss on the original earnings.

CHAPTER XI

TRANSACTIONS IN CORPORATE SECURITIES

Corporate securities may be purchased and sold by direct negotiation between buyer and seller, but such transactions take place frequently through the medium of a broker or dealer whose facilities are organized to provide such service for the general public.

Stocks and bonds bought and sold on established exchanges are known as "on-board" or "listed" securities. Stocks and bonds not sold on established exchanges are known as "off-board," "unlisted," or "over-the-counter" securities.

Stock Exchanges. Stock exchanges operate in most of the principal cities of the United States, but the New York Stock Exchange is by far the largest, in both number and value of transactions. Commission charges for transactions in corporate securities are generally the same as those of the New York Stock Exchange on the Boston, Detroit, Midwest, Pacific Coast, Philadelphia-Baltimore, and Pittsburgh exchanges.

Aside from mining and oil securities exchanges to be found in a number of cities, the two other principal exchanges in North America are the American Exchange located in New York City and the Toronto Exchange of Toronto, Ontario, Canada—all of which have commission charges varying slightly from the schedule established by the New York Stock Exchange.

Because of its importance in size and in leadership, the discussion that follows will be confined to transactions on the New York Stock Exchange.

UNIT 1. Odd-lot Differentials and Commission Rates

For his services the broker charges a fee or commission called *brokerage.* Additional expenses to the purchaser or seller of stocks may include Federal transfer taxes, Federal Securities and Exchange Commission charges, state transfer taxes, postage, and other fees. Such expenses are added to the cost to the purchaser and are deducted from the remittance to the seller.

Odd-lot Differentials. The unit of trading used most commonly on the New York Stock Exchange is 100 shares. A limited number of usually inactive issues is traded in units of 10 shares instead of 100 shares. Therefore in 100-share unit stocks, odd lots are any number of shares from 1 to 99; and in 10-share unit stocks, odd lots are any number of shares from 1 to 9 (on the American Stock Exchange, stocks are traded in units of 100, 50, 25, and 10 shares).

When an individual places an order with his broker to buy or sell an odd lot of stock, the broker *must* buy that stock from an odd-lot dealer who performs a kind of wholesaling function by breaking up round lots of securities into smaller groupings. Such odd-lot dealers do business only with brokers on the exchange floor, not with the general public. For this service the odd-lot dealer charges a *differential,* an additional cost to the individual buyer or charge to the seller.

Odd-lot transactions are subject to normal brokers' commissions and taxes. In the case of purchase orders only, the cost of the Federal transfer taxes and the Securities and Exchange Commission (SEC) charges paid by the odd-lot dealer are charged to the purchaser (pages 370–371). The prices of odd-lot transactions are determined by the round-lot trades (full units of trading as 100 shares or 10 shares) made on the floor of the exchange, modified by a differential determined as follows.

Differential—100-share Unit Stocks. With minor exceptions for extremely low-priced stocks, the odd-lot differential on a 100-share unit of trading stock is one-eighth point ($12\frac{1}{2}$ cents) when the round-lot price is $39\frac{7}{8}$ (\$39.875) or below.

The odd-lot differential is one-fourth point (25 cents) when the round-lot price is 40 (\$40) or above.

On purchase (buying) orders, the odd-lot differential is added to this round-lot transaction price. On sales (selling) orders, the odd-lot differential is subtracted from the round-lot transaction price.

The statement of price, known as the execution price, by the broker to the individual purchaser or seller of an odd lot includes the differential.

Example 1: Execution price on an odd lot when effective round-lot price is less than 40. Find the execution price on an odd lot of a 100-share unit stock if the effective round-lot price is 28 to (*a*) the individual buyer and (*b*) the individual seller.

(*a*) execution price per share $= 28 + \frac{1}{8} = 28\frac{1}{8} = \$28.125$ per share

(*b*) execution price per share $= 28 - \frac{1}{8} = 27\frac{7}{8} = \$27.875$ per share

Example 2: Execution price on an odd lot when the effective round-lot price is 40 or more. Find the execution price on an odd lot of a 100-share unit stock if the effective round-lot price is $71\frac{1}{2}$ to (*a*) the individual buyer and (*b*) the individual seller.

(*a*) execution price per share $= 71\frac{1}{2} + \frac{1}{4} = 71\frac{3}{4} =$ \$71.75 per share

(*b*) execution price per share $= 71\frac{1}{2} - \frac{1}{4} = 71\frac{1}{4} =$ \$71.25 per share

Differential—10-share Unit Stocks. The differentials in 10-share unit of trading stocks are as follows:

Effective round-lot price:	*Odd-lot differential*
25 and under	$\frac{1}{4}$
$25\frac{1}{8}$ to $74\frac{3}{4}$ inclusive	$\frac{3}{8}$
$74\frac{7}{8}$	$\frac{1}{2}$
75	$\frac{5}{8}$
$75\frac{1}{8}$ and over	$\frac{3}{4}$

Examples of execution prices on odd lots of 10-share unit stocks:

Effective round-lot prices:	*Execution price per share on purchases*	*Execution price per share on sales*
$17\frac{7}{8}$	$18\frac{1}{8}$	$17\frac{5}{8}$
$54\frac{5}{8}$	55	$54\frac{1}{4}$
$74\frac{7}{8}$	$75\frac{3}{8}$	$74\frac{3}{8}$
75	$75\frac{5}{8}$	$74\frac{3}{8}$
$108\frac{3}{4}$	$109\frac{1}{2}$	108

Commission Rates. The New York Stock Exchange commission rates charged to the general public by member brokers are as follows:

NEW YORK STOCK EXCHANGE—COMMISSION RATES

On stocks, rights, and warrants selling at \$1 per share and above, commissions on single transactions *not exceeding* 100 *shares* are based upon the amount of money involved as follows:

100-*share unit or* 10-*share unit Round Lots.* For a unit of trading, a combination of units of trading, or a combination of a unit or units of trading plus an odd lot, amounting to 100 shares or less:

Money value	*Commission*
Under $100	As mutually agreed
$100 to $1,999.99	1% plus $5
$2,000 to $4,999.99	$\frac{1}{2}$% plus $15
$5,000 and above	$\frac{1}{10}$% plus $35

To compute the commission *on multiples of* 100 *shares,* multiply the commission charge for 100 shares by the number of 100's involved.

1–99-*share odd lots and* 1–9-*share odd lots.* For less than 100 shares of a stock with a 100-share unit of trading, the commission charges are computed on the same money-value schedule and commission rates as for round lots *less* a deduction of $2.

For less than 10 shares of a stock with 10-share unit of trading, the commission charges are computed on the same money-value schedule and commission rates as for round lots *less* a deduction of $2.

Note that the aforementioned deduction of $2 is not applied to a unit of trading, a combination of units of trading, or a combination of a unit or units of trading plus an odd lot, amounting to 100 shares or less.

Minimum Commission Rates. On stocks, rights, and warrants selling at less than $1 per share, commissions are on a per share basis whether purchased in full units of trading or in odd lots. Purchase or sale of stocks priced at less than $1 per share are not considered in examples or in problems in this text and further discussion of such stocks is omitted.

Notwithstanding the schedules of commission rates preceding, when the money value of the transaction is $100 or more, the commission may not be reduced by the $2 odd-lot deduction to less than a minimum of $6.

Commissions, taxes, or other expenses are not included in determining the money value involved in a transaction.

Example 1: Round lots in 100-share units of trading. Find the commission charge in transactions of (*a*) 100 shares priced at $16\frac{1}{2}$, (*b*) 300 shares priced at 34, and (*c*) 200 shares priced at $73\frac{1}{8}$.

(*a*) $16\frac{1}{2} \times 100 = \$1,650$ Money value per 100 shares

$\$1,650 \times .01 = \$16.50$
$+ \; 5.00$
$\$21.50$ Commission charge for 100 shares

(*b*) $34 \times 100 = \$3,400$ Money value per 100 shares

$\$3,400 \times .005 = \$17 \quad \left(\text{or } \$3,400 \times .00\frac{1}{2} = \$17\right)$
$+ \; 15$
$\$32$ Commission charge for 100 shares
$\times \; 3$
$\$96$ Commission charge for 300 shares

(*c*) $73\frac{1}{8} \times 100 = \$7{,}312.50$ Money value per 100 shares

$\$7{,}312.50 \times .001 = \quad \$\ 7.31 \quad \left(\text{or } \$7{,}312.50 \times .00\frac{1}{10} = \$7.31\right)$

$+\ 35.00$

$\$42.31$ Commission charge for 100 shares

$\times\ 2$

$\$84.62$ Commission charge for 200 shares

Example 2: 10-share units and combinations of 10-share units plus an odd lot. Find the commission charges in transactions of (*a*) 80 shares of 10-share units of trading at 19, (*b*) 54 shares of 10-share units of trading *bought* at the effective round-lot price of 70, and (*c*) 54 shares of 10-share units of trading *sold* at the effective round-lot price of 70.

(*a*) $19 \times 80 = \$1{,}520$ Money value per 80 shares

$\$1{,}520 \times .01 = \quad \$15.20$

$+\ 5.00$

$\$20.20$ Commission charge for 80 shares

(*b*) $70 \times 50 = \quad \$3{,}500.00$ Money value per 50 shares

$70\frac{3}{8} \times 4 = + \quad 281.50$ Money value on execution price for 4-share odd lot

$\$3{,}781.50$ Money value per 54 shares

$\$3{,}781.50 \times .005 = \quad \$18.91$

$+\ 15.00$

$\$33.91$ Commission charge for purchase of 54 shares

(*c*) $70 \times 50 = \quad \$3{,}500.00$ Money value per 50 shares

$69\frac{5}{8} \times 4 = + \quad 278.50$ Money value on execution price for 4-share odd lot

$\$3{,}778.50$ Money value per 54 shares

$\$3{,}778.50 \times .005 = \quad \$18.89$

$+\ 15.00$

$\$33.89$ Commission charge for sale of 54 shares

Example 3. Odd lots of 100-share and 10-share units of trading. Find the commission charges in transactions of (*a*) 35 shares of 100-share units of trading *bought* at the effective round-lot price of $22\frac{5}{8}$, (*b*) 90 shares of 100-share units of trading *sold* at the effective round-lot price of 108, (*c*) 8 shares of 10-share units of trading *bought* at the effective round-lot price of $212\frac{1}{2}$, and (*d*) 7 shares of 10-share units of trading *sold* at the effective round-lot price of $18\frac{3}{4}$.

(*a*) $22\frac{5}{8} + \frac{1}{8}$ differential $= 22\frac{3}{4}$

$22\frac{3}{4} \times 35 = \$796.25$ Money value per 35 shares

$$
\begin{array}{lrl}
\$796.25 \times .01 = & \$\ 7.96 & \\
 & +\ \ 5.00 & \\
\hline
 & \$12.96 & \\
 & -\ \ 2.00 & \text{Odd-lot commission deduction} \\
\hline
 & \$10.96 & \text{Commission charge for purchase of 35 shares}
\end{array}
$$

(*b*) $108 - \frac{1}{4}$ differential $= 107\frac{3}{4}$

$107\frac{3}{4} \times 90 = \$9{,}697.50$ Money value per 90 shares

$$
\begin{array}{lrl}
\$9{,}697.50 \times .001 = & \$\ 9.70 & \\
 & +\ 35.00 & \\
\hline
 & \$44.70 & \\
 & -\ \ 2.00 & \text{Odd-lot commission deduction} \\
\hline
 & \$42.70 & \text{Commission charge for sale of 90 shares}
\end{array}
$$

(*c*) $212\frac{1}{2} + \frac{3}{4}$ differential $= 213\frac{1}{4}$

$213\frac{1}{4} \times 8 = \$1{,}706$ Money value per 8 shares

$$
\begin{array}{lrl}
\$1{,}706 \times .01 = & \$17.06 & \\
 & +\ \ 5.00 & \\
\hline
 & \$22.06 & \\
 & -\ \ 2.00 & \text{Odd-lot commission deduction} \\
\hline
 & \$20.06 & \text{Commission charge for purchase of 8 shares}
\end{array}
$$

(*d*) $18\frac{3}{4} - \frac{1}{4}$ differential $= 18\frac{1}{2}$

$18\frac{1}{2} \times 7 = \$129.50$ Money value per 7 shares

$$
\begin{array}{lr}
\$129.50 \times .01 = & \$1.30 \\
 & +\ 5.00 \\
\hline
 & \$6.30 \\
 & -\ 2.00 \\
\hline
 & \$4.30
\end{array}
$$

But the minimum charge is \$6 when the money value is \$100 or more. Therefore the commission charge for the sale of 7 shares is \$6.

Example 4: More than 100 shares plus an odd lot. Find the commission charges in transactions of (*a*) 130 shares of 100-share units of trading *bought* at the effective round-lot price of 52 and (*b*) 218 shares of 100-share units of trading *sold* at the effective round-lot price of $34\frac{1}{2}$.

(*a*) This is treated as two separate purchases of 100 and of 30 shares.

$52 \times 100 = \$5{,}200$ Money value per 100 shares

$\$5{,}200 \times .001 = \quad \$\ 5.20$

$+\ 35.00$

$\$40.20$ Commission charge for purchase of 100 shares

$52\frac{1}{4} \times 30 = \$1{,}567.50$ Money value on execution price for 30-share odd lot

$\$1{,}567.50 \times .01 = \quad \$15.68$

$+\ \ 5.00$

$\$20.68$

$-\ \ 2.00$ Odd-lot commission deduction

$\$18.68$ Commission charge for purchase of 30 shares

(*b*) This is treated as two separate sales of 200 and of 18 shares.

$34\frac{1}{2} \times 100 = \$3{,}450$ Money value per 100 shares

$\$3{,}450 \times .005 = \quad \$17.25$

$+\ 15.00$

$\$32.25$ Commission charge for sale of 100 shares

$\times\ \ 2$

$\$64.50$ Commission charge for sale of 200 shares

$34\frac{3}{8} \times 18 = \$618.75$ Money value on execution price for 18-share odd lot

$\$618.75 \times .01 = \quad \$\ 6.19$

$+\ \ 5.00$

$\$11.19$

$-\ \ 2.00$ Odd-lot commission deduction

$\$\ 9.19$ Commission charge for sale of 18 shares

EXERCISE 1

Solve the following, assuming all transactions take place on the New York Stock Exchange.

1. Find the execution prices per share to the purchaser on odd lots of 100-share unit stocks if the effective round-lot prices are (*a*) $31\frac{5}{8}$, (*b*) 260, (*c*) $16\frac{1}{2}$, and (*d*) 40.
2. Find the execution prices per share to the seller on odd lots of 100-share unit stocks if the effective round-lot prices are (*a*) $21\frac{7}{8}$, (*b*) $77\frac{1}{8}$, (*c*) 12, and (*d*) $134\frac{3}{4}$.
3. Find the execution prices per share to the purchaser on odd lots of 10-share

unit stocks if the effective round-lot prices are (*a*) $109\frac{1}{8}$, (*b*) $74\frac{7}{8}$, (*c*) $15\frac{7}{8}$, (*d*) 75, and (*e*) $61\frac{3}{4}$.

4. Find the execution prices per share to the seller on odd lots of 10-share unit stocks if the effective round-lot prices are (*a*) $229\frac{3}{8}$, (*b*) 75, (*c*) 25, (*d*) $49\frac{1}{8}$, and (*e*) $74\frac{7}{8}$.
5. Find the commission charges in the purchase or sale in transactions of (*a*) 100 shares priced at $21\frac{7}{8}$, (*b*) 400 shares priced at $16\frac{1}{2}$, and (*c*) 200 shares priced at $86\frac{1}{4}$.
6. Find the commission charges in the purchase or sale in transactions of (*a*) 60 shares of 10-share units of trading at $91\frac{7}{8}$ and (*b*) 120 shares of 10-share units of trading at $31\frac{3}{4}$.
7. Find the commission charges in (*a*) the purchase of 88 shares of 10-share units of trading bought at the effective round-lot price of 46 and (*b*) the sale of 46 shares of 10-share units of trading sold at the effective round-lot price of $181\frac{1}{8}$.
8. Find the commission charges in the purchase of (*a*) 65 shares of 100-share units of trading bought at the effective round-lot price of $17\frac{5}{8}$ and (*b*) 9 shares of 10-share units of trading bought at the effective round-lot price of $122\frac{7}{8}$.
9. Find the commission charges in the sale of (*a*) 32 shares of 100-share units of trading sold at the effective round-lot price of $92\frac{3}{4}$ and (*b*) 6 shares of 10-share units of trading sold at the effective round-lot price of $23\frac{1}{8}$.
10. Find the commission charges in purchases of the following 100-share unit of trading stocks for (*a*) 360 shares bought at the effective round-lot price of $17\frac{1}{2}$ and (*b*) 155 shares bought at the effective round-lot price of $102\frac{1}{8}$.
11. Find the commission charges in sales of the following 100-share unit of trading stocks for (*a*) 225 shares sold at the effective round-lot price of $91\frac{7}{8}$ and (*b*) 140 shares sold at the effective round-lot price of 40.

UNIT 2. Stock Purchases

The day on which a transaction takes place is known as the *actual date*.

The day on which the purchaser is expected to make payment in full to this broker for the securities he has ordered bought and the seller is expected to deliver to his broker the securities that he has ordered sold is known as the *settlement date*.

Ordinarily, the settlement date is the fourth business day following the actual date. When the settlement date is to be longer than the fourth business day following the actual date, the seller must have so stipulated and a later settlement date known and agreeable to the buyer must have been determined.

Federal Taxes on Odd-lot Purchases. When an odd-lot dealer transmits stock to a broker, this transfer is considered by the Federal government as a sale by the odd-lot dealer to the broker, and Federal transfer taxes must be paid by the odd-lot dealer. He charges these taxes to the regular broker who in turn passes them on to the odd-lot purchaser.

There are no taxes charged on purchases of full units of trading, but the purchaser of an odd lot must pay, in addition to the odd-lot differential and commission charges, the following two Federal taxes:

Federal Transfer Tax

1. If the market price is less than $20 per share, 5 cents tax per each $100 of total par value or fraction thereof.

Example: Find the Federal transfer tax on 6 shares of $40 par stock priced at 19 including differential.

Total par value = 40 × 6 = $240
$240 = 2.4 hundreds
Tax is 5¢ for each hundred or fraction thereof
Therefore Federal transfer tax is $.05 × 3 = $.15

2. If the market price is $20 or more, 6 cents tax per each $100 of total par value or fraction thereof.

Example: Find the Federal transfer tax on an odd lot of 61 shares of $30 par stock priced at $42\frac{1}{2}$ including differential.

Total par value = 30 × 61 = $1,830
$1,830 = 18.3 hundreds
Tax is 6¢ for each hundred or fraction thereof.
Therefore Federal transfer tax is $.06 × 19 = $1.14

3. If no-par stock and the market price is less than $20, 5 cents tax per share.

Example: Find the Federal transfer tax on an odd lot of 96 shares of no-par stock priced at $12\frac{1}{8}$ including differential.

The Federal transfer tax is $.05 × 96 = $4.80

4. If no-par stock and the market price is $20 or more, 6 cents tax per share.

Example: Find the Federal transfer tax on 9 shares of no-par stock priced at 146 including differential.

The Federal transfer tax is $.06 × 9 = $.54

Federal Securities and Exchange Commission Charge. To help defray the expenses of the Securities and Exchange Commission (SEC) 1 cent per $500 or fraction thereof is charged the seller (the odd-lot dealer in the case of odd-lot purchases who passes it on to the exchange broker who in turn passes it on to the odd-lot purchaser) in all transactions on any registered exchange.

Examples: Find the SEC charge on sales (or odd-lot purchases) totaling $300, $501, and $2,735.

SEC charge on $300 = $.01 × 1 = $.01
SEC charge on $501 = $.01 × 2 = $.02
SEC charge on $2,735 = $.01 × 6 = $.06

Take special note that *transfer taxes are not charged* for the purchase of a full unit or full units of trading.

Example of a Stock Purchase. Find the total cost to the purchaser of 160 shares of Square D Company $5 par common stock (100-share unit of trading) purchased through a broker on the New York Stock Exchange, if the effective round-lot price is $52\frac{1}{2}$.

Actual date, Oct. 3, 1960 Settlement date, Oct. 7

Exc.	Bot.	Description	Price	Tax	Amount	Commission	Total
NYS	100	Square D	$52\frac{1}{2}$		5,250	40.25	5,290.25
NYS	60		$52\frac{3}{4}$	.25	3,165.25	28.83	3,194.08

Explanation

Actual date: Oct. 3, 1960. The date on which the broker made the purchase.

Settlement date: Oct. 7. As is ordinarily the case, the fourth business day following the actual date.

Exc.: NYS. The transaction took place on the New York Stock Exchange.
Bot.: 100. A full unit of trading in this instance.
60. An odd lot.

Description: Square D. The abbreviation for Square D Company common stock.

Price: $52\frac{1}{2}$. Purchase price per share on full unit of trading.
$52\frac{3}{4}$. Purchase price per share including differential on odd lot.
Tax: None for the full unit of trading
.25. Transfer taxes on the odd-lot purchase of 60 shares is $.25.

Federal transfer tax: par of $5 × 60 = $300 = 3 hundreds of par, and since the price is more than 20, the tax is 6¢ per 100 of par. SEC charge based on $52\frac{3}{4} \times 60$ = $3,165 = 6 and a fraction $500's. Thus,

Federal transfer tax is $.06 × 3 = $.18
SEC charge is $.01 × 7 = .07
Total tax = $.25

Amount: 5,250. $52\frac{1}{2} \times 100$ = $5,250

3,165.25. $52\frac{3}{4} \times 60$ plus $.25 tax = $3,165 + $.25 = $3,165.25

Effective Round-lot Prices for Certain Stocks on the New York Stock Exchange

Par value, dollars	Today's sales, no. of shares	Stock, 100-share units of trading except as noted[1]	Today's quotations[2]			Change since yesterday[3]
			High	Low	Last	
100	40	Abbott Laboratories 4% pfd.	107 1/8	107	107	none
no-par	200	Adams-Millis Corp.	39 1/8	37 1/2	37 1/2	+1/8
50	70	Amalgamated Leather 6% pfd.	41	39 7/8	40 3/8	−1/2
1	800	American Cable & Radio	3 1/2	3 1/4	3 1/2	+1/8
.40	65	American Export Lines	19 1/2	19	19 1/8	−3/8
no-par	30	American Potash & Chemical	70 1/4	69 3/4	70	−1/2
100	18	Amer. Smelting & Refin. 7% pfd[1]	171	170	170 1/2	none
100	100	American Telephone & Telegraph	154 3/8	153 3/4	154 3/8	+3/8
25	100	American Tobacco	61 7/8	61 1/2	61 5/8	−1/8
100	80	do. 6% pfd.[1]	146 7/8	146 3/4	146 7/8	none
5	300	Armour & Co.	23 7/8	23 7/8	23 7/8	none
25	40	Chrysler Corporation	69 3/4	69 1/8	69 1/2	−3/8
100	50	City Stores Co. 4 1/2% pfd.[1]	85 1/2	85	85	−1/2
no-par	120	Consumers Power Co.	53 7/8	53 1/8	53 3/4	+2
100	70	Corn Products 7% pfd.[1]	149 1/2	149 1/2	149 1/2	+1 1/2
10	65	Eastern Corporation	43	42 1/2	42 3/4	−1/4
no-par	10	Fairbanks, Morse & Co.	47	46 7/8	46 7/8	none
no-par	100	First National Stores	52 3/4	52 1/4	52 3/4	+5/8
5	80	Flintkote Co.	33 7/8	33 1/2	33 1/2	+1/4
7.50	300	Florida Power Corp.	50 7/8	50 1/4	50 1/2	none
no-par	230	Florida Power & Light Co.	53	52 5/8	53	+1/2
2	30	Foremost Dairies, Inc.	16 1/2	16	16 1/2	+3 1/4
no-par	400	General Cable Corp.	44 3/8	43 1/4	43 1/2	−3/4
no-par	200	General Foods Corporation	49 1/4	49 1/8	49 1/8	−3/4
no-par	160	General Mills, Inc.	71 5/8	71 1/8	71 1/8	−3/4
25	30	Great Northern Paper Co.	111 1/4	110 5/8	110 5/8	+1
no-par	100	Hercules Motors Corp.	14	14	14	+1/8
no-par	20	Houston Lighting & Power Co.	55 1/2	54 3/8	55 1/2	+3/4
no-par	200	Household Finance Corp.	34 5/8	34 1/8	34 1/4	−1 3/8
no-par	160	Ingersoll-Rand Co.	81 7/8	79 3/4	81	+5/8
no-par	100	International Nickel of Can.	114	114	114	−1 1/2
15	300	International Packers	12 5/8	12 1/2	12 5/8	+3/4
10	50	Kresge (S.S.) Co.	37 7/8	37 5/8	37 3/4	none
100	60	Long Island Lighting 5% pfd.[1]	105 1/4	105 1/4	105 1/4	+1/4
5	200	May Department Stores Co.	36	36	36	none
1	90	National Auto. Fibres	17 5/8	17 3/8	17 5/8	+1/4
no-par	90	Panhandle Eastern Pipe Line	102 7/8	102 7/8	102 7/8	none
no-par	50	Pet Milk Company	63 1/8	62 1/2	63	+1 1/8
1	25	Phillips-Jones Corp.[1]	11 3/4	11	11	none
no-par	70	Pullman, Inc.	63 1/8	63	63 1/8	+1

NOTE: Data presented here are not factual as of any date, and changes have been made for purposes of problem diversification. *pfd.* = preferred.

[1] Unit of trading (round lot) is 10 shares.

[2] Stock prices are quoted in dollars: 37 1/4 = \$37.25; 16 7/8 = \$16.875; etc.

[3] *Change since yesterday* = the increase or decrease in dollars in today's last quotation as compared with yesterday's last quotation.

Commission: 40.25 commission on the full unit of trading computed as follows:

$52\frac{1}{2} \times 100 = \$5{,}250$

$$\begin{array}{rr} \$5{,}250 \times .001 = & \$\ 5.25 \\ & +\ 35.00 \\ \hline & \$40.25 \end{array} \text{ per 100 shares}$$

28.83 commission on the 60-share odd lot computed as follows:

$52\frac{3}{4} \times 60 = \$3{,}165$

$$\begin{array}{rrl} \$3{,}165 \times .005 = & \$15.83 & \text{(note that tax is excluded)} \\ & +\ 15.00 & \\ \hline & \$30.83 & \\ & -\ \ 2.00 & \text{Odd lot deduction} \\ \hline & \$28.83 & \text{per 60 shares} \end{array}$$

Total: 5,290.25. The amount of $5,250 plus $40.25 commission for the purchase of 100 shares = $5,250 + $40.25 = $5,290.25 total cost.

3,194.08. The amount of $3,165.25 plus $28.83 commission for the purchase of the odd lot of 60 shares = $3,165.25 + $28.83 = $3,194.08 total cost.

EXERCISE 2

A. Solve the following problems in transfer taxes on the purchase of odd lots.

1. Compute (*a*) the Federal transfer tax, (*b*) the SEC charge, and (*c*) the total transfer taxes on 83 shares of a 100-share unit of trading with par value of $3 per share if purchased at $24\frac{1}{8}$ including differential.
2. Compute (*a*) the Federal transfer tax, (*b*) the SEC charge, and (*c*) the total transfer taxes on 9 shares of stock with par value of $70 per share if purchased at $19\frac{5}{8}$ including differential.
3. Compute (*a*) the Federal transfer tax, (*b*) the SEC charge, and (*c*) the total transfer taxes on the purchase of 85 shares of 100-share unit of trading stock if it is no-par stock and the effective round-lot price is $129\frac{1}{4}$.
4. Compute (*a*) the Federal transfer tax, (*b*) the SEC charge, and (*c*) the total transfer taxes on the purchase of 7 shares of 100-share unit of trading stock if it is no-par stock and the effective round-lot price is $16\frac{3}{4}$.

B. In solving the following stock purchases on the New York Stock Exchange, use the stock listings on page 372 and assume quantities of shares purchased to be as indicated under the column "Today's sales, no. of shares." For each purchase, **find** (*a*) number of shares bought, (*b*) execution price per share, (*c*) total transfer taxes, if any, (*d*) amount, (*e*) commission, and (*f*) total cost to purchaser.

1. American Tobacco at yesterday's last effective round-lot quotation.
2. Adams-Millis Corp. at today's high effective round-lot quotation.

3. Armour & Co. at today's low effective round-lot quotation.
4. Corn Products 7% pfd. at today's last effective round-lot quotation.
5. Amalgamated Leather 6% pfd. at today's last effective round-lot quotation.
6. Foremost Dairies, Inc., at yesterday's last effective round-lot quotation.
7. American Smelting & Refining 7% pfd. at today's low effective round-lot quotation.
8. Ingersoll-Rand Co. at today's last effective round-lot quotation.

UNIT 3. Stock Sales

Unlike stock purchases, in which odd lots only are subject to the Federal transfer tax and the SEC charge, *all stock sales* through registered exchanges, whether full units of trading or odd lots, are liable for the Federal transfer tax and the SEC charge. Additionally, *all stock sales* made on registered exchanges in the states of New York, Florida, Pennsylvania, South Carolina, and Texas require the payment of state transfer taxes.

The Federal transfer tax and the SEC charge are computed in the same manner for sales as for the purchase of odd lots (see pages 370 and 371). The discussion here is limited to the New York State transfer tax on stock sales (state transfer taxes are not levied against stock purchases of full or odd lots).

New York State Transfer Tax

The transfer tax charged by New York State on stock sales is computed as follows:

1 cent per share selling under \$5
2 cents per share selling at \$5 but under \$10
3 cents per share selling at \$10 but under \$20
4 cents per share selling at \$20 or more

Examples: Find the New York State transfer tax on (*a*) 60 shares selling at $3\frac{1}{2}$, (*b*) 100 shares selling at 7, (*c*) 25 shares selling at $16\frac{1}{4}$, and (*d*) 240 shares selling at 83.

(*a*)	$\$.01 \times 60 = \$\ .60$
(*b*)	$\$.02 \times 100 = \$2.00$
(*c*)	$\$.03 \times 25 = \$.\ 75$
(*d*)	$\$.04 \times 240 = \$9.60$

Example of a stock sale. Find the net proceeds to the seller of 215 shares of Smith-Corona, Inc., \$10 par common stock (100-share unit of trading) sold through a broker on the New York Stock Exchange, if the effective round-lot price is $16\frac{7}{8}$.

Actual date, Nov. 9, 1960 Settlement date, Nov. 16

Exc.	Sold	Description	Price	Tax	Amount	Commission	Proceeds
NYS	200	Smith-Cor.	$16\frac{7}{8}$	7.07	3,367.93	43.76	3,324.17
NYS	15		$16\frac{3}{4}$	.56	250.69	6.00	244.69

Explanation

Actual date: Nov. 9, 1960. The date on which the broker made the sale.

Settlement date: Nov. 16. As is ordinarily the case, the fourth business day following the actual date. Nov. 11 was a legal holiday; Nov. 12 and 13 were Saturday and Sunday, always nonbusiness days; and thus the fourth business day following Nov. 9 was Nov. 16.

Exc.: NYS. The transaction took place on the New York Stock Exchange.

Sold: 200. Two full units of trading in this instance.

15. An odd lot.

Description: Smith-Cor. The abbreviation for Smith-Corona, Inc.

Price: $16\frac{7}{8}$. Selling price per share for full unit of trading.

$16\frac{3}{4}$. Selling price per share including differential on odd lot.

Tax: 7.07. Transfer taxes on the sale of 200 shares. Federal transfer tax: par of $10 × 200 = $2,000 = 20 hundreds of par, and since the price is less than 20, the tax is 5¢ per 100 of par. SEC charge is based on $16\frac{7}{8}$ × 200 = $3,375 = 6 and a fraction $500's. New York State transfer tax is based on the price of $16\frac{7}{8}$ (at least $10 but less than $20), and the tax is 3¢ times the number of shares. Thus,

Federal transfer tax is	$.05 × 20 =	$1.00
SEC charge is	.01 × 7 =	.07
New York State transfer tax is	.03 × 200 =	6.00
Total tax on 200 shares	=	$7.07

.56. Transfer taxes on the sale of 15 shares. Federal transfer tax: par of $10 × 15 = $150 = 1.5 hundreds of par and since the price is less than 20, the tax is 5¢ per 100 or fraction thereof of par. SEC charge is based on $16\frac{3}{4}$ × 15 = $251.25 = a fraction of $500. New York State transfer tax is based on the price of $16\frac{3}{4}$ (at least $10 but less than $20), and the tax is 3¢ times the number of shares. Thus,

Federal transfer tax is	$.05 × 2 =	$.10
SEC charge is	.01 × 1 =	.01
New York State transfer tax is	.03 × 15 =	.45
Total tax on 15 shares	=	$.56

Amount: 3,367.93. $16\frac{7}{8}$ × 200 minus $7.07 tax = $3,375 − $7.07 = $3,367.93

250.69. $16\frac{3}{4}$ × 15 minus $.56 tax = $251.25 − $.56 = $250.69

Commission: 43.76 commission on the 200 shares (2 full units of trading) computed as follows:

$$16\frac{7}{8} \times 100 = \$1{,}687.50$$

$$\begin{array}{rrl} \$1{,}687.50 \times .01 = & \$16.88 & \\ & +\ \ 5.00 & \\ \hline & \$21.88 & \text{per 100 shares} \\ & \times\ \ 2 & \\ \hline & \$43.76 & \text{per 200 shares} \end{array}$$

6.00 commission on the 15-share odd lot computed as follows:

$$16\frac{3}{4} \times 15 = \$251.25$$

$$\begin{array}{rrl} \$251.25 \times .01 = & \$2.51 & \\ & +\ 5.00 & \\ \hline & \$7.51 & \\ & -\ 2.00 & \text{odd-lot deduction} \\ \hline & \$5.51 & \end{array}$$

But the minimum commission is \$6 when the money value is \$100 or more.

Proceeds: 3,324.17. The amount of \$3,367.93 less \$43.76 commission for the sale of 200 shares = \$3,367.93 − \$43.76 = \$3,324.17 net proceeds.

244.69. The amount of \$250.69 less \$6.00 minimum commission for the odd-lot sale of 15 shares = \$250.69 − \$6.00 = \$244.69 net proceeds.

EXERCISE 3

A. Solve the following problems in transfer taxes in the sale of stocks:

1. Compute (*a*) the Federal transfer tax, (*b*) the SEC charge, (*c*) the New York State transfer tax, and (*d*) the total transfer taxes on the sale of 100 shares of stock with a par value of \$100 per share if the selling price is $15\frac{1}{2}$.
2. Compute (*a*) the Federal transfer tax, (*b*) the SEC charge, (*c*) the New York State transfer tax, and (*d*) the total transfer taxes on the sale of 200 shares of stock with par value of \$25 per share if the selling price is $33\frac{1}{4}$.
3. Compute (*a*) the Federal transfer tax, (*b*) the SEC charge, (*c*) the New York State transfer tax, and (*d*) the total transfer taxes on the sale of an odd lot of 58 shares of a 100-share unit of trading stock with no-par value if the effective round-lot price is $17\frac{1}{4}$.
4. Compute (*a*) the Federal transfer tax, (*b*) the SEC charge, (*c*) the New York State transfer tax, and (*d*) the total transfer taxes on the sale of 8 shares of a 10-share unit of trading stock with no-par value if the effective round-lot price is $113\frac{1}{4}$.

B. In solving the following stock sales on the New York Stock Exchange, use the stock listings on page 372 and assume quantities of shares sold to be as indicated under the column "Today's sales, no. of shares." For each sale, **find** (*a*) number of shares sold, (*b*) execution price per share, (*c*) total Federal, SEC, and New York State transfer taxes, (*d*) amount (remainder after taxes), (*e*) commission, and (*f*) net proceeds to seller.

1. American Telephone & Telegraph at yesterday's last effective round-lot quotation.
2. International Packers at yesterday's last effective round-lot quotation.
3. American Cable & Radio at today's low effective round-lot quotation.
4. General Cable Corp. at today's low effective round-lot quotation.
5. American Potash & Chemical at today's high effective round-lot quotation.
6. Great Northern Paper Co. at today's last effective round-lot quotation.
7. Consumers Power Co. at today's high effective round-lot quotation.
8. Phillips-Jones Corp. at today's high effective round-lot quotation.

UNIT 4. Purchase and Sale of Bonds

Corporate bonds as well as stocks are usually purchased or sold through the medium of a broker who charges a commission for his services. If the bonds are coupon bonds and delivered by mail, there will also be an insured postage charge made to the buyer. A Federal transfer tax and an SEC charge are additional expenses to the seller, but there are no state transfer taxes on bond sales and there are no transfer taxes (Federal, SEC, or state) on bond purchases.

Unlike most stock transactions, a bond transfer may include an element other than market price. In stocks, the market price ordinarily reflects (includes) the value of any earnings accruing since the last dividend payment. In the case of bonds, accrued interest is not included in the market price, and thus accrued interest is added to the cost to the purchaser and to the remittance to the seller.

Interest on Bond Transfers. Since the market price of a bond does not include any interest which may have accumulated, it is usually necessary to make this calculation in bond transfers. Exceptions to this statement are:

1. Registered bonds in which the settlement date is after the final date of record for any given payment. To explain more fully, if a bond is registered, the holder's name is recorded by the registrars or trustees who make payment of interest to the holder of record. A final date is set, usually about 1 month prior to the interest date for change of registration of holders for the next interest payment. It is obvious that a cer-

tain amount of time is required to complete the accounting processes necessary in transferring ownership from one party to another.

2. If the settlement date of a coupon bond is the interest date, it is required that the coupon due on the settlement date be attached, and thus an interest computation is not necessary. The new holder presents the coupon due for payment. In such instance, the bond is sold *flat* (see 3 following).

3. Perhaps the most frequent exception to the need to make interest calculations occurs when a bond is *flat* and is in default, that is, interest payments are in arrears and one or more interest payments have not been made when due. In such instance, on a registered bond all interest payments due are accumulated and on a coupon bond all coupons unpaid when due are attached, and the accumulated interest if paid in the future goes to the registered holder of record at that time if a registered bond, and to the bearer at that time if a coupon bond.

Computing Interest on Bond Transfers. Assuming that the three exceptions as noted in the preceding do not obtain, bond interest due to the seller and owed by the buyer in addition to the selling price is computed on the following basis.

Bond interest is based on the par (redemption) value of the bond at the specified interest rate for the number of days including the date of the last interest payment up to and including the day before the settlement date. As with stocks, the settlement date of a bond transaction is ordinarily the fourth business day following the actual date. When the settlement date is to be longer than 4 full business days following the actual date of the transaction, the seller must have so stipulated and a later date known and agreeable to the buyer must have been determined.

In making interest calculations, note that nonbusiness days are not considered in counting the number of days to the settlement date. Thus a bond transaction with an actual date on a Thursday has a settlement date on the following Wednesday, and if Friday, Monday, or Tuesday is a legal holiday (nonbusiness day) the settlement date would be delayed until the following Thursday.

On corporate bonds, the interest is computed as ordinary interest at 30-day-month time (on U. S. bonds exact interest is used)—the numerator of the time element being computed at 30-day-month time with a denominator of 360 days. Thus it is obvious why ordinary interest at 30-day-month time is frequently called *ordinary interest at bond time.*

Bond interest payments are usually made semiannually. Interest dates and redemption (maturity) dates of bonds are usually symbolized as follows: *MS 70, AO* 68, *JJ 80; the capital letters indicating the months in which semiannual interest payments are due (the first day of the month unless otherwise indicated); the asterisk (*) indicating the month of maturity; and the figures indicating the year of maturity. Thus the preceding symbols mean: *MS 70, semiannual interest payable Mar. 1 and Sept. 1, maturity date of Mar. 1, 1970; AO* 68, semiannual interest payable Apr. 1 and Oct. 1, maturity date of Oct. 1, 1968; and *JJ 80, semiannual interest payable Jan. 1 and July 1, maturity date of Jan. 1, 1980.

Example 1: Compute the accrued interest on a 4 per cent, $1,000 par corporate bond FA* 72 with actual date of Apr. 9.

The time period is from and including Feb. 1, the date of the last interest payment, to and including Apr. 12, the day preceding the settlement date of Apr. 13: 2 mo. 12 da. = 72 da.

$$\$1{,}000 \times \frac{72}{360} \times \frac{4}{100} = \$8 \quad \text{accrued interest}$$

Example 2: Compute the accrued interest on six $1,000 par, $4\frac{1}{2}$ per cent corporate bonds *JD 75 with actual date of Oct. 29.

The time period is from and including June 1, the date of the last interest payment to and including Nov. 1, the day preceding the settlement date of Nov. 2 (note that the exact number of days following Oct. 29 including Oct. 31 are counted in determining the settlement date): 5 mo. 1 da. = 151 da.

$$\$1{,}000 \times 6 = \$6{,}000$$

$$\$6{,}000 \times \frac{151}{360} \times \frac{45}{1{,}000} = \$113.25 \quad \text{accrued interest}$$

Example 3: Compute the accrued interest, if any, that is added to the purchaser's cost or to the seller's proceeds on a bond that is *flat*.

When a bond is purchased or sold flat, it means that interest payments due have not been made and the market price reflects the value of the bond including all interest payments not yet paid. Therefore, interest is not computed.

Bond Quotations. Bond quotations are per bond, there being no such thing as an odd lot. Quotations are a per cent of par, not in dollars. Most corporate bonds are $1,000 par, though a few are in denominations of $100 or $500, the most notable exception being American Telephone & Telegraph Co. $100 par debentures.

Examples 1: quotations on $100 par bonds

$$102\frac{1}{2} = \$100 \times 1.02\frac{1}{2} = \$102.50 \text{ per bond}$$

$$90\frac{3}{4} = \$100 \times .90\frac{3}{4} = \$\ 90.75 \text{ per bond}$$

Examples 2: quotations on $1,000 par bonds

$$110\frac{1}{8} = \$1{,}000 \times 1.10\frac{1}{8} = \$1{,}101.25 \text{ per bond}$$

$$83\frac{1}{4} = \$1{,}000 \times .83\frac{1}{4} = \$\ \ 832.50 \text{ per bond}$$

$$22\frac{5}{8} = \$1{,}000 \times .22\frac{5}{8} = \$\ \ 226.25 \text{ per bond}$$

Federal Taxes Only on Bond Transactions. The seller of bonds on a recognized exchange must pay both a Federal transfer tax of $.05 per $100 of par value ($.50 on a $1,000 bond) plus an SEC charge of 1 cent for each $500 or fraction thereof of the amount involved.

There are no state taxes on bond sales or purchases, nor are there any Federal transfer taxes or SEC charges on bond purchases.

The Federal transfer tax and SEC charge paid by the broker on bond sales are deducted by the broker from his remittance to the seller.

Example: Find (*a*) the Federal transfer tax, (*b*) the SEC charge, and (*c*) the total transfer taxes on the sale of four $1,000 par bonds at $91\frac{1}{2}$.

(*a*) $1,000 × 4 = $4,000 = 40 hundreds
$.05 × 40 = $2.00 Federal transfer tax

(*b*) $\$1{,}000 \times .91\frac{1}{2} = \$915$ Selling price per bond
$915 × 4 = $3,660 Total selling price of 4 bonds
$3,660 = 7 and a fraction $500's
$.01 × 8 = $.08 SEC charge

(*c*) $2.00 + $.08 = $2.08 Total transfer taxes

Commission Rates on Purchase or Sale of Bonds. Unlike stocks, the computation of brokerage charges for the purchase or sale of bonds is relatively simple. With certain exceptions, the following charges are applied:

New York Stock Exchange Bond Commission Rates per $1,000 of Par

Price per $1,000 of par	Commission per each bond:			
	1 or 2	3	4	5 or more
Selling at less than $10 (1%)...........	$1.50	$1.20	$ .90	$ .75
Selling at $10 (1%) and above but under $100 (10%).........................	2.50	2.00	1.50	1.25
Selling at $100 and above (10% and above)............................	5.00	4.00	3.00	2.50

Examples: Find the commission charges on $1,000 par bonds purchased or sold in quantities and at prices as follows: (*a*) 1 bond at 91, (*b*) 3 bonds at $108\frac{1}{2}$, (*c*) 4 bonds at 120, (*d*) 2 bonds at $22\frac{1}{4}$, (*e*) 9 bonds at $87\frac{5}{8}$, (*f*) 3 bonds at $9\frac{7}{8}$, (*g*) 12 bonds at $8\frac{3}{4}$, and (*h*) 4 bonds at $6\frac{1}{8}$.

(*a*) $5 × 1 = $5 (*b*) $4 × 3 = $12
(*c*) $3 × 4 = $12 (*d*) $5 × 2 = $10
(*e*) $2.50 × 9 = $22.50 (*f*) $2 × 3 = $6
(*g*) $1.25 × 12 = $15 (*h*) $1.50 × 4 = $6

A Listing and Quotations on Certain $1,000 Par Corporate Bonds[1]

Interest now in default[2]	Today's sales, $1,000 of par	$1,000 par bonds and interest rates	Interest dates and maturity	Today's quotations in per cents of par		
				High	Low	Last
No	1	Alabama Power Co. Mtg. 3 1/4's	*MS 81	95 7/8	95 7/8	95 7/8
No	7	American Tobacco Co. Deb. 3 1/4's	*FA 77	103	102 3/4	102 3/4
No	3	Boston & Maine R.R. Mtg. 4 1/2's	AO* 70	105 3/4	105 1/2	105 3/4
No	1	Boston & Maine R.R. Deb. 5's	*MN 75	85 1/2	85 1/2	85 1/2
No	1	Borden Co. Deb. 2 7/8's	*MS 81	92 7/8	92 7/8	92 7/8
No	10	Canadian Pac. Ry. Coll. Trust 4's	*JD 69	93	93	93
No	8	C.I.T. Financial Corp Deb. 3 5/8's	MS* 70	101 1/8	100 3/4	101 1/8
No	13	Commonwealth Edison Co. Mtg. 3 1/2's	JD* 86	110	110	110
No	10	Crampton Mfg. Co. Mtg. 5 1/2's	*MN 72	100	99 7/8	100
No	6	Foremost Dairies Deb. 4 1/2's	*JJ 80	90	89 3/4	90
No	4	Grand Union Co. Deb. 3 1/2's	*MS 69	102 1/2	102 1/2	102 1/2
No	1	Great Northern Ry. Mtg. 4 1/2's	JJ* 96	82 1/2	82 1/2	82 1/2
Yes	10	Greek Government 6's	*FA 85	24	24	24
No	16	Mo. Pacific R.R. Coll. Trust 4 1/4's	MS* 76	102 5/8	102 1/4	102 1/4
No	1	Norwich & Worcester R.R. Mtg. 4 1/2's	*FA 67	92	92	92
Yes	28	N.Y. Ont. & West'n Ry. 4's	*JD 95	26 3/4	25	25
No	8	Penn. Power & Light Deb. 4 1/2's	FA* 94	106 1/2	106 1/4	106 1/2
No	7	Pitt. Cinn. Chg. & St. L. R.R. "B" 5's	*AO 75	105	104 7/8	105
No	3	St. Lawrence & Adirond. Ry. Mtg. 6's	*AO 75	105 3/8	105	105
No	2	Textron American Deb. 5's	FA* 71	120	120	120

[1] Data presented in this listing are not factual as of any date. Interest dates, maturity dates, and quotations have been changed for purposes of problem diversification.

[2] When the interest is in default, the bond is bought or sold *flat*, that is, accrued interest is not computed, the quotation reflecting the market value of the bond including all interest due or in default.

Deb.: abbreviation of debenture. *Mtg.:* abbreviation of mortgage. *Coll.:* abbreviation of collateral. "*B*": an "A" issue of bonds if still outstanding may have prior preference.

Example of a bond purchase: Find the cost to the purchaser of a Chicago and Western Indiana Consolidated $1,000, 4 per cent, AO* 78, if purchased through a member of the New York Stock Exchange at $93\frac{5}{8}$.

Actual date, Mar. 7, 1960 Settlement date, Mar. 11

Exc.	Bot.	Description	Price	Interest	Amount	Commission	Total
NYS	1,000	ChgWestInd 4-78	$93\frac{5}{8}$	17.78 5 mo. 10 da.	954.03	5.00	959.03

Explanation

Actual date: Mar. 7, 1960. The date the broker made the purchase.

Settlement date: Mar. 11. The fourth business day after the actual date. The date that the buyer is to make payment and the seller is to deliver the bond.

Exc.: NYS. The transaction took place on the New York Stock Exchange.

Bot.: 1,000. Bought $1,000 of par value. Note that 1,000 refers to the total par value of the bond, not to the number of bonds purchased.

Description: ChgWestInd 4-78. Abbreviation of Chicago and Western Indiana Consolidated, 4 per cent interest-bearing bond due Oct. 1, 1978 with semiannual interest payment dates of Apr. 1 and Oct. 1.

Price: $93\frac{5}{8}$. The per cent of $1,000 par value at which the bond was purchased, meaning in dollars: $\$1,000 \times .93\frac{5}{8} = \$936.25$.

Interest: 17.78.

5 mo. 10 da. Interest computed at 30-day month time (160 days) = $17.78

from and including the date of the last interest payment, Oct. 1, 1959 to and including Mar. 10, 1960, the day before settlement date of Mar. 11.

Amount: 954.03. The sum of $\$936.25 + \$17.78 = \$954.03$.

Commission: 5.00. The commission on one $1,000 par bond selling at $100 or above is $5.

Total: 959.03. The cost to the purchaser is $\$954.03 + \$5.00 = \$959.03$.

Example of a bond sale: Find the proceeds to the seller of four $1,000 par, $4\frac{1}{2}$ per cent mortgage bonds of the Acme Railroad, *FA 76, if sold through a member of the New York Stock Exchange at $112\frac{1}{4}$.

Actual date, Nov. 30, 1960 Settlement date, Dec. 6

Exc.	Sold	Description	Price	Interest	Tax	Amount	Commission	Proceeds
NYS	4,000	Acme R.R. $4\frac{1}{2}$-76	$112\frac{1}{4}$	62.50 4 mo. 5 da.	2.10	4,550.50	12.00	4,538.40

Explanation

Actual date: Nov. 30, 1960. The date the broker made the sale.

Settlement date: Dec. 6. The fourth business day after the actual date, there being an intervening Saturday and Sunday. The day that the seller is to deliver the bonds and receive payment.

Exc.: NYS. The transaction took place on the New York Stock Exchange.

Sold: 4,000. Sold \$4,000 of par value. Note that 4,000 refers to the total par value of the four bonds, not to the number of bonds sold.

Description: Acme R.R. $4\frac{1}{2}$-76. Abbreviation of Acme Railroad $4\frac{1}{2}$ per cent mortgage bonds due Feb. 1, 1976 with interest payment dates of Feb. 1 and Aug. 1.

Price: $112\frac{1}{4}$. The per cent of par value at which the bonds were sold meaning a total in dollars: $\$4{,}000 \times 1.12\frac{1}{4} = \$4{,}490$.

Interest: 62.50.

4 mo. 5 da. Interest computed at 30-day month time (125 days) = \$62.50

from and including the date of the last interest payment, Aug. 1 to and including Dec. 5, the day before the settlement date of Dec. 6.

Tax: 2.10. Sum of the Federal transfer tax of \$2.00 and the S.E.C. charge of \$.10. Federal transfer tax computed as follows: \$4,000 of par = 40 hundreds; and $\$.05 \times 40 = \$2.00$. SEC charge computed as follows: the price of the four bonds plus interest totaling \$4,552.50 (\$4,490 + \$62.50) contains 9 and a fraction \$500's; and $\$.01 \times 10 = \$.10$.

Amount: 4,550.40. Price plus interest minus tax: $\$4{,}490 + \$62.50 - \$2.10 =$ 4,550.40.

Commission: 12.00. The commission on four bonds selling at \$100 or above $= \$3 \times 4 = \$12.00$.

Proceeds: 4,538.40. Proceeds to the seller is $\$4{,}550.40 - \$12.00 = \$4{,}538.40$.

EXERCISE 4A

For each of the following bond purchases, **find** (*a*) dollars of par purchased, (*b*) price in per cent, (*c*) interest, if any, (*d*) amount, (*e*) commission at New York Stock Exchange bond commission rates, and (*f*) total cost to purchaser. Use bond listings from page 381 and assume that quantities purchased are as indicated under the column "Today's sales, \$1,000 of par" and that settlement dates are 4 days after actual dates.

1. Boston & Maine R.R. Mtg. 4 1/2's at today's low quotation, actual date Oct. 8.
2. American Tobacco Co. Deb. 3 1/4's at today's high quotation, actual date July 12.
3. Commonwealth Edison Co. Mtg. 3 1/2's at today's last quotation, actual date June 19.
4. N.Y. Ont. & West's Ry. 4's at today's high quotation, actual date Nov. 14.
5. Mo. Pacific R.R. Coll. Trust 4 1/4's at today's last quotation, actual date Mar. 29.
6. Crampton Mfg. Co. 1st Mtg. 5 1/2's at today's low quotation, actual date Dec. 18.
7. Great Northern Ry. Mtg. 4 1/2's at today's high quotation, actual date Mar. 31.
8. St. Lawrence & Adirond. Ry. Mtg. 6's at today's last quotation, actual date Dec. 4.

EXERCISE 4B

For each of the following bond sales, **find** (*a*) dollars of par sold, (*b*) price in per cent, (*c*) interest, if any, (*d*) transfer taxes, (*e*) amount, (*f*) commission at New York Stock Exchange bond commission rates, and (*g*) net proceeds to the seller. Use bond listings from page 381 and assume that quantities sold are as indicated under the column "Today's sales, $1,000 of par" and that settlement dates are 4 days after actual dates.

1. Alabama Power Co. Mtg. 3 1/4's at today's last quotation, actual date Aug. 3.
2. C.I.T. Financial Corp. Deb. 3 5/8's at today's low quotation, actual date July 21.
3. Canadian Pac. Ry. Coll. Trust 4's at today's high quotation, actual date Aug. 11.
4. Borden Co. Deb. 2 7/8 at today's last quotation, actual date Nov. 9.
5. Grand Union Co. Deb. 3 1/2's at today's low quotation, actual date July 29.
6. Pitt. Cinn. Chg. & St. L. R.R. Gen. "B" 5's at today's high quotation, actual date May 12.
7. Penn. Power & Light Deb. 4 1/2's at today's high quotation, actual date Sept. 17.
8. Foremost Dairies Deb. 4 1/2's at today's last quotation, actual date Oct. 21

UNIT 5. Stock Rights; Dollar and Per Cent Gain or Loss on Securities

In order to obtain additional capital, the directors of a corporation may determine to raise such capital by the sale of unissued or treasury stock.

Stock Rights. The laws of most states require that a corporation increasing the amount of its common stock must allow the existing stockholders a right known as "stockholder's right" to purchase such new stock in the ratio that their present holdings are to the total shares of the corporation.

Such rights, known as "stock rights," may be exercised by all persons who are shown on the records of the company to be stockholders at the close of business on the "record date," a date ordinarily set several weeks after the board of directors have declared their intent to issue such rights. Since the subscription price of the new stock is usually offered at less than the current market price in order to ensure its sale, stock rights are valuable, but they must be exercised or sold before their expiration date or they become worthless.

Between the declaration date and the time when the stockholders actually have possession of the certificate representing their rights, such rights may be sold on a "when issued" basis. From the date of delivery of the rights to the expiration date, the actual certificates for the rights may be exercised or sold.

Prior to the delivery of the rights (during this period the stock is quoted "cum-rights" or "rights-on"), the value of a right may be computed as follows:

$$\text{Value of a right} = \frac{\text{market price} - \text{subscription price}}{\text{number of rights to purchase 1 share} + 1}$$

Example: A corporation offered at $120 a share, one share of its new stock for each five shares held. The stock was selling at $150 following the declaration date. Find the value of a right.

$$\frac{\$150 - \$120}{5 + 1} = \frac{\$30}{6} = \$5$$

After delivery of the certificate of rights (during this period the stock is quoted "ex-rights" or "rights-off"), the value of a right may be computed as follows:

$$\text{Value of a right} = \frac{\text{market price} - \text{subscription price}}{\text{number of rights to purchase one share}}$$

Example: Following the delivery of the certificates representing the stock rights in the preceding example (the stock was then ex-rights), the market price of the stock dropped to $145. Find the value of a right.

$$\frac{\$145 - \$120}{5} = \frac{\$25}{5} = \$5$$

Note that the rights in both examples had the same value. Assuming that the general market for this stock was unchanged between the rights-on price of $150 and the ex-rights price of $145, the market values of the rights for both periods tend to coincide for any appreciable difference would create an opportunity for profit. It should also be apparent that such rights offer a buyer considerably more opportunity for speculation than does the stock itself. Thus, if the market price of the stock should fall to $120, the rights would be worthless; if the market price should rise to $180 during the rights-on period or to $170 during the ex-rights period and before their expiration date, the value of the rights would double.

To Find Gain or Loss on Securities. Gain on stocks or bonds may be derived from two sources: (1) dividends or interest and (2) increment in value. Loss may occur through depreciation in value. The calculations in dollars and cents are very simple.

Example 1: Continental Insurance Co. common stock is purchased at 105 and is sold for 115, dividends received being $6. What was gain per share?

Gain from dividends		= $ 6
Gain through increment	= $115 − $105 =	10
	Total gain =	$16

Example 2: Florida Power Corp. 1st Mtg. 4's 66 purchased at $106\frac{1}{2}$ are sold for $98\frac{1}{4}$, 1 year's interest being received. What is the gain or loss per bond?

Gain from interest	= $1,000 × .04	= $40
Loss from depreciated value	= $1,065 − $982.50 =	82.50
	Net loss =	$42.50

To Find Per Cent of Gain or Loss on Securities. Per cent of gain or loss on stocks and bonds is also computed easily. To express the relationship of gain or loss to cost, divide gain or loss by cost.

Example 1: Southern California Edison common stock purchased at $23\frac{1}{4}$ is sold for $30\frac{1}{2}$, no dividends having been received. What is the per cent of gain or loss on cost per share?

No gain from dividends		= $0.00
Gain from increment	= $30.50 − $23.25 =	7.25
	Total gain =	$7.25

$$\text{Per cent gain on cost} = \frac{\$\ 7.25}{\$23.25} = .3118 = 31.18\%$$

Example 2: Iowa Public Service Co. Deb. 6's 60 purchased at 108 are sold at 100, 5 years' interest being received. What is the per cent of gain or loss on cost per bond?

Gain from interest	= $1,000 × .06 × 5	= $300
Loss from depreciated value	= $1,080 − $1,000 =	80
	Net gain =	$220

$$\text{Per cent gain on cost} = \frac{\$220}{\$1{,}080} = .2037 = 20.37\%$$

EXERCISE 5

A. Solve the following problems in stock rights:

1. A corporation offered at $40 per share, 1 share of its new stock for each 3 shares held. The stock was selling at $52 per share following the declaration date. Find the value of a right.
2. Following the delivery of the certificates representing the stock rights, a stock selling at $96 per share was quoted ex-rights. If 6 rights entitled the possessor to purchase 1 share of new stock at $84, find the value of a right.

3. The issued capital stock of a company was $500,000 divided into 20,000 common shares with a par value of $25 per share. Finding that $100,000 of additional capital is needed, the board of directors determine to issue 4,000 shares of new common stock at par. If the market price of the stock is then $42 per share, find (*a*) the number of rights required to subscribe for each new share, (*b*) the value of a right during the on-right period, and (*c*) the market price per share that the stock may be expected to sell for during the ex-right period.

4. A corporation has a capital stock consisting of 30,000 issued shares of $10 par common stock with a then market quotation of $59. The board of directors determine to issue 6,000 new shares permitting present stockholders to purchase at $50 per share 1 share of new stock for each 5 shares of the old stock held on date of record. Find (*a*) the total dollars of new capital the directors expect the company to obtain, (*b*) the value of a stock right during the on-right period, and (*c*) the market price per share that the stock may be expected to sell for during the ex-right period.

B. Solve the following without consideration of taxes, odd lots, commissions, or any brokerage costs:

1. 100 shares of American Tel. and Tel. common stock were purchased on May 1, 1952 at $178\frac{1}{4}$ and sold on Nov. 1, 1959 at $165\frac{7}{8}$. If dividends per quarter per share were $2.25, find (*a*) gain from dividends, (*b*) loss from depreciated value, and (*c*) net gain considering both dividends and loss from depreciated value.

2. 80 shares of Pacific Gas & Electric Co. 6 per cent $100 par-value preferred stock were purchased on June 1, 1952 at $102\frac{1}{2}$ and sold on Dec. 1, 1960 at $108\frac{3}{4}$. If dividends payable quarterly were not in arrears, find (*a*) gain from dividends, (*b*) gain from increment in value, and (*c*) net gain considering both dividends and gain through increment.

3. Five 4 per cent interest-bearing, $1,000 mortgage bonds of the Southern Pacific Railway Company were purchased on May 15, 1953 at $102\frac{1}{2}$ and sold on Nov. 15, 1961 at $98\frac{1}{8}$. If the interest was not flat, find (*a*) gain from interest, (*b*) loss from depreciated value, and (*c*) net gain considering both interest and loss from depreciated value.

C. Solve the following to nearest hundredth per cent without consideration of taxes, odd lots, commissions, or any brokerage costs:

1. 300 shares of Rheem Company common stock were purchased on Mar. 8, 1954 at $22\frac{3}{4}$ and sold on Sept. 8, 1960 at $19\frac{7}{8}$. If total dividends received over the period had been $7.80 per share, find the per cent of gain on cost.

2. 200 shares of Raphael Weill & Company, Inc., 7 per cent $100 par-value, cumulative preferred stock were bought on June 19, 1954 at $102\frac{1}{8}$ and sold on June 19, 1961 at $75\frac{1}{2}$. If dividends became in arrears $42 per share, find the per cent of loss on cost.

3. Eight Canada Dry Ginger Ale Deb. 4's, $1,000 par value, were purchased on June 2, 1959 at $99\frac{7}{8}$ and sold on Dec. 2, 1962 at $104\frac{1}{2}$. If the interest, payable semiannually, was not flat, find the per cent of gain on cost.

UNIT 6. Rate of Gain or Loss on Securities

Finding the rate of gain or loss on stocks or bonds introduces the factor of time into the calculations, making computation much more difficult than simply finding the gain or loss in dollars and per cent of gain or loss.

Rate of current yield is the term used to express the per cent of annual return at the present market price.

Rate of yield to maturity is the term used to express the per cent of average annual return with not only present market price but also future selling price considered. The term is used most frequently in reference to bonds selling at a premium or discount that presumably will be redeemed at par on their maturity date.

The dividend rates on preferred stocks and the interest rates on bonds are usually nominal rates, since the market or purchase price is rarely exactly at par. Thus a 5 per cent, \$100 par share of preferred stock pays dividends of \$5 per year, and a 4 per cent, \$500 bond pays interest of \$20 per year; but the real rate of return on the preferred share will be more or less than 5 per cent as the market price is less or more than \$100, and the real rate of return on the bond will be more or less than 4 per cent as the market price is less or more than \$500.

To Find Rate of Current Yield. To find the rate of current yield on a common stock, preferred stock, or bond, divide the annual return (dividend or interest) by the market price.

Example 1: What is the rate of current yield on a 6 per cent, \$100 par share of preferred stock selling at \$105?

$$\text{Current yield} = \$100 \times .06 = \$6$$

$$\text{Rate of current yield} = \frac{\$6}{\$105} = .0571 = 5.71\%$$

Example 2: What is the rate of current yield on a 4 per cent, \$1,000 bond if the market price is \$920?

$$\text{Current yield} = \$1{,}000 \times .04 = \$40$$

$$\text{Rate of current yield} = \frac{\$40}{\$920} = .0435 = 4.35\%$$

To Find Rate of Yield to Maturity. Yield to maturity on bonds may be found through the use of prepared tables of bond yields or of bond values. Formulas using logarithms or annuity tables may also be employed.

However, such tables may not be available, and it is possible to obtain a close approximation of yield to maturity by the use of a convenient, easily computed, rule-of-thumb method. Since this approximation is ordinarily exact to within the nearest $\frac{1}{10}$ of 1 per cent (.001), most individuals find the rule-of-thumb method sufficiently accurate.

For Premium Bonds. If the bond is purchased at more than the redemption (par) value, find yield to maturity as follows:

1. Subtract the par value from the cost to obtain the *premium.*
2. Divide the premium by the number of years to maturity to obtain approximate *annual amortization* of the premium.
3. Find the *remainder* of the annual yield less the annual amortization.
4. Find the *quotients* of the remainder divided by (*a*) the cost, (*b*) the par value plus annual amortization.
5. Average the two obtained quotients.

Example: Yield to maturity of premium bonds. Find yield to maturity of \$1,000 par, Appalachian Elec. Power Co. 1st Mtg. $3\frac{1}{2}$'s, JD* 83 if purchased immediately following the first interest payment in 1962 at 110.

Price: 110 = \$1,100.

Interest periods and maturity: JD* 83 = June 1 and Dec. 1 interest payment dates; Dec. 1, 1983 the date of the final interest payment and the redemption date. Therefore the number of years to maturity from June 1, 1962 to Dec. 1, 1983 is 21.5.

Annual yield: \$1,000 × .035 = \$35.

Steps in solution:

$$(1)\quad \$1{,}100 - \$1{,}000 = \$100$$

$$(2)\quad \frac{\$100}{21.5} = \$4.65$$

$$(3)\quad \$35 - \$4.65 = \$30.35$$

$$(4a)\quad \frac{\$30.35}{\$1{,}100} = .0276$$

$$(4b)\quad \frac{\$30.35}{\$1{,}000 + \$4.65} = .0302$$

$$(5)\quad \frac{.0276 + .0302}{2} = \frac{.0578}{2} = .0289 = 2.9\%$$

For Discount Bonds. If the bond is purchased at less than the redemption (par) value, find yield to maturity as follows:

1. Subtract the cost from the par value to find *discount.*
2. Divide the discount by the number of years to maturity to obtain approximate *annual accumulation* of the discount.
3. Find the *sum* of the annual yield plus the annual accumulation.
4. Find the *quotients* of the sum divided by (*a*) the cost, (*b*) the par value minus annual accumulation.
5. Average the two obtained quotients.

Example: Yield to maturity of discount bonds. Find yield to maturity of $1,000 par, Webb & Knapp Inc. Deb. 5's, *JD 74 if purchased immediately following the second interest payment in 1961 at $85\frac{1}{2}$.

Price: $85\frac{1}{2}$ = $855.

Interest periods and maturity: *JD 74 = June 1 and Dec. 1 interest payment dates; June 1, 1974 the date of the final interest payment and the redemption date. Therefore the number of years to maturity from Dec. 1, 1961 to June 1, 1974 is 12.5.

Annual yield: $1,000 × .05 = $50.

Steps in solution:

$$(1)\ \$1{,}000 - \$855 = \$145$$

$$(2)\ \frac{\$145}{12.5} = \$11.60$$

$$(3)\ \$50 + \$11.60 = \$61.60$$

$$(4a)\ \frac{\$61.60}{\$855} = .0720$$

$$(4b)\ \frac{\$61.60}{\$1{,}000 - \$11.60} = .0623$$

$$(5)\ \frac{.0720 + .0623}{2} = \frac{.1343}{2} = .06715 = 6.7\%$$

The same method of determining yield to maturity could be used for stock transactions if dividend returns are fairly constant in amount each year. However, in the preceding examples, the assumption has been made that the bonds would continue to pay interest and would be held to maturity, when they would be redeemed at par. Ordinarily, neither the price of a stock nor its dividends at some given date in the future can be readily forecast, and so such a computation is impractical with stocks. If it is desired to determine the true annual yield earned on a stock transaction over a preceding period of time, the same method of computation may be used.[1]

EXERCISE 6

A. Find rate of current yield (in per cents to nearest tenths) on each of the following stocks and bonds. Use today's last quotations from the stock listing on page 372 and from the bond listings on page 381. Assume that dividends as indicated following and interest payments are annual. *Do not consider any taxes or brokerage costs.*

[1] For further information on "yield to maturity" of bonds, the student is referred to the standard texts on investments or business finance which are available in most school libraries and which present a thorough discussion of the various prepared bond tables, interpolation, and the use of annuity tables and logarithms.

1. American Tobacco 6%, $100 par pfd.
2. Consumers Power Co. ($2.20 dividend).
3. Ingersoll-Rand Co. ($3 dividend).
4. Long Island Lighting 5%, $100 par pfd.
5. Foremost Dairies Deb. $4\frac{1}{2}$'s.
6. Penn. Power and Light Deb. $4\frac{1}{2}$'s.
7. Borden Co. Deb. $2\frac{7}{8}$'s.
8. St. Lawrence & Adirond. Ry. Mtg. 6's.

B. Determine the rate of yield to maturity (in per cents to nearest tenths) on the following bonds listed on page 381. Use today's last quotation and assume date of settlement on purchase to be the day immediately following the first interest payment due on each bond in 1963. *Do not consider any tax or brokerage costs.*

1. Boston & Maine R.R. Mtg. $4\frac{1}{2}$'s.
2. Canadian Pac. Ry. Coll. Trust 4's.
3. Norwich & Worcester R.R. Mtg. $4\frac{1}{2}$'s.
4. Mo. Pacific R.R. Coll. Trust $4\frac{1}{4}$'s.
5. Crampton Mfg. Co. Mtg. $5\frac{1}{2}$'s.
6. Pitt. Cinn. Chg. & St. L. R.R. "B" 5's.
7. Textron American Deb. 5's.
8. Foremost Dairies Deb. $4\frac{1}{2}$'s.

CHAPTER XII

PERIODIC AND COMPOUND INTEREST, ANNUITIES, SINKING FUNDS, AMORTIZATION

UNIT 1. Kinds of Interest

There are three kinds of interest in common use: (1) simple interest, (2) periodic interest, and (3) compound interest. Simple interest is the least and compound interest the greatest for the same principal, rate, and time.

Simple Interest. Interest on the principal for the given time at the given rate is known as *simple interest.* It varies directly with the rate, the time, and the principal.

Example: What is the simple interest due on a note for $500, running for 4 years at 5 per cent, if nothing is paid until date of maturity?

$$I = \$500 \times .05 \times 4 = \$100$$

Periodic Interest. Interest on the principal for the entire time plus interest on each interest payment if deferred from the time it is due and not paid until maturity is known as *periodic interest.* (This is sometimes called "annual interest" if the interest payments are due annually.)

Periodic interest is not in frequent use and is not legal in some states. However, if legal, and if a note stipulates the due date of interest payments as "payable annually," "payable semiannually," "payable quarterly," etc., it is known as periodic interest.

Example 1: What is the periodic interest due on a note of $500, running for 4 years at 5 per cent payable annually, if nothing is paid until date of maturity?

$500 × .05 × 4 = $100 Simple interest
$500 × .05 = $ 25 Yearly payment
$25 × .05 = $1.25 Interest on interest payment deferred 1 year

This $1.25 is to be taken 3 + 2 + 1 = 6 times.

Then $1.25 × 6 = $7.50, or interest on deferred interest payments.

Then simple interest = $100
Interest on interest = 7.50
Annual or periodic interest = $107.50

Or illustrated in Fig. 8.

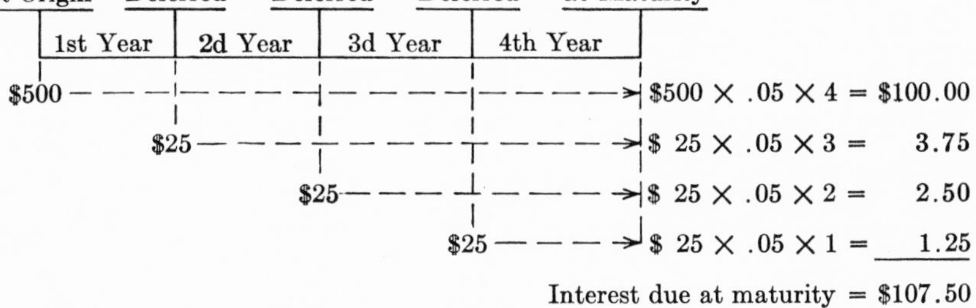

FIG. 8.

In computing periodic interest it is necessary to make allowances for interest paid when due.

Example 2: What is the periodic interest due at maturity on a note of $500, running for 4 years at 5 per cent payable annually, if only the second interest payment has been made when due?

Simple interest due is for only 3 years, since 1 year has been paid.

$500 × .05 × 3	= $75	Simple interest
$500 × .05	= $25	Yearly payment
$ 25 × .05	= $1.25	Interest on interest payment deferred 1 year

This $1.25 is to be taken 3 times (or 3 years) for the payment due at the end of the first year; as the second payment is made when due, there is no interest due on it; on the third payment $1.25 is to be taken 1 time (or 1 year) for the payment due at the end of the third year. Thus:

$1.25 is to be taken 3 + 1 = 4 times

Then $1.25 × 4 = $5, or interest on deferred interest payments.

Simple interest	= $75
Interest on interest	= 5
Annual or periodic interest	= $80

In visualizing periodic interest you may find it helpful to think of it as an original note at simple interest plus a series of additional notes at simple interest for the deferred payments. Thus in Example 2:

(*a*) $500 is borrowed for 4 − 1, or 3 years, since the second payment is made.

(*b*) $25, or first interest payment, is borrowed from end of first year to end of fourth year = 4 − 1 = 3 years.

(*c*) $25, or second interest payment, is paid when due; therefore neither it nor interest on it is due at maturity.

(*d*) $25, or third interest payment, is borrowed from end of third year to end of fourth year = 4 − 3 = 1 year.

(*e*) \$25, or fourth interest payment, does not fall due until maturity date, and therefore no interest on this payment is accumulated.

Or illustrated in Fig. 9.

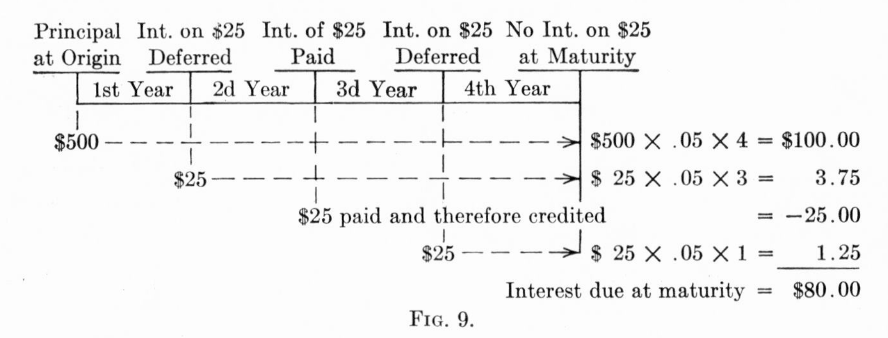

Fig. 9.

Compound Interest. Interest on the principal plus interest combined at regular intervals is known as *compound interest.*

Example: What is the compound interest due on a note of \$500 running 4 years at 5 per cent compounded annually, if nothing is paid until date of maturity?

	Principal + interest		= *maturity value*
1st yr.	= \$500 + \$25	(500 × .05)	= \$525
2d yr.	= \$525 + \$26.25	(525 × .05)	= \$551.25
3d yr.	= \$551.25 + \$27.56	(551.25 × .05)	= \$578.81
4th yr.	= \$578.81 + \$28.94	(578.81 × .05)	= \$607.75

$$I = S - P$$
$$I = \$607.75 - 500 = \$107.75$$

Note that the difference between periodic interest and compound interest is the compounding of interest on the interest in the latter. This accounts for the difference of \$.25 in Example 1 of periodic interest and this example of compound interest.

Compound interest periods may be other than annual. In such instances it is usual to quote a nominal annual rate of interest and then to stipulate the number of compounding periods per year. Thus interest at

6% compounded semiannually = 3% compounded each 6 months
2% compounded semiannually = 1% compounded each 6 months
4% compounded quarterly = 1% compounded each 3 months
6% compounded monthly = $\frac{1}{2}$% compounded each month

Banks usually divide interest-earning periods on deposits into half years or quarters of the year. Thus if the quarters begin Jan. 1, Apr. 1, July 1, and Oct. 1, deposits between these dates do not draw interest until the following quarterly period begins, and withdrawals between dates receive interest only up to the end of the preceding quarter. Therefore, if interest-earning periods are quarterly, a deposit on Feb. 8, withdrawn July 12, would earn interest only from Apr. 1 through June 30, and if interest-earning periods are semiannual, a deposit on Apr. 20, withdrawn the following Apr. 20, would earn interest only from July 1 through Dec. 31.

Furthermore, banks ordinarily do not consider anything but whole dollars in computing interest earnings on deposits. Restated, cents are not considered in interest computation. Thus 99 cents does not earn interest; $1 earns the same interest as $1.25; $23 earns the same interest as $23.82, etc. In the preceding example, if cents had not been considered, the interest would have been $27.55 for the third year and $28.90 for the fourth year, and the total compound interest $107.70 instead of $107.75.

EXERCISE 1

Solve the following. Consider cents as well as whole dollars in computing.

1. Find the total interest due at maturity on a $900, 6 per cent interest-bearing, 3-year note if no payments on either principal or interest are made until date of maturity and the interest is computed as (*a*) simple interest, (*b*) periodic interest payable annually, and (*c*) interest compounded annually.
2. If no payments on either principal or interest are made until date of maturity on a 5-year, $1,260 note, find the maturity value of the note if interest at $4\frac{1}{2}$ per cent is computed as (*a*) simple interest, (*b*) periodic interest payable annually, and (*c*) interest compounded annually.
3. Find the periodic interest due at maturity on a 2-year 6-month note for $2,600 if interest is computed at 10 per cent payable semiannually and only the second and fourth interest payments are made when due.
4. Find the interest due at maturity on a $7,200, 2-year note if interest at 4 per cent is compounded (*a*) semiannually and (*b*) quarterly.
5. Find the interest due at maturity on a 6-month note for $10,000 if interest at 12 per cent is computed as (*a*) simple interest and (*b*) interest compounded monthly.

UNIT 2. Finding Compound Interest; Accumulation Factor; and Tables

Accumulation Factor or the Compound Amount of $1. As has been previously illustrated (page 394), compound amount (and thence compound interest) may be determined by computing a designated per cent of the principal and adding this obtained percentage (interest) to the principal to find an amount (or new principal) at the end of each period of conversion. This process may be simplified by the use of the following rule:

To find the amount of any sum at compound interest, multiply the principal by the amount of $1 at the given rate of compound interest for the given number of time periods.

The following symbols will be recalled: P = principal; n = time, in years; i = interest rate per annum; S = maturity value (or compound amount); and I = interest. By formula, the amount at compound interest is

$$S = P(1 + i)^n$$

Compound interest may then be obtained by the use of the formula applied in simple interest:

$$I = S - P$$

Example 1: Find (*a*) what $500 will amount to in 4 years at 5 per cent interest compounded annually and (*b*) the compound interest.

(*a*) $S = P(1 + i)^n$

$= \$500(1 + .05)^4$

and $(1 + .05)^4 = 1.05 \times 1.05 \times 1.05 \times 1.05 = 1.21550625$

Therefore $S = \$500 \times 1.21550625 = \$607.75$

(*b*) $I = S - P$

$= \$607.75 - \$500 = \$107.75$ (see example on page 394)

In the preceding example, the number of years (4) is a small factor in the computation, and thus the calculation of $1.05 \times 1.05 \times 1.05 \times 1.05$ is not difficult. However, if the number of years had been many, this calculation would have been laborious. Mathematicians, actuaries, accountants, and businessmen have compiled specially prepared tables that eliminate the necessity of such computations for all common rates of compound interest.

In the formula $S = P(1 + i)^n$, if the principal is $1, it is customary to replace S by s. Thus the formula would become $s = 1(1 + i)^n$. Since $1 \times (1 + i)^n$ is equivalent to $(1 + i)^n$, the formula for the compound amount of $1, when interest is compounded annually, is

$$s = (1 + i)^n$$

$(1 + i)^n$ is known as the *accumulation factor.*

It is apparent that the rule for finding the amount of any sum at compound interest may also be stated:

To find compound amount of any principal, multiply the principal by the accumulation factor, or

$$S = P(1 + i)^n$$

And interest may be found by the use of either of the following formulas:

$$I = S - P$$
$$\text{or } I = P[(1 + i)^n - 1]$$

Table I (page 398) is an excerpt from a more complete table of accumulation factors.

In using such a table, find under n the number of periods during which interest is accumulated (compounded) and then locate the point at which this number of periods meets (horizontally) the given rate of interest per period. Thus \$1 for 1 year at 4 per cent interest compounded annually would amount to \$1.04; \$1 for 6 years at 3 per cent interest compounded annually would amount to \$1.1940523; \$1 for 4 years at 5 per cent interest compounded annually (as in the preceding Example 1) would amount to \$1.2155062.

Example 2: Same problem as Example 1.

(*a*)
$$\begin{aligned} S &= P(1 + i)^n \\ &= \$500(1 + .05)^4 \\ &= \$500 \times 1.2155062 = \$607.75 \end{aligned}$$

(*b*)
$$\begin{aligned} I &= S - P \\ &= \$607.75 - \$500 = \$107.75 \end{aligned}$$

or (*b*)
$$\begin{aligned} I &= P[(1 + i)^n - 1] \\ &= \$500[(1 + .05)^4 - 1] \\ &= \$500[1.2155062 - 1] \\ &= \$500 \times .2155062 = \$107.75 \end{aligned}$$

Example 3: Find what \$600 will amount to in 7 years at 4 per cent interest compounded annually.

$$\begin{aligned} S &= P(1 + i)^n \\ &= \$600(1 + .04)^7 \\ &= \$600 \times 1.3159318 = \$789.56 \end{aligned}$$

When Interest Is Compounded More Than Once per Year. Interest may be compounded more frequently than once each year, *e.g.*, semiannually, quarterly, etc. In such an instance the stated rate of interest is merely a nominal rate of interest and the higher rate of interest actually earned during the year is the *effective* annual rate.

Even though the interest conversion periods are not annual, the table of the compound amount of \$1 may be used to find the accumulation factor. When interest conversion periods are other than 1 year, it is

Table I. Amount of $1 at Compound Interest

$s = (1 + i)^n$

Formulas:

To find amount $S = P(1 + i)^n$

To find interest $I = S - P$

$= P[(1 + i)^n - 1]$

To find time or rate $(1 + i)^n = \frac{S}{P}$

To find present value $P = \frac{S}{(1+i)^n}$ { Also see Table II on page 402 which is preferable when available.

n	½%	1%	2%	3%	4%	5%	6%
1	1.005 0000	1.010 0000	1.020 0000	1.030 0000	1.040 0000	1.050 0000	1.060 0000
2	1.010 0250	1.020 1000	1.040 4000	1.060 9000	1.081 6000	1.102 5000	1.123 6000
3	1.015 0751	1.030 3010	1.061 2080	1.092 7270	1.124 8640	1.157 6250	1.191 0160
4	1.020 1505	1.040 6040	1.082 4322	1.125 5088	1.169 8586	1.215 5062	1.262 4770
5	1.025 2513	1.051 0100	1.104 0808	1.159 2741	1.216 6529	1.276 2816	1.338 2256
6	1.030 3775	1.061 5202	1.126 1624	1.194 0523	1.265 3190	1.340 0956	1.418 5191
7	1.035 5294	1.072 1354	1.148 6857	1.229 8739	1.315 9318	1.407 1004	1.503 6303
8	1.040 7070	1.082 8567	1.171 6594	1.266 7701	1.368 5690	1.477 4554	1.593 8481
9	1.045 9106	1.093 6853	1.195 0926	1.304 7732	1.423 3118	1.551 3282	1.689 4790
10	1.051 1401	1.104 6221	1.218 9944	1.343 9164	1.480 2443	1.628 8946	1.790 8477
11	1.056 3958	1.115 6684	1.243 3743	1.384 2339	1.539 4541	1.710 3394	1.898 2986
12	1.061 6778	1.126 8250	1.268 2418	1.425 7609	1.601 0322	1.795 8563	2.012 1965
13	1.066 9862	1.138 0933	1.293 6066	1.468 5337	1.665 0735	1.885 6491	2.132 9283
14	1.072 3211	1.149 4742	1.319 4788	1.512 5897	1.731 6764	1.979 9316	2.260 9040
15	1.007 6827	1.160 9690	1.345 8683	1.557 9674	1.800 9435	2.078 9282	2.396 5582
16	1.083 0712	1.172 5786	1.372 7857	1.604 7064	1.872 9812	2.182 8746	2.540 3517
17	1.088 4865	1.184 3044	1.400 2414	1.652 8476	1.947 9005	2.292 0183	2.692 7728
18	1.093 9289	1.196 1475	1.428 2462	1.702 4331	2.025 8165	2.406 6192	2.854 3392
19	1.099 3986	1.208 1090	1.456 8112	1.753 5061	2.106 8492	2.526 9502	3.025 5995
20	1.104 8956	1.220 1900	1.485 9474	1.806 1112	2.191 1231	2.653 2977	3.207 1355
21	1.110 4201	1.232 3919	1.515 6663	1.860 2946	2.278 7681	2.785 9626	3.399 5636
22	1.115 9722	1.224 7159	1.545 9797	1.916 1034	2.369 9188	2.925 2607	3.603 5374
23	1.121 5520	1.257 1630	1.576 8993	1.973 5865	2.464 7155	3.071 5238	3.819 7497
24	1.127 1598	1.269 7346	1.608 4372	2.032 7941	2.563 3042	3.225 0999	4.048 9346
25	1.132 7956	1.282 4320	1.640 6060	2.093 7779	2.665 8363	3.386 3549	4.291 8707
26	1.138 4596	1.295 2563	1.673 4181	2.156 5913	2.772 4698	3.555 6727	4.549 3830
27	1.144 1519	1.308 2089	1.706 8865	2.221 2890	2.883 3686	3.773 4563	4.822 3459
28	1.149 8726	1.321 2910	1.741 0242	2.287 9277	2.998 7033	3.920 1291	5.111 6867
29	1.155 6220	1.334 5039	1.775 8447	2.356 5655	3.118 6514	4.116 1356	5.418 3879
30	1.161 4001	1.347 8489	1.811 3616	2.427 2625	3.243 3975	4.321 9424	5.743 4912
40	1.220 7942	1.488 8637	2.208 0397	3.262 0378	4.801 0206	7.039 9887	10.285 7179
50	1.283 2258	1.644 6318	2.691 5880	4.383 9060	7.106 6834	11.467 3998	18.420 1543
60	1.348 8502	1.816 6967	3.281 0308	5.891 6031	10.519 6274	18.679 1859	32.987 6908
70	1.417 8305	2.006 7634	3.999 5582	7.917 8219	15.571 6184	30.426 4255	59.075 9302
80	1.490 3386	2.216 7152	4.875 4392	10.640 8906	23.049 7991	49.561 4411	105.795 9935
90	1.566 5547	2.448 6327	5.943 1331	14.300 4671	34.119 3333	80.730 3650	189.464 5112
100	1.646 6685	2.704 8138	7.244 6461	19.218 6320	50.504 9482	131.501 2578	339.302 0835

common practice to symbolize the nominal rate of interest by j and the number of converting periods per year by m. The formula for the amount at compound interest becomes

$$S = P\left(1 + \frac{j}{m}\right)^{mn}$$

And the formulas for compound interest are

$$I = S - P$$

$$\text{or } I = P\left[\left(1 + \frac{j}{m}\right)^{mn} - 1\right]$$

Example 4: Find (a) what \$750 will amount to in 4 years at 6 per cent interest compounded semiannually and (b) the compound interest.

(a)
$$S = P\left(1 + \frac{j}{m}\right)^{mn}$$
$$= \$750\left(1 + \frac{.06}{2}\right)^{2\times 4}$$
$$= \$750(1 + .03)^{8}$$
$$= \$750 \times 1.2667701 = \$950.08$$

(b)
$$I = S - P$$
$$= \$950.08 - \$750 = \$200.08$$

$$\text{or } (b)\ I = P\left[\left(1 + \frac{j}{m}\right)^{mn} - 1\right]$$
$$= \$750\left[\left(1 + \frac{.06}{2}\right)^{2\times 4} - 1\right]$$
$$= \$750[(1 + .03)^{8} - 1]$$
$$= \$750[1.2667701 - 1]$$
$$= \$750 \times .2667701 = \$200.08$$

To Find Time or Rate at Compound Interest. The time or rate at compound interest may be determined from an equation derived from the basic formula of $S = P(1 + i)^n$ and the use of Table I.

$$\text{If } S = P(1 + i)^n$$
$$\text{then } P(1 + i)^n = S$$
$$\text{and } (1 + i)^n = \frac{S}{P}$$

The use of this equation is illustrated in the following examples:

Example 1: If \$800 is deposited in a building and loan association at 4 per cent interest compounded semiannually, in how many years will this deposit accumulate to an amount of \$1,076.69?

$$(1 + i)^n = \frac{S}{P}$$

$$= \frac{\$1{,}076.79}{\$800} = 1.34586$$

Since 4 per cent interest compounded semiannually is equivalent to 2 per cent per period, reference is made to the 2 per cent column in Table I. The entry 1.34586(83) is found opposite the 15th period under n.

It is evident that \$800 would accumulate to the amount of \$1,076.79 in 15 periods at 2 per cent. Since 2 per cent represents the interest for 6 months ($\frac{1}{2}$ year), the deposit of \$800 will amount to \$1,076.79 in $15 \times \frac{1}{2} = 7\frac{1}{2}$ years.

Example 2: Five years after borrowing \$500, Mr. Hobbs repaid the loan with interest, the amount required being \$610.10. What rate of interest compounded quarterly did Mr. Hobbs pay?

$$(1 + i)^n = \frac{S}{P}$$

$$= \frac{\$610.10}{\$500} = \$1.2202$$

Since compounding quarterly for 5 years is equivalent to 20 periods, reference is made to the 20th period under the n column in Table I. The entry 1.2201900 is found in the 1 per cent column.

It is evident that \$1 accumulates to \$1.2202 in 20 periods at 1 per cent. Therefore Mr. Hobbs paid 1 per cent interest each quarter or 4 per cent interest compounded quarterly.

When the values of $(1 + i)^n$, as obtained in Examples 1 and 2, do not occur in Table I, these values may be found by ascertaining by simple ratio the relation of the intermediate (obtained) value to the two bracketing (nearest) values in the table.

Suppose that in Example 1, $(1 + i)^n = 1.35486$ instead of 1.34586. The factor 1.35486 does not appear in the table under the 2 per cent column. However, note the following:

$$\text{Where } (1.02)^n = 1.3458683,\ n = 15$$
$$\text{Where } (1.02)^n = 1.3727857,\ n = 16$$

The difference between 1.3458683 and 1.3727857 is .0269174
The difference between 1.3458683 and 1.35486 is .0089917

It is apparent that n is in excess of 15 periods by approximately $\frac{.0089917}{.0269174}$

And $15 + \frac{.0089917}{.0269174} = 15.33405$ periods

Therefore, since each period represents 6 months or $\frac{1}{2}$ year,

$$n = 15.33405 \times \frac{1}{2} = 7.667025 \text{ years} = 7 \text{ years } 8 \text{ months}$$

To Find Present Value at Compound Interest. Present value or the principal (P) that will amount to a given maturity value at some specified future date and rate of compound interest may be determined from an equation derived from the basic formula of $S = P(1 + i)^n$ and the use of Table I.

$$\text{If } S = P(1 + i)^n$$
$$\text{then } P(1 + i)^n = S$$
$$\text{and } P = \frac{S}{(1 + i)^n}$$

Example 1: Find (a) the principal which will amount to \$3,581.70 in 10 years at 6 per cent interest compounded annually and (b) the compound interest.

(a)

$$P = \frac{S}{(1 + i)^n}$$
$$= \frac{\$3,581.70}{(1 + .06)^{10}}$$
$$= \frac{\$3,581.70}{1.7908477} = \$2,000.00$$

(b)

$$I = S - P$$
$$= \$3,581.70 - \$2,000 = \$1,581.70$$

However, a prepared table of the present value of \$1 at compound interest $\left[\text{equivalent to } \frac{\$1}{(1 + i)^n}\right]$ may be used instead of Table I. It is customary to use the symbol v^n instead of $\frac{1}{(1 + i)^n}$. Generally, such a table is preferred because present value is computed by the process of multiplication rather than by the process of division. Table II (page 402) is an excerpt from the more complete tables that are available.

Example 2: Same problem as in Example 1a.

$$P = Sv^n$$
$$= \$3,581.70 \times 0.5583948 = \$2,000.00$$

Example 3: A non-interest-bearing note for \$1,801.86 is due in 3 years. Find the present value of the note at 4 per cent interest compounded semiannually. (4 per cent interest compounded semiannually for 3 years is equivalent to 2 per cent interest compounded annually for 6 years.)

$$P = Sv^n$$
$$= \$1,801.86 \times 0.8879714 = \$1,600.00$$

Table II. Present Value of $1 at Compound Interest[1]

$$v^n = \frac{1}{(1+i)^n}$$

Formula:

To find present value $\quad P = S\left[\frac{1}{(1+i)^n}\right] = Sv^n$

n	½%	1%	2%	3%	4%	5%	6%
1	0.9950 249	0.990 0990	0.980 3922	0.970 8738	0.961 5385	0.952 3810	0.943 3962
2	0.9900 745	0.980 2960	9.961 1688	0.942 5959	0.924 5562	0.907 0295	0.889 9964
3	0.9851 488	0.970 5902	0.942 3223	0.915 1417	0.888 9964	0.863 8376	0.839 6193
4	0.9802 475	0.960 9803	0.923 8454	0.888 4870	0.854 8042	0.822 7025	0.792 0937
5	0.9753 707	0.951 4657	0.905 7308	0.862 6088	0.821 9271	0.783 5262	0.747 2582
6	0.9705 181	0.942 0452	0.887 9714	0.837 4843	0.790 3145	0.746 2154	0.704 9605
7	0.9656 896	0.932 7180	0.870 5602	0.813 0915	0.759 9178	0.710 6813	0.665 0571
8	0.9608 852	0.923 4832	0.853 4904	0.789 4092	0.730 6902	0.676 8394	0.627 4124
9	0.9561 047	0.914 3398	0.836 7553	0.766 4167	0.702 5867	0.644 6089	0.591 8985
10	0.9513 479	0.905 2870	0.820 3483	0.744 0939	0.675 5642	0.613 9132	0.558 3948
11	0.9466 149	0.896 3237	0.804 2630	0.722 4213	0.649 5809	0.584 6793	0.526 7875
12	0.9419 053	0.887 4492	0.788 4932	0.701 3799	0.624 5970	0.556 8374	0.496 9694
13	0.9372 192	0.878 6626	0.773 0325	0.680 9513	0.600 5741	0.530 3214	0.468 8390
14	0.9325 565	0.869 9630	0.757 8750	0.661 1178	0.577 4751	0.505 0680	0.442 3010
15	0.9279 169	0.861 3495	0.743 0147	0.641 8619	0.555 2645	0.481 0171	0.417 2651
16	0.9233 004	0.852 8213	0.728 4458	0.623 1669	0.533 9082	0.458 1115	0.393 6463
17	0.9187 068	0.844 3775	0.714 1626	0.605 0164	0.513 3732	0.436 2967	0.371 3644
18	0.9141 362	0.836 0173	0.700 1594	0.587 3946	0.493 6281	0.415 5206	0.350 3438
19	0.9095 882	0.827 7399	0.686 4308	0.570 2860	0.474 6424	0.395 7340	0.330 5130
20	0.9050 629	0.819 5445	0.672 9713	0.553 6758	0.456 3870	0.376 8895	0.311 8047
21	0.9005 601	0.811 4302	0.659 7758	0.537 5493	0.438 8336	0.358 9424	0.294 1554
22	0.8960 797	0.803 3962	0.646 8390	0.521.8925	0.421 9554	0.341 8499	0.277 5051
23	0.8916 216	0.795 4418	0.634 1559	0.506 6917	0.405 7263	0.325 5713	0.261 7973
24	0.8871 857	0.787 5661	0.621 7215	0.491 9337	0.390 1215	0.310 0679	0.246 9786
25	0.8827 718	0.779 7684	0.609 5309	0.477 6056	0.375 1168	0.295 3028	0.232 9986
26	0.8783 799	0.772 0480	0.597 5793	0.463 6947	0.360 6892	0.219 8100	0.281 2407
27	0.8740 099	0.764 4039	0.585 8620	0.450 1891	0.346 8166	0.207 3680	0.267 8483
28	0.8696 616	0.756 8356	0.574 3746	0.437 0768	0.333.4775	0.195 6301	0.255 0936
29	0.8653 349	0.749 3422	0.563 1123	0.424 3464	0.320 6514	0.184 5567	0.242 9463
30	0.8610 297	0.741 9229	0.552 0709	0.411 9868	0.308 3187	0.174 1101	0.231 3774
40	0.819 1389	0.671 6531	0.452 8908	0.306 5568	0.208 2890	0.142 0457	0.097 2222
50	0.779 2861	0.608 0388	0.371 5279	0.228 1071	0.140 7126	0.087 2037	0.054 2884
60	0.741 3722	0.550 4496	0.304 7823	0.169 7331	0.095 0604	0.053 5355	0.030 3143
70	0.705 3029	0.498 3149	0.250 0276	0.126 2974	0.064 2194	0.032 8662	0.016 9274
80	0.670 9885	0.451 1179	0.205 1097	0.093 9771	0.043 3843	0.020 1770	0.009 4522
90	0.638 3435	0.408 3912	0.168 2614	0.069 9278	0.029 3089	0.012 3869	0.005 2780
100	0.607 2868	0.369 7112	0.138 0330	0.052 0328	0.019 8000	0.007 6045	0.002 9472

[1] Note that each factor in this table is reciprocal to the accumulation factor in Table I.

EXERCISE 2A

Solve the following, using Table I:

1. $1,650 is invested at 5 per cent interest compounded annually. After 19 years, what are (*a*) the amount and (*b*) the compound interest?
2. On Donald's tenth birthday his father placed $300 in a building and loan association which paid 4 per cent interest compounded semiannually. What was the amount on Donald's twenty-first birthday?
3. The Arnold Savings Bank paid 2 per cent interest compounded quarterly. Mr. Whiteaker deposited $875 on Apr. 1, 1953. If no further deposits or withdrawals were made, what was the accumulated amount on deposit on July 1, 1959?
4. By how much does the amount of $3,375 at 3 per cent interest compounded annually for 60 years exceed the amount of $3,375 at 3 per cent simple interest for 60 years?
5. How long does it take $1,200 to amount to $2,277.96 at 6 per cent interest compounded annually?
6. $2,650 will amount to $4,523.25 in how many years at 4 per cent interest compounded semiannually?
7. A deposit of $1,511 accumulated interest of $527.11 in 5 years at interest compounded monthly. What rate of interest did the deposit earn?
8. After 15 years, a loan of $860 was repaid by an amount of $2,087.45. If compounded semiannually, what rate of interest did the loan earn?

EXERCISE 2B

Solve the following, using Table I and/or Table II:

1. $8,000 will amount to $11,313.95 in how many years and months at 2 per cent interest compounded annually with simple interest at 2 per cent earned on the maturity value as of the beginning of the final partial period?
2. Interest of $4,718.91 was accumulated on a deposit of $3,600 after 14 years and 2 months. If compounded semiannually with simple interest at the same nominal rate per annum paid on the maturity value as of the beginning of the final 2-month partial period, what rate of interest did the deposit earn?
3. A non-interest-bearing note for $2,240 is due in 17 years. Find the present value of the note at 5 per cent interest compounded annually.
4. The Emporium Drug Store holds a contract to purchase a store building 12 years hence for $37,500. If money is worth 4 per cent compounded annually, what is the present value of the contract?
5. Find the present value of a non-interest-bearing note for $1,800 due in $11\frac{1}{2}$ years if money is worth 6 per cent interest compounded semiannually.
6. The State Savings Bank pays depositors 4 per cent interest compounded quarterly. On the day of his son's birth Mr. Cranston wishes to deposit a sum of money that will accumulate to $5,000 on the boy's twentieth birthday. How much money must he deposit?

7. Find the price paid by the purchaser of a 5-year note with a face of $900 bearing interest at 5 per cent compounded annually if it is bought $3\frac{1}{2}$ years before due at a price that yields the purchaser 6 per cent interest compounded semiannually.
8. On Oct. 1, 1959, Mr. Nelson purchased a $1,130 note dated Apr. 1, 1953, and due Apr. 1, 1967, with interest at 4 per cent compounded semiannually. If the then current interest rates were 6 per cent compounded monthly, find the purchase price of the note.

UNIT 3. Ordinary Annuities, Annuities Due, and Tables

Although many individuals tend to think of the word "annuity" as being typified only by retirement income for life (such as that purchasable from a life-insurance company), the meaning of the term is much broader and is properly applied to include such topics as wages, salaries, pensions, bond interest payments, preferred stock dividends, installment payments, and endowments.

An *annuity* is a series of payments (usually equal) at regular intervals of time. Although the word indicates that payments must be annual, its meaning in common use has been broadened to include payments at regular intervals which may be more or less than 1 year.

Annuities that have an indefinite duration in which beginning or termination is dependent on some uncertain event are known as *contingent annuities.* Thus an agreement by a life-insurance company to pay a stipulated monthly sum to an individual for life is a life annuity contingent in that the length of time that the payments will continue is determined by the uncertain life span of the individual.

Annuities that have a definite duration not dependent on some outside contingency are known as *annuities certain.* Thus most bond interest payments (which cease at maturity of the bonds) are *terminable* annuities certain. Interest payments on bonds that never mature, as in the case of certain foreign government bonds, are perpetual annuities certain and are called *perpetuities.*

Terminology of Annuities

The *rent* is the value of each periodic payment.

The *rent period* is the unit of time for which any one payment is made.

The *annual rent* is the sum of the payments made in one year.

The *term* of an annuity is the time from the beginning of the first rent period to the end of the last rent period.

An *ordinary annuity* is a series of payments, each of which is made at the *end* of each of the rent periods.

An *annuity due* is a series of payments, each of which is made at the *beginning* of each of the rent periods.

The *amount* of an annuity is the accumulated value at its termination.

The *present value* of an annuity is the amortized value at its beginning.

To Find the Amount of an Ordinary Annuity and of an Annuity Due. Compound interest on the rent of an annuity due begins with the *first day* of the first rent period whereas compound interest on the rent of an ordinary annuity does not begin until the *last day* of the first rent period. Therefore, an annuity due exceeds an ordinary annuity by the compound interest at the given rate for each dollar of the first rent for the term of the annuity. Thus, the value of an annuity due may be found by first finding the value of an ordinary annuity which has *one more* rent period and then subtracting the value of one rent.

In Example 1 which follows, Table I was used to simplify the computations. As you know, the same results could be obtained without the use of this table, but the required calculations would be many and laborious.

Example 1: Find the amount of $500 invested each of 4 years at 3 per cent interest compounded annually (*a*) if invested at the end of each year and (*b*) if invested at the beginning of each year.

(*a*) *Ordinary annuity:*

Annuity or investment	No. of years accumulated	Amounts	
$500	3	$\$500(1 + .03)^3 =$	$ 546.36
500	2	$500(1 + .03)^2 =$	530.45
500	1	$500(1 + .03) =$	515.00
500	0	500 =	500.00
		Total	$2,091.81

(*b*) *Annuity due:*

Annuity or investment	No. of years accumulated	Amounts	
$500	4	$\$500(1 + .03)^4 =$	$ 562.754
500	3	$500(1 + .03)^3 =$	546.364
500	2	$500(1 + .03)^2 =$	530.45
500	1	$500(1 + .03) =$	515.00
		Total	$2,154.57

The solutions indicated in Example 1 may be further simplified by using Table I and by applying the following formulas in which R is the rent per period and S is the sum of the compound amounts of the payments:

$$\text{Ordinary annuity,} \quad S = R\,\frac{(1+i)^n - 1}{i}$$

$$\text{Annuity due,} \quad S = R\,\frac{(1+i)^{n+1} - 1}{i} - R$$

Example 2: Same problem as Example 1*a* and 1*b*.

(*a*) *Ordinary annuity:*

$$\begin{aligned} S &= R\,\frac{(1+i)^n - 1}{i} \\ &= \$500\left[\frac{(1+.03)^4 - 1}{.03}\right] \\ &= 500\left[\frac{1.1255088 - 1}{.03}\right] \\ &= 500\left[\frac{.1255088}{0.3}\right] \\ &= 500 \times 4.186362\frac{2}{3} = \$2{,}091.81 \end{aligned}$$

(*b*) *Annuity due:*

$$\begin{aligned} S &= R\,\frac{(1+i)^{n+1} - 1}{i} \\ &= \$500\left[\frac{(1+.03)^{4+1} - 1}{.03}\right] - \$500 \\ &= 500\left[\frac{1.1592741 - 1}{.03}\right] - 500 \\ &= 500\left[\frac{.1592741}{.03}\right] - 500 \\ &= 500 \times 5.30913\frac{2}{3} - 500 \\ &= 2{,}654.57 - 500 = \$2{,}154.57 \end{aligned}$$

Just as special tables are available for the solution of problems in compound interest, so are there tables prepared to simplify the solution of problems in annuities. Table III is an excerpt from the more complete tables that are available. It is customary to use $s_{\overline{n}|i}$ instead of $\frac{(1+i)^n - 1}{i}$. The symbol $s_{\overline{n}|i}$ is read "s sub n at the rate i" and means

Table III. Amount of $1 per Annum at Compound Interest

$$s_{\overline{n}|i} = \frac{(1+i)^n - 1}{i}$$

Formulas:

To find amount of an ordinary annuity $S = R\,\frac{(1+i)n - 1}{i} = Rs_{\overline{n}|i}$

To find amount of an annuity due $S = R\,\frac{(1+i)^{n+1} - 1}{i} - R = R(s_{\overline{n+1}|i} - 1)$

n	½ %	1 %	2 %	3 %	4 %	5 %	6 %
1	1.000 0000	1.000 0000	1.000 0000	1.000 0000	1.000 0000	1.000 0000	1.000 0000
2	2.005 0000	2.010 0000	2.020 0000	2.030 0000	2.040 0000	2.050 0000	2.060 0000
3	3.015 0250	3.030 1000	3.060 4000	3.090 9000	3.121 6000	3.152 5000	3.183 6000
4	4.030 1001	4.060 4010	4.121 6080	4.183 6270	4.246 4640	4.310 1250	4.374 6160
5	5.050 2506	5.101 0050	5.204 0402	5.309 1358	5.416 3226	5.525.6312	5.637 0930
6	6.075 5019	6.152 0151	6.308 1210	6.468 4099	6.632 9755	6.801 9128	6.975 3185
7	7.105 8794	7.213 5352	7.434 2834	7.662 4622	7.898 2945	8.142 0084	8.393 8376
8	8.141 4088	8.285 6706	8.582 9691	8.892 3360	9.214 2263	9.549 1089	9.897 4679
9	9 182 1158	9 368 5273	9.754 6284	10.159 1061	10.582 7953	11.026 5643	11.491 3160
10	10.228 0264	10.462 2125	10.949 7210	11.463 8793	12.006 1071	12.577 8925	13.180 7949
11	11.279 1665	11.566 8347	12.168 7154	12.807 7957	13.486 3514	14.206 7872	14.971 6426
12	12.335 5624	12.682 5030	13.412 0897	14.192 0296	15.025 8055	15.917 1265	16.869 9412
13	13.397 2402	13.809 3280	14.680 3315	15.617 7904	16.626 8377	17.712 9828	18.882 1377
14	14.464 2264	14.947 4213	15.973 9382	17.086 3242	18.291 9112	19.558 6320	21.015 0659
15	15.536 5475	16.096 8955	17.293 4169	18.598 9139	20.023 5876	21.578 5636	23.275 9699
16	16.614 2303	17.257 8645	18.639 2853	20.156 8813	21.824 5311	23.657 4918	25.672 5281
17	17.697 3014	18.430 4431	20.012 0710	21.761 5877	23.697 5124	25.840 3664	28.212 8798
18	18.785 7879	19.614 7476	21.412 3124	23.414 4354	25.645 4129	28.132 3847	30.905 6526
19	19.879 7168	20.810 8950	22.840 5586	25.116 8684	27.671 2294	30.539 0039	33.759 9917
20	20.979 1154	22.019 0040	24.297 3698	26.870 3745	29.778 0786	33.065 9541	36.785 5912
21	22.084 0110	22.239 1940	25.783 3172	28.676 4857	31.969 2017	35.719 2518	39.992 7267
22	23.194 4311	24.471 5860	27.298 9835	30.536 7803	34.247 9698	38.505 2144	43.392 2903
23	24.310 4032	25.716 3018	28.844 9632	32.452 8837	36.617 8886	41.430 4751	46.995 8277
24	25.431 9552	26.973 4648	30.421 8625	34.426 4702	39.082 6041	44.501 9989	50.815 5774
25	26.559 1150	28.243 1995	32.030 2997	36.459 2643	41.645 9083	47.727 0988	54.864 5120
26	27.691 9106	29.525 6315	33.670 9057	38.553 0423	44.311 7446	51.113 4538	59.156 3827
27	28.830 3702	30.820 8878	35.344 3238	40.709 6335	47.084 2144	54.669 1264	63.705 7657
28	29.974 5220	32.129 0967	37.015 2103	42.930 9225	49.967 5830	58.402 5828	68.528 1116
29	31.124 3946	33.450 3877	38.792 2345	45.218 8502	52.966 2863	62.322 7119	73.639 7983
30	32.280 0166	34.784 8915	40.568 0792	47.575 4157	56.084 9378	66.438 8475	79.058 1862
40	44.158 8473	48.886 3734	60.401 9832	75.401 2597	95.025 5157	120.799 7742	154.761 9656
50	56.645 1630	64.463 1822	84.579 4015	112.796 8673	152.667 0837	209.347 9957	290.335 9046
60	69.770 0305	81.669 6699	114.051 5394	163.053 4368	237.990 6852	353.583 7179	533.128 1809
70	83.566 1055	100.676 3368	149.977 9111	230.594 0637	364.290 4588	588.528 5107	967.932 1696
80	98.067 7136	121.671 5217	193.771 9578	321.363 0185	551.244 9768	971.228 8213	1746.599 8914
90	113.310 9358	144.863 2675	247.156 6563	443.348 9037	827.983 3335	1594.607 3010	3141.075 1872
100	129.333 6984	170.481 3829	312.232 3059	607.287 7327	1237.623 7046	2610.025 1569	5638.368 0586

Table IV. Present Value of $1 per Annum at Compound Interest

$$a_{\overline{n}|i} = \frac{1 - \frac{1}{(1+i)^n}}{i}$$

Formulas:

To find present value of an ordinary annuity $A = R(a_{\overline{n}|i})$

To find present value of an annuity due $A = R(1 + a_{\overline{n-1}|i})$

n	½ %	1 %	2 %	3 %	4 %	5 %	6 %
1	0.995 0249	0.990 0990	0.980 3922	0.970 8738	0.961 5385	0.952 3810	0.943 3962
2	1.985 0994	1.970 3951	1.941 5609	1.913 4697	1.886 0947	1.859 4104	1.833 3927
3	2.970 2481	2.940 9852	2.883 8833	2.828 6114	2.775 0910	2.723 2480	2.673 0120
4	3.950 4957	3.901 9656	3.807 7287	3.717 0984	3.629 8952	3.545 9505	3.465 1056
5	4.925 8663	4.853 4312	4.713 4595	4.579 7072	4.451 8223	4.329 4767	4.212 3638
6	5.896 3844	5.795 4765	5.601 4309	5.417 1914	5.242 1369	5.075 6921	4.917 3243
7	6.862 0740	6.728 1945	6.471 9911	6.230 2830	6.002 0547	5.786 3734	5.582 3814
8	7.822 9592	7.651 6778	7.325 4814	7.019 6922	6.732 7449	6.463 2128	6.209 7938
9	8.779 0639	8.566 0176	8.162 2367	7.786 1089	7.435 3316	7.107 8217	6.801 6923
10	9.730 4119	9.471 3045	8.982 5850	8.530 2028	8.110 8958	7.721 7349	7.360 0870
11	10.677 0267	10.367 6282	9.786 8480	9.252 6241	8.760 4767	8.306 4142	7.886 8746
12	11.618 9321	11.255 0775	10.575 3412	9.954 0040	9.385 0738	8.863 2516	8.383 8439
13	12.556 1513	12.133 7401	11.348 3737	10.634 9553	9.985 6478	9.393 5730	8.852 6830
14	13.488 7078	13.003 7030	12.106 2488	11.296 0731	10.563 1229	9.898 6409	9.294 9839
15	14.416 6246	13.865 0525	12.849 2635	11.937 9351	11.118 3874	10.379 6580	9.712 2490
16	15.339 9250	14.717 8738	13.577 7093	12.561 1020	11.652 2956	10.837 7696	10.105 8953
17	16.258 6319	15.562 2513	14.291 8719	13.166 1185	12.165 6688	11.274 0662	10.477 2597
18	17.172 7680	16.398 2686	14.992 0313	13.753 5131	12.659 2970	11.689 5869	10.827 6035
19	18.082 3562	17.226 0085	15.678 4620	14.323 7991	13.133 9394	12.085 3209	11.158 1165
20	18.987 4192	18.045 5530	16.351 4333	14.877 4749	13.590 3263	12.462 2103	11.469 9212
21	19.887 9792	18.856 9831	17.011 2092	15.415 0241	14.029 1600	12.821 1527	11.764 0766
22	20.784 0590	19.660 3793	17.658 0482	15.936 9166	14.451 1153	13.163 0026	12.041 5817
23	21.675 6806	20.455 8211	18.292 2041	16.443 6084	14.856 8417	13.488 5739	12.303 3790
24	22.562 8662	21.243 3873	18.913 9256	16.935 5421	15.246 9631	13.798 6418	12.550 3575
25	23.445 6380	22.023 1557	19.523 4565	17.413 1477	15.622 0799	14.093 9446	12.783 3562
26	24.324 0179	22.795 2037	20.121 0358	17.876 8424	15.982 7692	14.375 1853	13.003 1662
27	25.198 0278	23.559 6076	20.706 8978	18.327 0315	16.329 5858	14.643 0336	13.210 5341
28	26.067 6894	24.316 4432	21.281 2724	18.764 1082	16.663 0632	14.898 1273	13.406 1643
29	26.933 0242	25.065 7853	21.844 3847	19.188 4546	16.983 7146	15.141 0736	13.590 7210
30	27.794 0540	25.807 7082	22.396 4556	19.600 4414	17.292 0333	15.372 4510	13.764 8312
40	36.172 2279	32.834 6861	27.355 4792	23.114 7720	19.792 7739	17.159 0864	15.046 2969
50	44.142 7864	39.196 1175	31.423 6059	25.729 7640	21.482 1846	18.255 9255	15.761 8606
60	51.725 5608	44.955 0384	34.760 8867	27.675 5637	22.623 4900	18.929 2895	16.161 4277
70	58.939 4176	50.168 5144	37.493 6193	29.123 4214	23.394 5150	19.342 6766	16.384 5439
80	65.802 3054	54.888 2061	39.744 5136	30.200 7634	23.915 3918	19.596 4605	16.509 1308
90	72.331 2996	59.160 8815	41.586 9292	31.002 4071	24.267 2776	19.752 2617	16.578 6994
100	78.542 6448	63.028 8788	43.098 3516	31.598 9053	24.504 9990	19.847 9102	16.617 5462

the amount of an ordinary annuity of \$1 per year payable for n years at the effective interest rate i.

Example 3: Same problem as Examples 1 and 2.

(a) *Ordinary annuity:*

$$\begin{aligned} S &= Rs_{\overline{n}|i} \\ &= \$500(s_{\overline{4}|.03}) \\ &= 500 \times 4.1836270 = \$2,091.81 \end{aligned}$$

(b) *Annuity due:*

$$\begin{aligned} S &= R(s_{\overline{n+1}|i} - 1) \\ &= \$500(s_{\overline{4+1}|.03} - 1) \\ &= 500 \times 5.3091358 - 1 \\ &= 500 \times 4.3091358 = \$2,154.57 \end{aligned}$$

To Find Present Value of an Ordinary Annuity and of an Annuity Due. The present value of an annuity symbolized by A is the sum of the present value of all the payments. Although it is possible to compute the present value of either an ordinary annuity or an annuity due without the aid of prepared tables or by applying Table I (Amount of \$1 at Compound Interest) or Table II (Present Value of \$1 at Compound Interest), it is desirable to use Table IV which is an excerpt from the more complete tables that have been specially prepared for this computation. It is customary to use $a_{\overline{n}|i}$ instead of $\dfrac{1 - \dfrac{1}{(1+i)^n}}{i}$. The symbol $a_{\overline{n}|i}$ is read "a sub n at the rate i" and means the present value of \$1 per year payable for n years at the effective rate of interest i.

Example 1: An ordinary annuity. Find the present value of \$500 per year if received at the end of the next 15 years and if the compound interest rate is 6 per cent per annum.

$$\begin{aligned} A &= Ra_{\overline{n}|i} \\ &= \$500(a_{\overline{15}|.00}) \\ &= 500 \times 9.7122490 = \$4,856.12 \end{aligned}$$

Example 2: An annuity due. A store is leased for 11 years at \$1,500 per annum payable in advance each year. Find the cash value of the lease on a 4 per cent annual compound interest basis.

$$\begin{aligned} A &= R(1 + a_{\overline{n-1}|i}) \\ &= \$1,500(1 + a_{\overline{11-1}|.04}) \\ &= 1,500(1 + a_{\overline{10}|.04}) \\ &= 1,500(1 + 8.1108958) \\ &= 1,500 \times 9.1108958 = \$13,666.34 \end{aligned}$$

EXERCISE 3A

Solve the following by the use of Table III unless otherwise stipulated:

1. Find the amount of $200 invested at the end of each of 5 successive years at 6 per cent interest compounded annually (*a*) using only Table I, (*b*) using Table I and the formula $S = R\frac{(1+i)^n - 1}{i}$, and (*c*) using Table III.
2. Miss Edith Murphy saved $540 per year which she deposited in a savings bank at the end of each year. If the bank paid 2 per cent interest compounded annually on all deposits, what was the amount on deposit at the end of 11 years?
3. On his son's twelfth birthday, a father invested in his son's name $40 at 4 per cent interest compounded quarterly. If every 3 months following the father made a similar investment, how much would the account amount to after a final $40 had been deposited on the son's eighteenth birthday?
4. To provide for depreciation on equipment, a trucking firm beginning in 1958 set aside $3,350 on June 30 and Dec. 31 of each year. If the fund and its income were invested at 6 per cent interest compounded semiannually, what was the amount in the fund at the end of 1963?
5. Find the amount at the end of 5 years of $600 invested at the beginning of each year at 5 per cent interest compounded annually (*a*) using only Table I, (*b*) using Table I and the formula $S = R\frac{(1+i)^{n+1} - 1}{i} - R$, and (*c*) using Table III.
6. How much money would be accumulated at the end of 23 years by William Brown if he invested $325 on the first day of each year at 4 per cent interest compounded annually?
7. On his fifty-first birthday and each third month thereafter, Dr. F. Grant Marsh invested $475 at 2 per cent interest compounded quarterly. On the day before his fifty-eighth birthday, what was the amount on deposit?
8. A young married couple in order to provide funds with which to make a down payment on a new home set aside $180 on Jan. 1 and July of each year at 6 per cent interest compounded semiannually. What did their fund amount to on Dec. 31 of the ninth year?

EXERCISE 3B

Solve the following by the use of Table IV:

1. Find the present value of $750 per year if received at the end of the next 17 years and if the compound interest rate is 4 per cent per annum.
2. The installment price of a television set is nothing down and $20 per month for 18 months. Find the cash price equivalent (present value) of the installment price if money is worth 6 per cent interest compounded monthly.

3. The estimated return from a piece of mining property is $50,000 net per year at the end of each of the next 14 years. If money is worth 5 per cent interest compounded annually, what is the present value of the property?
4. Mr. Pickett, who wishes to buy a home, is offered a house for $8,000 cash or $1,600 down and payments of $1,250 at the end of each year for 6 years. Which is the better offer to Mr. Pickett and by how much now if the present value of the payments is computed at 5 per cent interest compounded annually?
5. What is the present value of an annuity of $300 per year if the first payment is received today and yearly for a total of 10 consecutive payments, and money is worth 6 per cent interest compounded annually?
6. Find the present value of a 15-year lease on a store building at $2,400 per annum, payable in advance each year, if money is worth 4 per cent interest compounded annually.
7. For the title to his property on April 1, 1960, the owner of an apartment house is offered $1,000 as an immediate down payment and $1,000 per quarter to and including Apr. 1, 1970. What is the cash value of the offer if money is worth 4 per cent interest compounded quarterly?
8. Through inheritance, Mr. Conlan received a bequest of $1,840 on Oct. 1, 1954, and $1,840 each 6 months thereafter through and including Oct. 1, 1968. At 4 per cent interest compounded semiannually, what was the value of the inheritance on Oct. 1, 1968?

UNIT 4. Sinking Funds, Amortization, and Tables

A *sinking fund* is money accumulated by means of equal periodic deposits at compound interest for the purpose of meeting an obligation (principal) at maturity. Among the many examples of sinking funds to be found in business are the accumulations of moneys through periodic savings in order to meet bond obligations or real-estate mortgages at maturity or periodic savings to provide replacement of capital loss through depreciation or obsolescence.

Amortization is a method of payment in which borrowings with current interest (amounts) are repaid in equal periodic installments. Excellent examples of amortization are such periodic payments as those made on installment purchases or personal borrowings and the monthly payments to both principal and interest on real-estate loans.

Although there is some disagreement among authorities as to the scope of the meaning of the term *sinking fund*, it is rather generally agreed that if the obligation is interest bearing (that is, if the principal earns interest until maturity), the problem is one of *amortization* rather than of a sinking fund.

Note the following differences which distinguish a sinking fund from amortization:

In a sinking fund:

1. The principal equals the maturity value or amount; that is, the debt does not earn interest.
2. Installments (rent) are sufficient to accumulate a fund equal to the principal due at maturity.
3. The debt or principal remains constant to maturity.
4. Finally, the mathematical problem is that of determining what rent must be provided to accumulate the sum of the principal at maturity.

In amortization:

1. The principal earns interest to maturity.
2. Installments are sufficient to pay interest on the outstanding debt (decreasing principal) and a partial payment of the principal.
3. The amount (principal + interest) is reduced with each payment, the final payment at maturity retiring the debt obligation.
4. Finally, the mathematical problem is that of determining what rent must be provided to retire by maturity the present value of an amount (interest-bearing obligation).

From the preceding it will be apparent that a series of payments into a sinking fund or amortization, if made at regular intervals and in identical amounts, constitutes an annuity in which the mathematical problem will be the determination of the required value of each periodic payment (rent).

To Find Rent in a Sinking Fund (when Amount of the Annuity Is Known). You will recall (see Table III) that the amount of an ordinary annuity may be determined by the use of the formula $S = Rs_{\overline{n}|i}$. If $S = Rs_{\overline{n}|i}$ then $R = \frac{S}{s_{\overline{n}|i}}$. Obviously rent may be determined by the use of Table III (Amount of $1 per Annum at Compound Interest) if the values of S, n, and i are known. However the equation $R = \frac{S}{s_{\overline{n}|i}}$ may be written $R = S\frac{1}{s_{\overline{n}|i}}$. Since prepared tables of the values of $\frac{1}{s_{\overline{n}|i}}$ are available, it is possible to solve for R by multiplication rather than by the more tedious process of division required if the equation $R = \frac{S}{s_{\overline{n}|i}}$ is used. Table V is an excerpt from such a table.

Example of sinking fund. Mr. Monaco desires to accumulate $5,000 at the end of 10 years. How much money must be put aside at the end of each year if it will earn 4 per cent interest compounded annually?

$$R = S\frac{1}{s_{\overline{n|}i}}$$

$$= \$5,000\frac{1}{s_{\overline{10|}.04}}$$

$$= 5,000 \times 0.0832909 = \$416.45$$

To Find Rent in Amortization (when Present Value of the Annuity Is Known). As you will recall (see Table IV), the present value of an ordinary annuity may be determined by the use of the formula $A = Ra_{\overline{n|}i}$. If $A = Ra_{\overline{n|}i}$, then $R = \frac{A}{a_{\overline{n|}i}}$. Thus rent may be determined by application of Table IV (Present Value of $1 per Annum at Compound Interest) if A, n, and i are known. However, $\frac{A}{a_{\overline{n|}i}} = A\frac{1}{a_{\overline{n|}i}}$ and, since prepared tables of the values of $\frac{1}{a_{\overline{n|}i}}$ are available, it is desirable to use such tables because multiplication is generally preferable to division. Table VI is an excerpt from such a table.

Example of amortization. Mr. Frustuck purchased a home priced at $7,000 paying $3,000 down and agreeing to pay the balance with interest at 5 per cent compounded annually in equal payments at the end of each of the next 6 years. Find the size of each annual payment.

$$R = A\frac{1}{a_{\overline{n|}i}}$$

$$\text{The balance of } A = \$7,000 - \$3,000 = \$4,000$$

$$R = \$4,000\frac{1}{a_{\overline{6|}.05}}$$

$$= 4,000 \times 0.1970175 = \$788.07$$

EXERCISE 4

Solve the following by the use of Table V or VI:

1. Mr. and Mrs. Stewart desire to accumulate $6,500 at the end of 8 years. How much money must be put aside in equal installments at the end of each year if it will earn 5 per cent interest compounded annually?
2. Mr. Buttimer plans to accumulate $10,000 in 20 years by depositing an equal amount at the end of each 6-month period in a building and loan association

Table V. Annuity Which at Compound Interest Amounts to $1

$$\frac{1}{s_{\overline{n}|i}} = \frac{i}{(1+i)^n - 1} \qquad \left[\frac{1}{a_{\overline{n}|i}} = \frac{1}{s_{\overline{n}|i}} + i\right]$$ [1]

Formula:

To find rent in a sinking fund $R = S\,\frac{1}{s_{\overline{n}|i}}$

n	½%	1%	2%	3%	4%	5%	6%
1	1.000 0000	1.000 0000	1.000 0000	1.000 0000	1.000 0000	1.000 0000	1.000 0000
2	0.498 7531	0.497 5124	0.495 0495	0.492 6108	0.490 1961	0.487 8049	0.485 4369
3	0.331 6722	0.330 0221	0.326 7547	0.323 5304	0.320 3485	0.317 2086	0.314 1098
4	0.248 1328	0.246 2811	0.242 6238	0.239 0271	0.235 4901	0.232 0118	0.228 5915
5	0.198 0100	0.196 0398	0.192 1584	0.188 3546	0.184 6271	0.180 9748	0.177 3964
6	0.164 5955	0.162 5484	0.158 5258	0.154 5975	0.150 7619	0.147 0175	0.143 3626
7	0.140 7285	0.138 6283	0.134 5120	0.130 5064	0.126 6096	0.122 8198	0.119 1350
8	0.122 8289	0.120 6903	0.116 5098	0.112 4564	0.108 5278	0.104 7218	0.101 0359
9	0.108 9074	0.106 7404	0.102 5154	0.098 4339	0.094 4930	0.090 6901	0.087 0222
10	0.097 7706	0.095 5821	0.091 3265	0.087 2305	0.083 2909	0.079 5046	0.075 8680
11	0.088 6590	0.086 4541	0.082 1779	0.078 0775	0.074 1490	0.070 3889	0.066 7929
12	0.081 0664	0.078 8488	0.074 5596	0.070 4621	0.066 5522	0.062 8254	0.059 2770
13	0.074 6422	0.072 4148	0.068 1184	0.064 0295	0.060 1437	0.056 4558	0.052 9601
14	0.069 1361	0.066 9012	0.062 6020	0.058 5263	0.054 6690	0.051 0240	0.047 5849
15	0.064 3644	0.062 1238	0.057 8255	0.053 7666	0.049 9411	0.046 3423	0.042 9628
16	0.060 1894	0.057 9446	0.053 6501	0.049 6109	0.045 8200	0.042 2699	0.038 9521
17	0.056 5058	0.054 2581	0.049 9698	0.045 9525	0.042 1985	0.038 6991	0.035 4448
18	0.053 2317	0.050 9821	0.046 7021	0.042 7087	0.038 9933	0.035 5462	0.032 3565
19	0.050 3025	0.048 0518	0.043 7818	0.039 8139	0.036 1386	0.032 7450	0.029 6209
20	0.047 6665	0.045 4153	0.041 1567	0.037 2157	0.033 5818	0.030 2426	0.027 1846
21	0.045 2816	0.043 0308	0.038 7848	0.034 8718	0.031 2801	0.027 9961	0.025 0046
22	0.043 1138	0.040 8637	0.036 6314	0.032 7474	0.029 1988	0.025 9705	0.023 0456
23	0.041 1347	0.038 8858	0.034 6681	0.030 8139	0.027 3091	0.024 1368	0.021 2785
24	0.039 3206	0.037 0734	0.032 8711	0.029 0474	0.025 5868	0.022 4709	0.019 6790
25	0.037 6519	0.035 4068	0.031 2204	0.027 4279	0.024 0120	0.020 9525	0.018 2267
26	0.036 1116	0.033 8689	0.029 6992	0.025 9383	0.022 5674	0.019 5643	0.016 9044
27	0.034 6857	0.032 4455	0.028 2931	0.024 5642	0.021 2385	0.018 2919	0.015 6972
28	0.033 3617	0.031 1244	0.026 9897	0.023 2932	0.020 0130	0.017 1225	0.014 5926
29	0.032 1291	0.029 8950	0.025 7784	0.022 1147	0.018 8799	0.016 0455	0.013 5796
30	0.030 9789	0.028 7481	0.024 6499	0.021 0193	0.017 8301	0.015 0514	0.012 6489
40	0.022 6455	0.020 4556	0.016 5558	0.013 2624	0.010 5235	0.008 2782	0.006 4615
50	0.017 6538	0.015 5127	0.011 8232	0.008 8655	0.006 5502	0.004 7767	0.003 4443
60	0.014 3328	0.012 2445	0.008 7680	0.006 1330	0.004 2019	0.002 8282	0.001 8757
70	0.011 9666	0.009 9328	0.006 6677	0.004 3366	0.002 7451	0.001 6992	0.001 0331
80	0.010 1970	0.008 2189	0.005 1607	0.003 1118	0.001 8141	0.001 0296	0.000 5725
90	0.008 8253	0.006 9031	0.004 0460	0.002 2556	0.001 2078	0.000 6271	0.000 3184
100	0.007 3319	0.005 8657	0.003 2027	0.001 6467	0.000 8080	0.000 3831	0.000 1774

[1] Note that through slight modification in the formula presented, Tables V and VI may be used interchangeably. This is due to the fact that the rent of the present value of an annuity of $1 is equal to the rent of the amount of an annuity of $1 plus the interest rate per period.

Table VI. Annuity That $1 Will Purchase or Annuity Whose Present Value is $1

$$\frac{1}{a_{\overline{n}|i}} = \frac{i}{1-(1+i)^{n}} \qquad \left[\frac{1}{s_{\overline{n}|i}} = \frac{1}{a_{\overline{n}|i}} - i\right]^{1}$$

Formula:

To find rent in amortization $R = A \frac{1}{a_{\overline{n}|i}}$

n	½%	1%	2%	3%	4%	5%	6%
1	1.005 0000	1.010 0000	1.020 0000	1.030 0000	1.040 0000	1.050 0000	1.060 0000
2	0.503 7531	0.507 5124	0.515 0495	0.522 6108	0.530 1961	0.537 8049	0.545 4369
3	0.336 6722	0.340 0221	0.346 7547	0.353 5304	0.360 3485	0.367 2086	0.374 1098
4	0.253 1328	0.256 2811	0.262 6238	0.269 0271	0.275 4901	0.282 0118	0.288 5915
5	0.203 0100	0.206 0398	0.212 1584	0.218 3646	0.224 6271	0.230 9748	0.237 3964
6	0.169 5955	0.172 5484	0.178 5258	0.184 5975	0.190 7619	0.197 0175	0.203 3626
7	0.145 7285	0.148 6283	0.154 5120	0.160 5064	0.166 6096	0.172 8198	0.179 1350
8	0.127 8289	0.130 6903	0.136 5098	0.142 4564	0.148 5278	0.154 7218	0.161 0359
9	0.113 9074	0.116 7404	0.122 5154	0.128 4339	0.134 4930	0.140 6901	0.147 0222
10	0.102 7706	0.105 5821	0.111 3265	0.117 2305	0.123 2909	0.129 5046	0.135 8680
11	0.093 6590	0.096 4541	0.102 1779	0.108 0775	0.114 1490	0.120 3889	0.126 7929
12	0.086 0664	0.088 8488	0.094 5596	0.100 4621	0.106 5522	0.112 8254	0.119 2770
13	0.079 6422	0.082 4148	0.088 1184	0.094 0295	0.100 1437	0.106 4558	0.112 9601
14	0.074 1361	0.076 9012	0.082 6020	0.088 5263	0.094 6690	0.101 0240	0.107 5849
15	0.069 3644	0.072 1238	0.077 8255	0.083 7666	0.089 9411	0.096 3423	0.102 9628
16	0.065 1894	0.067 9446	0.073 6501	0.079 6109	0.085 8200	0.092 2699	0.098 9521
17	0.061 5058	0.064 2581	0.069 9698	0.075 9525	0.082 1985	0.088 6991	0.095 4448
18	0.058 2317	0.060 9821	0.066 7021	0.072 7087	0.078 9933	0.085 5462	0.092 3565
19	0.055 3025	0.058 0518	0.063 7818	0.069 8139	0.076 1386	0.082 7450	0.089 6209
20	0.052 6665	0.055 4153	0.061 1567	0.067 2157	0.073 5818	0.080 2426	0.087 1846
21	0.050 2816	0.053 0308	0.058 7848	0.064 8718	0.071 2801	0.077 9961	0.085 0046
22	0.048 1138	0.050 8637	0.056 6314	0.062 7474	0.069 1988	0.075 9705	0.083 0456
23	0.046 1347	0.048 8858	0.054 6681	0.060 8139	0.067 3091	0.074 1368	0.081 2785
24	0.044 3206	0.047 0735	0.052 8711	0.059 0474	0.065 5868	0.072 4709	0.079 6790
25	0.042 6519	0.045 4068	0.051 2204	0.057 4279	0.064 0120	0.070 9525	0.078 2267
26	0.041 1116	0.043 8689	0.049 6992	0.055 9383	0.062 5674	0.069 5643	0.076 9044
27	0.039 6857	0.042 4455	0.048 2931	0.054 5642	0.061 2385	0.068 2919	0.075 6972
28	0.038 3617	0.041 1244	0.046 9897	0.053 2932	0.060 0130	0.067 1225	0.074 5926
29	0.037 1291	0.039 8950	0.045 7784	0.052 1147	0.058 8799	0.066 0455	0.073 5796
30	0.035 9789	0.038 7481	0.044 6499	0.051 0193	0.057 8301	0.065 0514	0.072 6489
40	0.027 6455	0.030 4556	0.036 5558	0.043 2624	0.050 5235	0.058 2782	0.066 4615
50	0.022 6538	0.025 5127	0.031 8232	0.038 8655	0.046 5502	0.054 7767	0.063 4443
60	0.019 3328	0.022 2445	0.028 7680	0.036 1330	0.044 2019	0.052 8282	0.061 8757
70	0.016 9666	0.019 9328	0.026 6677	0.034 3366	0.042 7451	0.051 6992	0.061 0331
80	0.015 1970	0.018 2189	0.025 1607	0.033 1118	0.041 8141	0.051 0296	0.060 5725
90	0.013 8253	0.016 9031	0.024 0460	0.032 2557	0.041 2078	0.050 6271	0.060 3184
100	0.012 7319	0.015 8657	0.023 2027	0.031 6467	0.040 8080	0.050 3831	0.060 1774

[1] Note that through slight modification in the formulas presented, Tables VI and V may be used interchangeably. This is due to the fact that the rent of the amount of an annuity of $1 is equal to the rent of the present value of an annuity of $1 minus the interest rate per period.

that pays 4 per cent interest compounded semiannually. Find the amount of the semiannual deposit he must make.

3. To provide for the redemption in 25 years at maturity of a $140,000 bond issue, the Rainier Corporation plans to establish a sinking fund in which equal semiannual payments will earn 6 per cent interest compounded semiannually. How much money must be placed in the sinking fund at the end of each 6-month period?
4. On the day of his fiftieth birthday, Mr. Muscio determines to accumulate a fund of $25,000 at age 65. What equal amounts must he deposit at the end of each 3-month period following his fiftieth birthday to and including his sixty-fifth birthday in an investment corporation which pays 4 per cent interest compounded quarterly?
5. Mr. McMillan borrows $4,500 at 6 per cent interest compounded annually, agreeing to amortize the loan in equal installments at the end of each of the next 10 years. Find the size of each annual payment.
6. The Anderson Manufacturing Company agrees to repay in equal installments at the end of each 6-month period for the next 40 years a loan of $360,000 bearing 4 per cent interest compounded semiannually. Find the size of each payment.
7. Mr. and Mrs. Stoll agree to amortize a $6,300 mortgage on their home, the loan bearing interest at 5 per cent compounded annually. If yearly payments are due at the end of each of the succeeding 12 years, what will be the amount of each payment?
8. To repay a loan of $2,275 bearing interest at 6 per cent compounded monthly, Mr. and Mrs. Ancker agree to amortize the debt in 2 years by means of equal payments at the end of each month. Find the size of each payment.

APPENDIX I

MULTIPLICATION SHORT CUTS AND SHORT METHODS OF ADDING TWO FRACTIONS OR SUBTRACTING FRACTIONS

Short Cuts in Multiplication

The following short cuts in multiplication will often prove useful. While they are not so essential as those described on page 17, students who familiarize themselves with them may increase their speed considerably. A careful analysis of the steps of solution given in the examples should suffice as an explanation of the methods used. Recommended as most practical in this group of short cuts are those numbered 3, 5, 6, 9, and 14.

1. **Multiplication** by 11, 111, etc.:

Example a:
825 × 11 = 9 0 7 5

Solution a:
(*a*) Write 5
(*b*) 5 + 2 = 7
(*c*) 2 + 8 = 10, carry 1
(*d*) 8 + 1 = 9

Example b:
9635 × 111 = 10 6 9 4 8 5

Solution b:
(*a*) Write 5
(*b*) 5 + 3 = 8
(*c*) 5 + 3 + 6 = 14, carry 1
(*d*) 3 + 6 + 9 + 1 = 19, carry 1
(*e*) 6 + 9 + 1 = 16, carry 1
(*f*) 9 + 1 = 10

Example c: (multiplier 22, 33, 44, etc.):
264 × 22 = 5 8 0 8

Solution c:
Double each number in multiplicand, thus:
(4), (12), (8)
(*a*) Write 8
(*b*) 8 + 12 = 20, carry 2
(*c*) 12 + 4 + 2 = 18, carry 1
(*d*) 4 + 1 = 5

Or solve by multiplying 264 by 11 (as in Example a) and then multiplying this product by 2. Thus: 264 × 11 × 2 = 2,904 × 2 = 5,808.

2. **Multiplication** by 89, 111, etc.:

This method is a combination of the preceding method and multiplication by 10 or a power of 10. Thus:

Example a:
765 × 89 =
  76500
− 8415
  68085

Solution a:
(*a*) Multiply by 100 (765 × 100)
(*b*) Subtract 765 × 11

Example b: (see Example b of Group 1, preceding)

$9635 \times 111 =$

$$\begin{array}{r} 963500 \\ +\ \underline{105985} \\ 1069485 \end{array}$$

Solution b:

(*a*) 9635×100

(*b*) Add 9635×11

3. **Multiplication** of two-digit numbers by two-digit numbers when first digits (tens) are alike and second digits (units) add to 10:

Example a:

$35 \times 35 = \underline{12}\ \underline{25}$

Solution a:

(*a*) $5 \times 5 = 25$

(*b*) $3 \times (3 + 1) = 12$

Example b:

$81 \times 89 = \underline{72}\ \underline{09}$

Solution b:

(*a*) $9 \times 1 = 09$

(*b*) $8 \times (8 + 1) = 72$

Example c:

$23 \times 27 = \underline{6}\ \underline{21}$

Solution c:

(*a*) $7 \times 3 = 21$

(*b*) $2 \times (2 + 1) = 6$

Example d (*an extension of above*):

$124 \times 126 = \underline{156}\ \underline{24}$

Solution d:

(*a*) $6 \times 4 = 24$

(*b*) $12 \times (12 + 1) = 156$

NOTE: This method is useful in fractions. Thus:

$$4\frac{1}{2} \times 4\frac{1}{2} = 20\frac{1}{4};\ 3\frac{1}{3} \times 3\frac{2}{3} = 12\frac{2}{9}$$

4. **Multiplication** of two-digit numbers by two-digit numbers when first digits (tens) add to 10 and second digits (units) are alike:

Example a:

$47 \times 67 = \underline{31}\ \underline{49}$

Solution a:

(*a*) $7 \times 7 = 49$

(*b*) $(6 \times 4) + 7 = 31$

Example b:

$23 \times 83 = \underline{19}\ \underline{09}$

Solution b:

(*a*) $3 \times 3 = 09$

(*b*) $(8 \times 2) + 3 = 19$

5. **Multiplication** of two-digit numbers by two-digit numbers when first digits (tens) add to an even number and ending digits (units) are 5's:

Example a:

$85 \times 25 = \underline{21}\ \underline{25}$

Solution a:

(*a*) $5 \times 5 = 25$

(*b*) $(2 \times 8) + \frac{(8 + 2)}{2} = (2 \times 8) + 5 = 21$

Example b:
$75 \times 95 = \underline{71}\ \underline{25}$

Solution b:
(*a*) $5 \times 5 = 25$

(*b*) $(9 \times 7) + \frac{(9 + 7)}{2} = (9 \times 7) + 8 = 71$

NOTE: This method is useful in fractions. Thus:

$$6\frac{1}{2} \times 4\frac{1}{2} = 29\frac{1}{4};\ 3\frac{1}{2} \times 5\frac{1}{2} = 19\frac{1}{4}$$

6. **Multiplication** of two-digit numbers by two-digit numbers when first digits (tens) add to an odd number and ending digits (units) are 5's:

Example a:
$75 \times 25 = \underline{18}\ \underline{75}$

Solution a:
(*a*) Write 75

(*b*) $(2 \times 7) + \frac{(2 + 7)}{2}$ and drop the $\frac{1}{2}$
$= (2 \times 7) + 4 = 18$

NOTE: The writing or placing of 75 is equivalent to $25 + \frac{1}{2}$ of $100 = 75$. The $\frac{1}{2}$ dropped is $\frac{1}{2}$ of 100, and the 75 thus takes into account step (*b*) of the solution where the $\frac{1}{2}$ is dropped. The problem could be worked as follows:

(*a*) $5 \times 5 = 25$
(*b*) $(2 \times 7) + \frac{(7 + 2)}{2} = (2 \times 7) + 4\frac{1}{2} = 18\frac{1}{2}$ or 1,850; and
(*c*) $1{,}850 + 25 = 1{,}875$

Example b:
$45 \times 95 = \underline{42}\ \underline{75}$

Solution b:
(*a*) Write 75

(*b*) $(9 \times 4) + \frac{(9 + 4)}{2}$ and drop the $\frac{1}{2}$
$= (9 \times 4) + 6 = 42$

NOTE: This method is useful in fractions. Thus:

$$4\frac{1}{2} \times 7\frac{1}{2} = 33\frac{3}{4};\ 9\frac{1}{2} \times 8\frac{1}{2} = 80\frac{3}{4}$$

7. **Multiplication** of two-digit numbers with the same beginning figure:

Example a:
$36 \times 37 = \underline{13}\ \underline{3}\ \underline{2}$

Solution a:
(*a*) $6 \times 7 = 42$, carry 4
(*b*) $3 \times (6 + 7) + 4 = 43$, carry 4
(*c*) $(3 \times 3) + 4 = 13$

Example b:
$64 \times 68 = \underline{43}\ \underline{5}\ \underline{2}$

Solution b:
(*a*) $4 \times 8 = 32$, carry 3
(*b*) $6 \times (4 + 8) + 3 = 75$, carry 7
(*c*) $(6 \times 6) + 7 = 43$

8. **Multiplication** of two-digit numbers with the same ending figure:

Example a:
73 × 43 = 31 3 9

Solution a:
(*a*) 3 × 3 = 9
(*b*) 3 × (7 + 4) = 33, carry 3
(*c*) (7 × 4) + 3 = 31

Example b:
28 × 58 = 16 2 4

Solution b:
(*a*) 8 × 8 = 64, carry 6
(*b*) 8 × (2 + 5) + 6 = 62, carry 6
(*c*) (2 × 5) + 6 = 16

9. **Multiplication** when multiplier consists of multiples:

Example a:

```
   4327
    624
25962
 103848
2700048
```

Solution a:
Multiplier consists of 6 and 24 (4 × 6)
(*a*) 4327 × 6 = 25962, placed under 6
(*b*) 25962 × 4 = 103848, placed under 4
(*c*) Add

Example b:

```
   2483
    427
  17381
104286
1060241
```

Solution b:
Multiplier consists of 7 and 42 (6 × 7)
(*a*) 2483 × 7 = 17381, placed under 7
(*b*) 17381 × 6 = 104286, placed under 2
(*c*) Add

Example c:

```
      59437
      16832
    475496
   950992
     1901984
1000443584
```

Solution c:
Multiplier consists of 8, 16 (2 × 8), and 32 (4 × 8) or (2 × 16)
(*a*) 59437 × 8 = 475496, placed under 8
(*b*) 475496 × 2 = 950992, placed under 6
(*c*) 950992 × 2 =
or 475496 × 4 = 1901984, placed under 2
(*d*) Add

10. **To multiply** a multiplicand consisting of 9's by any other number:

Example:
9999 × 5327

```
       9999
       5327 6
5326   4673
```

Solution:
(*a*) Subtract 1 from multiplier
(*b*) Subtract multiplier (less the 1) from multiplicand
(*c*) Place multiplier (less the 1) to left of remainder

NOTE: This method is interesting, but obviously has limited practical value. It cannot be used if the multiplier has more digits than the multiplicand.

11. **Multiplying** numbers in "teens" by numbers in "teens":

Example:	*Solution:*
18	
16	
24	(*a*) 18 + 6 = 24
48	(*b*) 6 × 8 = 48, set one place to right
288	(*c*) Add

12. **Multiplication** by two-digit multiplier beginning with 1:

Example a:	*Solution* a:
934 × 15	
4670	(*a*) Multiply 934 by 5 and set one place to right
14010	(*b*) Add

Example b:	*Solution* b:
1273 × 16	
7638	(*a*) 1273 × 6, set one place to right
20368	(*b*) Add

NOTE: The only value of this short cut and the following short cut is to save the need of rewriting the multiplicand, for the solution is simply a transposition of the partial products as found in the ordinary method of multiplying.

13. **Multiplying** by two-digit multiplier ending in 1:

Example a:	*Solution* a:
9287 × 41	
37148	(*a*) Multiply 9287 by 4 and set one place to left
380767	(*b*) Add

Example b:	*Solution* b:
4236 × 91	
38124	(*a*) 4236 × 9, set one place to left
385476	(*b*) Add

14. **Cross multiplication** of two-digit numbers:

Example a:	*Solution* a:
7 4	(*a*) 4 × 3 = 12, carry 1
|×|	(*b*) (3 × 7) + (6 × 4) + 1 = 46, carry 4
6 3	(*c*) (6 × 7) + 4 = 46
46 6 2	

Example b:	*Solution* b:
5 2	(*a*) 5 × 2 = 10, carry 1
|×|	(*b*) (5 × 5) + (3 × 2) + 1 = 32, carry 3
3 5	(*c*) (3 × 5) + 3 = 18
18 2 0	

Cross multiplication of three-digit numbers may also be performed, but its value for most individuals is doubtful. Thus:

Example:

```
 3  4  5
 5  2  6
18 1 4 7 0
```

Solution:

(*a*) 6 × 5 = 30, carry 3
(*b*) (6 × 4) + (2 × 5) + 3 = 37, carry 3
(*c*) (6 × 3) + (5 × 5) + (2 × 4) + 3 = 45, carry 5
(*d*) (2 × 3) + (5 × 4) + 5 = 31, carry 3
(*e*) (5 × 3) + 3 = 18

15. **Cross multiplication** of three-digit numbers, middle numbers being zero:

Example a:

```
 6  0  5
 4  0  7
24 62 35
```

Solution a:

(*a*) 7 × 5 = 35
(*b*) (7 × 6) + (4 × 5) = 62
(*c*) 4 × 6 = 24

Example b:

```
 8  0  9
 7  0  8
57 27 72
```

Solution b:

(*a*) 8 × 9 = 72
(*b*) (8 × 8) + (7 × 9) = 127, carry 1
(*c*) (7 × 8) + 1 = 57

16. **Cross multiplication** of three-digit numbers, middle digit of multiplier being zero:

Example:

```
 7  1  5
 6  0  5
43 25 75
```

Solution:

(*a*) 5 × 15 = 75
(*b*) (6 × 15) + (5 × 7) = 125, carry 1
(*c*) (6 × 7) + 1 = 43

17. **Squaring** of three-digit numbers, middle numbers being zero:

Example a:

208^2

4 32 64

Solution a:

(*a*) 8 × 8 = 64
(*b*) (2 × 8) + (2 × 8) = 32
(*c*) 2 × 2 = 4

Example b:

403^2

16 24 09

Solution b:

(*a*) 3 × 3 = 09
(*b*) (4 × 3) + (4 × 3) = 24
(*c*) 4 × 4 = 16

Using the short cuts when there are decimals in the factors. All the preceding short cuts in multiplication are applicable even though there are decimals in either multiplicand and multiplier, or both. The general rule to be observed is, *A product will have as many decimal places as there are decimal places in the two factors together.*

Optional Exercise 1. Multiplication Short Cuts

A. The following problems offer opportunity for practice on the three short cuts in multiplication illustrated on page 17:

1.	2.	3.
a. 27 × 100	*a.* 85 × 25	*a.* 72 × 11
b. 342 × 1000	*b.* 973 × 50	*b.* 105 × 99
c. 4.76 × 10	*c.* 8.21 × 250	*c.* 3.08 × 102
d. .0052 × 10000	*d.* .0304 × 20	*d.* .7046 × 999

B. The following problems offer opportunity for practice on the 17 short cuts in multiplication illustrated on pages 419–424. NOTE: Problems are numbered in the same order as the illustrations of the short cuts appear on pages 419–424.

1.	2.	3.	4.
a. 38 × 11	*a.* 35 × 89	*a.* 45 × 45	*a.* 36 × 76
b. 7.46 × 11	*b.* 5.21 × 989	*b.* 73 × 77	*b.* 42 × 62
c. 852 × 22	*c.* 405 × 111	*c.* 65 × 65	*c.* 91 × 11
d. 97.89 × 11	*d.* 2.763 × 89	*d.* 29 × 21	*d.* 27 × 87
5.	**6.**	**7.**	**8.**
a. 65 × 45	*a.* 45 × 15	*a.* 22 × 27	*a.* 43 × 83
b. 95 × 75	*b.* 35 × 65	*b.* 63 × 62	*b.* 28 × 68
c. 85 × 25	*c.* 85 × 55	*c.* 54 × 53	*c.* 17 × 37
d. 55 × 35	*d.* 75 × 25	*d.* 71 × 76	*d.* 59 × 29
9.	**10.**	**11.**	**12.**
a. 472 × 147	*a.* 999 × 87	*a.* 12 × 14	*a.* 76 × 12
b. 592 × 824	*b.* 999 × 438	*b.* 16 × 19	*b.* 93 × 18
c. 8079 × 48126	*c.* 9999 × 742	*c.* 18 × 13	*c.* 235 × 13
d. 68943 × 83216	*d.* 99999 × 97267	*d.* 15 × 17	*d.* 624 × 16

13.	14.	15.	16.	17.
a. 27 × 31	*a.* 32 × 24	*a.* 302 × 204	*a.* 814 × 205	*a.* 503 × 503
b. 49 × 21	*b.* 25 × 43	*b.* 806 × 501	*b.* 722 × 403	*b.* 708 × 708
c. 743 × 61	*c.* 68 × 26	*c.* 708 × 905	*c.* 516 × 301	*c.* 206 × 206
d. 856 × 51	*d.* 87 × 98	*d.* 507 × 203	*d.* 324 × 802	*d.* 901 × 901

C. The following problems offer opportunity for practice in short cuts in multiplication, but require that you select an appropriate method:

1. 712 × 304	**2.** 75 × 55	**3.** 27 × 89	**4.** 85 × 85
5. 48 × 17	**6.** 239 × 126	**7.** 95 × 45	**8.** 35 × 35
9. 62 × 68	**10.** 48 × 71	**11.** 999 × 84	**12.** 52 × 56
13. 506 × 207	**14.** 609 × 609	**15.** 26 × 43	**16.** 13 × 17
17. 25 × 25	**18.** 58 × 58	**19.** 94 × 34	**20.** 86 × 11
21. 342 × 11	**22.** 85 × 65	**23.** 58 × 38	**24.** 83 × 24
25. 14 × 13	**26.** 37 × 41	**27.** 72 × 78	**28.** 702 × 702
29. 43 × 48	**30.** 605 × 403	**31.** 9999 × 846	**32.** 527 × 41
33. 59 × 51	**34.** 75 × 65	**35.** 783 × 147	**36.** 63 × 14
37. 45 × 35	**38.** 326 × 989	**39.** 85 × 45	**40.** 415 × 605

Short Method of Adding Two Fractions

The following method of adding two fractions will usually, but not always, save time:

1. To find the required numerator, multiply the denominator of each given fraction by the numerator of the other given fraction and add.
2. To find the required denominator, multiply the given denominators.
3. Unless already so expressed, reduce the result to lowest terms.

Example 1: Add $\frac{2}{3} + \frac{1}{4}$.

$$\frac{(2 \times 4) + (1 \times 3)}{3 \times 4} = \frac{11}{12}$$

Example 2: Add $\frac{3}{4} + \frac{5}{6}$.

$$\frac{(3 \times 6) + (5 \times 4)}{4 \times 6} = \frac{38}{24} = 1\frac{7}{12}$$

Example 3: Add $\frac{2}{7} + \frac{3}{5}$.

$$\frac{(2 \times 5) + (3 \times 7)}{7 \times 5} = \frac{31}{35}$$

Example 4: Add $\frac{5}{4} + \frac{9}{8}$.

$$\frac{(5 \times 8) + (9 \times 4)}{4 \times 8} = \frac{76}{32} = 2\frac{3}{8}$$

When this short method is used, the denominator of the obtained sum will be the lowest common denominator (of the fractions to be added) only when the denominators of the given fractions are prime to each other. Thus in Examples 1 and 3 the obtained denominators of the sums ($\frac{11}{12}$ and $\frac{31}{35}$, respectively) are the lowest common denominators; but in Examples 2 and 4 the obtained denominators of the sums ($\frac{38}{24}$ and $\frac{76}{32}$, respectively) are not the lowest common denominators.

As a general statement, it may be said that this short cut does save time when the denominators of the fractions to be added are prime to each other, and that it may or may not save time when the denominators are not prime. If the denominators of the fractions to be added are common to each other (the same), this short method would require considerably more time and therefore should not be used.

Short Method of Subtracting Fractions

The following method of subtracting one fraction from another is similar to the short method used in adding two fractions:

1. To find the required numerator, multiply the denominator of the given subtrahend by the numerator of the given minuend, and from this product subtract the product of the denominator of the given minuend and the numerator of the given subtrahend.
2. To find the required denominator, multiply the given denominators.
3. Unless it is already so expressed, reduce the result to lowest terms.

Example 1: From $\frac{3}{4}$ subtract $\frac{2}{3}$.

$$\frac{(3 \times 3) - (2 \times 4)}{4 \times 3} = \frac{1}{12}$$

Example 2: From $\frac{10}{3}$ subtract $\frac{5}{4}$.

$$\frac{(10 \times 4) - (5 \times 3)}{3 \times 4} = \frac{25}{12} = 2\frac{1}{12}$$

Optional Exercise 2. Short Methods of Adding Two Fractions or Subtracting Fractions

A. Add each of the following fractions, using the short method, and then express each obtained sum in lowest terms. (If a sum is an improper fraction, reduce it to a mixed number.)

1. $\frac{1}{4} + \frac{1}{3}$	2. $\frac{1}{5} + \frac{1}{2}$	3. $\frac{1}{8} + \frac{1}{9}$
4. $\frac{1}{7} + \frac{1}{6}$	5. $\frac{1}{5} + \frac{1}{3}$	6. $\frac{3}{4} + \frac{2}{3}$
7. $\frac{4}{5} + \frac{1}{2}$	8. $\frac{7}{8} + \frac{5}{9}$	9. $\frac{6}{7} + \frac{1}{6}$
10. $\frac{3}{5} + \frac{1}{3}$	11. $2\frac{1}{3} + \frac{1}{5}$	12. $5\frac{1}{7} + \frac{1}{6}$
13. $\frac{5}{6} + 8\frac{1}{5}$	14. $\frac{2}{3} + 9\frac{1}{9}$	15. $8\frac{1}{3} + 4\frac{1}{8}$

B. Subtract each of the following, using the short method, and then reduce each obtained remainder to lowest terms:

1. $\frac{2}{3} - \frac{2}{5}$	2. $\frac{7}{11} - \frac{5}{24}$	3. $\frac{6}{5} - \frac{11}{12}$
4. $\frac{11}{12} - \frac{5}{7}$	5. $\frac{2}{3} - \frac{1}{7}$	6. $\frac{7}{13} - \frac{5}{12}$
7. $\frac{9}{31} - \frac{22}{125}$	8. $\frac{15}{16} - \frac{12}{13}$	9. $\frac{13}{14} - \frac{11}{12}$
10. $\frac{19}{39} - \frac{3}{13}$	11. $\frac{14}{15} - \frac{2}{3}$	12. $\frac{3}{16} - \frac{1}{8}$
13. $\frac{5}{12} - \frac{1}{9}$	14. $\frac{4}{17} - \frac{2}{13}$	15. $\frac{5}{6} - \frac{2}{3}$

APPENDIX II

ROOTS AND POWERS AND MEASUREMENTS WITH REFERENCE TABLE

Tables of Measurements

Linear Measure

12 inches (in.)		= 1 foot (ft.)
3 feet		= 1 yard (yd.)
$5\frac{1}{2}$ yards	= $16\frac{1}{2}$ feet	= 1 rod (rd.)

320 rods	= 1 mile (mi.)
1,760 yards	= 1 mile
5,280 feet	= 1 mile

Surface Measure

144 square inches (sq. in.)		= 1 square foot (sq. ft.)
9 square feet		= 1 square yard (sq. yd.)
$30\frac{1}{4}$ square yards	= $272\frac{1}{4}$ square feet	= 1 square rod (sq. rd.)
160 square rods	= 43,560 square feet	= 1 acre (A.)
640 acres		= 1 square mile (sq. mi.) or section (Sec.)
36 sections (6 mi. by 6 mi. square)		= 1 township (T.)

Cubic Measure

1728 cubic inches (cu. in.)	= 1 cubic foot (cu. ft.)
27 cubic feet	= 1 cubic yard (cu. yd.)
128 cubic feet (4 by 4 by 8 ft.)	= 1 cord (cd.) of wood

Liquid Measure

4 gills (gi.)	= 1 pint (pt.)
2 pints	= 1 quart (qt.)
4 quarts	= 1 gallon (gal.)
$31\frac{1}{2}$ gallons	= 1 wine barrel (bbl.)
231 cubic inches	= 1 gallon; wt. about $8\frac{1}{3}$ lb.
1 cubic foot	= $7\frac{1}{2}$ gallons = $62\frac{1}{2}$ lb. approx.

Dry Measure

2 pints (pt.)	= 1 quart (qt.)
8 quarts	= 1 peck (pk.)
4 pecks	= 1 bushel (bu.)
1 bushel	= 2150.42 cu. in.
1 cubic foot	= 0.8 bushel approx.

Avoirdupois Weight

16 ounces (oz.)		= 1 pound (lb.)
100 pounds		= 1 hundredweight (cwt.)
20 hundredweight	= 2,000 pounds	= 1 ton (T.)
2,240 pounds		= 1 long ton

Measures of Time (see page 110)

Roots and Powers

The *root* of a given number is one of the *equal factors* of that given number. Restated, it is a number which multiplied by itself two or more times will produce the given number.

The term 6^2 means 6 to the second power, or 6 squared. This second power is obtained by using 6 twice as a factor, and $6 \times 6 = 36$. Thus 36 is the square of 6, or 6 to the second power.

The small 2 to the right of 6 (in 6^2) is called the *exponent*. .It indicates the number of times the *base* 6 is to be used as a factor. Thus

$$6^3 \text{ (6 to the third power or 6 cubed)} = 6 \times 6 \times 6 = 216$$

3^4 (or 3 to the fourth power) $= 3 \times 3 \times 3 \times 3 = 81$; and

$$2^5 \text{ (or 2 to the fifth power)} = 2 \times 2 \times 2 \times 2 \times 2 = 32$$

The *radical sign* $\sqrt{\ }$ placed above a number indicates that the root of that number is to be extracted. The index of the root indicates the power (or number of times) of the number to be extracted. Thus:

$\sqrt[2]{\ }$, ordinarily written simply $\sqrt{\ }$, indicates that the square root is to be extracted (2 is the index of the root).

$\sqrt[3]{\ }$ indicates that the cube root is to be extracted (3 is the index of the root).

$\sqrt[4]{\ }$ indicates that the fourth root is to be extracted (4 is the index of the root).

A number is a perfect power when the root can be extracted without leaving a remainder. Thus 25 is the perfect square of 5; 27 is the perfect cube of 3; 16 is the perfect fourth power of 2; etc.

A number is an imperfect power when the root cannot be extracted without leaving a remainder. Thus 26 is an imperfect square of 5; 26 is an imperfect cube of 3; 16.5 is an imperfect fourth power of 2; etc.

Square Root

In certain types of measurements, it becomes necessary to find the powers or roots of numbers. Since roots to higher powers than square root are infrequently required in business calculations, this discussion will be confined to the method of extracting the square root of perfect powers or the approximate square root of imperfect powers.

Method of Extracting the Square Root of a Number. To understand better the method used to find square root, consider the following:

(a)	(b)	(c)	(d)
$1^2 = 1$	$10^2 = 1\ 00$	$100^2 = 1\ 00\ 00$	$.1^2 = .01$
$3^2 = 9$	$15^2 = 2\ 25$	$250^2 = 6\ 25\ 00$	$.5^2 = .25$
$4^2 = 16$	$25^2 = 6\ 25$	$800^2 = 64\ 00\ 00$	$.25^2 = .06\ 25$
$8^2 = 64$	$80^2 = 64\ 00$	$930^2 = 86\ 49\ 00$	$2.5^2 = 6.\ 25$
$9^2 = 81$	$99^2 = 98\ 01$	$999^2 = 99\ 80\ 01$	$12.25^2 = 1\ 50.\ 06\ 25$

It is evident from the preceding that

(*a*) The square root of a one- or two-digit number is in units, that is, *one* place to the left of the decimal point.

(*b*) The square root of a three- or four-digit number is in tens, that is, *two* places to the left of the decimal point.

(*c*) The square root of a five- or six-digit number is in hundreds, that is, *three* places to the left of the decimal point.

(*d*) The number of decimal places in the square root of numbers expressed in decimals may also be determined. The square root of numbers one or two places to the right of the decimal is in tenths; the square root of numbers three or four places to the right of the decimal is in hundredths; etc.

From the preceding, the reason for the following first step in extracting the square root of a number is apparent.

First step: Point off two digits each to left and right of the decimal point in the number the square root of which is to be found. Thus to find the square root of

9 =	$\underline{9}$	; $\sqrt{9}$	will be in one digit
144 =	$\underline{1}\ \underline{44}$	; $\sqrt{144}$	will be in two digits
1225 =	$\underline{12}\ \underline{25}$	; $\sqrt{1225}$	will be in two digits
50625 =	$\underline{5}\ \underline{06}\ \underline{25}$	; $\sqrt{50625}$	will be in three digits
4914.1 =	$\underline{49}\ \underline{14}.\ \underline{10}$	; $\sqrt{4914.1}$	will be in two digits and one decimal place
27.5625 =	$\underline{27}.\ \underline{56}\ \underline{25}$	; $\sqrt{27.5625}$	will be in one digit and two decimal places

The procedure used to extract square root is illustrated by the following examples:

Example 1: Find the square root of 625.

(1) Largest square contained in 6 (or 600)	2 5.	
(2) Point off from decimal	$\sqrt{6\ 25.}$	
(3) 2 squared =	4	
(4) Subtract; bring down next grouping	2 25	
(5) 2 × 2, annex 0 = 40 + 5 = 45 × 5 =	2 25	40 is trial divisor; see solution following
(6) Remainder 0	0	

Since there is no remainder, 25 is the square root of 625, a perfect square.

Proof: 25 × 25 = 625

Solution:

1. Point off in groups of two digits each way from decimal. Thus 625. = $\underline{6}\ \underline{25}$ (the square will be in 2 digits).
2. Find the largest square contained in 6, the first grouping. (2 × 2 = 4, the largest perfect square contained in 6.) The number is 2; place it in quotient.
3. Square the quotient and subtract from 6 (6 − 4 = 2).
4. Bring down the next group of two digits (25).
5.* Double the quotient so far obtained (2 × 2 = 4). To 4 annex one zero:

* The actual process at this step is 20 × 2 = 40, for there are two groupings in the number 6 25, and the answer will be more than 20^2 (400) and less than 30^2 (900). The procedure of doubling the quotient obtained (2 × 2 = 4) and simply annexing a zero to determine the trial divisor as is illustrated in the fifth step is recommended as easier and less apt to result in error.

40. Use this as a trial divisor. Thus 225 ÷ 40 = 5. Add 5 to trial divisor (40 + 5 = 45). Place 5 in quotient and multiply 45 by 5 (45 × 5 = 225).

6. Subtract 225. Since there is no remainder, 625 is the perfect square of 25.

If the number 625 were not a perfect square, it would be necessary to annex two zeros at a time, and the process of solution would be continued until the desired degree of accuracy had been attained.

Example 2: Find the square root of 276,297.4096 to hundredths.

	5 2 5. 6 4
(1) Point off	$\sqrt{27\ 62\ 97.\ 40\ 96}$
(2) Nearest square (5^2) =	25
(3) Subtract; bring down next grouping	2 62
(4) 50 × 2 = 100 + 2 = 102 × 2 =	2 04 (100 is trial divisor)
(5) Subtract; bring down next grouping	58 97
(6) 520 × 2 = 1,040 + 5 = 1,045 × 5 =	52 25 (1040 is trial divisor)
(7) Subtract; bring down next grouping	6 72 40
(8) 5,250 × 2 = 10,500 + 6 = 10,506 × 6 =	6 30 36 (10500 is trial divisor)
(9) Subtract; bring down next grouping	42 04 96
(10) 52,560 × 2 = 105,120 + 4 = 105,124 × 4 =	42 04 96 (105120 is trial divisor)

Since there is no remainder, 525.64 is perfect square of 276,297.4096.

Proof: $525.64^2 = 276{,}297.4096$

Optional Exercise 1. Square Root

A. Find the square root of the following to nearest hundredths:

1. 345	2. 610	3. 7.03	4. 9.80	5. 1.567
6. 3,046.25	7. 748.967	8. 91.7563	9. 8,297.6	10. 45,678.329

B. Solve the following problems. NOTE: The square root of the square units of area will be the number of units of linear measure of each side of a square.

1. A square farm contains exactly 360 acres. What is the length of a side in yards? (Suggestion: Reduce the acreage to square yards before finding the square root.)
2. The floor of a square building contains exactly 31,152.25 sq. ft. What is the length of each side of the floor in feet and inches?
3. A two-story square building contains exactly 121,032 sq. ft. of inside flooring. If the outer walls are 8 in. thick, what is the outside length of each side of the building in yards, feet, and inches?
4. A square field contains exactly 121 acres. What is the length of a side to nearest feet?
5. A square building lot contains exactly 60,616 sq. ft. What is the length of a side in feet? (Find answer to nearest tenths.)
6. The floor of a dance pavilion contains exactly 30,925 sq. ft. What is the length of each side of the dance floor in feet? (Find answer to nearest hundredths.)
7. A square field contains exactly 372 acres. What is the length of a side to nearest whole feet in rods, yards, and feet? (Suggestion: Reduce to square feet before extracting square root.)

8. A farm in the shape of a square contains exactly 41 acres. What is the length of a side to nearest whole inches in rods, yards, feet, and inches?

9. A square exposition building contains exactly 89,888 sq. ft. of floor space on its two floors. What is the length of each side of each floor to nearest whole inches in rods, yards, feet, and inches?

Useful Formulas for Work in Measurements

Linear Measure and Area of Plane Figures:

Square

Perimeter, or $P = 4b$

$$b = \frac{P}{4}$$

Area, or $A = b^2$

$$b = \sqrt{A}$$

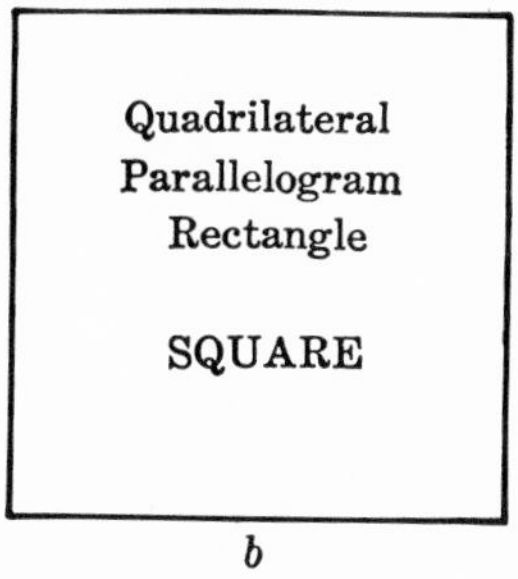

Quadrilateral
Parallelogram
Rectangle
SQUARE
b

FIG. 10.

Rectangle

Perimeter, or $P = 2b + 2h$

$$= 2(b + h)$$

$$b = \frac{P}{2} - h$$

$$h = \frac{P}{2} - b$$

Area, or $A = bh$

$$b = \frac{A}{h}$$

$$h = \frac{A}{b}$$

Quadrilateral
Parallelogram
RECTANGLE
h
b

FIG. 11.

Rhombus

Perimeter, or $P = 4b$

$$b = \frac{P}{4}$$

Area, or $A = bh$

$$b = \frac{A}{h}$$

$$h = \frac{A}{b}$$

Quadrilateral
Parallelogram
RHOMBUS
h
b

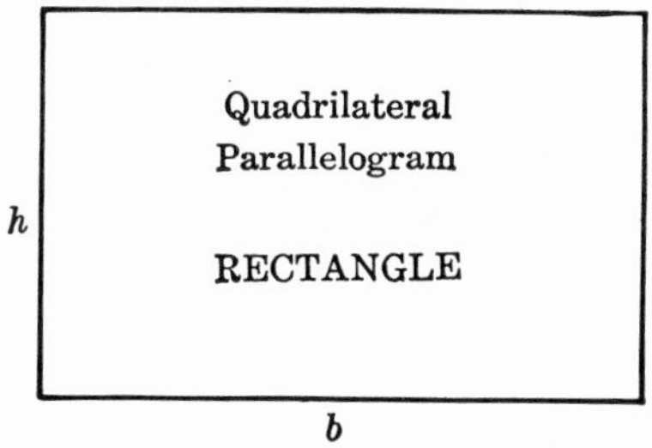

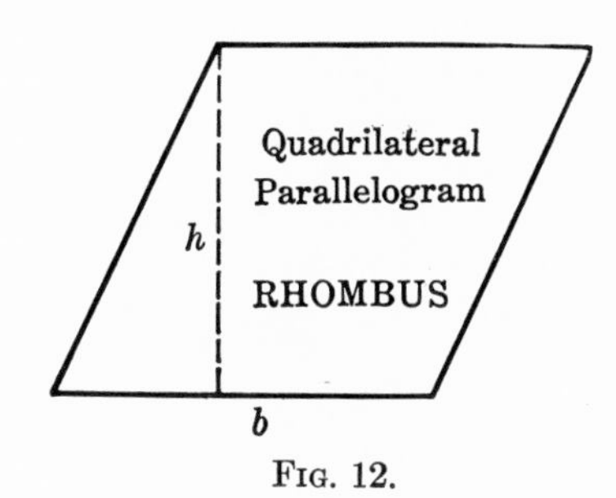

FIG. 12.

Rhomboid

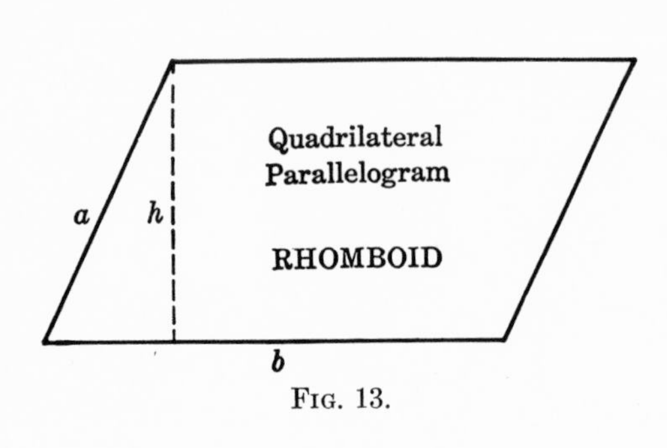

FIG. 13.

$$\text{Perimeter, or } P = 2b + 2a = 2(b + a)$$

$$b = \frac{P}{2} - a$$

$$a = \frac{P}{2} - b$$

$$\text{Area, or } A = bh$$

$$b = \frac{A}{h}$$

$$a = \frac{A}{b}$$

Trapezoid

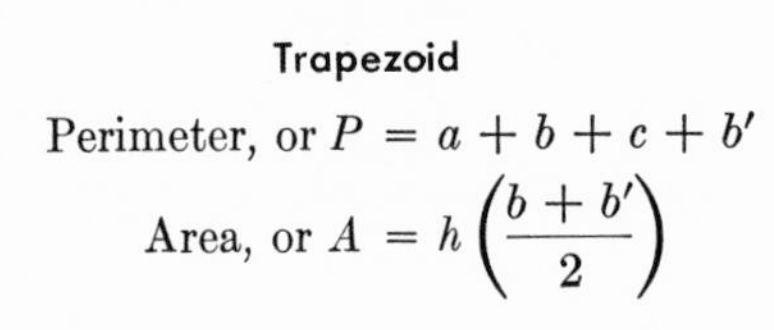

$$\text{Perimeter, or } P = a + b + c + b'$$

$$\text{Area, or } A = h\left(\frac{b + b'}{2}\right)$$

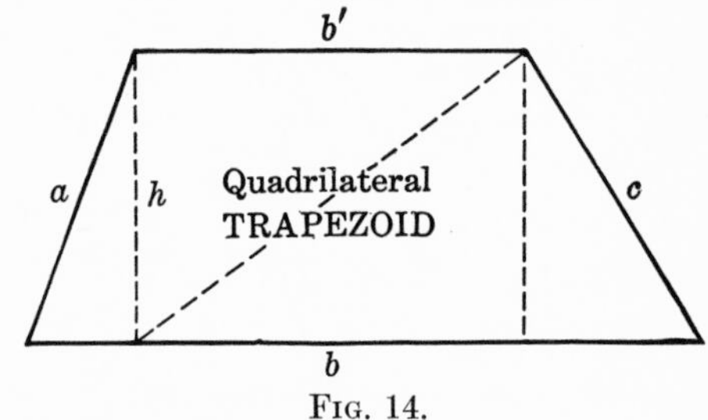

FIG. 14.

Triangles

$$\text{Perimeter, or } P = a + b + c$$

$$\text{Area, or } A = \frac{1}{2}bh = \frac{bh}{2}$$

$$b = A \div \frac{h}{2} = \frac{2A}{h}$$

$$h = A \div \frac{b}{2} = \frac{2A}{b}$$

Area may also be determined when the height is unknown if the length of the three sides be known.

$$\text{If} \quad s = \frac{a + b + c}{2}$$

$$\text{then } A = \sqrt{s(s - a)(s - b)(s - c)}$$

In a *right-angled* triangle, *the square of the hypotenuse is equal to the sum of the squares of other two sides.* Thus if c symbolizes the hypotenuse:

$$c^2 = b^2 + h^2$$

$$\text{and } c = \sqrt{b^2 + h^2}$$

$$b = \sqrt{c^2 - h^2}$$

$$h = \sqrt{c^2 - b^2}$$

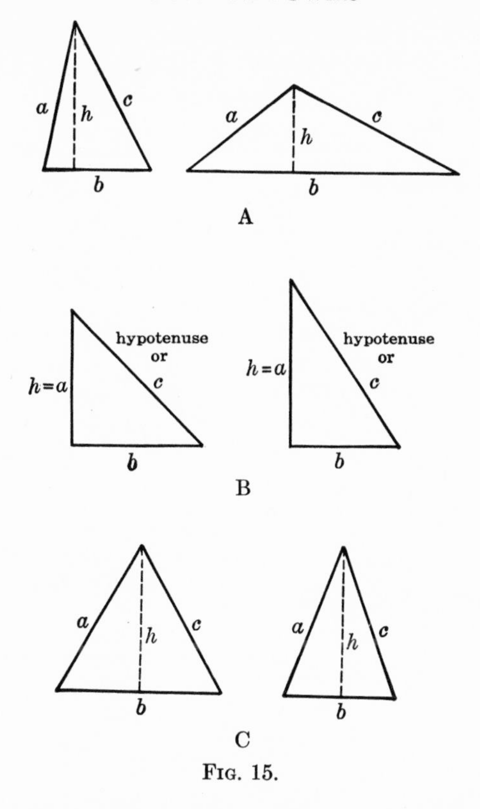

FIG. 15.

In an *isosceles* triangle, the height may be determined by first forming two equal right-angled triangles by means of a line bisecting the base to the vertex. Then

$$h^2 = c^2 - \left(\frac{b}{2}\right)^2 \qquad \text{or} \qquad h^2 = a^2 - \left(\frac{b}{2}\right)^2$$

$$h = \sqrt{c^2 - \left(\frac{b}{2}\right)^2} \qquad \text{and} \qquad h = \sqrt{a^2 - \left(\frac{b}{2}\right)^2}$$

Note also that in an isosceles triangle there are two equal sides; in an equilateral triangle, all three sides are equal.

Whenever a plane figure can be divided into triangles, squares, rectangles, parallelograms, or any combination of such figures, the area may be found if the needed dimensions of these figures are known or can be determined.

d = diameter of circle = $2r$
r = radius = $\frac{1}{2}d = \frac{d}{2}$

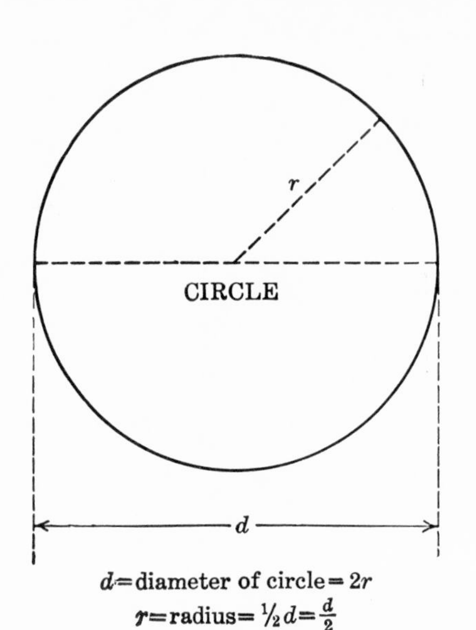

FIG. 16.

Circle

$$\text{Circumference, or } C = \pi d = 2\pi r$$

$$d = \frac{C}{\pi}$$

$$r = \frac{C \div \pi}{2} = \frac{C}{2\pi}$$

$$\text{Area, or } A = \pi r^2 = \frac{\pi d^2}{4} = \frac{Cr}{2} = \frac{\pi dr}{2}$$

$$r^2 = \frac{A}{\pi}$$

$$r = \sqrt{\frac{A}{\pi}}$$

$$d^2 = \frac{4A}{\pi}$$

$$d = \sqrt{\frac{4A}{\pi}}$$

Area and Volume of Solids:

Cubes

$$\text{Area, or } A = 6b^2$$
$$\text{Volume, or } V = b^3$$

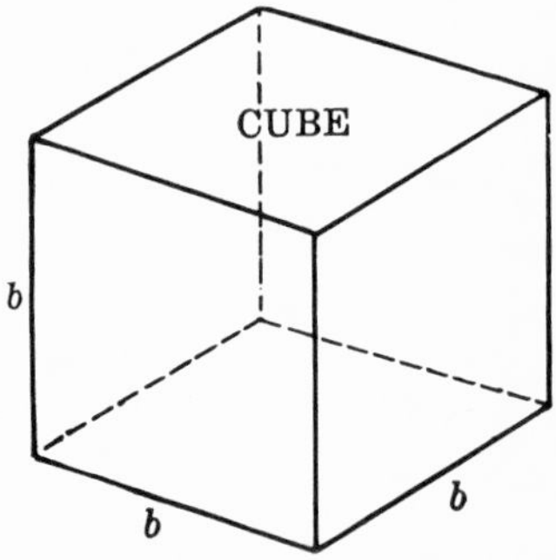

FIG. 17.

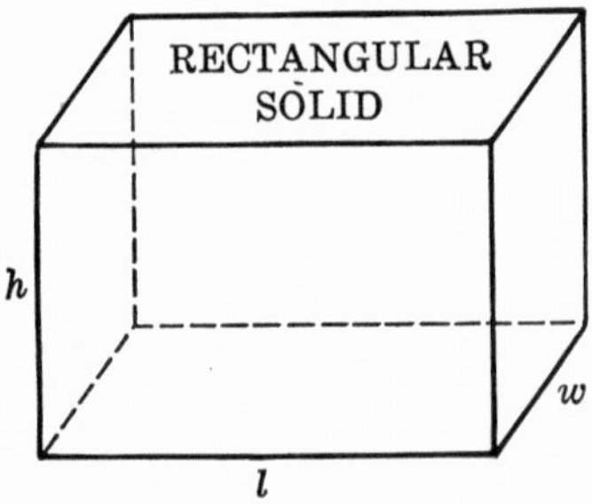

FIG. 18.

Rectangular Solids

$$\text{Lateral area} = 2(l + w) \times h = 2h(l + w)$$
$$\text{Area of both bases} = 2lw$$
$$\text{Entire surface area} = 2h(l + w) + 2lw$$
$$\text{Volume, or } V = lwh$$
$$\text{or} = \text{area of base} \times \text{height}$$

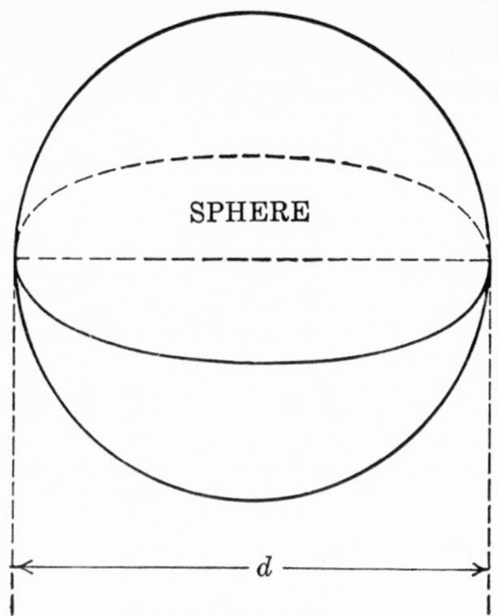

d = diameter of sphere = $2r$

r = radius = $\frac{1}{2}d = \frac{d}{2}$

FIG. 19.

Spheres

$$\text{Area, or } A = \text{circumference} \times \text{diameter}$$
$$= \pi d \times d = \pi d^2$$
$$= 4\pi r^2$$

$$\text{Volume, or } V = \pi d^2 \times \frac{1}{3} r = \pi d^2 \times \frac{1}{6} d = \frac{\pi d^3}{6}$$
$$= 4\pi r^2 \times \frac{1}{3} r = \frac{4\pi r^3}{3}$$

RIGHT CIRCULAR CYLINDER

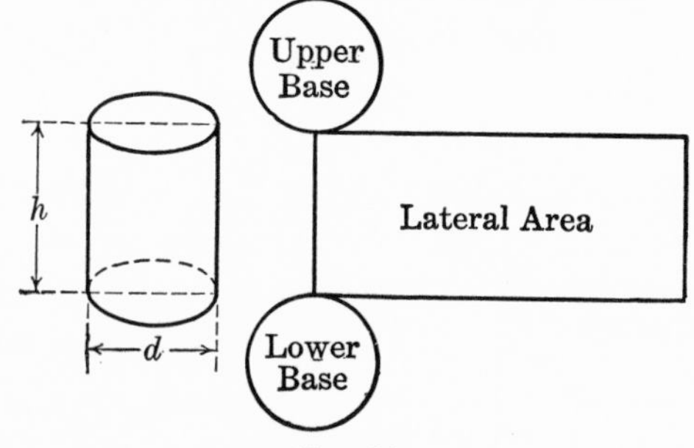

FIG. 20.

Right Circular Cylinders

$$\text{Lateral area} = \pi dh = 2\pi rh$$
$$\text{Area of both bases} = 2\pi r^2$$
$$\text{Total area} = \pi dh + 2\pi r^2$$
$$= 2\pi rh + 2\pi r^2$$
$$\text{Volume, or } V = \pi r^2 h$$

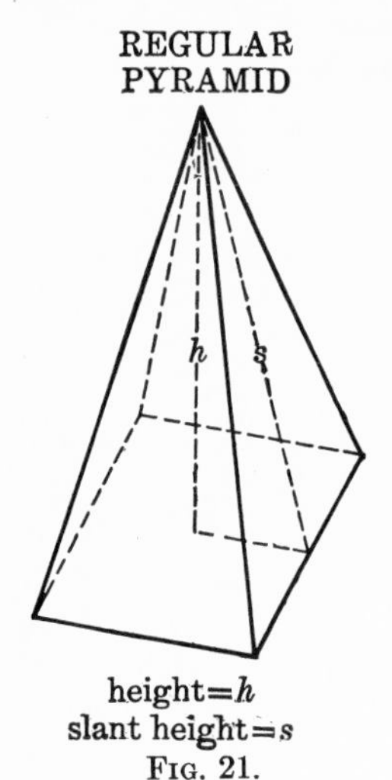

Fig. 21.

Regular Pyramids

Lateral area = $\frac{1}{2}$ perimeter of base × slant height
Area of base = as found for any plane polygon
Total area = sum of lateral area and area of base
Volume, or V = $\frac{1}{3}$ area of base × height

Right Circular Cone

Lateral area = $\frac{1}{2}$ circumference × slant height
= πr × slant height
Area of base = πr^2
Total area = sum of lateral area and area of base
Volume, or V = $\frac{1}{3}$ area of base × height

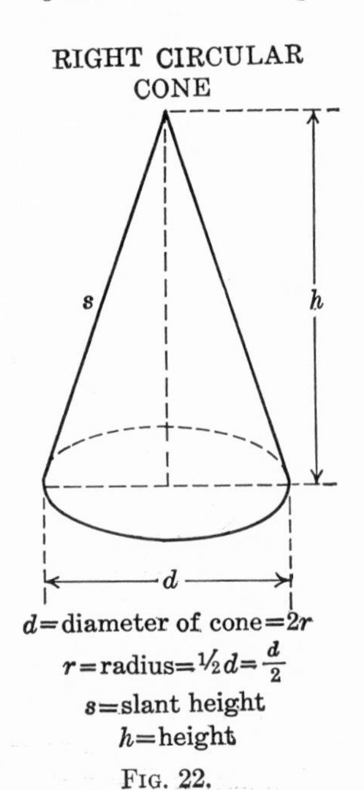

Fig. 22.

Optional Exercise 2A. Linear Measure

Solve the following:

1. A factory site in the shape of a rectangle is 250 ft. 0 in. long and 231 ft. 6 in. wide. If it is to be fenced, (*a*) how many rods of fencing will be required? If the wire costs $2.25 per linear rod and only whole rods may be purchased, (*b*) what will be the cost of the wire?
2. You are going to put 78 rd. 3 yd. 2 ft. of drain tile in a field at a cost of $.80 per yard. If 3-ft. tile is the shortest length that may be purchased (*a*) how many feet of drain tile must be bought and (*b*) what will be the total cost?
3. A field in the shape of a rhomboid has 450 ft. 6 in. bases and 231 ft. 9 in. sides. How many rods, yards, feet, and inches of fence would be required to enclose the field?
4. A room to be papered is 13 ft. 6 in. wide and 14 ft. 8 in. long. What minimum number of 18-in. strips of wallpaper will be required? (Disregard the length of the strips.)
5. A 2-ft.-wide sidewalk is placed 3 ft. inside the boundaries of a 70-ft.-square backyard. Find (*a*) the exterior perimeter of the walk in feet and (*b*) the interior perimeter of the walk in feet.
6. The owner of a chicken ranch plans to fence a rectangular chicken yard 32 rd. 8 ft. 0 in. long and 15 rd. 8 ft. 6 in. wide. What will be the cost of a wire fence at $.33 per linear foot?
7. A farmer plans to enclose a field of 160,000 sq. yd. with a fence. He considers fencing a 400-yd. square, or a rectangular area 800 yd. long and 200 yd. wide. If the cost is $.65 per linear yard, will the square or the rectangle be the cheaper, and by how much?
8. The edge of a roof in the shape of a rectangle is 33 ft. 0 in. long and 21 ft. 6 in. wide. 3-in.-wide rain gutters, costing $.35 per linear foot, are to be placed on the outer edge of the roof. If only one side of the rain gutters may be used for the external face, find (*a*) the minimum number of feet of gutter required and (*b*) the total cost of the gutter.
9. A pine baseboard in a room is to be replaced with $\frac{1}{2}$-in.-thick hardwood baseboard finished on one side only (corner joints are angle cut for fit), costing $.11 per linear foot. The room is of rectangular shape, 22 ft. 3 in. long and 14 ft. 9 in. wide. A 4-ft. opening into the room does not require any baseboard. Find (*a*) the number of linear feet of baseboard required and (*b*) the cost.

Optional Exercise 2B. Linear Measure

Solve the following:

1. The triangular sail on a small boat is 6 yd. 9 in. by 5 yd. 1 ft. 7 in. by 3 yd. 2 ft. 5 in. What is the perimeter in feet and inches?
2. On the campus of a certain school is a triangular plot of ground enclosed by a paved roadway. The dimensions of this plot are 47 rd. 4 yd. 2 ft. by 23

rd. 2 yd. 0 ft. by 34 rd. 3 yd. 1 ft. If the outer edges are to be planted with elm trees on each corner and evenly spaced on each side but not to exceed 23 ft. apart, what is the minimum number of trees required?

3. In an airplane race over a triangular course of 200 miles by 273 miles by 325 miles, the winner covered the distance in 3 hr. 45 min. What was his average speed in miles per hour? (To nearest tenths.)
4. The winner of a sailboat race covered the first leg of a triangular course in 1 hr. 45 min., averaging 9.50 knots per hour; on the next leg he averaged 8.75 knots per hour for 1 hr. 30 min; and on the return leg he averaged 10.50 knots per hour for 1 hr. 50 min. If a knot is a speed equal to 1 nautical mile and if a nautical mile is equivalent to approximately 1.15 common miles, how long was the course in common miles? (To nearest hundredths.)
5. A pressure tank for a water system has an external radius of 18 in. What is the external circumference in feet? (Let $\pi = 3.1416$.)
6. A water main is made of iron pipe $\frac{1}{2}$ in. thick, having an inside diameter of 12 in. What is the circumference of the exterior in inches? (Let $\pi = 3.1416$.)
7. A silo on a farm has an outside diameter of 14 ft. 0 in. The walls are built of concrete 12 in. thick. What are (*a*) the exterior and (*b*) interior circumferences in feet and inches (to nearest inches)? (Let $\pi = 3\frac{1}{7}$.)
8. The wheel of an automobile has a tire 6.25-16 or 28.5 in. in diameter. About how many revolutions does this wheel make in traveling 5 miles? (Let $\pi = 3\frac{1}{7}$.)

Optional Exercise 3A. Area of Plane Figures

Solve the following:

1. At $45 per acre, find (*a*) the number of acres to nearest thousandths and (*b*) the total cost of a rectangular field 370 rd. long and 150 rd. wide.
2. The surface of the face of a brick measures 4 by 8 in. Find the cost of the bricks required to pave a rectangular cellar floor 34 ft. 0 in. by 18 ft. 8 in., at $45 per M (thousand) brick. (Assume bricks to be laid without joining mortar.)
3. A rectangular field is 796 rd. long and has an area of 9,150,020 sq. yd. Find the width in feet.
4. A painting hanging in a prominent art gallery has an area of 3,960 sq. in. If one dimension is 4 ft. 6 in., what is the other dimension in feet and inches?
5. A triangular piece of land has a frontage of 150 ft. If the area is 9,000 sq. ft., what is the depth in feet?
6. If 90 ft. is the depth of a triangular piece of land and its area is 13,500 sq. ft., what is the length of the frontage in feet?
7. A triangular garden plot has sides of 35, 17, and 22 ft. What is the area to nearest square feet?
8. A house stands 41 ft. high. About how long in feet and inches must a ladder be if it is to reach approximately 1 ft. above the house and the base of the ladder is 10 ft. away from the house? (To nearest inches.)
9. An electric-light pole 38 ft. high is to be braced by a wire running from 3 ft.

below the top to an anchor 22 ft. from the base of the pole. Allowing 3 ft. for fastening the wire at the top and 2 ft. at the bottom, how many feet and inches of wire are necessary? (To nearest inches.)

10. A summer cabin in the mountains is to be 16 ft. by 32 ft., and the height of the ridge to run lengthwise is to be 4 ft. above the plate. How long in feet and inches must a rafter be? (To nearest inches.)

Optional Exercise 3B. Area of Plane Figures

Solve the following:

1. A triangular garden plot is 15 ft. 7 in. on each side. What is its area to nearest square feet?
2. A rectangular-shaped county is 15 mi. 300 rd. 4 yd. 2 ft. long and exactly 30 mi. wide. Find the area to nearest tenths of square miles.
3. A ranch in the shape of a rectangle is exactly 2 mi. wide and 3 mi. 15 rd. long. Find the area in acres.
4. A city park in the shape of a triangle extends 330 ft. on one side, 264 ft. on the second side, and 198 ft. on the third side. Find the area in square rods.
5. A three-story factory is built on a lot of the dimensions and shape of a trapezoid, as illustrated by Fig. 23. Find (*a*) area of each floor in square feet and (*b*) total area of the building in square yards.

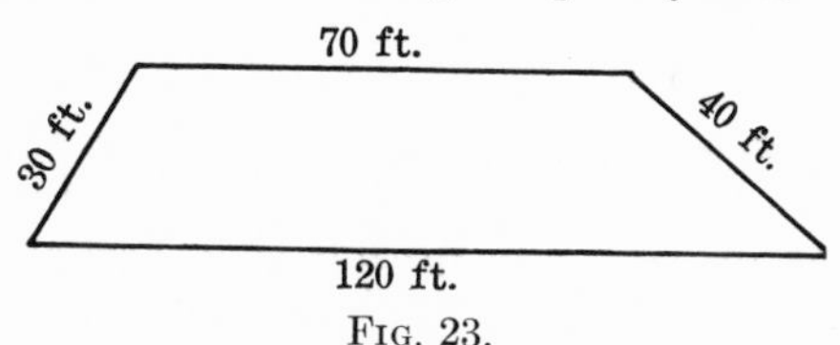

Fig. 23.

6. The floor of a circular tower is 90 ft. in diameter. What will it cost to pave at $.42 per square yard or fraction thereof? (Let $\pi = 3.1416$.)
7. A circular stage is to be covered with hardwood flooring. If the circumference is 235.62 ft., what will be the cost at $.28 per square foot or fraction thereof? (Let $\pi = 3.1416$.)
8. The radius of a roller-skating rink is 62 ft. 6 in. What is the surface area in square rods to nearest hundredths? (Let $\pi = 3.1416$.)
9. The flat top of a large cylindrical water tank is to be repainted. If two coats are necessary, how many gallons of paint must be purchased if the diameter is 80 ft. and it is estimated 1 gal. of paint will cover 450 sq. ft.? (Let $\pi = 3\frac{1}{7}$. Assume that only whole gallons are purchased.)
10. A walk 3 ft. wide encloses a circular flower garden 54 ft. in diameter. Find the area of the walk to the nearest square yard. (Let $\pi = 3\frac{1}{7}$.)

Optional Exercise 4A. Area and Volume of Solids

Solve the following:

1. A swimming pool is 60 ft. long, 20 ft. wide, and 8 ft. deep. (*a*) How many cubic feet of water will it hold? (*b*) How many gallons?

2. A grain elevator is 125 by 150 by 75 ft. high. (*a*) How many cubic feet of grain will it hold? (*b*) cubic yards? (*c*) bushels? (Assume that 1 cu. ft. = .8 bu.)
3. The excavation for the foundation of a building is to be 65 ft. long, 27 ft. wide, and 9 ft. deep. (*a*) How many cubic feet of ground must be removed? (*b*) cubic yards? (*c*) What will it cost at $2.05 per cubic yard?
4. Wood was stacked in a pile 16 ft. wide, 24 ft. high, and 168 ft. long. (*a*) What was the cubic contents in feet? (*b*) in cubic yards? (*c*) in cords?
5. A cloudburst deposited $2\frac{3}{4}$ in. of rain on a field of 7 acres. (*a*) What was the volume of the water in cubic feet and (*b*) the weight in pounds?
6. A wagon bed is 5 ft. wide and 15 ft. long. How many inches high must it be to hold 210 bu. of wheat? (Assume that 1 cu. ft. = .8 bu.)
7. The concrete foundation walls for a building are to have external measurements of 53 by 22 ft. If the walls are 1 ft. 6 in. thick and 7 ft. deep, find (*a*) the number of cubic yards of concrete required and (*b*) the cost at $4.25 per cubic yard.
8. A street 960 ft. long and 40 ft. wide is to be paved with concrete to a depth of 6 in. (*a*) How many cubic yards of concrete will be used? (*b*) What will it cost at $5.50 per cubic yard? (Assume a fraction of a cubic yard to cost the same as an entire cubic yard.)
9. A concrete driveway 12 ft. wide, 4 in. thick, and 96 ft. long is to be built from the street to the garage. (*a*) How many cubic feet of concrete will be required? (*b*) cubic yards? (*c*) What will it cost at $8.25 per cubic yard? (Assume a fraction of a cubic yard to cost the same as an entire cubic yard.) (*d*) What is the cost to nearest cents per square foot of surface area?
10. A room containing 102 cu. yd. of space is 27 ft. long and 12 ft. wide. (*a*) Find the height of the walls in feet and inches and (*b*) the surface area of the walls in square feet.
11. A rectangular ice-skating rink measures 150 ft. by 200 ft. Water $\frac{1}{4}$ in. deep is used each day to form new ice. The rink is open 365 days per year. 100 cu. ft. of water costs $.18. (*a*) What is the volume of water in cubic feet used per day? (*b*) per year? (*c*) What is the total weight in pounds of water used each year? (*d*) What is the average cost per day? (*e*) per year?

Optional Exercise 4B. Area and Volume of Solids

Solve the following:

1. The radius of the earth is approximately 4,000 miles. (*a*) To nearest thousands, how many square miles are there on its surface? (*b*) To nearest hundreds of thousands, how many cubic miles of material are there in the earth? (Let $\pi = 3\frac{1}{7}$.)
2. A spherical steel shell has an outer diameter of 11 ft. and an inner diameter of 10 ft. To nearest units, find (*a*) the number of square feet in the outer surface, (*b*) the weight of the water in pounds which could be contained within the spherical shell, and (*c*) the cubic feet of steel necessary to build such a spherical shell. (Let $\pi = 3.1416$.)

3. The surface area of a sphere is 180,956.16 sq. in. Find (*a*) the diameter in inches and (*b*) the volume in cubic inches. (Let $\pi = 3.1416$.)
4. A service-station owner is installing new equipment. He has replaced an underground cylindrical gas tank with a new one having outside dimensions of 5 ft. 10 in. in diameter and 12 ft. 6 in. in length. Find the total exterior area to nearest square feet. (Let $\pi = 3\frac{1}{7}$.)
5. A gasoline truck carries a tank with inside measurements of 5 ft. in diameter and 14 ft. in length. (*a*) How many cubic feet does it contain? (*b*) How many gallons of gasoline will it hold? (Let $\pi = 3\frac{1}{7}$.)
6. A silo stands 63 ft. high (inside measurement) and 22 ft. in diameter (outside measurement). The walls are 1 ft. thick. Find (*a*) the volume of the interior in cubic feet and (*b*) the number of bushels of ensilage it will hold. (Let $\pi = 3\frac{1}{7}$ and 1 cu. ft. = .8 bu.)
7. A grain elevator has seven cylindrical storage bins. The inside dimensions of each bin are 25 ft. in diameter and 46 ft. in height. A level bushel of grain contains 2150.42 cu. in. (*a*) What is the volume of the elevator in cubic feet? (*b*) in cubic inches? (*c*) How many whole level bushels will it hold? (Let $\pi = 3\frac{1}{7}$.)
8. A church spire is in the shape of a regular square pyramid. If each side of the base is 8 ft. and the height is 20 ft., (*a*) to nearest square feet, how much roofing does it require, and (*b*) how many cubic feet of space are there within the spire? (Do not consider thickness of the roof.)
9. A regular square pyramid has a base of 5 ft. on each side, and the slant height is 16 ft. Find (*a*) the lateral area in square feet and (*b*) the volume to nearest cubic feet.
10. A monument of solid concrete is in the shape of a right circular cone. The radius of the base is 3 ft. 6 in. and the height is 15 ft. Find (*a*) the lateral area in square feet and (*b*) the number of cubic feet of concrete in the monument. (Let $\pi = 3\frac{1}{7}$.)
11. A right circular cone is 6 in. in diameter at the base and has a slant height of 11 in. Find (*a*) the lateral area to nearest square inches and (*b*) the volume to nearest cubic inches. (Let $\pi = 3\frac{1}{7}$.)

ANSWERS TO ODD-NUMBERED PROBLEMS

Chapter I, Exercise 1, page 11

A. **1.** Three hundred seventy-four.
3. Five hundred forty-seven and four-ninths thousandths. Or: Five hundred forty-seven thousandths and four-ninths (of one) thousandth.

B. **1.** .0223
3. 8,507.06 1/3

C. *To hundredths*
1. 8.61
3. 73.21
To thousands
1. 4,338,000
3. 1,000
To tens
1. 470
3. 0
To tenths
1. .3
3. 921.1
To hundreds
1. 0
3. 24,700
To units
1. 704
3. 2

D. **1.** 6,251.48
3. 11,497.2193

E. **1.** 450.1739 (ck. 2)
3. 14,468.416 (ck. 7)

F. **1.** 67,831.41
3. 486.788.98
5. 737,888.93
7. 5,054.076
9. 8.945
11. 195.9791
13. 968.88976
15. 9,299.079

Chapter I, Exercise 2, page 23

A. **1.** 14,220,585.72

B. **1.** 15,898,272.48

C. **1.** 5,427.48090 (ck. 3)
3. 294,504.100 (ck. 7)
5. 38,658,239.46 (ck. 0)

D. **1.** 1,005; remainder 84
3. 122; remainder 100

E. **1.** 1,052; remainder 5 (ck. 1)
3. 101; remainder 264 (ck. 3)

Chapter I, Exercise 3, page 28

A. **1.** 2
3. 2 3 5
5. 2 5 7
7. 2 11
9. 2 3 7

B. **1.** 4 6 8
3. 6
5. 4 6 9
7. 4 6 10
9. none

C. **1.** 5 7 11
3. 2 4 7 8
5. 2 3 4 5 6 8 9 10 11
7. 2 3 4 5 6 8 9 10
9. 2 4 5 8 10

D. **1.** 3/11 (g.c.d. 13)
3. 2/5 (g.c.d. 71)
5. 7/11 (g.c.d. 59)
7. 11/170 (g.c.d. 17)
9. 5/21 (g.c.d. 53)

Chapter I, Exercise 4, page 34

A. 1. 240
3. 72
5. 22,680
B. 1. 378
3. 504
5. 3,780
C. 1. 4 1/2
3. 576
5. 405 cords
7. 35 sacks of flour
9. $192

Chapter I, Exercise 5, page 43

A. 1. 18/77
3. 1 30/77
5. 8 23/45
7. 10 1/4
9. 2/5
11. 1 8/39
13. 5 7/24
15. 11 13/15
17. 3/8
19. 1 7/72
21. 4 21/22
23. 13 7/45
B. 1. 1 19/20
3. 1 173/336
5. 2 59/840
7. 1 67/180
C. 1. 14 221/420
3. 204 1/15
5. 213 5/72

Chapter I, Exercise 6, page 48

A. 1. 5/24
3. 1 15/56
5. 1/1,000
7. 1/150
9. 15/76
11. 79/156
B. 1. 1
3. 4
5. 5
7. $2.00
C. 1. 22
3. 6
D. 1. 33 3/7
3. 52 17/26
5. 45 1/11
7. 93 8/13
9. 3 17/105
11. 6 7/9
13. 6 4/5
15. 14 21/44
17. 26
19. 12 14/75
21. 324 87/404
23. 7 5/9

Chapter I, Exercise 7, page 52

A. 1. 1/42
3. 1/10
5. 1/2
7. 4/9
9. 22/27
11. 63/100
13. 1/15
15. 55/153
B. 1. 1 7/26
3. 7/10
5. 1 7/20
7. 3 47/126
9. 3 61/63
11. 2 29/44
13. 49/52
15. 4 3/8
C. 1. 840
3. 400
5. 371 1/12
7. 3,666 26/27
9. 1,203
11. 888
13. 1,325 1/10
15. 2,414 9/49

Chapter I, Exercise 8, page 57

A. 1. 6/7
3. 8/9
5. 1 5/23
7. 1 2/3
9. 1/96
11. 1/135
13. 125

15. 51
17. 1 11/27
19. 3/5
21. 1 22/63
23. 1 85/147

B. 1. 3/4
3. 63/100
5. 1/32
7. 100
9. 232/287
11. 28/39

C. 1. 2 1/2
3. 1 1/9
5. 1/15
7. 12
9. 44/65
11. 1 31/60

Chapter I, Exercise 9, page 60

A. 1. 3/80
3. 12 117/280

B. 1. 11/200
3. 45/104

C. 1. 1/30
3. 33/65

D. 1. $3,062
3. A's profit is $3,080
B's profit is $4,200
C's profit is $1,960
5. $28,800

Chapter I, Exercise 10, page 66

A. 1. 71/100
3. 7/20
5. 5 13/25
7. 1/150
9. 77/90
11. 2 7/8

B. 1. .8750
3. .4800
5. .2683
7. 6.1429
9. 1.4000
11. 8.3922

C. 1. $.8\dot{3}$
3. $.\dot{5}7428\dot{5}$
5. $.14\dot{6}$
7. $3.58\dot{3}$

D. 1. 5/9
3. .1 2/3
5. .35 6/11
7. 4.8 7/9

E. 1. 43/90
3. 1/75
5. 47/550
7. 4 3/110

Chapter II, Exercise 1, page 70

A. 1. 147
3. 27 9/10
5. 8 4/27

B. 1. 45
3. 22 11/16
5. 25 5/18

C. (*a*)
1. 31 1/2
3. 534
5. $11 3/8 or $11.375

(*b*)
1. 52 1/2
3. 3,560
5. $6 1/15 or $6.06 2/3

(*c*)
1. 27
3. 22,250
5. $15 3/200 or $15.015

Chapter II, Exercise 2, page 76

A. 1. 80
3. 190
5. 8,700
7. 11
9. 44,250

B. 1. 45
3. 2,928
5. 11.52
7. 435.2
9. .243

C. 1. 4,400
3. 22.5

D. 1. 1.49 1/3
3. 1.23 3/7

E. 1. (*a*) $96.00
(*b*) $4.80
3. (*a*) $7,700.00
(*b*) $64.17
5. (*a*) $2,256.00
(*b*) $456.00

Chapter II, Exercise 3, page 82

A. 1. 18
3. 5
5. 30
7. 7

B. 1. 8
3. 2
5. 40
7. 1

C. 1. 1,200 sq. ft.
3. 18 3/4 (or 18.75) sq. yd.
5. $432
7. $1,173.33

Chapter II, Exercise 4, page 88

A. 1. 7/1
3. 4/11
5. 1/7
7. 64/33
9. 19/33

B. 1. 300
3. 17.1
5. 112
7. 12 3/4

C. 1. $1,155
3. $2,508.80
5. 36 men
7. A: $4,631.58
B: $5,210.53
C: $5,557.89

Chapter II, Exercise 5, page 96

A. 1. .50, 50%
3. 1/4, .25
5. 62.5%, 5/8
7. .075, 7.5%
9. 1 3/8, 1.375
11. .8%, 1/125

B. 1. 2/15 is greater by 1/75
3. 62.5% is less by 8 13/14% (or 8.9 2/7%)

C. 1. 64
3. 9
5. 42
7. .45
9. .07
11. $225
13. $15
15. $1.37

D. 1. 1,400.00
3. 300.00
5. 568.87

E. 1. (*a*) 13.0000
(*b*) 1300.00
3. (*a*) 2.8421
(*b*) 284.21
5. (*a*) 4.3467
(*b*) 434.67

F.

	(*a*)	(*b*)	(*c*)
1.	$8.50	$297.50	$1,054.00
3.	$19.23	$3.73	$10.82
5.	$2,041.98	$7.22	$16.23

Chapter II, Exercise 6A, page 101

A. 1. 1.92
3. 112.00
5. 30.69
7. 10.35
9. 46.50
11. 42.23
13. 40.00
15. 26.00

B. 1. 10%
3. 6 1/2%
5. 50%
7. 5%
9. 62 1/2%
11. 5%
13. 18%
15. 12%

C. 1. 400.00
3. 54.00
5. 400.00
7. 800.00
9. $1,300.00
11. $147.00
13. $400.00
15. $660.00

17. 160.00
19. $625.00

D.

	(*a*)	(*b*)
1.	$445.20	106%
3.	$187.20	104%
5.	$68.25	105%

E.

	(*a*)	(*b*)
1.	$174.15	96.75%
3.	$545.60	88%
5.	$432.45	93%

Chapter II, Exercise 6B, page 102

1. 1,032 lb.
3. $91.00
5. $8,875.01
7. $66.00 loss
9. 83%
11. 10%

Chapter II, Exercise 6C, page 103

1. A has 44 4/9%; B has 225%
3. 53%
5. $3,840.00
7. 7,500 miles
9. $32.00
11. $16,500.00

Chapter II, Exercise 6D, page 104

A.

	(*a*)	(*b*)	(*c*)	(*d*)
1.		25%	$75.00	$225.00
3.	$600.00	5%		$570.00
5.	$220.00		$17.60	$202.40

B. **1.** $134.90
3. $2,123.50

C.

	(*a*)	(*b*)	(*c*)	(*d*)
1.		4%	$16.80	$436.80
3.	$190.00	5%		$199.50
5.	$84.00		$2.73	$86.73

D. **1.** 53 11/13%
3. Gain of 16 2/3%

Chapter III, Exercise 1A, page 120

A.

	(*a*)			(*b*)
1.	13	1	6	4,716
3.	12	1	0	4,350
5.	4	4	16	1,576

B.

	(*a*)	(*b*)
1.	132	134
3.	73	74
5.	205	210

C. **1.** 10/9
3. 9/30
5. Apr. 13

D. **1.** 1/17
3. 1/30 or 1/31
5. July 18

E. **1.** 3/29
3. 4/30
5. Apr. 20

F. **1.** 4/26
3. 11/18
5. Jan. 16

G. **1.** $120.00
3. $2.88
5. $1.94

H. **1.** $160.00
3. $15.28
5. $5.56

Chapter III, Exercise 1B, page 122

A. **1.** $25.00
3. $2.36

B. **1.** $7,290.00
3. $81.73

C. **1.** $3.63
3. $44.88

D. **1.** $398.79
3. $8.63

E. **1.** $0.75
3. $19.66

F. **1.** $345.37
3. $4,407.19

G. **1.** (*a*) $12.26
(*b*) $420.91
3. $689.67

Chapter III, Exercise 2A, page 127

A. **1.** $1.50
3. $3.00
5. $2.46
7. $0.73
9. $4.58
11. $2.28

13. $3.38
15. $15.00
17. $92.40
19. $8.95

B. 1. $7.78
3. $9.32
5. $0.37
7. $28.52
9. $2.68

Chapter III, Exercise 2B, page 128

A. 1. $9.44
3. $3.81
5. $7.26
7. $0.38

B. 1. $5.50
3. $8.29
5. $5.21
7. $7.61

C. 1. (*a*) $153.49
(*b*) $8,621.97
3. (*a*) $62.91
(*b*) $3,745.62

Chapter III, Exercise 3, page 132

A. 1. $17.21
3. $5.74
5. $12.95
7. $1.61
9. $4.49

B. 1. $2.49
3. $5.67
5. $1.47
7. $0.88
9. $3.90

C. 1. $0.47
3. $2.66
5. $2.13
7. $7.67
9. $17.82

D. 1. (*a*) $15.23
(*b*) $471.98
3. (*a*) $79.44
(*b*) $8,333.44

Chapter III, Exercise 4, page 137

A. 1. $3.47
3. $11.94
5. $32.52
7. $39.50

B. 1. $0.73
3. $2.39
5. $5.09
7. $2.91

C. 1. $1,913.28
3. (*a*) $1.74
(*b*) $1.77
5. (*a*) $119.38
(*b*) $8,579.38

Chapter III, Exercise 5A, page 141

A. 1. 66 da.
3. 1,260 da.

B. 1. 185 da.
3. 1 yr. 4 mo. 14 da.

C. 1. 6%
3. 4 1/2%

D. 1. 4 1/2%
3. 10%

Chapter III, Exercise 5B, page 142

A. 1. (*a*) $548.38
(*b*) $568.67
3. (*a*) $349.94
(*b*) $356.72

B. 1. $764.09
3. $865.44

C. 1. $140.46
3. $640.00

D. 1. $9,303.13
3. $252.08

Chapter IV, Exercise 1, page 148

A. 1. (*a*) Apr. 3
(*b*) $200.00
(*c*) 60 da.
(*d*) $2.00
(*e*) $198.00
3. (*a*) July 13
(*b*) $700.00
(*c*) 18 da.
(*d*) $1.40
(*e*) $698.60
5. (*a*) Feb. 21
(*b*) $575.00

(c) 57 da.
(d) $4.10
(e) $570.90

B. 1. (a) $12.12
(b) $1,200.00
3. (a) $231.11
(b) $9,768.89
5. $147.97

Chapter IV, Exercise 2, page 150

A. 1. (a) June 5
(b) 180 da.
(c) $13.53
(d) $464.53
(e) 54 da.
(f) $4.18
(g) $460.35
3. (a) May 16
(b) 120 da.
(c) $18.58
(d) $761.58
(e) 14 da.
(f) $1.48
(g) $760.10
5. (a) June 7
(b) 90 da.
(c) $3.75
(d) $378.75
(e) 44 da.
(f) $1.39
(g) $337.36

B. 1. (a) $700.62
(b) $2.82
(c) $697.80
3. $617.30
5. $350.49

Chapter IV, Exercise 3, page 154

A. 1. (a) $5,750.00
(b) $5,729.87
(c) $5,729.95

B. 1. $444.59
3. (a) $110.91
(b) $109.94

C. 1. (a) $3,526.25
(b) $3,508.62
(c) $3,508.71

D. 1. $8,996.01
3. (a) $21.66
(b) $21.43

Chapter IV, Exercise 4, page 157

1. 66 da
3. 36 da.
5. 5%
7. 3%
9. $920.00
11. $3,645.00

Chapter IV, Exercise 5, page 161

1. $960.00
3. $315.00
5. $6,400.00
7. $4,800.00

Chapter IV, Exercise 6, page 165

1. $1,839.21
3. $1,229.29

Chapter IV, Exercise 7, page 172

1. 19.2%
3. 20.6%
5. 41.1%
7. 8.0%
9. 14.4%

Chapter V, Exercise 1, page 181

A. 1. $10.72
3. (a) $115.50
(b) $49.39
(c) $49.39
5. (a) $4.80
(b) $1.20
(c) $30.00
7. (a) $249.60
(b) $452.40
9. $101.34

B. Total wages $597.47
Total notes $594
Total specie $3.47

Chapter V, Exercise 2, page 186

1. $105.09
3. $114.19

5. (*a*) $180.00
   (*b*) $40.50
   (*c*) $220.50
7. (*a*) $19.01 (exactly 19.0125)
   (*b*) $5.36 (exactly 5.3625)
   (*c*) $24.37

Chapter V, Exercise 3, page 191

1. $62.51
3. $116.10
5. (*a*) $21.24
   (*b*) $29.92
   (*c*) $26.40
7. $112.67

Chapter V, Exercise 4, page 198

1. (*a*) $22.00
   (*b*) $28.60
   (*c*) $31.20
3. (*a*) $104.00
   (*b*) $110.50
5. (*a*) $26.40
   (*b*) $28.88 (exactly 28.875)
   (*c*) $0.50 (exactly .495)
7. (*a*) $27.00
   (*b*) $29.70
   (*c*) $0.90
9. (*a*) $100.80
   (*b*) $105.76
   (*c*) $142.24
11. (*a*) $26.00
    (*b*) $36.59

Chapter V, Exercise 5, page 201

1. $1,641.60
3. $144.60
5. $3,542.50
7. (*a*) $91.00
   (*b*) $1,521.00
   (*c*) $117.00

Chapter V, Exercise 6, page 205

1.

May 5	$604.80		
7	726.40		
8	896.50		
9	352.00		
Gross proceeds			$2,579.70
Commission		103.19	183.39
Net proceeds			$2,396.31

3.

Feb. 16	$7,275.00		
16	1,393.88		
19	2,542.50		
Prime cost			$11,211.38
Commission		168.17	473.02
Gross cost			$11,684.40

Chapter VI, Exercise 1, page 213

1. Age 21: (*a*) $41.95, (*b*) $98.10, (*c*) $74.30, (*d*) $149.20, (*e*) $118.05, (*f*) $243.15, (*g*) $214.60; answers omitted for ages 30 and 50
3. $49.70
5. (*a*) $1,242.85
   (*b*) $646.28
   (*c*) $110.30
7. $0.96
9. (*a*) $33.56
   (*b*) $34.90
   (*c*) $35.56
   (*d*) $35.76

Chapter VI, Exercise 2, page 219

1. $189.00
3. (*a*) $3,924
   (*b*) $7,308
   (*c*) $12,000
5. (*a*) $597.68
   (*b*) $604.00
7. (*a*) Return of $611.37
   (*b*) Return of $426.60
9. (*a*) $735.00
   (*b*) $1,837.50
   (*c*) 13 yr. 139 da.

Chapter VI, Exercise 3, page 227

1. $30.00
3. $93.70
5. $108.50
7. (*a*) $51.70
   (*b*) $41.40
   (*c*) $44.90
   (*d*) $48.30
9. (*a*) $101.50
   (*b*) $102.50

Chapter VI, Exercise 4, page 237

1. $215.10

3. (*a*) $45.50
(*b*) $34.20
(*c*) $38.00
(*d*) $41.80

5. (*a*) $6.70
(*b*) $50.10

7. (*a*) $29.40
(*b*) $129.70 (theoretical maximum is $129.60)

9. (*a*) $72.60 ($48.40 × 1 1/2 is maximum)
(*b*) $12.10
(*c*) $36.30

11. (*a*) $200.00 (theoretical maximum)
(*b*) $23.20 (actual maximum is $200.30)
(*c*) $60.00
(*d*) $46.70 (actual maximum is $200.10)

Chapter VI, Exercise 5, page 246

A.

	(*a*)	(*b*)	(*c*)
1.		$0.1925	$0.275
3.	$0.18	.315	
5.	.30	.525	.75

	(*d*)	(*e*)
1.	$0.3575	$0.44
3.	.585	.72
5.	.975	

B. **1.** (*a*) $13.50
(*b*) $23.63
(*c*) $33.75
(*d*) $43.88
(*e*) $54.00

3. Company A: $28.00
Company B: 12.60
Company C: 21.00
Total $61.60

C. **1.** $10.03
3. $22.68
5. $13.76

Chapter VI, Exercise 6, page 250

A. **1.** A: $1,333.33
B: $9,000.00
C: $5,166.67

3. $12,000.00

5. A: $103,571.43
B: $62.142.86
C: $69,047.62
D: $55,238.09

B. **1.** $4,000.00
3. $5,600.00
5. $215,625.00

Chapter VI, Exercise 7, page 260

1. (*a*) $25.00
(*b*) $33.88
(*c*) $16.80
(*d*) $75.68

3. (*a*) $31.00
(*b*) $47.36
(*c*) $25.00
(*d*) $103.36

5. (*a*) $44.00
(*b*) $120.00
(*c*) $52.36
(*d*) $27.60
(*e*) $243.96

7. (*a*) $36.83
(*b*) $85.92

9. (*a*) $117.39
(*b*) $102.34

Chapter VI, Exercise 8, page 264

1. $1,510

3. Refund due of $30.44

5. (*a*) $702.00
(*b*) $112.00
(*c*) $1,960.00

7. (*a*) $975.00
(*b*) $4,675.00
(*c*) $2,075.00
(*d*) $6,000.00

Chapter VII, Exercise 1, page 271

A. **1.** $0.71
3. $7.59

B. 1. $2.55
3. (*a*) 2.812%
(*b*) 28.12 mills (or $0.02812)
(*c*) $2.812
(*d*) $28.12
5. $204.40
7. $51,909,433.96
9. $13,250.00

Chapter VII, Exercise 2, page 276

1. (*a*) $350
(*b*) $700
3. (*a*) $3,600
(*b*) $3,000
5. (*a*)

1.	2.	3.	4.
12/31/58	1/1/58	$6,561.00	$ none
12/31/59	1/1/58	6,561.00	2,187.00
12/31/60	1/1/58	6,561.00	3,645.00
12/31/61	1/1/58	6,561.00	4,617.00
12/31/62	1/1/58	6,561.00	5,265.00
12/31/63	1/1/58	6,561.00	5,697.00

5.	6.	7.	8.
$6,561.00	6 yr.	6 yr.	$2,187.00
4,374.00	6 yr.	5 yr.	1,458.00
2,916.00	6 yr.	4 yr.	972.00
1,944.00	6 yr.	3 yr.	648.00
1,296.00	6 yr.	2 yr.	432.00
864.00	6 yr.	1 yr.	288.00

(*b*) $576.00

Chapter VIII, Exercise 1, page 280

A. 1. $123.12 for (*a*), (*b*), (*c*), (*d*)
B. 1. $130.63 (or 130.62)
3. $446.40
5. (*a*) $252.45
(*b*) $201.96

Chapter VIII, Exercise 2, page 285

A. 1. .45
3. .43605
B. 1. .1925
3. .5236 1/9
C. 1. 40%
3. 41.5%
D.

	(*a*)	(*b*)
1.	$40.00	15%
3.	$210.60	5%

(*c*)
1. 33 1/3%, 25%, and 15%
3. 35%, 20%, 10%, and 5%

E. 1. (*a*) $0.61
(*b*) $18.02
(*c*) $100.64
F. 1. $1,440.00
G. 1. (*a*) $21.44
(*b*) and (*c*) omitted
2. (*a*) $86.00

Chapter VIII, Exercise 3A, page 291

A. 1. (*a*) June 9
(*b*) $286.15
3. (*a*) Oct. 11
(*b*) $14.62
(*c*) $350.88
5. $1,813.90
B.

	(*a*)	(*b*)
1.	$4.81	$235.69
3.	$0.45	$22.05
5.	$1.28	$126.37
7.	$72.98	$839.32
9.	$1.41	$45.75
11.	$3.09	$100.00
13.	$8.13	$398.27

	(*c*)	(*d*)
1.	$240.50	none
3.	$22.50	none
5.	$127.65	none
7.	$912.30	none
9.	$47.16	none
11.	$103.09	$185.11
13.	$406.40	none

Chapter VIII, Exercise 3B, page 293

1. (*a*) 73.0%
(*b*) 76.0%
3. (*a*) $171.20
(*b*) $172.97

(c) $174.73
(d) $176.50
5. $18.80
7. $787.71
9. $529.63

Chapter VIII, Exercise 4, page 298

1. (a) $5.07
   (b) $501.78
3. (a) $3.83
   (b) $0.88
   (c) $91.01
4. #1(a) $4.27
   (b) $1.42
   (c) $79.67
5. #1(a) $4.27
   (b) $1.35
   (c) $79.74
   #2, #3 omitted
7. $1,023.02

Chapter VIII, Exercise 5A, page 301

1. (a) $33.75
   (b) 35%
   (c) 135%
3. (a) $22.00
   (b) 26.5%
   (c) 126.5%
5. (a) $16.56
   (b) $9.20
   (c) 125%
7. (a) 32%
   (b) $3.75
   (c) $4.95
9. (a) 127.5%
   (b) $15.20
   (c) $4.18

Chapter VIII, Exercise 5B, page 302

1. (a) $5.50
   (b) 32%
   (c) 68%
3. (a) $34.50
   (b) 42.5%
   (c) 57.5%
5. (a) $5.95
   (b) $2.80
   (c) 32%
7. (a) 36%
   (b) $5.50 dz.
   (c) $3.52 dz.
9. (a) 73.6%
   (b) $37.50
   (c) $9.90

Chapter VIII, Exercise 6, page 305

A. 1. 1/10
   3. 2/5
B. 1. 3/5
   3. 9
C. 1. 35.06%
   3. 60.00%
D. 1. 108.33%
   3. 170.27%

E.

	Cost	+ *markup* =	*sales*
1.		$80.00	$200.00
	100%	66.67%	166.67%
		40.00%	100%
3.		$ 1.09	$ 2.95
	100%	58.60%	158.60%
	63.10%		100%
5.	$ 2.25		$ 3.95
	100%	75.56%	175.56%
		43.04%	100%
7.	$ 1.15		$ 2.00
	100%	73.91%	173.91%
	57.50%		100%
9.	$117.49	$72.01	
	100%	61.29%	161.29%
		38.00%	100%
11.	$ 0.75	$ 0.64	
	100%	85.33%	185.33%
	53.96%		100%

Chapter IX, Exercise 1, page 311

A.

	Retail =	*cost*	+ *markup*
1.		$76.35	$48.65
			38.92%
3.	$84.80		$24.38
			38.75%
5.	$62.50	$35.85	
			42.64%

B. 1. $10.50
   3. $1.95

5. $2.50
7. 19.16%

Chapter IX, Exercise 2, page 314

1. 39.81%
3. 41.76%
5. (*a*) $8,062.00
   (*b*) $19,488.00
7. $986.76

Chapter IX, Exercise 3, page 319

1. 46.90%
3. 39.41%
5. 41.49%
7. $9.72

Chapter IX, Exercise 4, page 322

1. (*a*) 42.22%
   (*b*) 33.33%
3. (*a*) 30.38%
   (*b*) 38.89%
5. 31.80%
7. $5,747.00
9. (*a*) 44.43%
   (*b*) 45.28%

Chapter IX, Exercise 5, page 326

1. (*a*) $310.00
   (*b*) 20.35%
3. (*a*) $53.55
   (*b*) 8.23%
5. (*a*) 6.95%
   (*b*) 7.09%
7. 5.69%

Chapter IX, Exercise 6, page 328

1. $119,505.99
3. $89,694.38
5. $21,555.32
7. $1,247.03 profit

Chapter IX, Exercise 7, page 333

1. $7,352.00
3. (*a*) $15,352.50
   (*b*) $8,976.08
5. 2.72 times
7. 1.83 times

Chapter IX, Exercise 8, page 338

1. (*a*) 2.50%
   (*b*) $25,000.00
   (*c*) 1.50%
   (*d*) $90,000.00
   (*e*) 3.00%
3. $119,700.00
5. $22,800.00
7. $31,565.00
9. $83,335.24
11. (*a*) $8,637.00
    (*b*) $4,663.98

Chapter X, Exercise 1, page 342

A. 1. $3,299
   3. $8,210
   5. $528

B. 1. $15,750.00
   3. Jones: $3,172.03
      Smith: $3,700.70
      Brown: $5,727.27
   5. (*a*) $5,481.08
      (*b*) $2,951.35
   7. (*a*) $342,000.00
      (*b*) $3,182.50

Chapter X, Exercise 2, page 347

1. (*a*) Cate: $2,057.14
        Stout: $1,542.86
   (*b*) Cate: $2,571.425
        Stout: $1,928.575
3. (*a*) Cate: $2,057.14
        Stout: $1,542.86
   (*b*) Cate: $2,316.18
        Stout: $2,183.82
5. (*a*) James: $5,000 profit
        Evans: $5,120 profit
   (*b*) James: $2,500 loss
        Evans: $3,000 loss
7. Kilham: $870.00
   Reed: $880.00

Chapter X, Exercise 3, page 352

1. (*a*) $32,500.00
   (*b*) $49.63
3. (*a*) $35,000.00
   (*b*) $31.11

5. (*a*) $72,380.00
   (*b*) $60.32
7. (*a*) $117,040
   (*b*) $639,040

Chapter X, Exercise 4, page 354

1. (*a*) $12.50
   (*b*) none
3. (*a*) $8.25
   (*b*) $1.00
5. (*a*) $3.00
   (*b*) $0.86
7. (*a*) $150,000
   (*b*) $58,800
   (*c*) $326,400
   (*d*) $451,400

Chapter X, Exercise 5, page 360

1. (*a*) $325.00
   (*b*) 21.67%
   (*c*) 15.21%
3. (*a*) $0.40
   (*b*) 17.78%
   (*c*) 10.60%
5. (*a*) $6.60
   (*b*) 10.00%
   (*c*) 13.20%
7. (*a*) $43,200
   (*b*) $13,500
   (*c*) $56,700
   (*d*) 31.25%
   (*e*) 10.50%

Chapter XI, Exercise 1, page 368

1. (*a*) 31 3/4
   (*b*) 260 1/4
   (*c*) 16 5/8
   (*d*) 40 1/4
3. (*a*) 109 7/8
   (*b*) 75 3/8
   (*c*) 16 1/8
   (*d*) 75 5/8
   (*e*) 62 1/8
5. (*a*) $25.94
   (*b*) $86.00
   (*c*) $87.26
7. (*a*) $35.26
   (*b*) $43.33
9. (*a*) $27.80
   (*b*) $6.00 (minimum)
11. (*a*) $ 88.38
    24.45
    Total = $112.83
    (*b*) $35.00
    18.90
    Total = $53.90

Chapter XI, Exercise 2, page 373

A. 1. (*a*) $0.18
   (*b*) $0.05
   (*c*) $0.23
3. (*a*) $5.10
   (*b*) $0.23
   (*c*) $5.33

B. 1. (*a*) 100 shares
   (*b*) 61 3/4
   (*c*) none
   (*d*) $6,175.00
   (*e*) $41.18
   (*f*) $6,216.18
3. (*a*) 300 shares
   (*b*) 23 7/8
   (*c*) none
   (*d*) $7,162.50
   (*e*) $80.82
   (*f*) $7,243.32
5. (*a*) 70 shares (odd lot)
   (*b*) 40 5/8
   (*c*) $2.16
   (*d*) $2,845.91
   (*e*) $27.22
   (*f*) $2,873.13
7. (*a*) 10 shares (round lot)
   8 shares (odd lot)
   (*b*) 170 170 3/4
   (*c*) none $0.51
   (*d*) $1,700.00 $1,366.51
   (*e*) $30.33 commission on cost of 18 shares
   (*f*) $3,096.84 (for 18 shares)

Chapter XI, Exercise 3, page 376

A. 1. (*a*) $5.00
(*b*) $0.04
(*c*) $3.00
(*d*) $8.04
3. (*a*) $2.90
(*b*) $0.02
(*c*) $1.74
(*d*) $4.66

B. 1. (*a*) 100 shares
(*b*) 154
(*c*) $10.31
(*d*) $15,389.69
(*e*) $50.40
(*f*) $15,339.29
3. (*a*) 800 shares
(*b*) 3 1/4
(*c*) $8.46
(*d*) $2,591.54
(*e*) $66.00
(*f*) $2,525.54
5. (*a*) 30 shares (odd lot)
(*b*) 70
(*c*) $3.05
(*d*) $2,096.95
(*e*) $23.50
(*f*) $2,073.45
7. (*a*) 100 shares
20 shares (odd lot)

(*b*)	53 7/8	53 5/8
(*c*)	$10.11	$2.03
(*d*)	$5,377.39	$1,070.47
(*e*)	$40.39	$13.73
(*f*)	$5,337.00	$1,056.74

Total proceeds are $6,393.74

Chapter XI, Exercise 4A, page 383

1. (*a*) $3000
(*b*) 105 1/2
(*c*) $4.13
(*d*) $3,169.13
(*e*) $12.00
(*f*) $3,181.13
3. (*a*) $13,000
(*b*) 110
(*c*) $27.81
(*d*) $14,327.81
(*e*) $32.50
(*f*) $14,360.41
5. (*a*) $16,000
(*b*) 102 1/4
(*c*) $58.56
(*d*) $16,418.56
(*e*) $40.00
(*f*) $16,458.56
7. (*a*) $1,000
(*b*) 82 1/2
(*c*) $11.63
(*d*) $836.63
(*e*) $5.00
(*f*) $841.63

Chapter XI, Exercise 4B, page 384

1. (*a*) $1,000
(*b*) 95 7/8
(*c*) $14.08
(*d*) $0.52
(*e*) $972.31
(*f*) $5.00
(*g*) $967.31
3. (*a*) $10,000
(*b*) 93
(*c*) $82.22
(*d*) $5.19
(*e*) $9,377.03
(*f*) $25.00
(*g*) $9,352.03
5. (*a*) $4,000
(*b*) 102 1/2
(*c*) $58.72
(*d*) $2.09
(*e*) $4,156.63
(*f*) $12.00
(*g*) $4,144.63
7. (*a*) $8,000
(*b*) 106 1/2
(*c*) $50.00
(*d*) $4.18
(*e*) $8,565.82
(*f*) $20.00
(*g*) $8,545.82

Chapter XI, Exercise 5, page 386

A. 1. $3.00
   3. (*a*) 5 rights
      (*b*) $2.83 (approx.)
      (*c*) $39.17 (approx.)

B. 1. (*a*) $6,750.00
      (*b*) $1,237.50
      (*c*) $5,512.50
   3. (*a*) $1,700.00
      (*b*) $218.75
      (*c*) $1,481.25

C. 1. 21.65%
   3. 18.65%

Chapter XI, Exercise 6, page 390

A. 1. 4.1%
   3. 3.7%
   5. 5.0%
   7. 3.1%

B. 1. 3.6%
   3. 6.8%
   5. 5.5%
   7. 2.4%

Chapter XII, Exercise 1, page 395

1. (*a*) $162.00
   (*b*) $171.72
   (*c*) $171.91
3. $429.00
5. (*a*) $600.00
   (*b*) $615.20

Chapter XII, Exercise 2A, page 403

1. (*a*) $4,169.47
   (*b*) $2,519.47
3. $991.20
5. 11 years
7. 6% compounded monthly

Chapter XII, Exercise 2B, page 403

1. 17 1/2 years
3. $977.30
5. $912.05
7. $933.96

Chapter XII, Exercise 3A, page 410

1. (*a*) $1,127.42
   (*b*) $1,127.42
   (*c*) $1,127.42
3. $1,129.73
5. (*a*) $3,481.15
   (*b*) $3,481.15
   (*c*) $3,481.15
7. $14,309.09

Chapter XII, Exercise 3B, page 410

1. $9,124.25
3. $494,932.05
5. $2,340.51
7. $33,834.69

Chapter XII, Exercise 4, page 413

1. $680.69
3. $1,241.17
5. $611.41
7. $710.80

Appendix I, Optional Exercise 1, page 425

A. 1. (*a*) 2,700
      (*b*) 342,000
      (*c*) 47.6
      (*d*) 52
   3. (*a*) 792
      (*b*) 10,395
      (*c*) 314.16
      (*d*) 703.8954

B. 1. (*a*) 418
      (*b*) 82.06
      (*c*) 18,744
      (*d*) 1,076.79
   3. (*a*) 2,025
      (*b*) 5,621
      (*c*) 4,225
      (*d*) 609
   5. (*a*) 2,925
      (*b*) 7,125
      (*c*) 2,125
      (*d*) 1,925
   7. (*a*) 594
      (*b*) 3,906

(c) 2,862
(d) 5,396
9. (a) 69,384
(b) 487,808
(c) 388,809,954
(d) 573,716,088
11. (a) 168
(b) 304
(c) 234
(d) 255
13. (a) 837
(b) 1,029
(c) 45,323
(d) 43,656
15. (a) 61,608
(b) 403,806
(c) 640,740
(d) 102,921
17. (a) 253,009
(b) 501,264
(c) 42,436
(d) 811,801

C. 1. 216,448
3. 2,403
5. 816
7. 4,275
9. 4,216
11. 83,916
13. 104,742
15. 1,118
17. 625
19. 3,196
21. 3,762
23. 2,204
25. 182
27. 5,616
29. 2,064
31. 8,459,154
33. 3,009
35. 115,101
37. 1,575
39. 3,825

Appendix I, Optional Exercise 2, page 427

A. 1. 7/12
3. 17/72
5. 8/15
7. 1 3/10
9. 1 1/42
11. 2 8/15
13. 9 1/30
15. 12 11/24

B. 1. 4/15
3. 17/60
5. 11/21
7. 443/3,875
9. 1/84
11. 4/15
13. 11/36
15. 1/6

Appendix II, Optional Exercise 1, page 434

A. 1. 18.57
3. 2.65
5. 39.59
7. 27.37
9. 91.09

B. 1. 1,320 yd.
3. 82 yd. 1 ft. 4 in.
5. 246.2 ft.
7. 243 rd. 5 yd. 1 ft.
9. 12 rd. 4 yd. 2 ft. 0 in.

Appendix II, Optional Exercise 2A, page 441

1. (a) 58 4/11 rd. (or 59 rd.)
(b) $132.75
3. 82 rd. 3 yd. 2 ft. 6 in.
5. (a) 256 ft.
(b) 240 ft.
7. Square is cheaper by $260
9. (a) 70 ft.
(b) $7.70

Appendix II, Optional Exercise 2B, page 441

1. 46 ft. 9 in.
3. 212.8 m.p.h.
5. 9.4248 ft.
7. (a) 44 ft. 0 in.
(b) 37 ft. 9 in.

Appendix II, Optional Exercise 3A, page 442

1. (*a*) 346.875 acres
   (*b*) $15,609.38
3. 6,270 ft.
5. 120 ft.
7. 149 sq. ft.
9. 46 ft. 4 in.

Appendix II, Optional Exercise 3B, page 443

1. 105 sq. ft.
3. 3,900 acres
5. (*a*) 2,280 sq. ft.
   (*b*) 760 sq. yd.
7. $1,237.04
9. 23 gal.

Appendix II, Optional Exercise 4A, page 443

1. (*a*) 9,600 cu. ft.
   (*b*) 72,000 gal.
3. (*a*) 15,795 cu. ft.
   (*b*) 585 cu. yd.
   (*c*) $1,199.25
5. (*a*) 69,877.5 cu. ft.
   (*b*) 4,367,343.75 lb.
7. (*a*) 56 cu. yd.
   (*b*) $238.00
9. (*a*) 384 cu. ft.
   (*b*) 14 2/9 cu. yd.
   (*c*) $123.75
   (*d*) $0.11 per sq. ft.
11. (*a*) 625 cu. ft. per day
    (*b*) 228,125 cu. ft. per year
    (*c*) 14,257,812.5 lb. per year
    (*d*) $1.13 per day
    (*e*) $410.63 per year

Appendix II, Optional Exercise 4B, page 444

1. (*a*) 201,143 (000) sq. miles
   (*b*) 268,190 (000,000) cu. miles
3. (*a*) 240 in.
   (*b*) 7,238,246.4 cu. in.
5. (*a*) 275 cu. ft.
   (*b*) 2,062.5 gal.
7. (*a*) 158.125 cu. ft.
   (*b*) 273,240,000 cu. in.
   (*c*) 127,063 bu.
9. (*a*) 160 sq. ft.
   (*b*) 132 cu. ft.
11. (*a*) 104 sq. in.
    (*b*) 100 cu. in.

INDEX